add

D0983953

NEMATODE PARASITES
OF VERTEBRATES

THE
NEMATODE PARASITES
OF VERTEBRATES

BY

WARRINGTON YORKE, M.D.

*Professor of Parasitology, University of Liverpool and Liverpool
School of Tropical Medicine*

AND

P. A. MAPLESTONE

M.D., D.S.O.

With a Foreword by

C. W. STILES

Professor of Zoology, United States Public Health Service

WITH 307 ILLUSTRATIONS

HAFNER PUBLISHING COMPANY

NEW YORK

1962

Originally published in 1926 by

J. & A. CHURCHILL

LONDON

REPRINTED BY ARRANGEMENT

Published by

HAFNER PUBLISHING CO., INC.

31 East 10th Street

New York 3, N. Y.

Printed in the U.S.A.

NOBLE OFFSET PRINTERS, INC.

NEW YORK 3, N. Y.

FOREWORD

So long as a given group of animals retains its status as of only academic interest, the taxonomic literature dealing with it remains relatively restricted and the authors relatively few, so that it is not especially difficult for systematists to keep themselves informed in respect to current publication. Thus, in the days of Rudolphi, Dujàrdin, and Diesing, the nematodes were of interest chiefly as zoological objects, and authors sought knowledge regarding them primarily for the sake of knowledge. True, a few genera like "*Ascaris*" and "*Strongylus*" were of some slight interest in human and veterinary medicine, but this fact played a distinctly secondary *rôle* in nematological studies.

Gradually the point of view changed as Zenker, Leuckart, Cobbold, Manson, R. Blanchard, and others, pointed out the far-reaching medical and economic bearings of nematology. Some of us, whose hair has already turned gray, lived through the transitional stage of the subject, and can recall the days when our colleagues in other groups—still on an academic basis—looked upon us just a little askance and even expressed regret that we were drifting away from purely academic to applied science as we studied the effects produced by nematodes and sought measures to combat them.

What a changed viewpoint exists to-day ! With no disrespect to early authors, it may be truly said that the present tendency is to seek knowledge for the sake of the good it will do rather than for the sake of knowledge itself. And with this changed viewpoint, the number of workers has increased, the literature has grown, known genera and species have multiplied x-fold, and it is becoming increasingly difficult for an investigator to orientate himself in nematology. The seriousness of this situation becomes the more evident when the fact is considered that as the geographic distribution of the workers extends away from library centres, such as Berlin, London, Paris, Vienna, Washington, etc., the investigators on the periphery labour under a radially increasing handicap.

The authors of this book have kindly given me the opportunity of looking through their proof sheets, and in this perusal four thoughts in particular have occurred to me to which, as a member of the passing generation, I take the liberty of giving verbal expression.

As I compare the early history of helminthology, and its outstanding spirit to seek knowledge for the sake of knowledge, with the present tendency to seek knowledge for the sake of its potential practical application to human and animal welfare, it is difficult to escape a comparison between the man who seeks money for the sake of money and the man who seeks money in order to apply it to the practical benefit of mankind. This does not mean that I view Rudolphi as an Intellectual Miser ; far from it, for he bequeathed his accumulated knowledge to us. It does, however, mean that in the rising generation of helminthologists I see a motive which is not apparent in the early literature of Goeze, Batsch, Rudolphi, and Zeder. They dug the ground and laid the foundations which have made it possible for later generations to continue the structure, from the upper story of which the rising generation of students obtain a view denied to their fore-runners of the eighteenth century and of the early part of the nineteenth.

The second thought is that in this broadened view of the rising generation, it is to be confidently hoped that workers will not overlook the fact that the broader and more modern view of applied helminthology cannot widen indefinitely without extending the foundation in various horizontal radii. The time will never come when a man or woman can apply knowledge without first gaining it. Applied science can never divorce itself from abstract science. A man cannot give without first gaining, despite the fact that the Intellectual Miser can gain without later giving. Therefore, in our efforts to apply knowledge, let us not go to an extreme and exhaust our stock, but rather let there be a well-planned effort—as exampled by this book—continually to build up and systematize the knowledge which we hope to apply.

The third thought which arises in my mind in this pleasurable perusal of the proof sheets is a cold-blooded mathematical calculation. Here is a book which will enable many men on the periphery of library facilities to have telephone communication, so to speak, with the library centres ; and I am wondering what percentage of the working hours, of their colleagues, Yorke and Maplestone have saved by bringing together in condensed form this wealth of very technical information. In other words, have they made our lives, from now on, 5, 10, 15, or 20 per cent. more efficient ?

The fourth thought is addressed to the unborn helmintho-logist :—

MY DEAR UNBORN COLLEAGUE :

When you consult this book, you will find in it some views with which you will not agree. This will be the inevitable result of an advance in knowledge after the publication of this volume. And as you differ with taxonomic views expressed here, so will your successors modify your views as their knowledge increases. These changes of view from generation to generation are inevitable unless Science stagnates.

This work by Yorke and Maplestone was written in order to save your time and to make you more efficient in your professional life. It has cost them many hours and days of patient labour. It has not been prepared in order to gain a reputation. It is a labour of love on their part in order to help you. See that you do for the generation which follows you, what Yorke and Maple-stone have done for you.

CHARLES WARDELL STILES,

Professor of Zoology, U.S. Public Health Service.

WASHINGTON, D. C.

PREFACE

NOTWITHSTANDING the vast amount of work which has been done on the Nematode parasites of man and other vertebrate animals, it is remarkable that, since the time of Dujardin, Diesing, and Schneider, nobody has attempted to envisage the whole subject and bring together into a single volume an account of all the known Nematode parasites. In our work at the Liverpool School of Tropical Medicine, where we frequently have to deal with large collections of parasites, we have been forcibly impressed with the fact that the task of identification would be greatly simplified if we had at our disposal a volume of this nature. The literature on the subject is so enormous and so scattered that without the assistance of a large reference library even experts would find it almost impossible to place many nematodes in their proper genera, and for those who have no special knowledge of the subject the task is hopeless.

It was mainly with the object of simplifying the process of identifying Nematode parasites that we have undertaken this work. We have confined ourselves to a description and classification of the genera, not only because any attempt to deal with all the species would be a task far too great for the time at our disposal, but also because it is very doubtful whether, in view of the wholly inadequate description available of vast numbers of species, anything is to be gained by attempting so ambitious a work at the present moment. After the description of each genus we have, however, given a list of such species, together with their hosts, as can, with a reasonable degree of certainty, be ascribed to it. On further investigation it will probably be found that many of the species are merely synonyms, and it will of course be understood that no reference is made to large numbers of the earlier species, knowledge of which is not sufficient to permit of their classification.

In framing our generic definitions we have kept the type species prominently in mind and consequently in certain cases further knowledge will doubtless show that we have included points of merely specific value. Whilst in most cases we have illustrated the genus by drawings of the type species, in a few instances we have been compelled to use other species for this purpose.

In preparing this work, we have been fortunate in possessing, in the Museum of the Liverpool School of Tropical Medicine, a very large and representative collection of Nematodes, and have so far as is possible relied for our illustrations and descriptions on personal observation, but it need hardly be mentioned that we have of necessity borrowed copiously from the work of others whose names are too numerous to mention. We cannot, however, refrain from paying special tribute to Stiles and Hassall's " Index Catalogue of Nematodes "—a truly indispensable volume and one without which it would have been impossible for us to have undertaken this work. Amongst other modern authors to whom we must express particular obligation are Railliet and Henry, Baylis, Hall, Lane, Leiper, Ransom, Seurat, Skrjabin, and Travassos. We are also specially indebted to Dr. J. W. Scott Macfie, and Mr. Noel Pillers for much assistance and material, and to Professor Stiles, who has kindly read the proofs of this volume, for much friendly criticism and many valuable suggestions.

At the end of the volume is a list of references which, although it represents only a small fraction of the total literature, is nevertheless of considerable length and mentions those papers which we have found of value for the purpose in view. In order to avoid constant repetition of references throughout the text, we have adopted the plan of numbering the list, which is arranged alphabetically, and of placing after each genus the numbers relating to the references which bear upon it.

We offer no apologies for the presentation of this work, as we are satisfied that it will prove useful to the expert as a book of reference, and to the novice as a reliable guide in his endeavour to allocate the various Nematode parasites to their respective genera.

W. Y.
P. A. M.

TABLE OF CONTENTS

	PAGE
INTRODUCTION	1
SUPERFAMILY *RHABDIASOIDEA*	16
,, *TRICHUROIDEA*	20
,, *STRONGYLOIDEA*	33
,, *DIOCTOPHYMOIDEA*	176
,, *OXYUROIDEA*	181
,, *ASCAROIDEA*	254
,, *SPIRUROIDEA*	288
,, *FILARIOIDEA*	387
GENERA INSUFFICIENTLY KNOWN AND OF UNCERTAIN SYSTEMATIC POSITION	443
COLLECTIVE GROUP NAMES FOR IMMATURE NEMATODES	449
GLOSSARY AND EXPLANATORY NOTES	450
INDEX OF GENERIC NAMES AND SYNONYMS	452
INDEX OF SPECIFIC NAMES	468
REFERENCES	507

INTRODUCTION

ZOOLOGISTS have apparently not yet reached agreement even upon the question of the primary subdivision of the animal kingdom, and the NEMATHELMINTHES have been variously accorded the rank of Class, Phylum, and Subkingdom. If we accept the view that the proper status of the group is that of a Phylum, then its main subdivisions, NEMATODA and ACANTHOCEPHALA, will be Classes. Study of the literature reveals a certain justification for this view. Rudolphi (1808) divided the round worms into two Orders : the NEMATOIDEA including the genera *Filaria, Hamularia, Trichocephalus, Oxyuris, Cucullanus, Ophiostoma, Ascaris, Strongylus* and *Liorhynchus,* to which in 1819, he added *Trichosoma, Spiroptera* and *Physaloptera ;* and the ACANTHOCEPHALA including the genera *Echinorhynchus* and *Tetrarhynchus,* the second of which he transferred in 1819, to the CESTOIDEA.

Diesing (1861) in his " Revision der Nematoden " employs the same two Orders, except that he emends NEMATOIDEA to NEMATODA which he ascribes to Rudolphi. Accordingly, NEMATOIDEA and NEMATODA are absolute synonyms. The order NEMATODA as used by Diesing is however much more extensive than the Order NEMATOIDEA as employed by Rudolphi and includes in addition to many other genera, GORDIUS and MERMIS. Consequently, Diesing finds it necessary to divide the Order NEMATODA into two suborders, NEMATODA APROCTA containing *Gordius* and *Mermis,* and NEMATODA PROCTUCHA including the genera placed by Rudolphi in NEMATOIDEA together with many other allied genera. It is obvious therefore that Diesing's suborder NEMATODA PROCTUCHA corresponds to the Order NEMATOIDEA as employed by Rudolphi.

On account of its superfamily termination NEMATOIDEA is an unfortunate word, and we believe that we are justified in accepting Diesing's emendation. We therefore propose to raise the Orders NEMATODA Rudolphi, 1808, emend. Diesing, 1861, and ACANTHOCEPHALA Rudolphi, 1808, to the rank of Classes and to divide the former into two Orders corresponding to Diesing's NEMATODA APROCTA and NEMATODA PROCTUCHA. These are, however, homonyms of APROCTA Diesing, 1851, and PROCTUCHA Diesing, 1851, respectively, and cannot be used. For the former group the order GORDIACEA Siebold, 1848 (quoted in Carus, 1863) seems to be valid, and for the latter EUNEMATODA Ward, 1916.

When dealing with a large series of individuals which tend morphologically to merge gradually one into the other, it is obvious that no system of classification, which must of necessity be based on hard and fast characters, can be entirely satisfactory. Yet it is equally obvious that, for the identification of individuals, some system of classification is essential and must be attempted, however far the result falls short of idealism.

We have followed Railliet in dividing the nematode parasites of vertebrates into eight superfamilies. Railliet, however, gives no definition of the various superfamilies, but contents himself with enumerating the families and subfamilies they contain. The task of defining them is necessarily arbitrary, owing to the manner in which they tend to run one into the other (e.g., the SPIRUROIDEA into the FILARIOIDEA and the OXYUROIDEA into the ASCAROIDEA), and we have found it a matter of very great difficulty.

In the past from the time of Schneider onwards, much importance from the point of view of classification has been attached to the character of the subcutaneous musculature. This character appears to us to be of rather doubtful taxonomic value, as it is not one which is very easily observed and nothing is recorded about it in respect of the great majority of species. Moreover, it cannot have a superfamily value, as otherwise such a well-defined superfamily as the STRONGYLOIDEA would require division, and the polymyarian METASTRONGYLIDÆ have to be separated from the meromyarian TRICHOSTRONGYLIDÆ and STRONGYLIDÆ. Moreover, the genus *Spiroxys*, which is typically meromyarian, would require to be removed from the superfamily SPIRUROIDEA, many of which are typically polymyarian. Further evidence indicating the difficulty of basing any classification on this character is found in such worms as *Cruzia tentaculata* (Rud., 1819) which Travassos, 1921, describes as being incompletely polymyarian ; and finally Seurat (1920), in discussing the great importance in classification attributed by Schneider to myological characters, states that in reality these characters are not absolute and that the two types of structure can exist not only in forms belonging to the same genus, but also in the same species, e.g., in *Falcaustra lambdiensis* Seurat, 1918, the subventral muscle fields exhibit one polymyarian sublateral area and one meromyarian sublateral area. We have, therefore, decided to ignore this character in our definitions and to have recourse to characters which are more easily determined and more generally recorded.

The first superfamily RHABDIASOIDEA differs from all the others in that it is based on a biological character and not on particular morphological features. Railliet created the RHABDIA-SOIDEA to include all the heterogenetic parasitic nematodes. In these forms the parasitic stage is not differentiated into males and females, but is hermaphroditic or parthenogenetic, whilst the free-living stages may or may not exhibit sexual differentiation before reaching the infective stage. It might be noted here that Travassos (1919) has placed the ATRACTIDÆ in this superfamily, but as hardly anything is known of the life-history of these parasites, except that the parasitic forms are sexually differentiated, nothing seemed to be gained by following Travassos in this respect and we have preferred to leave them in the superfamily OXYUROIDEA.

As the superfamily name ANGIOSTOMOIDEA Hall, 1916, is still used by some modern writers, it seems desirable to point out that Dujardin placed in his genus *Angiostoma* two species, viz.—*A. entomelas* and *A. limacis*, the former of which is heterogenetic, but not the latter. The type of the genus has been decided both by designation and by absolute tautonymy (Stiles and Hassall, 1905) to be the non-heterogenetic form *A. limacis* from *Limax rufa*, and consequently *A. entomelas* and the heterogenetic forms which have been ascribed by various authors to the genus *Angiostoma* must be removed from it. In 1905, Stiles and Hassall erected the genus *Rhabdias* for the heterogenetic nematode *Ascaris bufonis* Schrank, 1788, found in the lung of the toad, and it is to this genus that *Angiostoma entomelas* Duj. now belongs (Seurat, 1916) ; the superfamily name of the heterogenetic group is consequently RHABDIASOIDEA and not ANGIOSTOMOIDEA.

With regard to the remaining seven superfamilies, an attempt must be made to define them on morphological characters and this is a somewhat arbitrary and difficult task.

The TRICHUROIDEA form a well-defined group based on the character of the œsophagus, which is peculiar in that it consists of a delicate membranous tube running in part of its length at least through the centre of a chain of single cells, thus giving an effilate appearance to the anterior (œsophageal) portion of the worms.

The worms belonging to this superfamily are divided into two families, viz., TRICHURIDÆ and TRICHINELLIDÆ, depending on whether or not the male possesses a spicule or copulatory sheath. The former family is conveniently subdivided into two subfamilies, viz., the TRICHURINÆ, in which the anterior (œsophageal) part of the body is longer and much more delicate than the posterior, and the CAPILLARIINÆ, in which the anterior (œsophageal) part of the body is not longer, and only slightly more delicate, than the posterior. We have decided to separate off the genus *Trichosomoides* from the second family TRICHINELLIDÆ, which is characterized by the absence of a spicule and a copulatory sheath, and to place it in a new family TRICHOSOMOIDIDÆ, because the two sexes are of very different sizes and during the greater part of its adult life the male is parasitic in the vagina or uterus of the female, and because they are parasites of the genito-urinary system. It is to be noted that Hall (1916) has already created for this nematode a subfamily TRICHOSOMOIDINÆ, which he placed in the TRICHINELLIDÆ.

There is some doubt regarding the correct name of this superfamily, since TRICHINELLOIDEA Hall, 1916, preceded TRI-CHUROIDEA Railliet, 1916. Hall based his superfamily on the family TRICHINELLIDÆ Ward, 1907, in which he places all the genera belonging to the superfamily, apparently not recognizing the family TRICHURIDÆ Railliet, 1915. As Railliet (1916) points out the genus *Trichuris*, based on the species *Ascaris trichiura* Linnæus, 1771, is undoubtedly the central genus of the super-family, and Baird (1853) actually made a family TRICHOCEPHALIDÆ for the genus *Trichocephalus*, of which *Ascaria trichiura* Linnæus is the type. For these reasons it seems to us desirable to accept TRICHUROIDEA as the superfamily name.

The STRONGYLOIDEA form another well-defined superfamily characterized by the presence in the male of a cuticular bursa copulatrix. This is a cuticular formation completely surrounding the posterior extremity of the worm on its dorsal and lateral surfaces and sometimes also on the ventral surface, not extending forwards along the body laterally, but prolonged beyond the posterior extremity which it encloses. It consists typically of two lateral lobes united dorsally by a dorsal lobe, but the latter is frequently small or even undefined, and sometimes the lateral lobes are united ventrally by a special ventral lobe or lobes. It is supported by prolongations of subcuticular substance known as rays. The term bursa is sometimes used in referring to the lateral cuticular expansions (caudal alæ) seen on the tails of many of the OXYUROIDEA, SPIRUROIDEA, and FILARIOIDEA, *e.g.*, in the genus *Physaloptera*, but it is better limited to the terminal cuticular formation seen in the STRONGYLOIDEA.

The numerous nematodes constituting the superfamily

STRONGYLOIDEA can conveniently be divided into two groups according to whether they are parasites of the alimentary canal or of the respiratory system, and those belonging to each group can again be subdivided on the character of the buccal cavity. It is upon these points that the various families are separated one from the other. Railliet (1916) considers that the bursate nematodes found in the alimentary canal should be divided into two families only, TRICHOSTRONGYLIDÆ and STRONGYLIDÆ. Whilst we have accepted the first of these in the sense in which it is employed by Railliet, i.e., for all the strongyl parasites of the alimentary canal in which the buccal capsule is rudimentary or absent, we agree with Lane (1917) and others that it is desirable to limit the definition of the STRONGYLIDÆ, and to separate off from them into other families those worms in which the oral margin of the buccal capsule is armed by ventral teeth or cutting plates—ANCYLOSTOMIDÆ, and those in which the buccal capsule is definitely bivalvular and of a complex character—DIAPHANO-CEPHALIDÆ.

The division of the family STRONGYLIDÆ into subfamilies is very necessary on account of the numerous and widely different genera it contains. The procedure is, however, a matter of great difficulty whether it is based on cephalic or on bursal characters. Railliet and Henry maintain that the form and disposition of the buccal capsule are secondary adaptations, and are consequently of less importance in classification than variations in the sexual apparatus ; they therefore have divided up the family into subfamilies on bursal characters, and on certain female characters, e.g., the position of the vulva, and the direction of the uterine tubes. Lane (1917) has clearly shown there are numerous objections to this scheme of classification ; and, indeed, the more one puts it to the test the more unsatisfactory does it appear. In our definitions of Railliet's subfamilies STRONGYLINÆ, TRICHONE-MINÆ, and ŒSOPHAGOSTOMINÆ, we have therefore relied entirely on cephalic characters, and have completely ignored the sexual characters. The definitions given are admittedly somewhat arbitrary and even unsatisfactory, but we are convinced that such a procedure gives rise to fewer difficulties, and to less ambiguity due to differences of interpretation depending on the personal element, than any attempt to base the definitions on sexual characters. Emphasis of the transverse ventral cervical groove as the essential character of the ŒSOPHAGOSTOMINÆ may at first sight appear unfortunate, as it necessitates the grouping together of genera with the buccal capsule so widely different as those exhibited by *Œsophagostomum* and *Chabertia* ; but if we exclude bursal characters, there appears to be nothing left on which to base a definition ; whereas if we do not exclude bursal characters, then we must range in the subfamily some four or five genera from marsupials, all of which exhibit a bursal formula similar to *Œsophagostomum*, but have widely different cephalic characters, and none of which possesses a transverse ventral cervical groove. Strict adherence to the above definitions has of course necessitated some reshuffling of the genera and the transference of such genera as *Œsophagodontus*, *Triodontophorus*, and *Craterostomum* from the TRICHONEMINÆ to the STRONGYLINÆ. The creation of a special subfamily KILULUMINÆ Thapar, 1923, for the genus *Kiluluma* appears to us to be unnecessary and undesirable. For the genus *Stephanurus*, which is met with in renal and perirenal tissue, Railliet, Henry, and Bauche (1919) created the subfamily STEPHANURINÆ, which is placed in the STRONGYLIDÆ.

The ANCYLOSTOMIDÆ are divided, as suggested by Lane (1917), into the subfamilies ANCYLOSTOMINÆ and NECATORINÆ, according to whether the ventral cutting organs on the oral margin of the buccal capsule are teeth or plates. We adhere to the name NECATORINÆ, although it is preceded by BUNOSTOMINÆ Looss, 1911, on account of the considerable discussion which still continues concerning the status of the generic name *Bunostomum*. More recently Lane (1923) has created a third subfamily AGRIO-STOMINÆ for the genus *Agriostomum*, but we have been unable to discover any particular advantage for this. For the genus *Strongylacantha* we have found it necessary, on account of its peculiar buccal armature, to erect a new subfamily STRONGYLACANTHINÆ, which we have with some diffidence placed in the ANCYLOSTOMIDÆ, although possibly it should be referred to the TRICHOSTRONGYLIDÆ.

Railliet (1916) has created the subfamily DELETROCEPHALINÆ for the genera *Deletrocephalus* and *Codiostomum*, which are parasites of birds, and to this subfamily Baylis and Daubney (1922) have referred tentatively the genus *Diaphanocephalus*. The genus *Deletrocephalus* requires re-investigation, and *Codiostomum*, which we have had the opportunity of studying, undoubtedly resembles very closely the genus *Strongylus*, and we have therefore transferred it to the STRONGYLINÆ. For these reasons we have adopted the family DIAPHANOCEPHALIDÆ Travassos, 1919, to include the bursate nematodes with a bivalvular buccal capsule, parasitic in reptiles, and we have left unplaced, pending further investigation, the genus *Deletrocephalus*, which is found in the American ostrich.

In subdividing the family TRICHOSTRONGYLIDÆ, it is convenient, as Travassos (1914) has suggested, to unite into one sub-family HELIGMOSOMINÆ Travassos, 1914, all those genera with a single set of female genitalia ; and to divide the remainder into two other subfamilies TRICHOSTRONGYLINÆ Leiper, 1908, and AMIDO-STOMINÆ Travassos, 1919, according to whether the buccal capsule is absent or rudimentary, or whether it is relatively well-developed ; the last group, AMIDOSTOMINÆ, obviously occupies an intermediate position between the STRONGYLIDÆ and the TRICHOSTRONGYLIDÆ.

On studying the TRICHOSTRONGYLIDÆ as a whole, and more especially the TRICHOSTRONGYLINÆ, one cannot but be impressed with the almost ludicrous extent to which minute differences in the bursal formula have been made a pretext for the erection of new genera, and in view of the variations in minor detail of the bursal formula, which are now known to be exhibited by certain species of the STRONGYLOIDEA, it does not seem unlikely that further knowledge will necessitate the sinking of many of the genera of this subfamily. A somewhat similar state of things is seen in the TRICHONEMINÆ, where we ourselves have found it necessary to sink a number of genera, the sole claim for existence of which depended on minutiæ of the bursal formula, which we are satisfied in certain cases is hardly even of specific value.

The bursate nematodes in the respiratory system are similarly divided into two families, viz., SYNGAMIDÆ, in which there is a well-developed chitinous buccal capsule, and METASTRONGYLIDÆ, in which the buccal capsule is rudimentary or absent. Both these families are small and they do not require further subdivision into subfamilies. The hitherto incompletely known genera *Pseudalius*, *Stenurus*, and *Prosthecosacter*, parasitic in the respiratory system of marine mammals, have recently been re-investigated by Baylis and Daubney (1925). Although these authors have placed these genera in the METASTRONGYLIDÆ, we have, on account of the rudimentary development of the bursa, followed Railliet in grouping them in a family PSEUDALIIDÆ.

The superfamily DIOCTOPHYMOIDEA, characterized by the presence in the male of a bell-shaped muscular copulatory bursa, is a small group and contains but a single family.

Considerable difficulty is involved in separating the next two superfamilies, viz., OXYUROIDEA and ASCAROIDEA. Railliet con-siders that the essential distinction between the two is that the first is meromyarian and the second polymyarian. We have, however, already referred to certain objections to emphasizing this character in classification and also to the fact that it cannot be regarded as of superfamily value ; and we prefer therefore to follow Travassos (1920) in regarding the presence of a posterior bulb in the œsophagus as the essential characteristic of the superfamily OXYUROIDEA. The adoption of this definition of the OXYUROIDEA has necessitated the removal of the genus *Ascaridia* from the family HETERAKIDÆ, and the transference of the rest of this family from the ASCAROIDEA to the OXYUROIDEA. It must be confessed, however, that we have not been absolutely consistent in regard to the above definition of the OXYUROIDEA : the genus *Dujardinia*, although it possesses a definite œsophageal bulb, resembles so closely the ANISAKINÆ in other respects, that we have been compelled to leave it in this subfamily of the ASCAROIDEA. Moreover, certain of the ATRACTIDÆ, which we have placed in the OXYUROIDEA, exhibit but a very ill-defined bulb at the posterior end of the œsophagus, but taking the family as a whole, there seems to us to be no reasonable ground for not including it in the OXYUROIDEA. With these qualifications, however, we have adhered strictly to the conception that the presence of a posterior œsophageal bulb is the essential character of the superfamily OXYUROIDEA.

In considering the primary divisions of the OXYUROIDEA, it appears reasonable to divide them into two groups, the first including those forms which possess single female genitalia, and the second including those which possess double female genitalia. For the first group Travassos (1919) has erected the family ATRACTIDÆ. With regard to the second group, which comprises the great majority of the worms belonging to the superfamily, we consider there is ample precedent for adopting the family CRUZIIDÆ erected by Travassos (1917) for the genus *Cruzia*, on the ground that it exhibits an intestinal diverticulum ; and we have separated the remainder into the OXYURIDÆ Cobbold, 1864, in which there is no special development of the precloacal musculature, and into three other families, viz., HETERAKIDÆ, SUBULURIDÆ, and KATHLANIIDÆ, in which the precloacal musculature is strongly developed—usually in the form of a sucker or pseudosucker.

We have felt it desirable to separate the genus *Subulura* and its allied genera from the HETERAKIDÆ, and to erect for them a new family SUBULURIDÆ, owing to the absence in the latter worms of the three large lips characteristic of the HETERAKIDÆ, the presence of a definite cylindrical vestibule armed with teeth at its base, and the more feeble development of its precloacal sucker, which is neither circular nor surrounded by a chitinous rim as in the HETERAKIDÆ. The family KATHLANIIDÆ Travassos, 1918,

seems to occupy an intermediate position between the HETERA-
KIDÆ and the SUBULURIDÆ. It is characterized by the presence
of three definite lips, by a vestibule, and usually by a sucker
without a chitinous rim, although occasionally there may be no
definite sucker but merely a strongly-developed precloacal
musculature ; finally, the œsophageal bulb is usually preceded
by a definite swelling so that the end of the œsophagus presents
the appearance of an hour-glass.

In dealing with the very large family OXYURIDÆ, we have
followed Railliet and Henry in dividing it into four subfamilies,
according to the presence of one or two spicules and to the presence
or absence of a gubernaculum ; and similarly we have divided the
ATRACTIDÆ into three subfamilies on the same characters.

Whilst this procedure may be zoologically sound, and is cer-
tainly useful failing other more pronounced characters exhibited
by both sexes, it is in practice very unsatisfactory, because the
classification is based on the characters of the sex, which in the
case of worms belonging to this family, is notoriously the more
difficult to find ; and indeed in a large number of species now
placed in the genus *Oxyuris s.l.*, the male is still unknown. Nothing
appears to us to be gained by accepting the family PHARYNGO-
DONIDÆ which Travassos (1919) has erected for the genera
Pharyngodon, *Thelandros*, and *Tachygonetria*.

As we have removed the SUBULURINÆ from the HETERAKIDÆ,
this family now contains but a single subfamily, the HETERAKINÆ.
We have placed the genus *Hoplodontophorus* made by Turner
(1921) for the species *Oxyuris flagellum* Hemprich and Ehrenberg,
1828, in the family SUBULURIDÆ, but as it presents several well-
marked differences from the other members of this family, we
have thought it desirable to create for it a new subfamily HOPLO-
DONTOPHORINÆ. The genus *Cissophyllus* Railliet and Henry,
1912, appears to us to be more closely allied to the KATHLANIIDÆ
than to the SUBULURIDÆ, and we have therefore placed it in that
family, but in a new subfamily CISSOPHYLLINÆ.

Having eliminated the OXYUROIDEA, the definition of the
superfamily ASCAROIDEA becomes a comparatively simple matter
and we have restricted it to contain only those nematodes which
possess three large lips, and do not exhibit a bulb at the posterior
end of the œsophagus. This definition excludes the genera
Camallanus and *Cucullanus* and their allied forms from this superfamily where Railliet has tentatively placed them. Both these
genera are characterized by the bilateral symmetry of the mouth,
and for this reason we have referred them to the SPIRUROIDEA.

As regards *Camallanus* the character of the œsophagus affords strong support for this procedure, but in *Cucullanus* the structure of this organ resembles more that found in the ASCAROIDEA.

We have followed Railliet and Henry in dividing the ASCAROIDEA into two families : ASCARIDÆ, in which the alimentary canal is simple ; and HETEROCHEILIDÆ, in which it is not simple, but exhibits œsophageal, or intestinal, diverticula or cæca, or a post-œsophageal ventriculus. We have divided the ASCARIDÆ into two subfamilies, ASCARINÆ and ASCARIDIINÆ, depending on the absence or presence of a precloacal sucker. As regards the second family, we agree with Baylis that it is better to limit the sub-family HETEROCHEILINÆ Railliet and Henry, 1912, to include only the genera *Heterocheilus* and *Typhlophorus*, to place the genus *Gœzia* and the genus *Crossophorus* in special subfamilies GŒZIINÆ (Travassos, 1919) Baylis, 1920, and CROSSOPHORINÆ Baylis, 1920, and to group all the remaining genera which do not exhibit any special cuticular characters in the subfamily ANISA-KINÆ Railliet and Henry, 1912.

Whilst the two remaining superfamilies, viz., SPIRUROIDEA and FILARIOIDEA, are clearly separated from the previous super-families, it is by no means easy to draw a sharp line of demarcation between them, and both can be generally described as slender and filiform with a long slender œsophagus. The SPIRUROIDEA possess, as a rule, two lateral lips, they usually exhibit a chitinous buccal capsule or vestibule, so that the œsophagus does not approach the anterior extremity of the worm, and the vulva is usually situated in the middle of the body or posterior to it ; in the FILARIOIDEA the mouth is usually simple and without lips, the buccal cavity or vestibule is absent or rudimentary, so that the œsophagus approaches closely to the anterior extremity, and the vulva is almost invariably in, or close to, the œsophageal region of the body. Whilst these morphological distinctions suffice to separate the two superfamilies in the vast majority of instances, there are undoubtedly forms which appear to occupy an intermediate position, and to our mind the essential difference between the two is that whilst the SPIRUROIDEA are parasites of the alimentary canal, of the respiratory system, or of the oral or nasal cavities, the FILARIOIDEA are tissue parasites. The question is one of very great difficulty and it is only by carefully con-sidering morphological characters in conjunction with the site in which the parasite is found, that it is possible in some instances to reach a conclusion regarding the superfamily in which the worm should be classified.

In attempting to define the numerous families comprising the SPIRUROIDEA we have attached particular importance to the formation of the head, and to the presence of special cuticular structures such as cordons or spines. The TETRAMERIDÆ Travassos, 1914, form a well-defined family for those SPIRUROIDEA exhibiting marked sexual dimorphism. We have grouped together all those forms which are provided with prominent cephalic appendages into the family ANCYRACANTHIDÆ Railliet, 1916, and this, as will be referred to later, has necessitated the transference of a considerable number of genera previously placed in other families. The family HEDRURIDÆ Railliet, 1916, contains only the genus *Hedruris* which is characterized by its four highly specialized lips, and by the peculiar fixation organ on the tail of the female. We have limited the family CAMALLANIDÆ Railliet and Henry, 1915, to those forms which possess a large chitinous buccal capsule ; and we have accepted the family CUCULLANIDÆ Cobbold, 1864, for those worms in which the head consists of two large lateral lips and the œsophagus is dilated anteriorly to form a pseudo-buccal capsule.

It appears to us desirable to limit the family ACUARIIDÆ Seurat, 1913, to include only those SPIRUROIDEA which exhibit cuticular cordons, and to separate off into the family PHYSALOPTERIDÆ Leiper, 1908, those which, while they resemble the ACUARIIDÆ in possessing large simple lateral lips, do not exhibit cuticular cordons, but are usually provided with a cuticular collarette. We have accepted with some slight modification the definition of GNATHOSTOMIDÆ Railliet, 1895, given by Baylis and Lane (1920) ; but, while we regard the peculiar formation of the lips as one of the chief features of this family, it seems to us to be simpler to consider the presence of a cuticular head bulb as the essential character, and for this reason we have removed the genus *Spiroxys* from this family and placed it with the forms exhibiting somewhat similar lips, *e.g.*, *Hartertia* and *Protospirura*, in the family SPIRURIDÆ. We have extended the family RICTULARIIDÆ to include all the SPIRUROIDEA which do not possess cordons, but are armed with chitinous hook-like spines arranged in longitudinal rows or circles along the whole, or anterior portions, of the body. The family SEURATIDÆ was made by Railliet (1916) to include the genus *Seuratum*, which is peculiar in possessing a short entirely muscular œsophagus and in exhibiting longitudinal dark bands on the cuticle. The remaining families, SPIRURIDÆ Oerley, 1885, and THELAZIIDÆ Railliet, 1916, are based more or less on negative characters. Railliet, who erected the family THELAZIIDÆ, placed in it eight genera and gave a long definition which contains, however, only a single definite point, viz., that the tail of the male is provided on each side with a linear row of numerous preanal papillæ. He includes in the family, forms with cephalic appendages and forms without cephalic appendages, forms with caudal alæ in the male and forms without caudal alæ, and forms from such widely different sites as the orbital regions of mammals and birds and the alimentary canal and air vessels of birds and fishes. Railliet's definition of the family is therefore not entirely satisfactory, the more especially as when we turn to the genus *Oxyspirura*, which is included in the family, we find that the number of preanal papillæ varies from two to twenty-eight. In view of the somewhat ill-defined nature of this family, it appears to us better to remove from it those genera which are provided with cephalic appendages and to place them in a subfamily SCHISTOROPHINÆ Travassos, 1918, which we refer to the family ANCYRACANTHIDÆ. While the general distinction between the SPIRURIDÆ and the THELAZIIDÆ, viz., that in the former the male is always provided with caudal alæ supported by four pairs (rarely five or six) of pedunculated preanal papillæ, and in the latter the male is usually without caudal alæ and the preanal papillæ are sessile and numerous, undoubtedly holds good in the great majority of cases, yet it is not entirely satisfactory.

Most of the above mentioned families are small and contain but a limited number of genera and in only three cases is it necessary to subdivide the families by the formation of two or more subfamilies. As we have enlarged the family ANCYRA-CANTHIDÆ by the introduction of the subfamily SCHISTOROPHINÆ, into which we have placed seven genera removed from the THELAZIIDÆ and other families on account of their cephalic ornamentation, it became necessary to erect a new subfamily ANCYRACANTHINÆ for the genus *Ancyracanthus*, the most striking feature of which is its possession of four remarkable feathered processes arising from the head and directed outwards and backwards. We have subdivided the CUCULLANIDÆ into two new subfamilies, CUCULLANINÆ, for the genus *Cucullanus* and other allied forms without an intestinal cæcum and with two ovaries, and DACNITOIDINÆ, for the genus *Dacnitoides* Ward and Magath, 1916, which possesses an intestinal cæcum and only one ovary. Finally, the family SPIRURIDÆ is divided into the subfamilies, SPIRURINÆ Railliet, 1915, SPIROXYINÆ Baylis and Lane, 1920, ARDUENNINÆ Railliet and Henry, 1911, and GONGYLONEMINÆ Hall, 1916, according to the characters of the lips and vestibule, and whether or not the anterior portion of the body is ornamented with cuticular plaques.

The FILARIOIDEA are divided into two families, viz., FILARIIDÆ (Cobbold, 1864) Claus, 1885, in which the females are not enormously longer than the males and the vulva does not atrophy in the gravid worm, and DRACUNCULIDÆ Leiper, 1912, in which the female is enormously larger than the male and the vulva is atrophied in the gravid worm. Whilst the latter family contains only a couple of genera, the former is very large and contains numerous genera.

Up to the present the FILARIIDÆ have been divided into four subfamilies: FILARIINÆ Stiles, 1907, ONCHOCERCINÆ Leiper, 1911, DIPLOTRIÆNINÆ Skrjabin, 1916, and MICROPLEURINÆ Baylis and Daubney, 1922. The researches of Seurat, Skrjabin, and others during the past few years have, however, revealed the necessity for the creation of many new genera of filariid worms; and in attempting to classify the numerous genera now recognized, we have found it necessary to limit the scope of the existing sub-families which, with the exception of DIPLOTRIÆNINÆ Skrjabin, 1916, have not been defined, and to erect a number of others. Turning to *Filaria martis* Gmelin, 1790, which is the type species upon which the whole family is based, we find that the most striking characters are the simple mouth bounded by minute lips, the smooth cuticle without bosses or annular thickenings, the unequal and dissimilar spicules in the male, and the anterior position of the vulva in the female. We have therefore limited the subfamily FILARIINÆ to include FILARIIDÆ with these characters. A second group only differing from the above by the fact that the spicules are equal, or subequal and similar, we have united into a new subfamily APROCTINÆ. We have considered the existence of annular cuticular thickenings as characteristic of the subfamily ONCHOCERCINÆ Leiper, 1911, and similarly have erected a new subfamily LOAINÆ for those FILARIIDÆ which exhibit cuticular bosses. Skrjabin regards the presence of chitinous formations, exhibiting a tendency to divide into three portions, on each side of the head—situated either superficially on the cuticle, or in the interior of the body beside the œsophagus—as the essential character of his subfamily DIPLOTRIÆNINÆ; he includes in the subfamily the genera *Diplotriæna* Railliet and Henry, 1909, *Serratospiculum* Skrjabin, 1916, and *Contorto-spiculum* Skrjabin, 1916. We have carefully examined these genera, and also a number of allied forms, and have reached the conclusion, that the trident-like structures embedded in the body on each side of the anterior end of the œsophagus in *Diplotriæna* are so characteristic and essentially different from the superficial epaulette-like formations existing in *Serratospiculum* and *Contortospiculum*, that it is better to limit the subfamily DIPLOTRIÆNINÆ to the genus *Diplotriæna*. We have consequently removed the other two genera to a new subfamily SETARIINÆ, characterized by the fact that the mouth is surrounded by a chitinous ring, by lateral epaulette-like structures, or by small spinous teeth.

Baylis and Daubney (1922) mention a number of characters, viz., opposed uteri, vulva placed far back from the head, short ovaries, and equal spicules, as characteristic of *Micropleura*, and suggest on these grounds that it is justifiable to regard it as the type of a new subfamily MICROPLEURINÆ. On considering the FILARIIDÆ as a whole, however, we find that the position of the vulva is the only one of these characters which can be regarded as peculiar to *Micropleura*, and hence this feature must be regarded as the essential character of the subfamily. For a similar reason, we have erected a new subfamily CRASSICAUDINÆ for the genus *Crassicauda*, which is remarkable in that the vulva is situated near the posterior extremity.

It is, of course, obvious that although the family, subfamily, and generic names are ascribed to the author who first used them, the sense in which they were first used has been frequently modified by subsequent writers, and we ourselves have freely emended definitions wherever we considered it to be desirable. No reference to such emendations has been made in the text, as to have done so would have greatly complicated matters without serving any useful purpose.

Phylum NEMATHELMINTHES Vogt [Quoted by Carus, 1863].

Definition. — Unsegmented animals, without appendages arranged on a regularly segmental plan ; usually elongated, cylindrical, or filiform ; with a body cavity in which the organs float : sexes usually separate, but some forms are hermaphroditic.

CLASS I.—*Nematoda* Rudolphi, 1808, emend. Diesing, 1861. *Nemathelminthes ;* with a gut, but without a proboscis.

CLASS II.--*Acanthocephala* Rudolphi, 1808. *Nemathelminthes ;* without a gut, but with a proboscis usually protrusible and almost invariably furnished with hooks.

CLASS NEMATODA Rudolphi, 1808, emend. Diesing, 1861.

ORDER 1.—*Eunematoda* Ward, 1916. *Nematoda ;* in which the body cavity is not lined by epithelium, the gonads being continuous with their ducts. Occasionally the posterior portion of the alimentary canal may atrophy in the sexually mature worms. Lateral chords present ; cloaca absent in the female.

ORDER 2.—*Gordiacea* Siebold, 1848 (quoted by Carus, 1863). *Nematoda ;* in which the body cavity is lined by epithelium ; the gonads are not continuous with their ducts, the ova being discharged into the body cavity and then passing into the ducts. In sexually mature worms the alimentary canal is atrophied. Lateral chords absent ; cloaca present in the female.

Order EUNEMATODA Ward, 1916.

KEY TO SUPERFAMILIES.

1. Heterogenetic, parasitic form parthenogenetic .   .   .   .   Rhabdiasoidea, p. 16.
   Not heterogenetic, parasitic forms
   sexually differentiated   .   .   2
2. Œsophagus consisting of a narrow
   tube running through the centre
   of a row of single cells for most
   of its length .   .   .   .   Trichuroidea, p. 20.
   Œsophagus not consisting of a
   narrow tube running through
   the centre of a row of single cells   3
3. Males with a bursa copulatrix   .   4
   Males without a bursa copulatrix.   5
4. Bursa copulatrix cuticular and
   supported by rays .   .   .   Strongyloidea, p. 33
   Bursa copulatrix muscular and
   not supported by rays   .   .   Dioctophymoidea, p. 176.
5. Œsophagus dilated posteriorly
   into a bulb usually containing
   a denticular apparatus and frequently separated from the rest
   of the œsophagus by a con-
   striction   .   .   .   .   Oxyuroidea p. 181.
   Œsophagus not dilated posteriorly
   into a bulb   6

6. Head with three large lobes or
    lips : relatively stout worms   .   Ascaroidea, p. 254.
    Head without three large lobes or
    lips but with two lateral lips, or
    4 or 6 small lips, or lips absent ;
    relatively slender filiform worms   7
7. Usually with two lateral lips,
    chitinous buccal cavity or
    vestibule usually present, vulva
    usually in the middle of the body
    or posterior to it; parasites of
    alimentary canal, respiratory
    system, or orbital nasal or oral
    cavities   .   .   .   .   Spiruroidea, p. 288.
    Usually without lips, buccal cavity
    or vestibule absent or rudi-
    mentary, vulva almost invari-
    ably in the œsophageal region ;
    parasites of circulatory or lym-
    phatic systems, or muscular, or
    connective, tissue, or of serous
    cavities   .   .   .   .   Filarioidea, p. 387.
    Genera of uncertain position, p. 443.

Superfamily RHABDIASOIDEA Railliet, 1916.

Syn., *Angiostomoidea* Hall, 1916.

Definition.—EUNEMATODA : parasitic forms not differentiated into males and females but hermaphroditic or parthenogenetic ; the free living forms may or may not exhibit sexual differentiation before reaching the infective stage.

FAMILY RHABDIASIDÆ RAILLIET, 1915.

Syn., *Angiostomidæ* Braun, 1895, in part.

Definition.—With the characters of the superfamily.

KEY TO GENERA.

Parasitic form : vestibule present, œso-
    phagus short, vulva near middle of
    body   .   .   .   .   .   .   Rhabdias, p. 17.
Parasitic form : vestibule absent, œso-
    phagus long, vulva in posterior part
    of body   .   .   .   .   .   Strongyloides, p. 18.

Genus RHABDIAS Stiles and Hassall, 1905.

Syn., *Rhabdonema* Leuckart, 1879, preoccupied.
Angiostoma Dujardin, 1845, in part.
Leptodera Schneider, 1866, in part, not Dujardin, 1845.

Definition.—RHABDIASIDÆ : Parasitic form.—Mouth surrounded by six insignificant lips ; sometimes with lateral flanges which are broader anteriorly than posteriorly ; vestibule short and broad ; œsophagus short, exhibiting sometimes a differentiation into two parts, and ending in a club-shaped swelling posteriorly. Posterior extremity tapers rapidly behind the anus and ends in a finely conical point ; vulva near the middle of the body ; uteri divergent and ending in a receptaculum seminis, shortly after

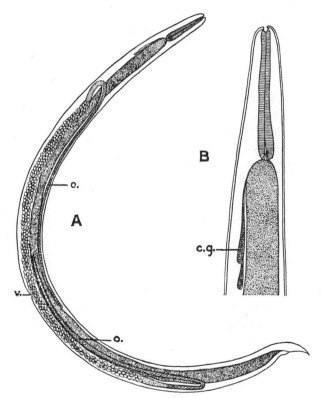

Fig. 1.—*Rhabdias bufonis.* A. Parasitic form, whole worm. *o,* ovary; *v,* vulva. × 18. B. Parasitic form, anterior extremity. *c.g,* cervical glands. × 50. (Orig.)

which the oviducts bend sharply back towards the middle of the body. Oviparous, eggs with a thin shell and containing either a fully-developed larva or a morula at deposition. Parasites of the lungs of amphibia and reptiles.

Outside the host the larvæ may develop directly into the infective stage or pass first through a sexual generation. The infective larvæ are sheathed, have a short cylindrical vestibule, and the œsophagus has two swellings.

Type species : *R. bufonis* (Schrank, 1788). 11–13 mm. In *Rana* sp., *Bufo* sp.

    Syn., *Ascaris bufonis* Schrank, 1788, not Gmelin, 1790.
        Ascaris nigrovenosa Gœze, 1800.
        Rhabdonema nigrovenosum (Gœze, 1800) Leuckart, 1879.
        Angiostomum nigrovenosum (Gœze, 1800) Linstow, 1882.
        Leptodera nigrovenosa (Gœze, 1800) Schneider 1866.

Other species :
    R. chamæleonis (Skrjabin, 1916). In *Chamæleon* sp.
    R. dujardini (Maupas, in Seurat, 1916). In *Anguis fragilis*.
    R. entomelas (Duj., 1845). In *Anguis fragilis*.
      Syn., *Angiostoma entomelas* Duj., 1845.
        Angiostoma macrostoma Linstow, 1875.
    R. fuscovenosa (Railliet, 1899). In *Tropidonotus natrix*.
    R. ophidia Goodey, 1924. In *Coluber* sp.
    R. rotundata (Linstow, 1906). In *Bufo viridis*.
    R. rubrovenosa (Schneider, 1866). In *Bufo* spp., *Pelobates* sp.
    R. sphærocephala Goodey, 1924. In *Bufo vulgaris*.

Refs. 131, 145, 186, 187, 190, 195, 304, 332, 400, 480, 481, 535, 557, 599.

Genus STRONGYLOIDES Grassi, 1879.

Syn., *Pseudorhabditis* Perroncito, 1880.

Stercoralis Tanaka, 1910.

Definition.—RHABDIASIDÆ : Parasitic form.—Body attenuated anteriorly, mouth with three small lips opening directly into a very long almost cylindrical œsophagus ; anus shortly in front of the pointed posterior extremity ; vulva in the posterior third of the body ; uteri divergent continued as the oviducts which eventually turn backwards and run towards the middle of the body as the ovaries. Oviparous, eggs containing larvæ at deposition. Parasites of the intestine of mammals.

Outside the host the larvæ may develop directly into the infective stage or pass first through a sexual generation. The infective larvæ are unsheathed, have a short cylindrical vestibule, and the œsophagus is long and almost cylindrical ; the tail ends in two small points. Free-living sexual forms.—Mouth with three very small lips, vestibule short and cylindrical ; œsophagus with two swellings separated by a constricted portion surrounded by the nerve ring, the anterior elongate and the posterior pear-shaped and containing a valvular apparatus ; anus a little distance in front of the pointed posterior extremity. Male : posterior

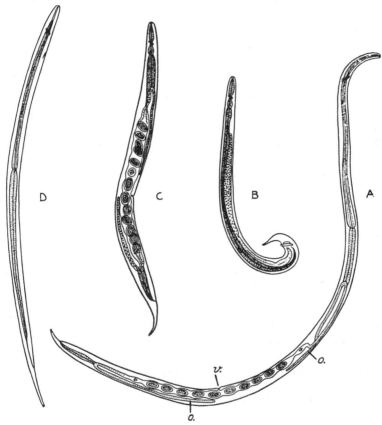

Fig. 2.—*Strongyloides stercoralis*. A. Parasitic form. *o*, ovary ; *v*, vulva. × 90. B. Free-living male. × 90. C. Free-living female. × 90. D. Infective larva. × 215. (Orig.)

extremity bent ; spicules short and equal ; gubernaculum present ; a few preanal papillæ. Female : posterior extremity tapering to a point ; vulva near the middle of the body ; uteri divergent. Usually oviparous, sometimes viviparous, eggs contain larvæ when deposited.

Type species : *S. stercoralis* (Bavay, 1876). In man. Parasitic form 2·2 mm. Free-living form ♂ 0·7 mm., ♀ 1·5 mm.

Syn., *Anguillula stercoralis* Bavay, 1876.
    Anguillula intestinalis Bavay, 1877, not Ehrenb., 1838.
    Leptodera intestinalis (Bavay, 1877) Cobbold, 1879.
    Pseudorhabditis intestinalis (Bavay, 1877) Perroncito,
      1881.
    Rhabdonema strongyloides Leuckart, 1883.
    Rhabdonema intestinale (Bavay, 1877) R. Bl. 1888.
Other species :
† *S. canis* Brumpt, 1922. In the dog.
* *S. cebus* Darling, 1911. In *Cebus* sp.
* *S. fülleborni* Linstow, 1905. In *Anthropopithecus* sp.
† *S. nasua* Darling, 1911. In *Nasua* sp.
* *S. ovocinctus* Ransom, 1911. In *Antilocapra americana*.
  S. papillosus (Wedl, 1856) Ransom, 1911. In *Capra* sp.,
    Lepus sp., *Ovis* sp., etc.
    Syn., *Rhabdonema longum* (Grassi and Segré, 1885).
* *S. Simiæ* Hung See Lu and Höppli, 1923. In macaques.
* *S. suis* (Lutz, 1894) Linstow, 1905. In ox, pig, rabbit.
  S. vituli Brumpt, 1921. In cattle.
  S. westeri Ihle, 1917. In *Equus caballus*.
Refs. 77b, 78, 90a, 200, 219, 342, 344, 375, 389.

Superfamily TRICHUROIDEA Railliet, 1916.

Syn., *Trichinelloidea* Hall, 1916.

Definition.—EUNEMATODA : anterior portion of body filiform, the œsophagus consisting of a delicate tube running, in part of its length at least, through the centre of a chain of single cells. Male : spicule single or absent. Female : one ovary.

KEY TO FAMILIES.

1. Males with a spicule or copulatory
    sheath .   .   .   .   . Trichuridæ, p. 21.
    Males without a spicule or copu-
    latory sheath .   .   . 2
2. Males parasitic in uterus of female :
    parasites of urinary system   . Trichosomoididæ, p. 31.
    Males not parasitic in uterus of
    female : parasites of gut .   . Trichinellidæ, p. 32.

---

* Chandler (1925) considers these worms varieties or sub-pecies of *papillosus,* and those marked † varieties of *Stercoralis.*

FAMILY TRICHURIDÆ RAILLIET, 1915.

Syn., *Trichocephalidæ* Baird, 1853.

Trichosomidæ Leiper, 1912.

Definition.—TRICHUROIDEA : medium to large worms ; the anterior (œsophageal) part of the body may be longer or shorter than the posterior ; posterior part of the body may be much thicker than the anterior or only slightly thicker ; mouth simple, lips inconspicuous or absent. Male : spicule single, or rarely with only a copulatory sheath. Female : vulva near termination of œsophagus. Oviparous, eggs with a thick shell, barrel-shaped, with plugs at each end, and containing when deposited an unsegmented ovum.

KEY TO SUBFAMILIES.

Anterior (œsophageal) part of body longer
 than posterior, which is much thicker . Trichurinæ, p. 21.
Anterior (œsophageal) part of body shorter
 than, or rarely equal to, posterior,
 which is only slightly thicker . . Capillariinæ, p. 23.
Trichuridæ insufficiently known, p 30.

Subfamily TRICHURINÆ Ransom, 1911.

Definition.—TRICHURIDÆ : anterior (œsophageal) portion of the body very slender and longer than the posterior part, which is much thicker and contains the reproductive organs ; posterior extremity of body blunt and rounded.

Genus TRICHURIS Roederer, 1761.

Syn., *Trichocephalus* Schrank, 1788.

Mastigodes Zeder, 1800.

Definition.—TRICHURINÆ : mouth simple ; cuticle transversely striated ; on the ventral portion of the anterior part of the body there is a broad longitudinal bacillary band formed of punctiform projections, which are the points of small rod-like structures originating in the subcuticular cells and penetrating the cuticle, they interrupt the transverse striations ; anus terminal or sub-terminal. Male : posterior end of body rolled dorsally in a spiral ; spicule surrounded by a prepuce-like sheath, which evaginates when the spicule is protruded ; external surface of sheath smooth or covered with spines. Female : posterior extremity slightly curved, but not spirally coiled ; vulva near the junction of the anterior and posterior portions of the body. Oviparous, eggs with thick brown shells, with plugs at both ends. Parasites of the intestine of mammals.

Type species : *T. trichiura* (Linnæus, 1771) Stiles, 1901.
♂ 40–45 mm., ♀ 45–50 mm.   In man.

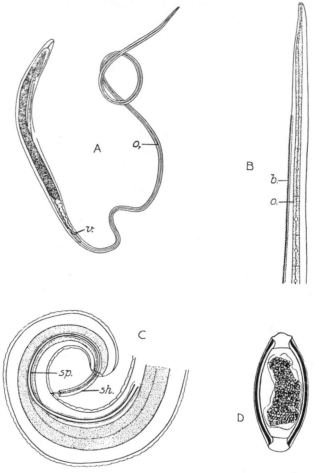

Fig. 3.—*Trichuris trichiura*.   A. Female. *o*, œsophagus ; *v*, vulva.   × 6.
     B. Anterior extremity. *b*, bacillary band ; *o*, œsophagus.   × 35.
     C. Posterior extremity of male. *sp*, spicule ; *sh*, spicule sheath.   × 35
     D. Egg.   × 560.   (Orig.)

Syn., *Ascaris trichiura* Linn., 1771.
        Trichocephalus hominis Schrank, 1788.
        Trichocephalus dispar Rud., 1802.
        Mastigodes hominis (Schrank, 1788) Zeder 1803.
Other species :
     T. alcocki (Linst., 1906).   In *Cervus eldi*.
     T. cameli (Rud., 1819).   In *Camelus* spp.

Syn., *T. echinophalla* (Nitzsch, 1849).

T. campanula (Linst., 1889). In *Felis dom.*

T. carlieri Gedoelst, 1916. In *Cricetomys gambianus.*

T. contorta (Rud., 1819). In *Georychus capensis.*

T. discolor (Linst., 1906). In *Bos indicus.*

T. fossor Hall, 1916. In *Thomomys fossor.*

T. giraffæ (Dies., 1851). In *Giraffa* sp.

T. globulosa (Linst., 1901). In *Camelus* sp.

T. gracilis (Rud., 1819). In *Dasyprocta aguti.*

T. infundibula (Linstow, 1906). In *Hystrix cristata.*

T. leporis (Froelich, 1789, Rud., 1809). In *Lepus* spp., etc.
Syn., *Trichocephalus unguiculatus* Rud., 1809.

T. megaloòn Gedoelst, 1917. In *Sciurus prevosti.*

T. muris (Schrank, 1788). In rats and mice.
Syn., *Trichocephalus nodosus* Rud., 1809.

T. opaca Barker and Noyes, 1915. In *Fiber* sp.

T. ovis (Abildg., 1795). In cattle, goat, sheep.
Syn., *T. affinis* (Rud., 1802).

T. serrata (Linst., 1879). In *Felis dom.*

T. skrjabini Baskakow, 1924. In *Camelus* spp.

T. suis (Schrank, 1788). In the pig.
Syn., *Trichocephalus apri* Gmelin, 1790.
Trichocephalus crenatus Rud., 1809.

T. vulpis (Froel., 1789). In the dog and fox.
Syn., *Trichocephalus depressiusculus* Rud., 1809.

Refs. 10, 16a, 152, 205, 403, 458, 470, 481, 593, 598, 610, 681.

Subfamily CAPILLARIINÆ Railliet, 1915.

Definition.—TRICHURIDÆ : anterior (œsophageal) portion of the body shorter than, or rarely equal to, the posterior part, which is only slightly thicker.

KEY TO GENERA.

1. With a spicule . . . . . Capillaria, p. 23.
   Without a spicule but with a copulatory
   sheath 2
2. Parasites of liver . . . . Hepaticola, p. 28.
   Parasites of lungs . . . . Eucoleus, p. 29.

Genus CAPILLARIA Zeder, 1800.

Syn., *Trichosoma* Rud., 1819.
Trichosomum Creplin, 1829.
Liniscus Duj., 1845.
Thominx Duj., 1845.
Calodium Duj., 1845.

Definition.—CAPILLARIINÆ : body capillary ; mouth simple ; cuticle with bacillary bands, dorsal, ventral, or lateral in position ; œsophagus long and gradually increasing in size posteriorly. Male : anus terminal or subterminal, small membranous caudal alæ or bursa-like structure present or absent ; spicule long and slender, surrounded by a sheath with or without spines on its

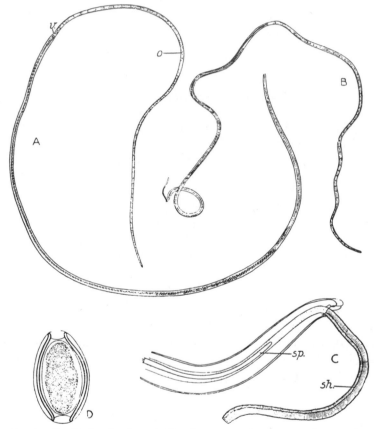

Fig. 4.—*Capillaria columbæ.* A. Female. *o*, œsophagus ; *v*, vulva. × 18. B. Male. × 18. C. Posterior extremity of male. *sh*, spicule sheath ; *sp*, spicule. × 160. D. Egg. × 500. (Orig.)

surface. Female : vulva near termination of œsophagus. Oviparous, eggs lemon-shaped, with the usual opercular plugs at the poles. Parasites of intestine, or urinary bladder of mammals, birds, etc.

Type species : *C. anatis* (Schrank, 1790). ♂ 11–13 mm., ♀ 21–28 mm. In *Anser ferus, Harelda* sp., *Merganser* spp., *Œdemia* sp., *Querquedula* sp.

Syn., *Trichocephalus anatis* Schrank, 1790.
    Trichocephalus capillaris Rud., 1809.
    Capillaria tumida Zeder, 1803.
    Trichosoma brevicolle Rud., 1819.

Other species :

C. angusta (Duj., 1845). In *Fringilla cælebs*.

C. annulosa (Duj., 1845). In rats.
    Syn., *Calodium annulosum* Duj., 1845.

C. auritæ Travassos, 1914. In *Didelphys aurita*.

C. bacillata (Eberth, 1863). In *Mus musculus*.
    Syn., *Trichosoma bacillatum* Ebert, 1863.

C. bombinatoris (Linst., 1892). In *Bombinator igneus*.

C. bovis (Schnyder, 1906). In cattle.

C. brevipes Ransom, 1911. In sheep.

C. brevis (Linst., 1877). In *Totanus fuscus*.

C. brevispicula (Linst., 1873). In *Blicca bjœrkna, Lota* sp.

C. caprimulgi (Rud., 1819). In *Caprimulgus europæus*.

C. carbonis (Rud., 1819). In *Phalacrocorax carbo*.

C. charadrii (Rud., 1819). In *Ægialitis* sp., *Himantopus* sp.

C. chrysotidis (Walter, 1866). In *Chrysotis amazonicus*.

C. collaris (Linst., 1873). In *Gallus dom.*

C. columbæ (Rud., 1819). In *Columba dom.*
    Syn., *Trichosoma columbæ* Rud., 1819.
        Calodium tenue Duj., 1845, not *Eucoleus tenuis* Duj., 1845.
        Trichosoma tenuissimum Dies., 1851, not Rud., 1803.
        Capillaria dujardini Trav., 1914.

C. contorta (Crep., 1839). In *Corvus* spp., *Sterna* sp., etc.

C. convoluta (Fourm., 1885). In *Ossifraga gigantea*.

C. corvorum (Rud., 1819). In *Corvus* sp., *Pica* sp., *Nucifraga* sp.

C. crotali (Rud., 1819). In *Crotalus terrificus*.

C. crypturi (Rud., 1819). In *Tinamus tao*.

C. curvicauda (Duj., 1845). In *Hirundo* sp., *Micropus* sp.

C. cylindrica (Eberth, 1863). In *Buteo vulgaris*.

C. dispar (Duj., 1845). In *Buteo* sp., *Falco* sp.

C. droummondi Trav., 1915. In *Cygnus* sp.

C. dubia Trav., 1917. In *Atilla cinerea*.

C. entomelas (Duj., 1845). In *Mustela foina*.

C. erinacei (Rud., 1819). In *Erinaceus europæus*

C. exigua (Duj., 1845). In *Erinaceus* sp.

C. exilis (Duj., 1845). In *Turdus merula*.
    Syn., *Trichosoma exile* Duj., 1845.

C. falconum (Rud., 1919). In *Buteo* sp., *Milvus* sp., *Circus* sp.,
  Accipiter sp.

C. feliscati Bellingham, 1844. In *Felis catus*.

C. filiformis (Linst., 1885). In *Triton* sp.

C. fringillæ (Rud., 1819). In *Fringilla cælebs*.

C. fritschi Trav., 1914. In *Malapterurus electricus*.

C. gracilis (Bellingham, 1840). In *Merluccius* spp.

C. hirundinis (Rud., 1819). In *Hirundo rustica*.

C. hydrochœri Trav., 1916. In *Hydrochœrus capibara*.

C. incrassata (Dies., 1851). In *Sorex araneus*.
  Syn., *Liniscus exilis* Duj., 1845 [homonym].

C. inflexa (Rud., 1819). In *Monticola* sp., *Turdus* sp.

C. leidyella Trav., 1915. In *Colaptes maximus*.
  Syn., *Trichosoma picorum* Leidy, 1856, not Rud., 1819.

C. leidyi (Trav., 1914). In *Mus norvegicus*.
  Syn., *Trichosomum tenuissimum* Leidy, 1891, not Rud.,
    1803, not Dies., 1851.

C. lemmi (Retzius, 1841). In *Microtus terrestris*.

C. leporis (Dies., 1851). In *Lepus timidus*.
  Syn., *Filaria pulmonalis* Froel., 1802, in part.

C. leucisci Hesse, 1923. In *Leuciscus phoxinus*.

C. linearis (Leidy, 1856). In *Felis catus*.

C. linstowi Trav., 1914. In *Talpa europæa, Crocidura* sp.

C. longevaginata (Linst., 1879). In *Alauda arvensis*.

C. longicollis (Rud., 1819). In *Gallus* sp., etc.

C. longifila (Duj., 1845). In *Accentor modularis*.

C. longipes Ransom, 1911. In antelope and sheep.

C. longispicula (Sonsino, 1889). In *Python molurus*.

C. longistriata Walton, 1923. In *Colaptes* sp.

C. manica (Duj., 1845). In *Fringilla cœlebs*.
  Syn., *Thominx manica* Duj., 1845.

C. meleagris-gallopavo (Barile, 1912). In *Meleagris* sp.

C. mingazzinii (Rizzo, 1902). In *Tropidonotus natrix*.

C. modiglianii (Parona, 1897). In *Lachesis sumatranus*.

C. mucronata (Molin, 1858). In *Mustela foina*.

C. murinæ Trav., 1914. In *Eunectes murina*.

C. muris-musculi (Dies., 1861). In *Mus musculus*.

C. muris-sylvatici (Dies., 1851). In *Mus sylvaticus*.

C. myoxi-nitelæ (Dies., 1851). In *Eliomys quercinus*.

C. obtusiuscula (Rud., 1819). In *Grus grus*.

C. ornata (Duj., 1843). In *Anthus pratensis*.

C. ovopunctata (Linst., 1873). In *Sturnus vulgaris*.

C. pachyderma (Linst., 1877). In *Podicipes fluviatilis*.

C. pachykeramota (Wedl, 1856). In *Felis tigrina.*

C. papillifer (Linst., 1877). In *Chelidon* sp., *Hirundo* sp.

C. papilligera (Raill. and Henry, 1911). In *Tetrao urogallus.*
  Syn., *Trichosoma papillosum* Blome, 1909, not Wedl, 1856.

C. blomei Travassos, 1914.

C. papillosa (Polonio, 1860). In *Mus norvegicus.*

C. parilis (Kowalewsky, 1903). In *Bubo ignavus.*

C. parvumspinosa Raill. and Henry, 1911. In *Rhea americana.*

C. picorum (Rud., 1819). In *Dendrocopus* sp., *Gecinus* spp.

C. plica (Rud., 1819). In *Canis* sp., *Vulpes* sp.

C. protracta (Duj., 1845). In *Vanellus* spp.

C. pusilla Trav., 1914. In *Sturnira lilium.*

C. putorii (Rud., 1819). In *Putorius putorius.*

C. ransomia Barker and Noyes, 1915. In *Fiber* sp.

C. recurva (Solger, 1877). In *Crocodilus americanus.*

C. resecta (Duj., 1843). In *Corous* sp., *Garrulus* sp., etc.

C. retusa (Raill., 1893). In *Gallus dom.*, *Numida* sp.

C. rigidula (Duj., 1845). In *Accentor modularis.*

C. rubra (Linton, 1892). In *Spizella socialis.*

C. schmidtii (Linstow, 1874). In *Mus norvegicus.*

C. similis (Kowalewsky, 1903). In *Turdus pilaris.*

C. sonsinoi (Parona, 1897). In *Zamenis gemonensis.*

C. speciosa (Beneden, 1873). In *Vespertilio* spp.

C. spinulosa (Linst., 1890). In *Nyroca ferina.*

C. spiralis (Molin, 1858). In *Plegadis falcinellus.*

C. splenæca (Duj., 1843). In *Sorex araneus.*
  Syn., *Trichosoma splenæcum* Duj., 1843.

Calodium splenæcum Duj., 1845.

C. striata (Linst., 1879). In *Accipiter nisus.*

C. strumosa (Reibisch, 1893). In *Gallus dom.*, *Phasianus* sp.

C. talpæ (Siebold, 1850). In *Talpa europæa.*

C. tenuissima (Rud., 1803). In *Strix* sp., *Asio* sp., *Bubo* sp.,etc.

C. tomentosa (Duj., 1843). In *Idus melanotus*, *Scardinius* sp.,
  Cyprinus sp.

C. totani (Linst., 1875). In *Tringoides* sp.

C. tridens (Duj., 1845). In *Sylvia luscinia.*

C. triloba (Linst., 1875). In *Vanellus* sp.

C. tritonis-cristati (Dies., 1861). In *Triton cristatus.*

C. tritonis-punctati (Dies., 1851). In *Triton* spp.

C. tuberculata (Linst., 1914). In *Acipenser ruthenus.*

C. turdi (Rud., 1819). In *Geocichla mollissima.*

C. vanelli (Rud., 1819). In *Vanellus vanellus.*

C. vespertilionis (Rud., 1819). In *Vespertilio noctula.*

Travassos (1915) has divided the genus *Capillaria* into two subgenera :—

Subgenus CAPILLARIA (Zeder, 1800) Travassos, 1915.

Definition.—CAPILLARIA in which the sheath of the spicule is not provided with spines. Contains the species : *anatis, angusta, annulosa, auritæ, brevispicula, chrysotidis, columbæ, convoluta, curvicauda, droummondi, entomelas, exigua, exilis, incrassata, inflexa, leidyella, longipes, longicollis, longevaginata, longifila, longispicula, mingazzinii, mucronata, murinæ, obtusiuscula, ornata, ovopunctata, pachykeramota, pusilla, resecta, retusa, rigidula, schmidtii, similis, speciosa, splenæca,* and *tuberculata.*

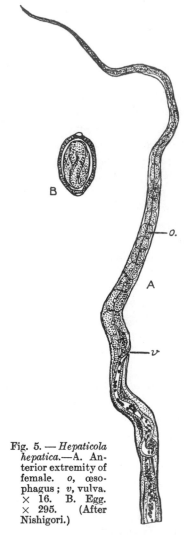

Subgenus THOMINX (Duj., 1845) Travassos, 1915.

Definition.—CAPILLARIA in which the sheath of the spicule is provided with spines. Contains the species : *manica, bacillata, collaris, contorta, dispar, dubia, falconua, filiformis, gracilis, hydrochœri, meleagris, pachyderma, papillifer, papilligera, parilis, spinulosa, striata, strumosa, tenuissima, totani, tridens,* and *triloba.*

Refs. 131, 205, 216, 403, 458, 477, 572, 627, 659, 681, 682.

Genus HEPATICOLA Hall, 1916.

Definition.—CAPILLARIINÆ: body capillary ; mouth simple ; cuticle apparently without bacillary band. Male : anterior and posterior portions of the body about equal ; spicule absent, but represented by a membranous sheath. Female : anterior portion of body half as long as the posterior portion ; vulva prominent, opening in œsophageal region. Oviparous, eggs of the usual type, but with the outer shell striate. Parasites of liver of rodents (and man).

Fig. 5. — *Hepaticola hepatica.*—A. Anterior extremity of female. *o*, œsophagus ; *v*, vulva. × 16. B. Egg. × 295. (After Nishigori.)

Type species : *H. hepatica* (Bancroft, 1893). ♂ and ♀ 40–50 mm. In *Rattus* spp., *Lepus* sp., man.

Syn., *Trichocephalus hepaticus* Bancroft, 1893.

Other species : *H. soricicola* Nishigori, 1924. In *Sorex* sp.

Refs. 9, 125a, 205, 373a, 403, 405.

Genus EUCOLEUS Dujardin, 1845.

Definition.—CAPILLARIINÆ : anterior (œsophageal) portion of the body much shorter than the posterior portion ; dorsal and ventral bacillary bands present. Male : tail consisting of two short lobes united by a delicate membrane ; spicule absent, represented by a copulatory sheath, protrusible and thickly armed with fine spines. Female : posterior extremity curved slightly, tail blunt ; vulva lateral, not projecting, and opening at the termination of the œsophagus. Oviparous, eggs whitish with

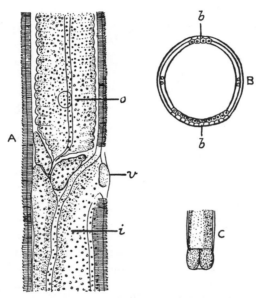

Fig. 6.—*Eucoleus ærophilus.* A. Vulvar region of female. *i,* intestine ; *o,* œsophagus ; *v,* vulva. B. Transverse section. *b,* bacillary band. (After Eberth.) C. Posterior extremity of male. × 200. (After Schneider.)

a thick granular shell, they are held on the surface of the worm by a kind of mucilage. Parasites of respiratory tract of mammals.

Type species : *E. ærophilus* (Creplin, 1839). ♂ 24·5 mm., ♀ 32 mm. In fox and cat.

Syn., *Trichosoma ærophilum* Creplin, 1839.

Other species : *E. tenuis* Duj., 1845. In *Erinaceus europæus.* Refs. 131, 132, 405, 480.

Possibly *Eucoleus* and *Hepaticola* are identical and Railliet states that *E. tenuis* has been found in the liver of *Erinaceus europæus.*

TRICHURIDÆ insufficiently known.

Genus SCLEROTRICHUM Rud.. 1819.

Definition.—TRICHURINÆ : body very long and composed of two parts, the anterior portion very thin, ending in a disc bordered with hooks in the centre of which the mouth opens, and the posterior portion swollen, rolled into a spiral, and nodular.

According to Dujardin (1845) the only species of this incompletely known genus, which itself appears doubtful, has been found by Pallas in the stomach of *Lacerta apus,* from Russia and named by this author *Tænia spirillum.* Gœze has reproduced the figures given by Pallas and has placed the worm in his genus *Trichocephalus,* of which Zeder changed the name to *Mastigodes.* Rudolphi, who also studied this hel-

Fig. 7. — *Sclerotrichum echinatum.* A. Head. B. Whole worm. (After Bremser.)

minth, preserved in alcohol, named it *Trichocephalus echinatus,* and made a distinct division for it from his other *Trichocephalus* species ; de Blainville made it a genus apart under the name *Mastigodes* already applied by Zeder to all the *Trichocephalus* spp. ; finally Nordmann, in his annotations in the third volume on invertebrates of Lamarck, also considered it should be a separate genus under the name *Sclerotrichum* proposed by Rudolphi. Dujardin also expresses the same opinion, but admits that the worm is not very well known.

Type species : *S. echinatum* (Rud., 1809). ♀ 54 mm. In the stomach of *Lacerta apus.*

Syn., *Trichocephalus echinatus* Rud., 1809.
  Tænia spirillum Pallas, 1781.
  Trichocephalus spirillum (Pallas, 1781) Bremser, 1824.
  Mastigodes spirillum (Pallas, 1781) Blainville, 1828.
  Trichocephalus lacertæ Schrank, 1788.
  Mastigodes lacertæ (Schrank, 1788) Zeder, 1803.
  Trichocephalus ophisauris Froriep MS. in Rud., 1809.
Refs. 53b, 77, 123, 131, 186, 477, 627.

Genus ONCOPHORA Diesing, 1851.

Definition.—TRICHURINÆ : body clearly divided into two portions, the anterior much longer than the posterior, but relatively thicker than in *Trichuris*. The posterior part of the body near its commencement is furnished with a humped-shaped swelling on which the vulva is situated ; the posterior extremity tapers to a fine point. The male is unknown. Viviprous. The above description is based on two females, the anterior portion of which was incomplete.

Type species : *O. neglecta* Dies., 1851. ♀ 67–95 mm. In gall bladder of *Thynnus vulgaris*.

Syn., *Trichocephalus gibbosus* Rud., 1819.

Refs. 123, 125, 131.

FAMILY TRICHOSOMOIDIDÆ n. f.

Definition.—TRICHUROIDEA : male much smaller than the female and found in the vagina or uterus of the latter ; spicule and

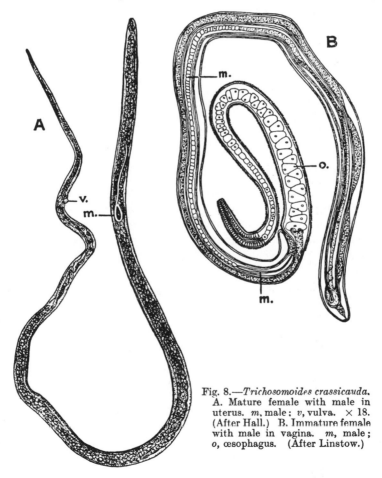

Fig. 8.—*Trichosomoides crassicauda.*
A. Mature female with male in uterus. *m,* male ; *v,* vulva. × 18. (After Hall.) B. Immature female with male in vagina. *m,* male ; *o,* œsophagus. (After Linstow.)

copulatory sheath absent. Female : vulva near posterior end of œsophagus. Oviparous, eggs with a thick shell and an operculum at each end, containing a fully-formed embryo when deposited. Parasites of urinary tract of rodents.

Subfamily TRICHOSOMOIDINÆ Hall, 1916.

Definition.—TRICHOSOMOIDIDÆ : with the characters of the family.

Genus TRICHOSOMOIDES Railliet, 1895.

Syn., *Trichodes* Linstow, 1874, preoccupied.

Definition.—TRICHOSOMOIDINÆ : males and females of very different size ; anterior portion of the œsophagus devoid of cell body, and remainder surrounded by a cell chain ; anus terminal in both sexes. Male : bursa, spicule, or copulatory organs of any sort, absent. Female : vulva just behind the termination of the œsophagus. Parasites of urinary tract of rodents.

Type species : *T. crassicauda* (Bellingham, 1840). ♂ 1·5–2·5 mm., ♀ 10·5–13 mm. In rats.

Syn., *Trichosoma crassicauda* Bellingham, 1840.

Trichodes crassicauda (Bellingham, 1840) Linstow, 1874.

Refs. 47, 205, 309, 399, 617.

FAMILY TRICHINELLIDÆ WARD, 1907.

Syn., *Trichinidæ* Cobbold, 1879.

Definition.—TRICHUROIDEA : small worms, posterior portion of body only slightly thicker than the anterior ; mouth simple. Male : spicule and copulatory sheath absent. Female : vulva in œsophageal region. Viviparous. Parasites of mammals ; adults in intestine and larvæ in muscles.

Subfamily TRICHINELLINÆ Ransom, 1911.

Definition.—TRICHINELLIDÆ : with the characters of the family.

Genus TRICHINELLA Railliet, 1895.

Syn., *Trichina* Owen, 1835, preoccupied.

Definition.—TRICHINELLINÆ : body of nearly uniform diameter throughout, becoming slightly thicker posteriorly. Mouth simple, unarmed ; œsophagus, anterior part consists of a simple membranous tube, the posterior part is surrounded by a single row of cells ; anus terminal in both sexes. Male : posterior extremity with a conical projection on each side of the protrusible cloaca, and between them lie four papillæ; spicule and sheath absent.

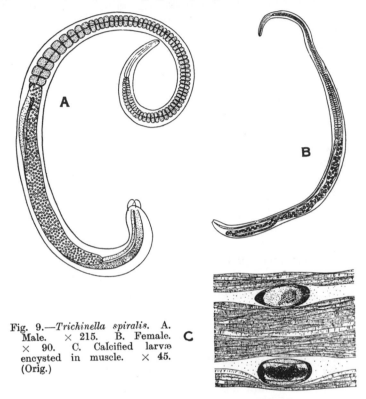

Fig. 9.—*Trichinella spiralis.* A. Male. × 215. B. Female. × 90. C. Calcified larvæ encysted in muscle. × 45. (Orig.)

Female : vulva about the middle of the cellular part of œsophagus. Viviparous. Parasites of intestine of mammals.

Type species : *T. spiralis* (Owen, 1835). ♂ 1·4–1·6 mm., ♀ 3–4 mm. In numerous mammals.

Syn., *Trichina spiralis* Owen, 1835.

Refs. 103, 205, 301, 383, 384, 399, 458, 660.

Superfamily STRONGYLOIDEA Weinland, 1858; Hall, 1916.

Definition.—EUNEMATODA : males with a cuticular bursa copulatrix supported by rays. Œsophagus usually more or less club-shaped posteriorly, but without a definite spherical bulb and without a valvular apparatus ; intestine almost always simple. Usually oviparous, occasionally viviparous.

KEY TO FAMILIES.

1. Parasites of alimentary canal or,
rarely, of renal tissue . . 2
Parasites of respiratory system . 5
2. More or less filiform worms with
buccal capsule feebly-developed
or absent . . . . Trichostrongylidæ, p. 115
Stouter worms with buccal cap-
sule well-developed . . 3
3. Buccal capsule bivalvular . . Diaphanocephalidæ, p. 111.
Buccal capsule continuous . . 4
4. Oral aperture guarded by ventral
cutting organs, *i.e.*, teeth, or
chitinous plates . . . Ancylostomidæ, p. 90.
Oral aperture not guarded by
ventral cutting organs ; with
or without a corona radiata . Strongylidæ, p. 34.
5. With a well-developed chitinous
buccal capsule . . . Syngamidæ, p. 156.
Buccal capsule rudimentary or
absent 6
6. With a well-developed bursa with
more or less typical rays . Metastrongylidæ, p. 158.
Bursa rudimentary supported by
a few atypical rays . . Pseudaliidæ, p. 166.
7. *Strongyloidea* insufficiently known, p. 172.

FAMILY STRONGYLIDÆ BAIRD, 1853.

Definition.—STRONGYLOIDEA : with a chitinous buccal capsule,
the oral aperture of which is not guarded by ventral cutting organs,
but is usually surrounded by a corona radiata (or leaf-crown).
Parasites of the alimentary canal, or, rarely, of renal tissue.

KEY TO SUBFAMILIES.

1. With a transverse ventral cervical
groove . . . . Œsophagostominæ, p. 85.
Without a transverse ventral
cervical groove . . . 2
2. Buccal capsule cylindrical or ring-
shaped . . . . Trichoneminæ, p. 52.
Buccal capsule globular, subglobular or infundibular . 3

3. Bursa copulatrix well-developed
   and terminal. Parasites of
   alimentary canal .   .   .   Strongylinæ, p. 35.
   Bursa copulatrix very short and
   subterminal. Parasites of renal
   and perirenal tissue   .   .   Stephanurinæ, p. 49.

Subfamily STRONGYLINÆ Railliet, 1893.

Definition.—STRONGYLIDÆ : without a transverse ventral
cervical groove ; buccal capsule large and globular, subglobular,
or infundibular. Duct of the dorsal œsophageal gland almost
always prolonged as a ridge on the dorsal wall of the buccal
capsule to open near its oral margin. Bursa copulatrix well-
developed and terminal. Parasites of alimentary canal.

KEY TO GENERA.

1. Buccal capsule funnel-shaped, much
   longer than broad   .   .   .   Choniangium, p. 40.
   Buccal capsule globular or sub-
   globular   2
2. With 3 simple lancets in œsophageal
   funnel not projecting into buccal
   capsule .   .   .   .   .   Œsophagodontus, p. 42.
   With 3 teeth, each consisting of two
   lamellæ, in œsophageal funnel,
   and projecting into buccal cap-
   sule   .   .   .   .   .   Triodontophorus, p. 44.
   Without teeth in œsophageal funnel   3
3. Mouth directed antero-ventrally   .   Ransomus, p. 41.
   Mouth directed straight forwards or
   antero-dorsally   .   .   .   4
4. Corona radiata absent or rudimentary   5
   Corona radiata well-developed   .   6
5. Mouth collar subterminal and very
   prominent   .   .   .   .   Acheilostoma, p. 49.
   Mouth collar absent   .   .   .   Globocephalus, p. 48.
6. Elements of external leaf-crown of
   two lengths ; externo-dorsal ray
   of bursa trifurcate   .   .   .   Equinurbia, p. 39.
   Elements of external leaf-crown all
   of same length ; externo-dorsal
   ray of bursa simple .   .   .   7

7. Without an internal leaf-crown;
vulva about commencement of
posterior third of body . . 8
With an internal leaf-crown; vulva
near anus 9
8. Dorsal ray of bursa undivided except at its tip; gubernaculum
absent . . . . . Decrusia, p. 38.
Dorsal ray of bursa divided to near
its base; gubernaculum present Strongylus, p. 37.
9. Elements of external leaf-crown
fimbriated . . . . Castorstrongylus, p. 46.

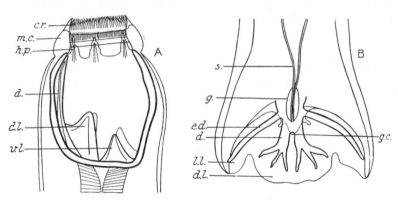

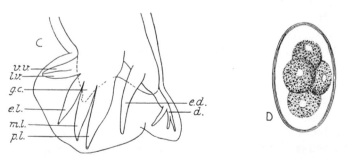

Fig. 10.—*Strongylus equinus.* A. Head, lateral view. *c.r*, corona radiata;
d, duct of dorsal œsophageal gland; *d.l*, subdorsal teeth; *h.p*, head
papillæ; *m.c*, mouth collar; *v.l*, subventral teeth. × 35. B. Bursa,
dorsal view. *s*, spicule; *g*, gubernaculum; *e.d*, externo-dorsal ray;
d, dorsal ray; *l.l*, lateral lobe of bursa; *d.l*, dorsal lobe; *g.c*, genital cone.
× 35. C. Bursa, lateral view. *v.v*, ventro-ventral ray; *l.v*, latero-
ventral ray; *g.c*, genital cone; *e.l*, externo-lateral ray; *m.l*, medio-
lateral ray; *p.l*, postero-lateral ray; *e.d*, externo-dorsal ray; *d*, dorsal
ray. × 35. D. Egg. × 325. (Orig.)

Elements of external leaf-crown
    not fimbriated   .   .   .   10.
10. Mouth directed straight forwards. Craterostomum, p. 45.
     Mouth directed antero-dorsally . Codiostomum, p. 45.

Genus STRONGYLUS Mueller, 1780, or Gœze, 1782.

Syn., *Sclerostoma* Rud., 1809.

Definition.—STRONGYLINÆ : mouth directed straight forwards, surrounded by a corona radiata or external leaf-crown arising from the mouth collar ; buccal capsule subglobular without an internal leaf-crown, and with or without teeth in its depth. Male : bursal formula—ventral ray cleft, externo-lateral and laterals arising from a common trunk, externo-dorsal arises from a common trunk with the dorsal, dorsal doubled almost as far as the origin of the externo-dorsal ray, each branch ending in three digitations ; spicules equal, gubernaculum present. Female : vulva near the commencement of the posterior third of the worm. Parasites of equines (and *Varanidæ*).

Type species : *S. equinus* Mueller, 1780. ♂ 27–30 mm., ♀ 35–55 mm. In equines.

    Syn., *Sclerostomum equinum* (Mueller, 1780) Looss, 1900.
        Strongylus armatus Rud., 1802.

Other species :

S. asini Boulenger, 1920. In equines.
S. edentatus (Looss, 1900). In equines.
S. intermedius Monnig, 1924. In *Varanus* sp.
S. vulgaris (Looss, 1900). In equines.

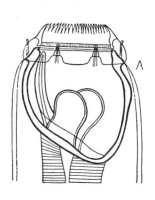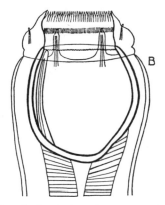

Fig. 11.—*Strongylus (Delafondia) vulgaris.* A. Head, lateral view. × 56.
   Strongylus (Alfortia) edentatus. B. Head, lateral view. × 35. (Orig.)

Railliet, 1923, has subdivided the genus *Strongylus* into the following subgenera : —

Subgenus STRONGYLUS (Gœze, 1782) Railliet, 1923.

Definition.—Head not swollen ; two subventral and two subdorsal teeth at the base of the buccal capsule. Contains the species *equinus*.

Subgenus ALFORTIA Railliet, 1923.

Definition.—Head slightly swollen ; without teeth at the base of the buccal capsule. Contains the species *edentatus*.

Subgenus DELAFONDIA Railliet, 1923.

Definition.—Head swollen or not ; without subventral teeth, but with two subdorsal teeth at the base of the buccal capsule. Contains the species *vulgaris* and *asini*.

Subgenus DECRUSIA (Lane, 1914) Railliet, 1923.

Definition.—*Vide Decrusia* Lane, 1914.

Refs. 63, 251, 338, 363, 366, 413.

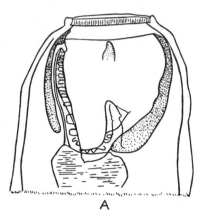 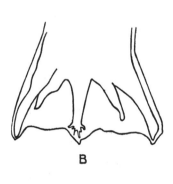

A

B

Fig. 12.—*Decrusia additicta.* A. Head, lateral view. × 75. B. Bursa, dorsal view. × 38. (After Lane.)

Genus DECRUSIA Lane, 1914.

Definition.—STRONGYLINÆ : closely resembles *Strongylus*, but differs in that the head is slightly tilted dorsally, the buccal capsule has two subventral teeth in its depth, there is no gubernaculum, the dorsal ray is undivided except at its tip where it terminates in four to six digitations, and the externo-dorsal ray is short. Parasites of elephants.

Type species : *D. additicta* (Railliet, Henry, and Bauche, 1914). ♂ 14 mm., ♀ 15 mm. In *Elephas indicus.*

Syn., *Strongylus additictus* Railliet, Henry, and Bauche, 1914. *D. decrusi* Lane, 1914.

Refs. 221, 251, 255, 257, 448.

Genus EQUINURBIA Lane, 1914.

Definition.—STRONGYLINÆ : mouth directed slightly dorsally, with an external leaf-crown consisting of elements of two different lengths arising from the mouth collar ; buccal capsule sub-globular, without an internal leaf-crown and without teeth in its

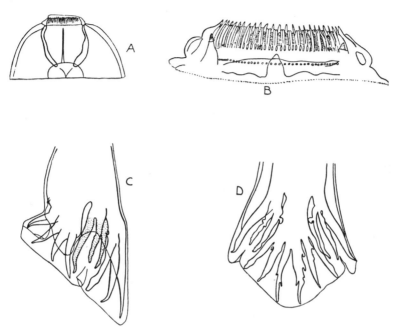

Fig. 13.—*Equinurbia sipunculiformis.* A. Head, dorsal view. × 28. B. Corona radiata and cephalic papillæ, from the left side. × 120. C. Bursa, lateral view. × 30. D. Bursa, dorsal view. × 30. (After Lane.)

depth. Male : bursal formula—ventral ray cleft, externo-lateral and laterals arising from a common trunk, externo-dorsal arises separately from the dorsal and almost immediately breaks up into three branches of which the first is longest, dorsal ray split for almost half its length with two lateral branches arising from the common trunk immediately before it bifurcates ; spicules equal, gubernaculum absent. Female : vulva opens on a pro-minence close to the anus. Parasites of elephants.

Type species : *E. sipunculiformis* (Baird, 1859). ♂ 15 mm., ♀ 27·5 mm. In elephants.

Syn., *Sclerostoma sipunculiforme* Baird, 1859.

Cylicostomum sipunculiforme (Baird, 1859) Railliet, Henry, and Bauche, 1914.

Refs. 251, 255, 257, 448.

Genus CHONIANGIUM Railliet, Henry, and Bauche, 1914.

Syn., *Asifia* Lane, 1914.

Definition.—STRONGYLINÆ : anterior extremity obliquely truncate, so that the mouth is directed antero-dorsally ; with an external leaf-crown arising from the mouth collar ; buccal

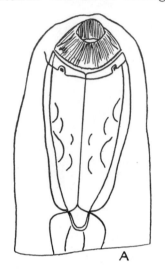

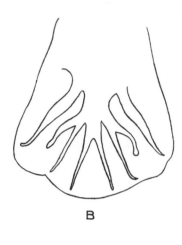

Fig. 14. — *Choniangium epistomum.* A. Head, dorsal view. × 60. B. Bursa, dorsal view. × 60. C. Bursa, lateral view. × 60. (After Lane.)

capsule very long and narrowing posteriorly, without an internal leaf-crown and without teeth in its depth, but with about five pairs of irregular cuticular prominences projecting into the cavity about the middle of its length. Male : bursal formula—ventral ray cleft, externo-lateral and laterals arising from a common trunk, externo-dorsal arising from a common trunk with the dorsal, dorsal bifurcate for about half its length the common trunk giving off a lateral branch on each side, which almost immediately bifurcates ; spicules equal ; gubernaculum present.   Female : vulva near the anus.   Parasites of elephants.

Type species : *C. epistomum* (Piana and Stazzi, 1900). ♂ 14 mm., ♀ 19 mm.   In elephants.

Syn., *Sclerostoma epistomum* Piana and Stazzi, 1900.

Asifia vasifa Lane, 1914.

Refs. 251, 255, 257, 392, 448.

Genus RANSOMUS * Hall, 1916.

Definition.—STRONGYLINÆ : anterior extremity obliquely truncate, so that the mouth is directed antero-ventrally ; with an

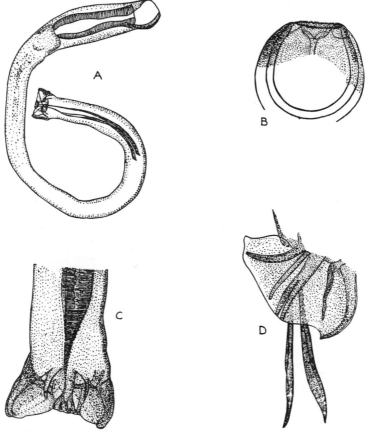

Fig. 15.—*Ransomus rodentorum.*   A. Male.   B. Head, dorsal view.   C. Bursa, dorsal view.   D. Bursa, lateral view.   (After Hall.)

* Hall, 1916, placed this genus in a special subfamily *Ransominæ.*

external leaf-crown ; buccal capsule globular, without teeth in its depth. Male : bursal formula—ventral ray cleft, externo-lateral arising separately from the laterals, lateral bifurcated for about half its length, externo-dorsal arises separately from the dorsal, dorsal ends in four almost equal digitations ; spicules equal and alate ; gubernaculum present. Female : vulva opens a short distance in front of the anus. Parasites of rodents.

Type species : *R. rodentorum* Hall, 1916. ♂ 4·64–8·2 mm. ♀ 8–9·2 mm. In rodents.

Ref. 205.

Genus ŒSOPHAGODONTUS Railliet and Henry, 1902.

Syn., *Pseudosclerostomum* Quiel, 1919.

Definition.—STRONGYLINÆ : mouth directed straight forwards with an external leaf-crown arising from the mouth collar ; buccal capsule infundibular with an internal leaf-crown arising from its

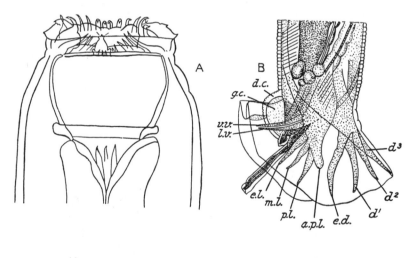

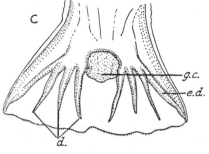

Fig. 16. — *Œsophagodontus robustus.*
A. Head. × 90. B. Bursa, lateral view. *g.c,* genital cone ; *d.c,* dermal collar of genital cone ; *v.v,* ventro-ventral ray ; *l.v,* latero-ventral ray : *e.l,* externo-lateral ray ; *m.l,* medio-lateral ray ; *p.l,* postero-lateral ray ; *e.d,* externo-dorsal ray ; *a.p.l,* accessory branch of postero-lateral ray ; *d,* dorsal ray. × 50. C. Bursa, dorsal view. *g.c,* genital cone ; *d,* dorsal ray ; *e.d,* externo-dorsal ray. × 50. (After Boulenger.)

anterior margin ; œsophageal funnel well-developed, containing three lancets not projecting into the capsule, duct of dorso-œsophageal gland not prolonged into the buccal capsule as a dorsal ridge. Male : bursa with large lateral lobes but without a dorsal lobe ; with the following formula—ventral ray cleft, externo-

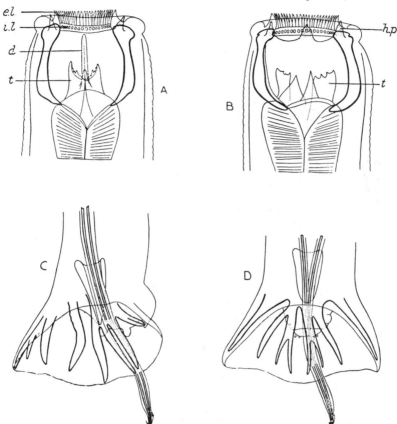

Fig. 17.—*Triodontophorus serratus.* A. Head, dorsal view. *e.l,* external leaf-crown ; *i.l,* internal leaf-crown ; *d,* duct of dorsal œsophageal gland ; *t,* œsophageal teeth. × 160. B. Head, lateral view. *h.p,* head papillæ ; *t,* œsophageal teeth. × 160. C. Bursa, lateral view. × 28. D. Bursa, dorsal view. × 28. (Orig.)

lateral and laterals arising from a common trunk, the postero-lateral giving off a short thick accessory branch, dorsal rays arising in two lateral groups, each consisting of four rays representing an externo-dorsal and three approximately equal dorsal rays ; spicules equal. Female : vulva near anus. Parasites of equines.

Type species : *O. robustus* (Giles, 1892). ♂ 13 mm., ♀ 22 mm. In equines.

Syn., *Sclerostoma robustum* Giles, 1892.

Pseudosclerostomum securiferum Quiel, 1919.

Refs. 61, 182, 232, 394, 414, 615.

Genus TRIODONTOPHORUS Looss, 1902.

Syn., *Triodontus* Looss, 1900, preoccupied.

Definition.—STRONGYLINÆ : mouth directed straight forwards with an external leaf-crown arising from mouth collar ; buccal

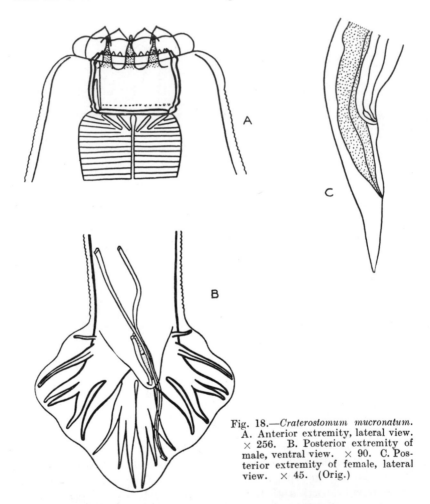

Fig. 18.—*Craterostomum mucronatum.* A. Anterior extremity, lateral view. × 256. B. Posterior extremity of male, ventral view. × 90. C. Posterior extremity of female, lateral view. × 45. (Orig.)

capsule subglobular, with an internal leaf-crown arising from its anterior margin and with three radially arranged teeth projecting into it from the œsophageal funnel, each tooth being composed of two lamellæ converging towards the axis of the body and meeting at an obtuse angle. Male : bursal formula—ventral ray cleft, externo-lateral and laterals arising from a common trunk, externo-dorsal arising from a common trunk with the dorsal, dorsal cleft almost to its base, each limb giving off two lateral branches ; spicules equal ; gubernaculum present. Female : vulva close to anus. Parasites of equines.

Type species : *T. serratus* (Looss, 1900). ♂ 18 mm., ♀ 25 mm. In equines.

> Syn., *Triodontus serratus* Looss, 1900.
> *T. intermedius* Sweet, 1909.

Other species :

> *T. brevicauda* Boulenger, 1916. In equines.
> *T. minor* (Looss, 1900). In equines.
> *T. tenuicollis* Boulenger, 1916. In equines.

Refs. 61, 232, 336, 338, 607, 615.

Genus CRATEROSTOMUM Boulenger, 1920.

Definition.—STRONGYLINÆ : closely allied to *Triodontophorus*, but differing in the absence of teeth projecting into the buccal capsule. Parasites of equines.

Type species : *C. acuticaudatum* (Kotlán, 1919). ♂ 9·5 mm., ♀ 9–11 mm. In equines.

> Syn., *Cylicostomum acuticaudatum* Kotlán, 1919.
> *Craterostomum tenuicauda* Boulenger, 1920.

Other species : *C. mucronatum* (Ihle, 1920). In equines.
Refs. 64, 232, 252, 615.

Genus CODIOSTOMUM Railliet and Henry, 1911.

Definition.—STRONGYLINÆ : mouth directed antero-dorsally with an external leaf-crown arising from the mouth collar and an internal leaf-crown arising from the anterior margin of the buccal capsule ; with 4 submedian and 2 lateral head papillæ ; buccal capsule subglobular with heavily chitinized walls and without teeth in its depth ; duct of dorsal œsophageal gland runs in a ridge in the wall of the capsule to open near its anterior margin. Male : bursa with a large dorsal lobe clearly marked off from the lateral lobes ; with the following formula—ventral rays close together, externo-lateral and laterals arising from a common trunk, externo-dorsal arises from a common trunk with the dorsal, dorsal bifurcate for more than half its length, each limb giving off near its origin a lateral branch, which immediately subdivides into two divisions; spicules long and equal; gubernaculum present. Female : vulva near anus, and just in front of it is a prominent cuticular elevation ; uteri parallel. Parasites of ostriches.

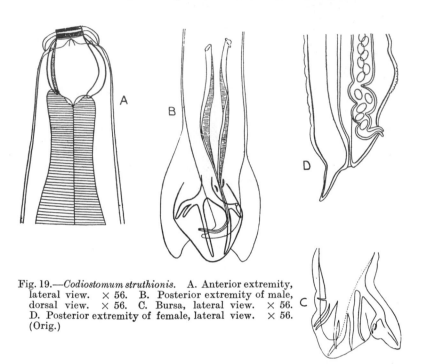

Fig. 19.—*Codiostomum struthionis*.   A. Anterior extremity, lateral view.   × 56.   B. Posterior extremity of male, dorsal view.   × 56.   C. Bursa, lateral view.   × 56. D. Posterior extremity of female, lateral view.   × 56. (Orig.)

Type species : *C. struthionis* (Horst, 1885).   ♂ 13 mm., ♀ 23 mm. In *Struthio australis*.

Syn., *Sclerostoma struthionis* Horst, 1885.

Refs. 217, 362, 431.

Genus CASTORSTRONGYLUS Chapin, 1925.

Definition.—STRONGYLINÆ : mouth directed slightly dorsally, external leaf-crown arises from the mouth collar and consists of long fimbriated elements, internal leaf-crown arises from the anterior margin of the buccal capsule and consists of numerous short, stout elements ; buccal capsule spherical with stout walls, and without teeth in its depth.   Male : bursa with large lateral lobes and a small dorsal lobe ; with the following formula—ventral rays cleft, externo-lateral arises from a common trunk with the other laterals, externo-dorsal arises separately from the dorsal,

dorsal bifurcated for about half its length, each limb being bidigitate ; spicules long, slender and somewhat twisted ; gubernaculum

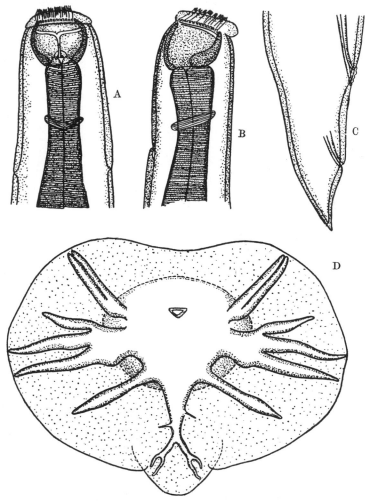

Fig. 20.—*Castorstrongylus castoris.* A. Anterior extremity, ventral view. × 65. B. Anterior extremity, lateral view. × 65. C. Tail of female, lateral view. × 65. D. Bursa, ventral view. × 130. (After Chapin.)

absent. Female : tail conical ; vulva near the anus. Oviparous. Parasites of rodents.

Type species : *C. castoris* (Chapin, 1925). ♂ 11 mm., ♀ 12 mm. In *Castor canadensis.*

Ref. 93*b*.

Genus GLOBOCEPHALUS Molin, 1861.

Syn., *Cystocephalus* Railliet, 1895.
Characostomum Railliet, 1902.
Crassisoma Alessandrini, 1909.
Raillietostrongylus Lane, 1923.

Definition.—STRONGYLINÆ : mouth directed antero-dorsally ; buccal capsule more or less globular with very stout walls ; sub-ventral lancets may or may not be present in the depth of the cavity, dorsal œsophageal ridge present and opening near the oral

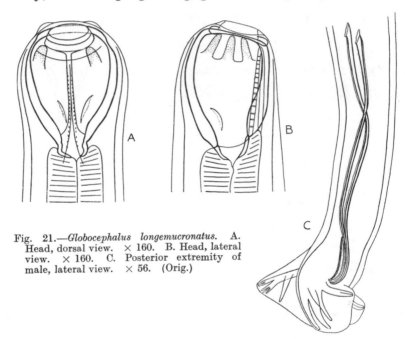

Fig. 21.—*Globocephalus longemucronatus.* A. Head, dorsal view. × 160. B. Head, lateral view. × 160. C. Posterior extremity of male, lateral view. × 56. (Orig.)

margin of the capsule. Male : bursal formula—ventral ray cleft, externo-lateral and laterals arising from a common trunk, externo-dorsal arising from a common trunk with the dorsal, dorsal bifurcate, each branch tridigitate ; spicules equal ; gubernaculum present. Female : vulva a little behind the middle of the body ; uteri opposed. Parasites of pigs and monkeys.

Type species : *G. longemucronatus* Molin, 1861. ♂ 7 mm., ♀ 8 mm. In pigs.

Syn., *Characostomum longemucronatum* (Molin, 1861) Railliet, 1902.

Cystocephalus longemucronatus (Molin, 1861) Railliet, 1895.

Other species :

   G. asmilius (Railliet, Henry, and Joyeux, 1913). In monkeys.

      Syn., *Characostomum asmilium* Railliet, Henry, and Joyeux, 1913.

   **G. samoensis* (Lane, 1922). In pigs.

      Syn., *Crassisoma samoense* Lane, 1922.

          Raillietostrongylus samoensis (Lane, 1922) Lane, 1923.

   G. urosubulatus (Alessandrini, 1909). In pigs.

      Syn., *Crassisoma urosubulatum* Alessandrini, 1909.

      G. connorfilii Lane, 1922.

Refs. 3, 84, 268, 269, 360, 402, 450, 656.

Genus ACHEILOSTOMA Leiper, 1911.

Definition.—STRONGYLINÆ : mouth directed slightly dorsally with a well-developed mouth collar, which is not quite terminal and surrounds the anterior portion of the buccal capsule ; this is globular with two subventral and two subdorsal triangular teeth in its depth ; dorsal cone prominent and flanked by two sharp teeth. Male : lateral lobes of bursa much longer than the dorsal ; bursal formula—ventral rays united almost to their tips, externo-lateral and lateral rays arising from a common trunk, externo-dorsal arises from a common trunk with the dorsal and is long and thin, dorsal bifurcate for about half its length or more, each branch being bidigitate ; spicules long and equal ; gubernaculum absent. Female : vulva about centre of body, uteri opposed.

Type species : *A. simpsoni* Leiper, 1911. ♂ 17 mm., ♀ 23 mm. In a large African rodent.

Other species :

   A. moucheti Railliet, 1918. In gall bladder of *Thryonomys swinderianus.*

   A. paranecator Travassos and Horta, 1915. In intestine of *Equus asinus.*

Refs. 286, 409, 648.

Subfamily STEPHANURINÆ Railliet, Henry, and Bauche, 1919.

Definition.—STRONGYLIDÆ : with a well-developed chitinous buccal capsule, the oral margin is not provided with teeth or other

---

* Possibly *G. samoensis* Lane, 1922, is identical with *G. longemucronatus* Molin, 1861, practically the only difference being that in Molin's species subventral lancets are not figured in the buccal capsule, but these may easily have escaped observation. Lane (1925) in a recent paper upholds his original opinion that *Raillietostrongylus* is a valid genus characterized by the presence of "rudimentary subventral semilunes" guarding the oval aperture.

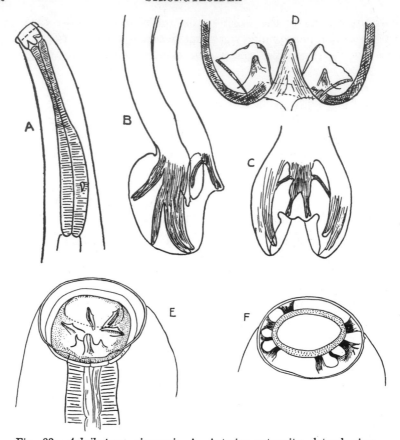

Fig. 22.—*Acheilostoma simpsoni.*—A. Anterior extremity, lateral view.
B. Posterior extremity of male, lateral view. C. Bursa, dorsal view. D.
Base of buccal capsule. (After Leiper.)
Acheilostoma moucheti. E. Head, dorsal surface, deep view. × 150.
F. Head, dorsal surface, superficial view. × 150. (After Railliet.)

cutting organs, but with a rudimentary corona radiata. Bursa copulatrix very short and subterminal. Parasites of renal and perirenal tissue, and occasionally of the liver.

Genus STEPHANURUS Dies., 1839.

Definition.—STEPHANURINÆ : mouth circular and directed straight forwards ; buccal capsule subglobular with thick walls, the anterior margin divided into six festoons, of which the dorsal and ventral are the most prominent, and furnished with a feebly-developed corona radiata ; at the base of the capsule surrounding the orifice of the œsophagus are six to ten triangular teeth. Cephalic glands very voluminous and extend backwards about

half the length of the worm ; the gut is much longer than the
worm and consequently is considerably convoluted.   Male :
bursa poorly-developed and placed subterminally ; with the follow-

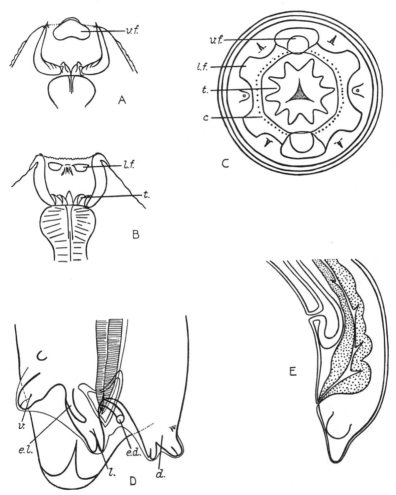

Fig. 23.—*Stephanurus dentatus*.—A. Head, ventral view. *v.f*, ventral
festoon. × 65. B. Head, lateral view. *l.f*, sub-lateral festoon ;
t, teeth. × 65. C. Head, end-on view. *v.f*, ventral festoon ; *l.f*, sublateral festoon ; *t*, teeth at base of buccal capsule ; *c*, corona radiata.
× 100. D. Posterior extremity of male, lateral view. *v*, ventral rays ;
e.l, externo-lateral ray ; *l*, lateral rays ; *e.d*, externo-dorsal ray ; *d*, dorsal
ray. × 135. E. Posterior extremity of female. × 24. (Orig.)

ing formula—ventral ray cleft, externo-lateral and other laterals
arising from a common trunk, medio-lateral and postero-lateral
thick and fused proximally, externo-dorsal arises separately from

the dorsal, dorsal thick and bifurcate in its distal portion, each branch bidigitate ; spicules equal, or subequal, and winged ; gubernaculum present. Female : vulva a little in front of the anus, posterior extremity bent ventrally, body narrows suddenly just behind anus and ends in a very small conical tail ; there is a large sublateral papilla on each side of the anus. Parasites of renal and perirenal tissue of pigs.

Type species : *S. dentatus* Diesing, 1839. ♂ 22–30 mm., ♀ 34–40 mm. In pigs.

> Syn., *Sclerostomum pinguicola* Verrill, 1870.
> *S. nattereri* Cobbold, 1879.
> *Sclerostomum renium* Drabble, 1922.

Refs. 53, 85, 103, 120, 122, 126, 449, 579, 612.

Subfamily TRICHONEMINÆ Railliet, 1916.

Syn., *Cylicostominæ* Railliet, 1915.

Definition.—STRONGYLIDÆ : without a transverse ventral cervical groove ; buccal capsule cylindrical and as a rule short or ring-shaped. Dorsal œsophageal ridge relatively short or absent, never reaching the anterior margin of the buccal capsule.

KEY TO GENERA.

1. Mouth surrounded by prominent anteriorly directed digitiform processes . . . . Labiostrongylus, p. 67.
   Mouth not surrounded by prominent digitiform processes . 2
2. Both sexes permanently spirally rolled. . . . . Spirostrongylus, p. 68.
   Not permanently spirally rolled 3
3. Buccal capsule relatively enormously long . . . Cylindropharynx, p. 64.
   Buccal capsule relatively short . 4
4. With a long cylindrical vestibule with ringed walls . . Pharyngostrongylus, p. 65.
   Without a vestibule . . 5
5. Anterior end of œsophagus greatly dilated and chitinized 6
   Anterior end of œsophagus not greatly dilated . . . 7

6. Chitinized œsophageal dilatation
with three large crescentic
teeth . . . . . Gyalocephalus, p. 62.
Chitinized œsophageal dilatation
covered with small papillæ . Trachypharynx, p. 63.
7. Mouth cavity much smaller than
buccal capsule from which it
is separated by parenchyma . 8
Mouth cavity not separated
from buccal capsule by parenchyma 9
8. Leaf-crown consists of 10–18
prominent elements . . Quilonia, p. 71.
Leaf-crown rudimentary . . Paraquilonia, p. 74.
9. Mouth collar absent, submedian
head papillæ absent or atrophied . . . . Buissonia, p. 80.
Mouth collar and submedian
head papillæ present . . 10
10. Buccal capsule divided transversely into anterior and
posterior portions . . Bourgelatia, p. 82.
Buccal capsule not divided into
anterior and posterior portions 11
11. Œsophageal cuticle provided
with numerous rose - thorn
like spines ; intestinal diverticula present . . . Sauricola, p. 61.
Œsophageal cuticle not provided
with rose-thorn like spines ;
intestinal diverticula absent . 12
12. Elements of leaf-crown much
longer laterally than dorsally
and ventrally, so that the
mouth opening when viewed
from the anterior aspect is
slit-like and when viewed
laterally is crescentic . . Murshidia, p. 78.
Elements of leaf-crown all of
approximately the same
length, so that the mouth
opening is circular or oval in
shape 13

13. Bursa closed ventrally by a
    ventral lobe clearly marked
    off from the lateral lobes   .   Macropostrongylus, p. 75.
    Bursa not closed ventrally by a
    ventral lobe   .   .   .   14
14. With a single leaf-crown arising
    from the base of the buccal
    capsule   15
    With two leaf-crowns, the
    external arising from the
    mouth collar and the internal
    from the buccal capsule   .   16
15. Leaf-crown consists of only six
    elements ; bursa with an
    extra lateral ray .   .   .   Kiluluma, p. 70.
    Leaf-crown consists of numerous
    elements ; bursa without an
    extra lateral ray .   .   .   Theileriana, p. 76.
16. Œsophagus hour-glass shaped ;
    bursa with the externo-lateral
    and lateral rays all very close
    together   .   .   .   .   Amira, p. 82.
    Œsophagus not hour-glass
    shaped ; bursa with the
    externo-lateral and lateral
    rays not very close together .   17
17. Dorsal ray of bursa cleft to base   Trichonema, p. 54.
    Dorsal ray of bursa cleft for only
    half its length   .   .   .   Poteriostomum, p. 60.
18. Insufficiently known   .   .   Eucyathostomum, p. 84.

Genus TRICHONEMA Cobbold, 1874.

Syn., *Cyathostomum* Molin, 1861 ; not *Cyathostoma* Blanchard,
    1849.
    Cylicostomum Railliet, 1901.
    Cylichnostomum Looss, 1901.

Definition.—TRICHONEMINÆ : mouth directed straight forwards, it may be circular or ellipsoidal with the long axis either
dorso-ventrally or laterally ; two leaf-crowns the elements of
which vary greatly in size and shape in the different species ;
buccal capsule more or less cylindrical, likewise varying greatly
in size and shape in the different species ; only very occasionally

are small triangular lancets present at the base of the capsule. Duct of dorsal œsophageal gland may or may not project into the buccal capsule. Male : bursal formula—ventral ray cleft, externo-lateral and laterals arising from a common trunk, externo-dorsal arising separately from the dorsal, dorsal cleft to the base, each branch giving off two lateral branches or very occasionally three ;

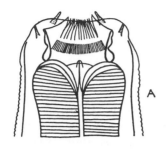
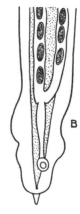

Fig. 24.—*Trichonema (Trichonema) tetracan-thum.* A. Head, dorsal view. × 215. B. Posterior extremity of female, ventral view. × 46. (Orig.)

spicules equal ; gubernaculum present. Female : vulva near anus ; uteri parallel ; posterior extremity varies greatly in shape. Parasites of equines.

Type species : *T. tetracanthum* (Mehlis, 1831, of Looss, 1900). ♂ 9 mm., ♀ 10–12 mm. In equines.

Syn., *Cylichnostomum tetracanthum* Mehlis, 1831, of Looss, 1900.

T. ægyptiacum Railliet, 1923.

Other species :

T. adersi (Boulenger, 1920).

T. alveatum (Looss, 1900).

T. asymmetricum (Theiler, 1923).

T. auriculatum (Looss, 1900).

T. barbatum (Smit and Notosoediro, 1923).

T. bicoronatum (Looss, 1900).

T. bidentatum (Ihle, 1925).

T. brevicapsulatum (Ihle, 1920).

T. calicatum (Looss, 1900).

T. catinatum (Looss, 1900).

T. catinatum var. *litoraurea* (Yorke and Macfie, 1920).

T. catinatum var. *pseudocatinata* (Yorke and Macfie, 1919).

T. coronatum (Looss, 1900).

T. elongatum (Looss, 1900).

   T. elongatum var. *kotláni* (Ihle, 1920).

      Syn., *C. elongatum* var. *macrobursata* Kotlán, 1920.

T. euproctum (Boulenger, 1917).

T. goldi (Boulenger, 1917).

   Syn., *T. tridentatum* (Yorke and Macfie, 1920).

T. hybridum (Kotlán, 1920).

T. insigne (Boulenger, 1917).

   Syn., *T. zebræ* (Boulenger, 1920).

T. labiatum (Looss, 1901).

   T. labiatum var. *digitata* (Ihle, 1921).

T. labratum (Looss, 1900).

T. leptostomum (Kotlán, 1920).

T. longibursatum (Yorke and Macfie, 1918).

   Syn., *Cylicostomum longibursatum* Yorke and Macfie, 1918.

      Cylicostomum calicatiforme Kotlán, 1919.

      Cylicostomum nanum Ihle, 1919.

T. mettami (Leiper, 1913).

   Syn., *T. ihlei* (Kotlán, 1921).

T. minutum (Yorke and Macfie, 1918).

   Syn., *C. calicatum* var. *minor* Kotlán, 1920.

T. montgomeryi (Boulenger, 1920).

T. nassatum (Looss, 1900).

   T. nassatum var. *parva* (Yorke and Macfie, 1918).

   Syn., *T. ashworthi* Le Roux, 1924.

T. ornatum (Kotlán, 1919).

T. pateratum (Yorke and Macfie, 1919).

   Syn., *T. cymatostomum* Kotlán, 1919.

T. poculatum (Looss, 1900).

T. prionodes (Kotlán, 1921).

T. radiatum (Looss, 1900).

T. sagittatum (Kotlán, 1920).

T. triramosum (Yorke and Macfie, 1920).

T. ultrajectinum (Ihle, 1920).

The genus has been divided into subgenera by Ihle (1922-1925) and the subdivision subsequently modified as follows by Le Roux (1924), and by Cram (1924).

Subgenus TRICHONEMA * (Cobbold, 1874) ; not Le Roux, 1924.

Syn., *Cylicostomum* (Railliet, 1901) Ihle, 1922.

Definition.—The external leaf-crown consists of 18–24 elements, mostly pointed ; those of the internal crown are thin triangular plates placed radially, and arising from the internal surface of the mouth capsule some

* Cram has raised this to a genus, viz.: *Cylicostomias* Cram, 1925.

distance from its anterior margin; "problematic structure" of Looss in the mouth collar present. Mouth capsule rather short, thick-walled. Posterior extremity of the body of the female straight or slightly bent dorsally. Contains the species : *tetracanthum* of Looss, *coronatum, labiatum, labratum, ornatum,* and *sagittatum.*

Subgenus CYLICOSTEPHANUS Ihle, 1922.

Syn., *Trichonema* (Cobbold, 1874) Le Roux, 1924.

Definition.—Mouth opening circular, mouth collar depressed, external leaf-crown consists of 8–18 elements (ca. 35 in *C. poculatum*). Mouth capsule generally long and cylindrical or somewhat narrower anteriorly

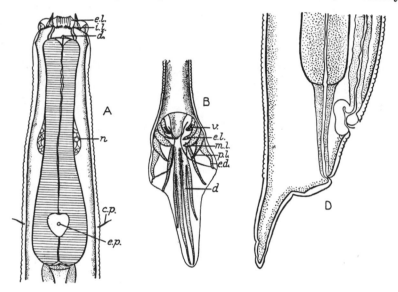

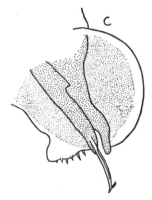

Fig. 25.—*Trichonema (Cylicostephanus) longibursatum.* A. Anterior extremity, ventral view. *e.l,* external leaf-crown; *i.l,* internal leaf-crown; *d,* duct of dorsal œsophageal gland; *n,* nerve ring; *c.p,* cervical papilla; *e.p,* excretory pore. × 205. B. Bursa, ventral view. *v,* ventral rays; *e.l,* externo-lateral ray; *m.l,* medio-lateral ray; *p.l,* postero-lateral ray; *e.d,* externo-dorsal ray; *d,* dorsal ray. × 58. C. Genital cone. × 275. D. Posterior extremity of female, lateral view. × 275. (After Yorke and Macfie.)

than posteriorly. The elements of the internal leaf-crown are short rods arising from near the anterior margin of the mouth capsule. Posterior extremity of the female mostly straight. Contains the species : *calicatum, barbatum, hybridum, longibursatum, minutum,* and *poculatum.*

Subgenus CYLICOCERCUS Ihle, 1922.

Definition.—The external leaf-crown consists of 20–29 elements, the elements of the internal crown resemble those of the subgenus *Trichonema;* their point of origin is sometimes far back in the capsule. Posterior

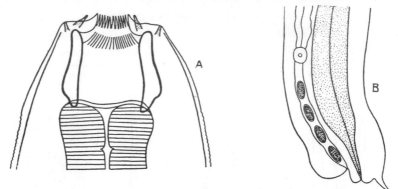

Fig. 26.—*Trichonema (Cylicocercus) alveatum.* A. Head, ventral view. × 215. B. Posterior extremity of female, lateral view. × 46. (Orig.)

extremity of the female strongly bent dorsally, with a swelling in front of the vulva, so as to resemble a human foot when seen laterally. Contains the species : *alveatum, catinatum, goldi,* and *pateratum.*

Subgenus CYLICOCYCLUS Ihle, 1922.

Definition.—The posterior margin of the mouth capsule has a hoop-like thickening, the elements of the internal leaf-crown are usually small and numerous ; they are generally fine rods, originating near the anterior

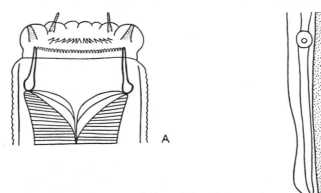

Fig. 27.—*Trichonema (Cylicocyclus) radiatum.* A. Head, ventral view. × 215. B. Posterior extremity of female, lateral view. × 46. (Orig.)

margin of the mouth capsule. The posterior extremity of the female is usually straight or slightly bent dorsally, rarely greatly bent dorsally. Contains the species : *radiatum, adersi, auriculatum, elongatum, insigne, leptostomum, nassatum* and *triramosum.*

Subgenus CYLICODONTOPHORUS Ihle, 1922.

Definition.—Submedian papillæ generally conical, their distal part mostly small and globular ; elements of the external leaf-crown generally small and numerous, those of the internal leaf-crown very large and broad consisting of plates radially arranged and arising close to the anterior

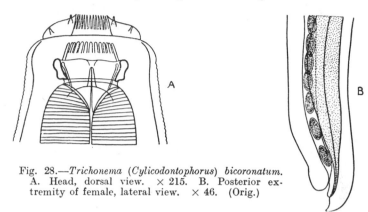

Fig. 28.—*Trichonema (Cylicodontophorus) bicoronatum.* A. Head, dorsal view. × 215. B. Posterior extremity of female, lateral view. × 46. (Orig.)

margin of the buccal capsule. Mouth capsule short and wide, thick-walled. Posterior extremity of the female generally straight ; anus and vulva often some distance apart. Contains the species : *bicoronatum, euproctum, mettami,* and *ultrajectinum.*

Subgenus CYLICOTETRAPEDON Ihle, 1925.

Definition.—The external leaf-crown consists of 15 or 16 elements ; those of the internal leaf-crown are short and broad ; the wall of the mouth capsule is thicker anteriorly than posteriorly and somewhat larger ventrally than dorsally. Posterior extremity of female straight. Contains the species *bidentatum* and *asymmetricum.*

The subdivision of this genus was first attempted by Ihle (1922) who based his effort on the assumption that the correct name for the genus is *Cylicostomum* and not *Trichonema.* Railliet (1923) endeavoured to show that *Strongylus tetracanthus* Mehlis, 1831, is *T. insigne* (Boulenger, 1917) and not *T. tetracanthum* (Mehlis of Looss, 1900) ; but as Le Roux (1924) has pointed out there is no more justification for this than for Looss' assumption that his Egyptian worm was the same as that described by Mehlis.

Le Roux considers that as *Strongylus tetracanthus* Mehlis, 1831, cannot be identified with certainty it automatically ceases to be the type of the genus *Trichonema,* and that *Str. tetracanthus* Mehlis of Looss assumes the name *Trichonema ægyptiacum* Railliet, 1923 ; he accordingly designates *Cylicostomum longibursatum* Yorke and Macfie, 1918, as the type of the genus *Trichonema.* This, however, is contrary to the International Code and it seems to us desirable to retain *Cylichnostomum tetracanthum* Mehlis of Looss, 1900, as the type of the genus *Trichonema.*

Cram (1924) has unfortunately still further complicated matters by raising Ihle's subgenera to generic rank, and has added two more to the list, viz., *Cylicotoichus* Cram, 1924, in which the dorsal and ventral walls of the mouth capsule are much higher than the lateral walls, containing the species *montgomeryi ;* and *Cylicobrachytus* Cram, 1924, for those *Trichonema* in which the mouth capsule is extremely short, and the elements of the internal leaf-crown are either inconspicuous or absent, containing the species *prionodes* and *brevicapsulatum.*

Refs. 62, 101, 111a, 111d, 220, 223, 224, 225, 227, 228, 230, 231, 232, 234, 235, 236a, 252, 253, 292, 336, 338, 351a, 412, 473, 582c, 615, 671, 673, 674, 676, 678.

Genus POTERIOSTOMUM Quiel, 1919.

Syn., *Hexodontostomum* Ihle, 1920.

Definition.—TRICHONEMINÆ : closely resembles *Trichonema*, differing from this genus in the arrangement of the dorsal rays of

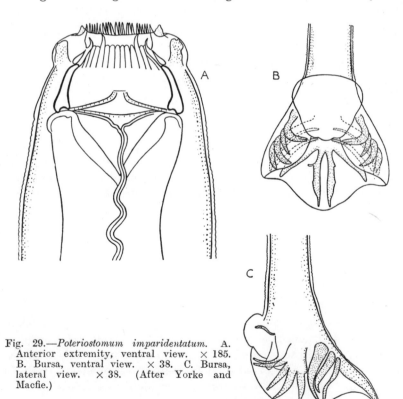

Fig. 29.—*Poteriostomum imparidentatum.* A. Anterior extremity, ventral view. × 185. B. Bursa, ventral view. × 38. C. Bursa, lateral view. × 38. (After Yorke and Macfie.)

the bursa, which is as follows—externo-dorsal ray arises from a common trunk with the dorsal, the main trunk of the dorsal ray is not cleft to its base, but only for about half its length, the two lateral branches arising from the undivided portion close to the point of origin of the externo-dorsal. Parasites of equines.

Type species : *P. imparidentatum* Quiel, 1919. ♂ 14 mm., ♀ 14–20 mm. In equines.

 Syn., *P. pluridentatum* Quiel, 1919.
  Hexodontostomum markusi Ihle, 1920.
  Cylichnostomum zebræ Turner, 1920.
Other species :
 P. rátzii (Kotlán, 1919). In equines.
  P. rátzii var. *nana* Theiler, 1923.
Refs. 222, 225, 232, 252, 393, 615, 675.

Genus SAURICOLA Chapin, 1924.

Syn., *Echinopharynx* Thapar, 1925.

Definition.—TRICHONEMINÆ: mouth directed straight forwards; buccal capsule very short, cylindrical or ring-shaped, and cut up

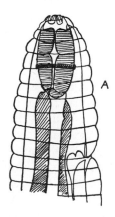
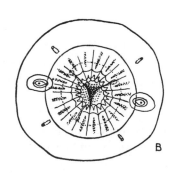

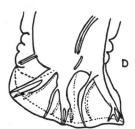

Fig. 30.—*Sauricola sauricola.* A. Anterior extremity, lateral view. × 60. B. Head, end-on view. × 240. C. Posterior extremity of female, lateral view. × 32. D. Bursa, lateral view. × 60. (After Chapin.)

into 36 distinct segments ; arising from the capsule is the corona-radiata consisting of 36 elements. Œsophagus very short and stout, and the cuticular lining is provided with numerous rose-thorn shaped spines. Intestine with a very thick cuticular lining and provided with three pocket-shaped diverticula directed posteriorly. Male : bursa well-developed ; with the following formula—ventro-ventral and ventro-lateral rays separate and parallel, externo-lateral and other laterals arising from a common trunk, the medio-lateral and postero-lateral separate in their distal portion only, and from the latter a short branch is directed posteriorly, externo-dorsal arises from the base of the dorsal, dorsal bifurcate in its distal portion, each branch being bidigitate ; preventral rays present ; spicules long, slender and simple ; gubernaculum present. Female : vulva near anus ; uteri parallel. Oviparous, eggs oval with thin shells. Parasites of reptiles.

Type species : *S. sauricola* Chapin, 1924. ♂ 7–7·5 mm., ♀ 8–10 mm. In *Testudo denticulata* (*T. tabulata*).

Other species : **S. echinopharynx* (Thapar, 1925). In *Testudo tabulata*.

Syn., *Echinopharynx echinopharynx* Thapar, 1925.

Refs. 92, 613a.

Genus GYALOCEPHALUS Looss, 1900.

Definition.—TRICHONEMINÆ : mouth directed straight forward with an external leaf-crown arising from the mouth collar ; buccal capsule short with an internal leaf-crown. Anterior end of the œsophagus enormously dilated and chitinous, and containing three large crescentic teeth which project forward into the buccal capsule. Male : bursal formula—ventral, externo-lateral and lateral rays arise from a common trunk, externo-dorsal arises separately from the dorsal, dorsal split almost to its base, each limb giving off two lateral branches : well-marked preventral rays ; spicules equal ; gubernaculum present. Female : vulva near anus ; posterior extremity straight and conical. Parasites of equines.

Type species : *G. capitatus* Looss, 1900. ♂ 7·5 mm., ♀ 9–10 mm. In equines.

Other species : *G. equi* Yorke and Macfie, 1918. In equines.

Refs. 232, 336, 338, 615, 672.

---

* Possibly this species is identical with *S. sauricola*, but the spicules are stated by Thapar to be 4·05 mm. in length as compared with 2·36 mm. in *S. sauricola*.

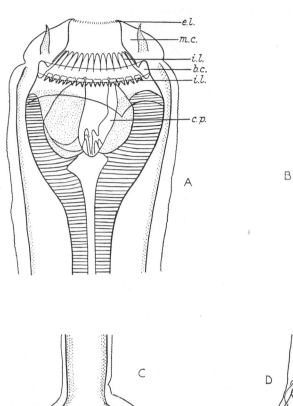
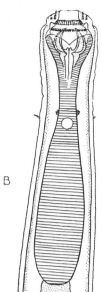
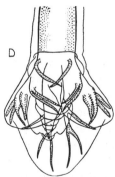

Fig. 31.—*Gyalocephalus capitatus.* A. Head, lateral view. *e.l,* external leaf-crown ; *m.c,* mouth collar ; *i.l,* internal leaf-crown ; *b.c,* buccal capsule ; *c.p,* crescentic plates. × 185. B. Anterior extremity, ventral view. × 62. C. Bursa, lateral view. *p.r,* preventral ray ; *v,* ventral rays ; *e.l,* externo-lateral ray ; *m.l,* medio-lateral ray ; *p.l,* postero-lateral ray ; *e.d,* externo-dorsal ray ; *d,* dorsal ray. × 62. D. Bursa, ventral view. × 62. (After Yorke and Macfie.)

Genus TRACHYPHARYNX Leiper, 1911.

Definition.—TRICHONEMINÆ : mouth directed straight forward, two leaf-crowns ; buccal capsule short ; anterior end of œsophagus greatly dilated, and lined by cuticle having a large number of rounded knobs. Male : undescribed. Female : vulva a short distance in front of the anus.

Fig. 32.—*Trachypharynx nigeriæ*. Anterior extremity, lateral view. (After Leiper.)

Type species : *T. nigeriæ* Leiper, 1911. ♂ 11 mm., ♀ 15 mm. In a large West African rodent.

Refs. 205, 286.

Genus CYLINDROPHARYNX Leiper, 1911.

Definition.—TRICHONEMINÆ : mouth directed straight forward ; the external leaf-crown which arises from the mouth collar is greatly modified and consists of six large elements corresponding to the head papillæ, dorsally and ventrally it is deficient, but from each of the prominent dorsal and ventral lips of the mouth collar there projects horizontally inwards a broad crescentic plate ; buccal capsule extremely long and cylindrical, with an internal leaf-crown at its anterior margin.   Male : bursal formula —ventral ray cleft, externo-lateral and laterals arise from a common trunk, externo-dorsal arising separately from the dorsal, dorsal doubled, each limb giving off one lateral branch, the extremity of which may be bifurcated ; spicules long, stout and barbed at their extremity.   Female : vulva a short distance in front of the anus.   Parasites of zebras.

Type species : *G. brevicauda* Leiper, 1911. ♂ 5–7 mm., ♀ 6–8 mm. In zebra.

Other species :

 C. intermedia Theiler, 1923.   In zebra.

 C. longicauda Leiper, 1911.   In zebra.

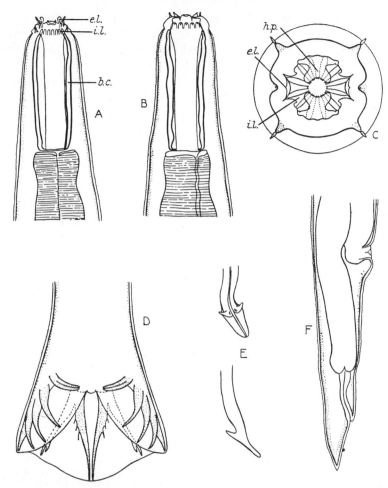

Fig. 33.—*Cylindropharynx rhodesiensis.* A. Anterior extremity, ventral view. *e.l*, external leaf-crown ; *i.l*, internal leaf-crown ; *b.c*, buccal capsule. × 58. B. Anterior extremity, lateral view. × 58. C. Head, end-on view. *h.p*, horizontal crescentic plate ; *e.l*, external leaf-crown ; *i.l*, internal leaf-crown. × 185. D. Bursa, ventral view. × 58. E. Ends of spicules. × 280. F. Posterior extremity of female, lateral view. × 30. (After Yorke and Macfie.)

C. ornata Cram, 1924. In zebra.

C. rhodesiensis Yorke and Macfie, 1920. In zebra.

Refs. 64, 111a, 232, 286, 615, 677.

Genus PHARYNGOSTRONGYLUS n. g.

Definition.—TRICHONEMINÆ : body tapering gradually ante-riorly, head directed straight forwards, mouth collar with two large broad lateral papillæ and four smaller submedian head papillæ. Cuticle smooth with a few fine striations anteriorly ; buccal capsule short and cylindrical with walls concave outwards. Corona radiata arising from near the anterior end of the buccal capsule ; the buccal capsule leads into a long cylindrical vestibule, with heavily chitinized ringed walls, which opens obliquely into

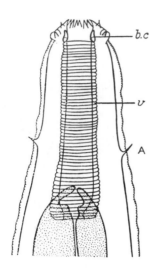

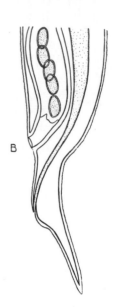

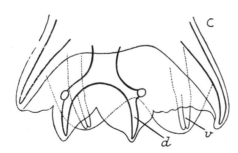

Fig. 34.—*Pharyngostrongylus macropodis*. A. Anterior extremity, dorsal view. *b.c,* buccal capsule ; *v,* vestibule. × 250. B. Posterior extremity of female, lateral view. × 56. C. Bursa, dorsal view. *d,* dorsal ray ; *v,* ventral ray. × 250. (Orig.)

the œsophagus the dorsal walls being longer than the ventral ; œsophagus very long and slender ; cervical papillæ long and thin, situated over the posterior part of the vestibule ; excretory pore behind the nerve ring about the end of the anterior fourth of œsophagus. Male : bursa very short and closed ventrally, with lateral lobes clearly marked off from the ventral and dorsal lobes ; with the following formula—ventral ray cleft in the distal part, externo-lateral, lateral and externo-dorsal all arise from a common trunk, medio-lateral and postero-lateral fused except in the distal portion, dorsal divided almost to its base, each limb giving off a short external appendage ; spicules long, thin, and striated with simple points ; gubernaculum present. Female : posterior extremity narrows suddenly behind the vulva and again behind the anus to end in a conical tail ; vulva a little distance in front of the anus ; uteri parallel. Oviparous. Parasites of marsupials.

Type species : *P. macropodis* n. sp. ♂ 11–12 mm., ♀ 14–17 mm. In *Macropus* sp.

Genus LABIOSTRONGYLUS n. g.

Definition.—TRICHONEMINÆ : large stout worms ; mouth directed straight forwards and surrounded by 4 very large bilobed processes arranged submedianly, by a large simple process on each side, and by a smaller process dorsally and ventrally ; buccal capsule large and cylindrical of rather greater diameter laterally than antero-posteriorly ; œsophagus long and rather slender. Male : bursa with lateral lobes clearly marked off from the dorsal lobe and also from two large ventral lobes, each of which is supported by a ventral ray ; with the following formula—ventral ray cleft distally, externo-lateral very short and arising from a common trunk with the laterals and externo-dorsal, lateral long, cleft distally and reaching the apex of the lateral lobes, externo-dorsal very short, dorsal divided for about half its length, and from the common trunk a long branch is given off on each side ; spicules long, thin, and striated, with simple points ; gubernaculum present. Female : posterior extremity tapers regularly behind the vulva to end in a conical process ; vulva a little distance in front of the anus ; uteri parallel ; oviparous. Parasites of marsupials.

Type species : *L. labiostrongylus* n. sp.† ♂ 42 mm., ♀ 50–70 mm. In *Macropus* sp.

---

* *Pharyngostrongylus macropodis* n. sp. Length of male 11–12 mm., female 14–17 mm.; mouth capsule about 15 μ in depth and definitely broader than deep. Corona radiata arises from near the anterior end of the buccal capsule, and consists of about 16 delicate triangular finely pointed elements. Length of pharynx or vestibule about 200–230 μ, breadth about 30 μ. Cervical papillæ about 140 μ from the anterior extremity. Length of œsophagus about 2–2·3 mm. Spicules about 1·9–2 mm. in length. In the female the anus is about 400 μ from the tip of the tail and the vulva about 350 μ in front of the anus.

† *Labiostrongylus labiostrongylus* n. sp. Length of male about 42 mm., female 50–70 mm. Length of œsophagus in male about 9·4 mm., and in female about 11·3 mm. Spicules about 5·2 mm. in length. In the female the anus is about 2·2 mm. from the tip of the tail and the vulva is about 1·9 mm. in front of the anus.

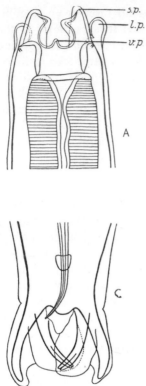

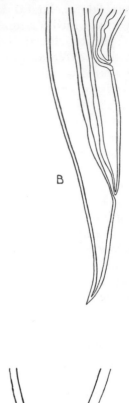

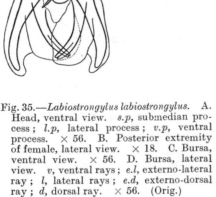

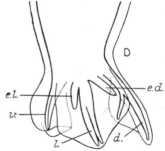

Fig. 35.—*Labiostrongylus labiostrongylus.* A.
Head, ventral view. *s.p*, submedian process ; *l.p*, lateral process ; *v.p*, ventral
process. × 56. B. Posterior extremity
of female, lateral view. × 18. C. Bursa,
ventral view. × 56. D. Bursa, lateral
view. *v*, ventral rays ; *e.l*, externo-lateral
ray ; *l*, lateral rays ; *e.d*, externo-dorsal
ray ; *d*, dorsal ray. × 56. (Orig.)

Genus SPIROSTRONGYLUS n. g.

Definition.—TRICHONEMINÆ : small worms, body spirally
rolled permanently ; mouth collar circular and shallow ; buccal
capsule almost cylindrical, slightly narrower posteriorly, with a
leaf-crown consisting of ten broad elements arising from the base
of the capsule and projecting forwards beyond the mouth collar.
Cervical papillæ and excretory pore about the posterior end of the
œsophagus ; œsophagus markedly constricted at the level of the
nerve ring about the commencement of the posterior fourth,

the anterior portion being slightly club-shaped posteriorly, and the posterior broad, short, and subglobular. Male : bursa well-developed, the lateral lobes being clearly marked off from the dorsal, and also from the small ventral lobes which are supported by the ventral rays ; with the following formula—ventral ray

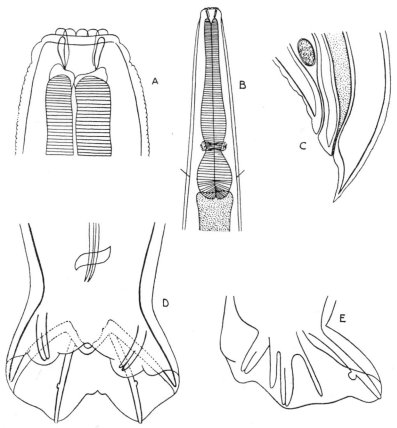

Fig. 36.—*Spirostrongylus spirostrongylus.* A. Head, ventral view. × 330. B. Anterior extremity, ventral view. × 75. C. Tail of female, lateral view. × 330. D. Bursa, ventral view. × 330. E. Bursa, lateral view. × 220. (Orig.)

cleft, externo-lateral, lateral and externo-dorsal all arise from a common trunk, medio-lateral and postero-lateral fused except in the distal part, dorsal ray divided almost to its base, the limbs being widely separated, projecting beyond the margin of the bursa, and each giving off a short lateral branch ; spicules very long, thin, and striated, with simple points ; gubernaculum present.

Female : posterior extremity conical, vulva near anus. Oviparous. Parasites of marsupials.

Type species : *S. spirostrongylus* n. sp. ♂ about 4 mm., ♀ about 5 mm. In *Macropus* sp.

Genus KILULUMA Skrjabin, 1916.

Definition.—TRICHONEMINÆ : mouth directed straight forwards and surrounded by a mouth collar subdivided into six sections,

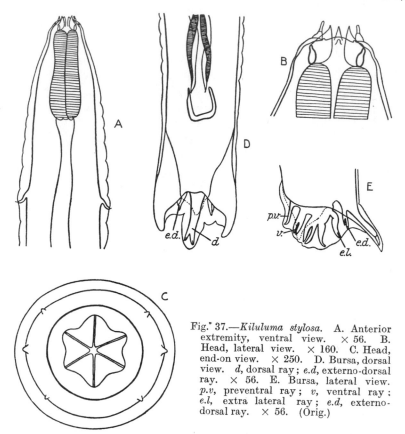

Fig. 37.—*Kiluluma stylosa.* A. Anterior extremity, ventral view. × 56. B. Head, lateral view. × 160. C. Head, end-on view. × 250. D. Bursa, dorsal view. *d*, dorsal ray ; *e.d*, externo-dorsal ray. × 56. E. Bursa, lateral view. *p.v*, preventral ray ; *v*, ventral ray ; *e.l*, extra lateral ray ; *e.d*, externo-dorsal ray. × 56. (Orig.)

2 lateral and 4 submedian, each bearing a head papilla ; the lateral head papillæ are small and the submedian long and projecting, with club-like terminations ; buccal capsule cylindrical and short, with stout walls ; there is a single leaf-crown con-

* *Spirostrongylus spirostrongylus* n. sp. Length of male about 4 mm., female about 5 mm. Mouth capsule about 25–27 μ in depth and distinctly deeper than broad. The corona radiata consists of about ten broad elements arising from the base of the capsule. Œsophagus about 650 μ in length, excretory pore and cervical papillæ about the posterior end of the œsophagus. Spicules about 1·2 mm. in length. In the female the anus is about 300 to 320 μ from the tip of the tail, and the vulva is about 200 μ in front of the anus.

sisting of six elements arising from the base of the capsule, sweeping inwards and forwards, and projecting beyond the mouth collar when the mouth is open. Cuticle of the anterior part of the worm inflated ; œsophagus short. Male : bursa short, lateral lobes clearly separated from the dorsal, which is longer ; with the following formula—there is a well-developed pre-ventral ray, ventro-ventral and latero-ventral rays fused proximally, close together and parallel distally, externo-lateral and other laterals arise from a common trunk, medio-lateral and postero-lateral separate, there is an extra lateral ray * between the postero-lateral and externo-dorsal, externo-dorsal arises from the base of the dorsal and is sometimes cleft distally, dorsal bifurcate in its distal portion ; spicules equal, broad, winged, and twisted distally, with simple points ; gubernaculum present. Female : posterior extremity narrows rapidly behind the anus to end in a conical tail ; vulva near anus ; vagina long ; uteri parallel. Oviparous. Parasites of rhinoceroses.

Type species : *K. stylosa* (Linstow, 1907). ♂ 12–19 mm. ♀ 17–21 mm. In *Rhinoceros africanus.*

Syn., *Deletrocephalus stylosus* Linstow, 1907.

Other species :

K. africana Thapar, 1924. In *Rhinoceros africanus.*

K. macdonaldi Thapar, 1924. In *Rhinoceros africanus.*

K. magna Thapar, 1924. In *Rhinoceros africanus.*

K. pachyderma Thapar, 1924. In *Rhinoceros africanus.*

K. rhinocerotis Thapar, 1924. In *Rhinoceros africanus.*

K. solitaria Thapar, 1924. In *Rhinoceros africanus.*

With the exception of *K. magna*, these species appear to us to be very similar to one another. We have examined a large collection of worms belonging to the genus obtained from five rhinoceroses, and although the individual worms were found to exhibit considerable variation we have been unable to satisfy ourselves that more than one species was present. Thapar made a new subfamily *Kiluluminæ* for this genus, but this appears to us to be unnecessary.†

Refs. 371, 573, 613, 613b.

Genus QUILONIA Lane, 1914.

Syn., *Evansia* Railliet, Henry, and Joyeux, 1913, preoccupied.

Nematevansia Ihle, 1919.

Definition.—TRICHONEMINÆ : mouth directed straight forwards, surrounded by a mouth collar bearing 4 prominent submedian

* It appears to us that this so-called extra lateral ray might well represent the externo-dorsal, and the so-called externo-dorsal be merely a branch of the dorsal ray.

† In a later paper Thapar (1925) has described four additional species of this genus from the African rhinoceros, viz., *K. goodeyi, K. brevicauda, K. brevivaginata,* and *K. cylindrica.*

head papillæ and a pair of lateral head papillæ ; the leaf-crown
is composed of a few characteristically curved elements arising
posteriorly from the cuticle covering the anterior end of the
œsophagus and continued anteriorly to surround the mouth.
The cuticular lining of the oral cavity does not lie directly in
contact with the mouth capsule, but is separated from it by

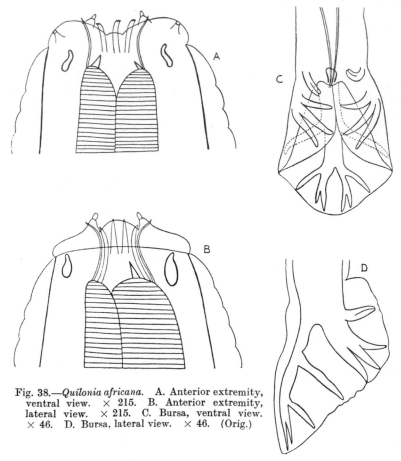

Fig. 38.—*Quilonia africana*. A. Anterior extremity,
ventral view. × 215. B. Anterior extremity,
lateral view. × 215. C. Bursa, ventral view.
× 46. D. Bursa, lateral view. × 46. (Orig.)

parenchyma, so that the mouth cavity is narrower than the buccal
capsule. Buccal capsule very short and ring-shaped ; two or
more teeth project into the oral cavity from the top of the œsophagus. Male : the dorsal lobe of the bursa is longer than the
lateral lobes ; bursal formula—ventral ray cleft, externo-lateral
and laterals arise from a common trunk, medio-lateral and postero-
lateral separated, externo-dorsal arises from a common trunk
with the dorsal, dorsal bifurcate for about half its length, each

branch trifurcate. Female : posterior extremity straight, long, and pointed ; vulva in the caudal third of the body. Parasites of elephants and rhinoceroses.

Type species : *Q. renniei* (Railliet, Henry, and Joyeux, 1913). ♂ 15 mm., ♀ 20 mm. In Indian elephant.

    Syn., *Evansia renniei* Railliet, Henry, and Joyeux, 1913.

        Nematevansia renniei (Railliet, Henry, and Joyeux, 1913).

        Q. quilona Lane, 1914.

Other species :

    Q. africana Lane, 1921.   In African elephant.

    Q. apiensis (Gedoelst, 1916).   In African elephant.

    Q. brevicauda Khalil, 1922.   In African elephant.

    Q. ethiopica Khalil, 1922.   In African elephant.

    Q. parva Neveu-Lemaire, 1925.   In African rhinoceros.

    Q. rhinocerotis Neveu-Lemaire, 1924.   In rhinoceros.

    Q. travancra Lane, 1914.   In Indian elephant.

    Q. uganda Khalil, 1922.   In African elephant.

Refs. 221, 251, 255, 257, 264, 371, 372a, 450.

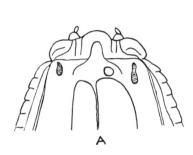

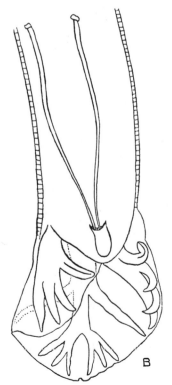

Fig. 39.—*Paraquilonia brumpti.* A. Anterior extremity, lateral view. × 150. B. Posterior extremity of male, ventral view. × 65. (After Neveu-Lemaire.)

Genus **PARAQUILONIA** Neveu-Lemaire, 1924.

Definition.—TRICHONEMINÆ : mouth directed straight forwards, and surrounded by a mouth collar giving the appearance of six thick and rounded lips, two dorsal and two ventral, each bearing a prominent papilla the last portion of which is separated from the rest by a constriction, and two lateral lips without papillæ : the

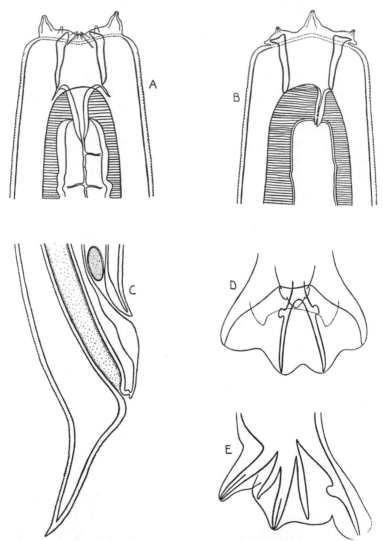

Fig. 40.—*Macropostrongylus macropostrongylus.*   A. Anterior extremity, ventral view.   × 250.   B. Anterior extremity, lateral view.   × 250. C. Tail of female, lateral view.   × 160.   D. Bursa, dorsal view.   × 160. E. Bursa, lateral view.   × 160.   (Orig.)

leaf-crown is rudimentary, buccal capsule short, ring-shaped and almost circular. Male : bursa with three well-developed lobes ; with the following formula—ventral ray cleft, externo-lateral and laterals arising from a common trunk, externo-dorsal arising from a common trunk with the dorsal, dorsal bifurcate for about half its length, each branch being tridigitate ; spicules equal, long, and thin ; gubernaculum present. Female : vulva in the posterior fourth of the body ; uteri opposed. Parasites of rhinoceroses.

Type species : *P. brumpti* Neveu-Lemaire, 1924. ♂ 14 mm., ♀ 22 mm. In *Rhinoceros bicornis*.

Ref. 371.

Genus MACROPOSTRONGYLUS n. g.

Definition.—TRICHONEMINÆ : mouth directed straight forwards, mouth collar with two large prominent lateral head papillæ, and four smaller submedian head papillæ ; buccal capsule cylindrical with a leaf-crown arising from the internal surface of the capsule, and projecting beyond the mouth collar ; œsophagus relatively long, and club-shaped posteriorly. Male : with a well-developed bursa completely closed ventrally by a ventral lobe, distinctly marked off from the lateral lobes, and supported by the ventral rays ; with the following formula—ventral rays cleft in the distal portion, externo-lateral, lateral, and externo-dorsal rays arise from a common trunk, medio-lateral and postero-lateral fused in the proximal portion, dorsal divided nearly to the base, the limbs being widely separated and each giving off a short lateral branch ; spicules long, delicate, striated, with simple points ; gubernaculum present. Female : body tapers rapidly behind the anus to end in a sharply conical tail ; vulva near anus ; uteri parallel. Oviparous. Parasites of marsupials.

Type species : **M. macropostrongylus* n. sp. ♂ 8–9 mm., ♀ 10–12 mm. In *Macropus* sp.

Other species : *†M. australis* n. sp. In *Macropus* sp.

---

* *Macropostrongylus macropostrongylus* n. sp. Length of male 8–9 mm., female 10–12 mm. ; buccal capsule about 40 μ in depth and definitely deeper than broad ; leaf-crown composed of relatively small elements only slightly projecting beyond the mouth collar. Excretory pore about 850–875 μ from the anterior extremity. Length of œsophagus about 1·6 mm. in the male, and 1·75 mm. in the female. Spicules about 1·5 mm. in length ; the lateral branch of the dorsal rays is given off shortly after the bifurcation. In the female the anus is about 250–275 μ from the tip of the tail, and the vulva is about 130–140 μ in front of the anus.

† *Macropostrongylus australis* n. sp. Length of male 7–8 mm., female 8–9 mm. ; buccal capsule about 12 μ in depth and definitely broader than deep ; leaf-crown composed of relatively long elements projecting considerably beyond the mouth collar. Excretory pore about 510–560 μ from the anterior extremity. Length of œsophagus about 650 μ in the male, and 720 μ in the female. Spicules about 2·7 mm. in length ; the lateral branch of the dorsal rays is given off about the commencement of the distal third of the main limbs. In the female the anus is about 160 μ from the tip of the tail, and the vulva is about 120 μ in front of the anus.

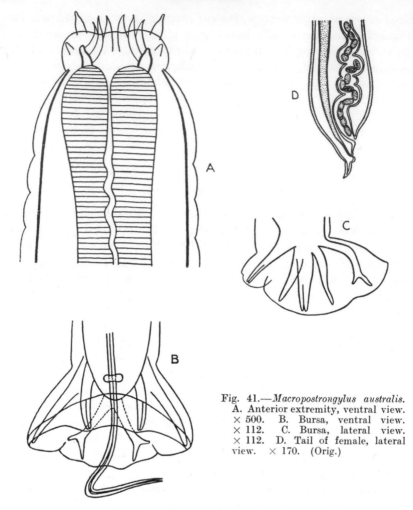

Fig. 41.—*Macropostrongylus australis.*
A. Anterior extremity, ventral view.
× 500.   B.   Bursa, ventral view.
× 112.   C.   Bursa, lateral view.
× 112.   D. Tail of female, lateral
view.   × 170.   (Orig.)

Genus THEILERIANA Monnig, 1924.

Definition.—TRICHONEMINÆ : mouth directed straight forwards,
slightly ellipsoidal with the long axis dorso-ventral, with a well-
developed mouth collar.   One leaf-crown arising from the base of
the buccal capsule ; buccal capsule very short, slightly ellipsoidal,
long axis dorso-ventral, walls stout ; duct of dorsal œsophageal
gland projects into the buccal capsule as a tooth-like tubercle ; œsophagus, very stout and short, and constricted at the level of nerve
ring ; cervical papillæ and excretory pore behind the posterior
extremity of œsophagus.   Male : bursa very large with two large
lateral lobes and a smaller dorsal lobe ; with the following formula
—ventral rays cleft, externo-lateral and laterals arising from a

common trunk, medio-lateral cleft for the greater part of its length, postero-lateral lies close and parallel to it, externo-dorsal arising from a common trunk with the dorsal, dorsal bifurcate almost to its base, each limb dividing into two processes ; spicules long and thin ; gubernaculum present.   Female : posterior extremity

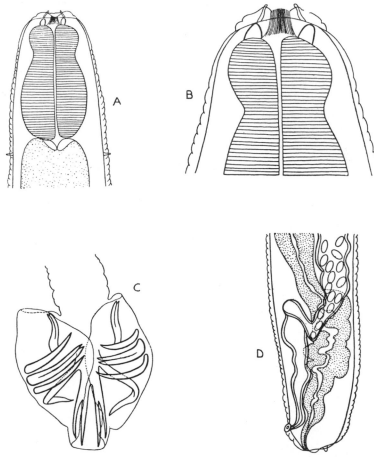

Fig. 42.—*Theileriana brachylaima*.   A. Anterior extremity, ventral view.   × 64.   B. Anterior extremity, lateral view.   × 180.   C.   Bursa, ventral view.   × 40.   D. Tail of female, lateral view.   × 40.   (Orig.)

rounded with a small conical terminal process ; vulva near anus. Oviparous, eggs with thin shell and containing a well-developed embryo when deposited.   Parasites of rodents.

Type species :   *T. brachylaima* (Linstow, 1901).   ♂ 9–13 mm., ♀ 11–20 mm.   In *Procavia* sp.

Syn., *Deletrocephalus brachylaimus* Linstow, 1901.

Other species :   ? *T. variabilis* (Chapin, 1924).   In *Testudo denticulata*.

Syn., *Deletrocephalus variabilis* Chapin, 1924.

Refs. 92, 320, 362, 652.

Genus MURSHIDIA Lane, 1914.

Syn., *Pteridopharynx* Lane, 1921.

Memphisia Khalil, 1922.

Henryella Neveu-Lemaire, 1924.

Pterygopharynx Witenberg, 1925.

Definition.—TRICHONEMINÆ : mouth directed straight forwards, mouth collar more prominent laterally giving the appearance of

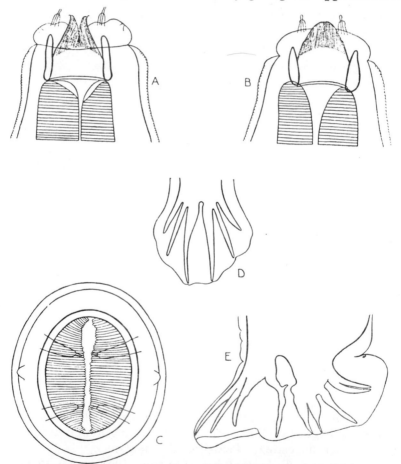

Fig. 43.—*Murshidia murshida.*   A. Anterior extremity, ventral view (optical section).   × 160.   B.   Anterior   extremity,   lateral   view.   × 160. C. Anterior extremity, end-on view.   × 260.   D. Bursa, dorsal view. × 56.   E. Bursa, lateral view.   × 56.   (Orig.)

two lateral lips, each of which bears a sessile lateral, and two prominent submedian, head papillæ ; the leaf-crown arises from the internal surface of the buccal capsule, the point of origin being more anterior laterally than dorsally and ventrally ; since the dorsal and ventral elements of the leaf-crown are much shorter than the lateral elements, their points, which form the boundary of the mouth, do not describe a circle, but produce a dorso-ventral slit, the mouth having a crescentic appearance when viewed laterally ; the buccal capsule is roughly cylindrical and may or may not have in its depth a few teeth arising from the anterior end of the œsophagus ; œsophagus short and stout, the cuticle lining the anterior portion may or may not exhibit a plumose sculpturing. Male : bursa with a well-developed dorsal lobe, and with the following formula—ventral, externo-lateral and lateral rays arising from a common trunk, the medio-lateral and postero-lateral separated in their distal portions, the externo-dorsal arises from the base of the dorsal, dorsal bifurcate for about half its length, and from about the point of bifurcation gives off either two lateral branches arising close together or a single lateral branch which is cleft to a greater or less extent, various small excrescences may be present on the postero-lateral or on the externo-dorsal ray ; spicules equal, with the points bent in one direction ; gubernaculum present. Female : posterior extremity long and tapering, vulva near anus. Parasites of elephants, rhinoceroses and warthogs.

Type species : *M. murshida* Lane, 1914. ♂ 18–20 mm., ♀ 22–28 mm. In Indian elephant.

Other species :

M. africana (Lane, 1921). In African elephant.
Syn., *Pteridopharynx africana* Lane, 1921.

M. anisa (Khalil, 1922). In African elephant.
Syn., *Pteridopharynx anisa* Khalil, 1922.

M. aziza (Khalil, 1922). In African elephant.
Syn., *Memphisia aziza* Khalil, 1922.

M. bozasi (Neveu-Lemaire, 1924). In African rhinoceros.
Syn., *Henryella bozasi* Neveu-Lemaire, 1924.

M. didieri (Neveu-Lemaire, 1924). In African rhinoceros.
Syn., *Henryella didieri* Neveu-Lemaire, 1924.

M. falcifera (Cobbold, 1882). In Indian elephant.

M. hadia Khalil, 1922. In African elephant.

M. hamata Daubney, 1923. In *Phacochœrus æthiopicus*.

M. indica (Ware, 1924). In Indian elephant.

M. lanei Witenberg, 1925. In elephant.

M. linstowi Khalil, 1922. In African elephant.

Syn., *Sclerostomum rectum* Linst., 1907, not *Strongylus rectus* Linst., 1906.

M. memphisia (Khalil, 1922). In African elephant.

Syn., *Memphisia memphisia* Khalil, 1922.

M. neveu-lemairei (Witenberg, 1925). In elephant.

M. omœnsis (Neveu-Lemaire, 1924). In African rhinoceros.

Syn., *Pteridopharynx omœnsis* Neveu-Lemaire, 1924.

M. pugnicaudata (Leiper, 1909). In *Phacochœrus œthiopicus*.

M. raillieti (Neveu-Lemaire, 1924). In African rhinoceros.

Syn., *Henryella raillieti* Neveu-Lemaire, 1924.

M. rhinocerotis (Neveu-Lemaire, 1924). In African rhinoceros.

Syn., *Memphisia rhinocerotis* Neveu-Lemaire, 1924.

M. zeltneri (Neveu-Lemaire, 1924). In African rhinoceros.

Syn., *Henryella zeltneri* Neveu-Lemaire, 1924.

Refs. 105, 118, 221, 251, 255, 257, 371, 448, 663, 666a.

Genus BUISSONIA Neveu-Lemaire, 1924.

Definition.—TRICHONEMINÆ: closely resembling *Murshidia* from which it apparently differs only in the absence of a definite

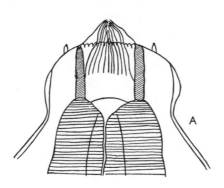
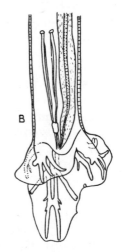

Fig. 44.—*Buissonia rhinocerotis*. A. Anterior extremity, lateral view. × 300. B. Bursa. × 45. (After Neveu-Lemaire.)

mouth collar, and in the absence or atrophy of the submedian head papillæ, with the result that the anterior margin of the capsule abuts directly on the end of the worm and the corona radiata, which consists of numerous converging elements, appears very prominent and projecting. Parasites of rhinoceroses.

Type species : *B. rhinocerotis* Neveu-Lemaire, 1924. ♂ 13 mm., ♀ 15 mm. In African rhinoceros.

Other species :

B. *africana* Neveu-Lemaire, 1924.   In African rhinoceros.

B. *longibursa* Neveu-Lemaire, 1924.   In African rhinoceros.

Ref. 371.

Lane (1921) differentiated *Pteridopharynx* from *Murshidia* on the grounds that in the former the cuticle lining the anterior part of the œsophagus exhibited a plumose sculpturing, and that the two external branches of the dorsal ray were almost completely fused. Khalil (1922) emended *Pteridopharynx* by stating that the plumose sculpturing of the œsophagus may or may not be present, but that the genus is characterized by the presence of a prominence or accessary ray on the posterior border of the lateral ray, and that the two external branches of the dorsal ray are fused almost to their tips.* Khalil then separated a number of worms closely resembling *Pteridopharynx* into a genus *Memphisia*, characterized by the presence of a cuticular collar round the anterior end of the body, and by the peculiarity of having a small branch on the externo-dorsal ray. The cuticular collar appears, however, to be a very variable character, and can hardly be seen in Khalil's figure of *Memphisia aziza*. Neveu-Lemaire (1924) expresses the opinion that the branch on the externo-dorsal ray is of only specific value, but adds another species to *Memphisia* on the ground of its having a cuticular collar. He then proceeds to erect a new genus *Henryella* closely resembling *Murshidia*, but differentiated from it by slight differences of the bursal formula. On comparing his drawing of the type species (*M. raillieti*) with Lane's drawing of the type of *Pteridopharynx* (*P. africana*), we were, however, unable to discover the slightest difference. Finally, Neveu-Lemaire created a second genus *Buissonia* for worms closely resembling *Henryella*, but differing by the greater anterior projection of the leaf-crown, and by the absence, or atrophy, of the submedian head papillæ. On studying the figures of the three species included in this genus, the most striking feature appears to be the absence of the mouth collar, the buccal capsule reaching the anterior end of the worm.

After carefully considering the various points raised, and after working through the large collection of worms from elephants and rhinoceroses in the Liverpool School of Tropical Medicine, we have

---

* In this connection, however, it must be noted that *Murshidia falcifera* (Cobbold, 1882) Lane, 1924, which Khalil includes in the genus *Murshidia*, exhibits a small prominence on the posterior border of the postero-lateral ray, and also one on the posterior border of the externo-dorsal ray, and furthermore that there is only a single branch of the dorsal ray, which is split for about half its length.

reached the conclusion that the genera *Pteridopharynx* Lane, 1914, *Memphisia* Khalil, 1922, and *Henryella* Neveu-Lemaire, 1924, are synonymous with *Murshidia* Lane, 1914. In view of the apparent absence of a mouth collar in *Buissonia*, we propose to leave this genus pending further investigation.

Genus BOURGELATIA Railliet, Henry, and Bauche, 1919.

Definition.—TRICHONEMINÆ : mouth circular directed straight forwards, two leaf-crowns ; buccal capsule cylindrical with thick walls consisting of an anterior and a posterior portion. Male :

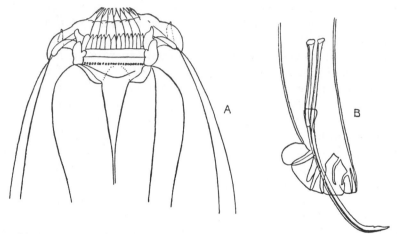

Fig. 45.—*Bourgelatia diducta.* A. Anterior extremity, dorsal view. × 200. B. Bursa, lateral view. × 50. (After Railliet, Henry, and Bauche.)

lateral lobes of bursa divided, giving the appearance of a five-lobed bursa ; bursal formula—ventral ray cleft, externo-lateral and laterals arising from a common trunk, externo-dorsal arises from a common trunk with the dorsal, dorsal cleft for about half its length, each branch giving off one lateral branch ; spicules equal, long, and winged ; inconspicuous gubernaculum present. Female : vulva near anus ; posterior extremity straight and ending in a sharp point. Parasites of pigs.

Type species : *B. diducta* Railliet, Henry, and Bauche, 1919. ♂ 9·3 mm., ♀ 11–13·5 mm. In pigs.

Ref. 449.

Genus AMIRA Lane, 1914.

Syn., *Khalilia* Neveu-Lemaire, 1924.

Definition.—TRICHONEMINÆ : mouth circular and directed straight forwards, with two leaf-crowns, the elements of the

external being long and thin, and all of equal size, and those of
the internal being short and stout, and arising from the anterior
orifice of the buccal capsule ; buccal capsule very short and ring-
shaped ; œsophagus stout and hour-glass shaped, with a thick
cuticular lining. Male : dorsal lobe of bursa may or may not be
enormously elongated, prebursal papillæ much elongated ; with
the following formula—ventral ray cleft near its extremity only,
externo-lateral and laterals arise from a common trunk and lie
close together, externo-dorsal arises from a common trunk with

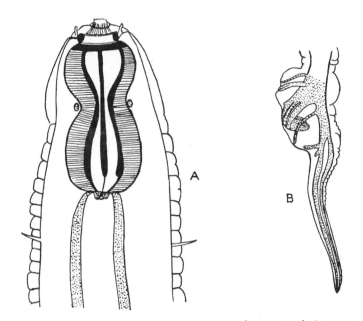

Fig. 46.—*Amira pileata*. A. Anterior extremity, dorso-ventral view. × 60.
    B. Bursa, dorso-lateral view.   × 30.   (After Khalil.)

the dorsal, dorsal bifurcate almost to its base, each branch giving
off two lateral twigs close together ; spicules of enormous length,
equal and very thin ; gubernaculum present. Female : posterior
extremity tapering to a rather blunt point ; vulva near anus ;
vagina very long ; uteri parallel. Parasites of elephants and
rhinoceroses.

Type species : *A. pileata* (Railliet, Henry, and Bauche, 1914).
♂ 10 mm., ♀ 13 mm. In Indian elephant.

   Syn., *Cylicostomum pileatum* Railliet, Henry, and Bauche,
        1914.
        Amira omra Lane, 1914.

Other species :

    A. rhinocerotis (Neveu-Lemaire, 1924). In rhinoceros.

    Syn., *Khalilia rhinocerotis* Neveu-Lemaire, 1924.

    A. sameera Khalil, 1922. In African elephant.

Refs. 251, 255, 257, 370, 371.

Neveu-Lemaire (1924) erected the genus *Khalilia* for *K. rhino-cerotis*, and afterwards added to it *Amira sameera* Khalil, 1922. He differentiated the genus *Khalilia* from *Amira*, because, firstly the head in the former genus is slightly inclined dorsally, whereas in the latter it is directed straight forwards, and secondly, in the former the dorsal lobe of the bursa is short, whereas in the latter it is very long. These characters appear to us to be purely specific. Neveu-Lemaire includes the two genera in a new subfamily *Amirinæ* based on the bursal formula.

TRICHONEMINÆ insufficiently known.

Genus EUCYATHOSTOMUM Molin, 1861.

Definition.—TRICHONEMINÆ : mouth circular, directed straight forwards, a single leaf-crown consisting of numerous slender

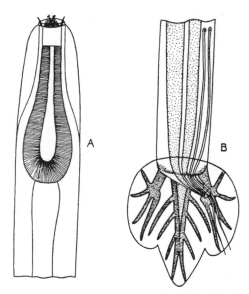

Fig. 47.—*Eucyathostomum longesubulatum.* A. Anterior extremity. B. Bursa.
(After Molin.)

elements ; buccal capsule large, cylindrical, without teeth in its depth. Male : dorsal lobe of bursa projecting beyond the lateral lobes ; bursal formula—ventral, externo-lateral, and lateral rays arise from a common trunk, ventral ray cleft at its extremity, externo-dorsal ray arises from a common trunk with the dorsal ; dorsal gives off two lateral branches from each side of the common trunk, which is bifurcate in its distal third ; spicules long, slender and equal. Female : vulva a short distance in front of the anus ; posterior extremity narrows gradually behind the anus to end in a long conical tail. Parasites of ungulates.

Type species : *E. longesubulatum* Molin, 1861. ♂ 10–12 mm., ♀ 15–20 mm. In *Cervus campestris* and *Mazama rufa*.

Other species : ? *E. spinulosum* (Linstow, 1879). In *Capra ibex*.

Syn., *Strongylus spinulosus* Linstow, 1879.

Refs. 360, 420, 458.

Subfamily ŒSOPHAGOSTOMINÆ Railliet, 1915.

Definition.—STRONGYLIDÆ : with a transverse, ventral cervical groove and a more or less pronounced cephalic vesicle. Buccal capsule cylindrical, ring-shaped, or subglobular.

KEY TO GENERA.

1. Mouth capsule cylindrical and
   shallow or ring-shaped . . Œsophagostomum, p. 85.
   Mouth capsule subglobular . . 3
2. Mouth directed antero-dorsally.
   Œsophageal funnel dilated and
   contains teeth . . . Ternidens, p. 88.
   Mouth directed antero-ventrally.
   Œsophageal funnel does not
   contain teeth . . . Chabertia, p. 89

Genus ŒSOPHAGOSTOMUM Molin, 1861.

Syn., *Hypostomum* Stewart, 1898.

Definition.—ŒSOPHAGOSTOMINÆ : mouth directed straight forwards and surrounded by a mouth collar, which bears the head papillæ, and is sharply delimited behind by a deep annular constriction ; shortly in front of the excretory pore is the ventral transverse groove extending round the body towards the dorsal surface ; the cuticle between the mouth collar and the ventral groove is dilated to a greater or lesser extent forming the cephalic vesicle ; usually there are two leaf-crowns, but occasionally the external is absent ; buccal capsule shallow, cylindrical, or ring-

shaped. Lateral cuticular flanges sometimes present. Œsophageal funnel sometimes dilated and containing lancets. Male :
bursal formula—ventral ray cleft, externo-lateral and laterals

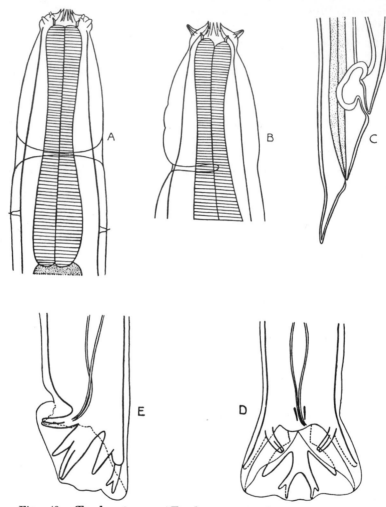

Fig. 48.—*Œsophagostomum* (*Œsophagostomum*) *dentatum*. A. Anterior
extremity, ventral view. × 160. B. Anterior extremity, lateral view.
× 160. C. Tail of female, lateral view. × 56. D. Bursa, ventral
view. × 84. E. Bursa, lateral view. × 84. (Orig.)

arise from a common trunk, medio-lateral and postero-lateral
fused proximally, externo-dorsal arising from a common trunk
with the dorsal, dorsal bifurcate for about half its length, each
branch giving off a short lateral twig ; spicules equal ; guber-

naculum present. Female : vulva a little distance from the anus.
Parasites of mammals.

Type species : *O. dentatum* (Rudolphi, 1803). ♂ 8–12 mm.,
♀ 12–15 mm. In the domesticated pig.

Syn., *O. subulatum* Molin, 1861.

Other species :

O. aculeatum (Linstow, 1879). In *Macacus* sp.

O. apiostomum (Willach, 1891). In man and monkeys.

O. asperum Railliet and Henry, 1913. In goats.

O. attenuatum (Leidy, 1856). In *Cynocephalus porcarius*.

O. bifurcum (Creplin, 1849). In *Cercopithecus patas*.

O. blanchardi Railliet and Henry, 1912. In orang outan.

O. brumpti Railliet and Henry, 1905. In man.

O. columbianum Curtice, 1890. In goat and sheep.

Syn., *Hypostomum columbiana* (Curtice, 1890) Stewart,
1898.

O. dentigerum Railliet and Henry, 1906. In chimpanzee.

O. eurycephalum Goodey, 1924. In roan antelope.

O. mwanzæ Daubney, 1924. In warthog and roan antelope.

O. oldi Goodey, 1924. In roan antelope and warthog.

O. ovatum (Linstow, 1906). In *Hylobates* spp.

O. pachycephalum Molin, 1861. In *Cercopithecus* sp.

O. radiatum (Rudolphi, 1803). In cattle.

Syn., *O. inflatum* (Schneider, 1866).

O. dilatatum (Railliet, 1884).

O. bovis Schnyder, 1906.

O. biramosum Cuillé, Marotel, and Panisset, 1911.

O. vesiculosum Rátz, 1898.

O. simpsoni Goodey, 1924. In warthog and roan antelope.

O. stephanostomum Stoss., 1904. In gorilla.

O. stephanostomum var. *thomasi* Railliet and Henry, 1909. In
man.

O. ventri Thornton, 1924. In Brazilian wild cat.

O. venulosum (Rud., 1809). In goat and sheep.

O. xeri Ortlepp, 1922. In *Xerus setosus*.

O. yorkei Thornton, 1924. In *Phacocœrus æthiopicus*.

Railliet and Henry (1913) and Ihle (1922) have divided the genus
into the following subgenera :—

Subgenus ŒSOPHAGOSTOMUM (Molin, 1861) Railliet and Henry, 1913.

Definition.—Cephalic vesicle well-developed, cervical papillæ at the level
of the posterior œsophageal swelling, cuticular flanges absent, vagina
short, almost transverse. Contains the species *dentatum*.

Subgenus HYSTERACRUM Railliet and Henry, 1913.

Definition.—Cephalic vesicle well-developed, cervical papillæ behind the œsophagus, cuticular lateral flanges absent or very narrow ; vagina long, directed forwards.   Contains the species *venulosum* and *asperum*.

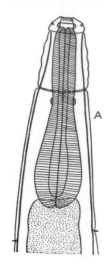 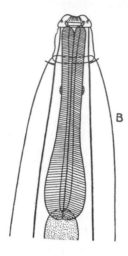 

Fig.   49.—*Œsophagostomum (Hysteracrum) venulosum.* A. Anterior extremity, ventral view. × 56. (Orig.) *Œsophagostomum (Proteracrum) columbianum.* B. Anterior extremity, ventral view.   × 56.   (Orig.) *Œsophagostomum (Conoweberia) apiostomum.* C. Anterior extremity.   × 115. (After Ihle.)

Subgenus PROTERACRUM Railliet and Henry, 1913.

Definition.—Cephalic vesicle small or absent, cervical papillæ in front of the œsophageal swelling, lateral cuticular flanges present ; vagina short, almost transverse.   Contains the species *columbianum* and *radiatum*.

Subgenus CONOWEBERIA Ihle, 1922.

Definition.—Cephalic vesicle well-developed, cervical papillæ close behind middle of œsophagus, cuticular lateral flanges absent ; the small buccal capsule has the shape of a truncated cone ; œsophageal funnel with three teeth behind the mouth capsule ; vagina long and directed forwards.   Contains the species *apiostomum* and *brumpti*.

Goodey (1924), who has studied the genus in great detail, reaches the conclusion that its division into the above subgenera is unnecessary and undesirable ; and Thornton (1924) is of the same opinion.

Refs. 121, 134, 189, 191, 192, 233, 283, 360, 377, 403, 416, 427, 435, 440, 449, 458, 605, 619, 654.

Genus TERNIDENS Railliet and Henry, 1909.

Definition.—ŒSOPHAGOSTOMINÆ :   mouth   directed   slightly dorsally, two leaf-crowns ; buccal capsule subglobular. Œsophageal funnel dilated and containing three teeth, each consisting of two lamellæ, projecting into the depth of the capsule.   Transverse ventral cervical groove present, cephalic vesicle very slight.

Male : bursal formula as in *Œsophagostomum ;* spicules equal.
Female : vulva near anus.   Parasites of primates.

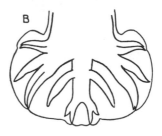

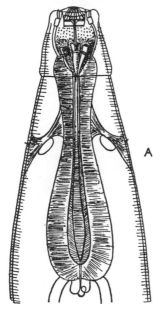

Fig. 50.—*Ternidens deminutus.*   A. Anterior extremity, ventral view.   × 180.
B. Bursa, ventral view.   × 180.
(After Railliet and Henry.)

Type species :   *T. deminutus* (Railliet and Henry, 1905).
♂ 9·5 mm., ♀ 11·7 mm.   In man and monkeys.

Syn., *Triodontophorus deminutus* Railliet and Henry, 1905.
? *Globocephalus macaci* Smith, Fox, and White, 1908.

Refs. 284, 415, 420, 435, 583.

Genus CHABERTIA Railliet and Henry, 1909.

Definition.—ŒSOPHAGOSTOMINÆ :   mouth directed anteroventrally, two very small leaf-crowns ; buccal capsule subglobular without teeth in its depth.   Œsophageal funnel does not contain teeth.   Transverse ventral cervical groove present, cephalic vesicle slight.   Male : bursal formula as in *Œsophagostomum ;* spicules equal ; gubernaculum present.   Female : vulva near anus.   Parasites of ungulates.

Type species : *C. ovina* (Fabricius, 1788 or 1794).   ♂ 13–14 mm., ♀ 17–20 mm.   In goats, sheep, cattle and deer.

Syn., *Strongylus ovinus* Fabricius, 1788 or 1794.
Strongylus ovinus Gmelin, 1790.
Strongylus hypostomus Rud., 1819.

Refs. 420, 458.

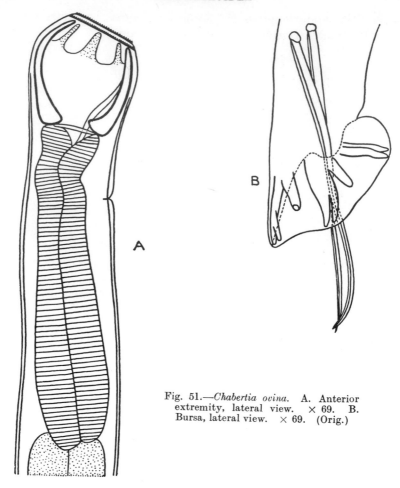

Fig. 51.—*Chabertia ovina*. A. Anterior extremity, lateral view. × 69. B. Bursa, lateral view. × 69. (Orig.)

Family ANCYLOSTOMIDÆ (Looss, 1905) Lane, 1917.

Syn., *Agchylostomidæ* Looss, 1905.

Definition.—STRONGYLOIDEA : with a well-developed chitinous buccal capsule, the oral aperture of which is guarded by ventral cutting organs. Parasites of the alimentary canal.

KEY TO SUBFAMILIES.

1. Ventral cutting organs plate-like   Necatorinæ, p. 96.
   Ventral cutting organs tooth-like   2
2. Mouth directed obliquely dorsally, ventral teeth directed
   into mouth cavity .   .   Ancylostominæ, p. 91.

Mouth directed obliquely ventrally, ventral teeth directed
outwards . . . . Strongylacanthinæ, p. 95.

Subfamily ANCYLOSTOMINÆ (Looss, 1905) Stephens, 1916.

Syn., *Agchylostominæ* Looss, 1905.
Ankylostominæ Railliet and Henry, 1909.

Definition.—ANCYLOSTOMIDÆ : mouth directed obliquely dorsally, the oral margin of the buccal capsule is provided ventrally
with teeth directed inwardly.

KEY TO GENERA.

1. Buccal capsule shallow, anterior end
   of œsophagus enormously dilated . Agriostomum, p. 95.
   Buccal capsule subglobular, anterior
   end of œsophagus not enormously
   dilated. 2
2. Buccal capsule completely chitinized,
   dorsal notch on oral margin . . Ancylostoma, p. 91.
   Buccal capsule chitinized only in latero-
   ventral regions, no dorsal notch on
   oral margin . . . . . Galoncus, p. 94.

Genus ANCYLOSTOMA * (Dubini, 1843) Creplin, 1845.

Syn., *Agchylostoma* Dubini, 1843.
Anchylostomum Diesing, 1851.
Ankylostoma Lutz, 1885.
Diploodon Molin, 1861.

Definition.—ANCYLOSTOMINÆ : anterior extremity bent dorsally ; buccal capsule infundibular, one to three pairs of ventral
teeth at the oral margin, and two triangular lancets in the depth
of the capsule. Duct of the dorsal œsophageal gland runs in a
ridge on the dorsal wall of the capsule, and opens at the bottom
of a deep notch on its oral margin. Male : bursal formula—
ventral ray cleft, externo-lateral and laterals arise from a common
trunk, medio-lateral and postero-lateral separate, externo-dorsal
arising from a common trunk with the dorsal, dorsal bifurcate,
each branch being tridigitate ; spicules equal ; gubernaculum

---

* Lane, 1916, divided the genus *Ancylostoma* into two subgenera, viz., the subgenus
Ancylostoma with *A. (Ancylostoma) duodenale* as the type, and the subgenus *Ceylancylostoma* with *A. (Ceylancylostoma) ceylanicum* as the type.

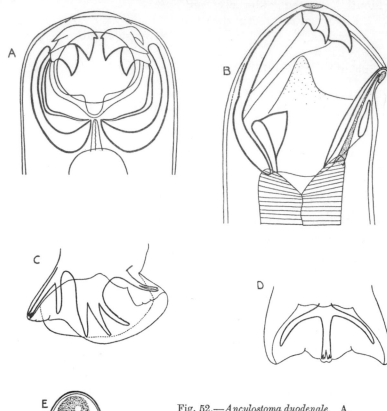

Fig. 52.—*Ancylostoma duodenale.* A.
Head, dorsal view. × 190. B.
Head, lateral view. × 190. C.
Bursa, lateral view. × 67. D.
Bursa, dorsal view. × 67. E.
Egg. × 440. (Orig.)

present. Female : vulva in posterior third of body. Parasites of the intestine of mammals.

Type species : *A. duodenale* (Dubini, 1843) Creplin, 1845. ♂ 9 mm., ♀ 12 mm. In man, *Felis* spp. and the pig.

Syn., *Agchylostoma duodenale* Dubini, 1843.

Strongylus quadridentatus Sieb., 1851.

Other species :

A. braziliense de Faria, 1910. In man, dog, cat, tiger, lion, leopard, wolf, and sloth bear.

Syn., *A. ceylanicum* (Looss, 1911).

A. caninum (Ercolani, 1859). In dog, jackal, wolf, fox, tiger, and sloth bear.

A. conepati (Solanet, 1911). In *Conepatus suffocans*.

A. gilsoni Gedoelst, 1917. In *Sciurus prevosti*.

A. malayanum (Alessandrini, 1905). In man and bear.

A. minimum (Linstow, 1906). In *Felis rubiginosa*.

A. mucronatum (Molin, 1861). In *Dasypus gilvipes*.

Syn., *Diploodon mucronatum* Molin, 1861.

A. mycetis nom. nov. In *Mycetes coraya*.

Syn., *Diploodon quadridentatum* Molin, 1861 [homonym].

A. pluridentatum (Alessandrini, 1905). In *Felis mitis*.

Refs. 115, 128, 130, 152, 197, 254, 259, 261, 263, 266, 293, 294, 328, 341, 344, 360, 669, 670.

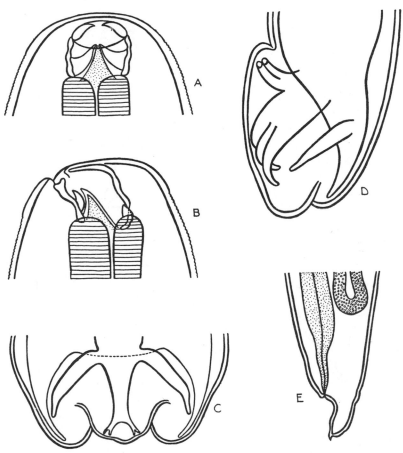

Fig. 53.—*Galoncus perniciosus*. A. Anterior extremity, dorsal view. × 215. B. Anterior extremity, lateral view. × 215. C. Bursa, dorsal view. × 215. D. Bursa, lateral view. × 215. E. Posterior extremity of female, lateral view. × 90. (Orig.)

Genus GALONCUS Railliet, 1918.

Definition.—ANCYLOSTOMINÆ : anterior extremity bent dorsally ; buccal capsule small in size as compared with the width of the head, and actually chitinized only in the latero-ventral regions ; one or more pairs of ventral teeth at its entrance ; in the depth of the capsule on the ventral wall are a pair of small triangular lancets, and on the dorsal wall are two long conical teeth, one on each side of the cone of the duct of the dorsal œsophageal gland. Male : bursal formula as in *Ancylostoma ;* spicules equal ; gubernaculum present. Female : vulva in the posterior fourth of the body. Parasites in submucous cysts in gut of *Felidæ*.

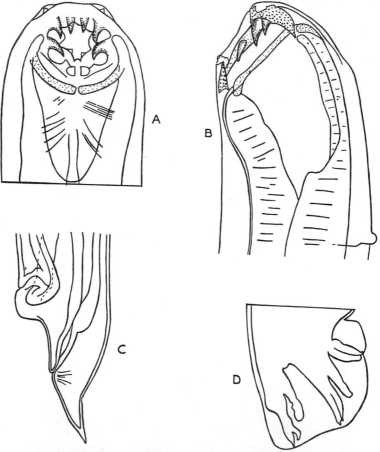

Fig. 54.—*Agriostomum vryburgi.* A. Anterior extremity, dorsal view. × 165. B. Anterior extremity, lateral view. × 165. C. Tail of female. × 37. D. Bursa, lateral view. × 120. (After Lane.)

Type species : *G. perniciosus* (Linstow, 1885).   ♂ 8–14 mm.
♀ 17–18 mm.   In submucous cysts in gut of *Felidæ*.
   Syn., *Ankylostomum perniciosum* Linstow, 1885.
Other species : *G. tridentatus* Khalil, 1922.   In a leopard.
Refs. 248, 314, 408.

Genus AGRIOSTOMUM* Railliet, 1902.

Definition.—ANCYLOSTOMINÆ : anterior extremity bent dorsally ; buccal capsule cylindrical and shallow, the oral margin
surrounded by four pairs of teeth [or according to Lane (1923),
by only three pairs].   Anterior extremity of the œsophagus
enormously dilated into a large funnel.   Well-marked cervical
ventral groove present.   Male : bursal formula—ventral ray
cleft, externo-lateral and laterals arising from a common trunk,
medio-lateral and postero lateral close together, externo-dorsal
arising from a common trunk with the dorsal, dorsal bifurcate,
each branch bidigitate ; spicules equal ; gubernaculum present.
Female : vulva near anus.   Parasites of ruminants.
   Type species : *A. vryburgi* Railliet, 1902.   ♂ 9 mm., ♀ 14·5–15·5
mm.   In *Bos zebu*.
   Refs. 268, 402, 440.

Subfamily STRONGYLACANTHINÆ n.sf.

Definition.—ANCYLOSTOMIDÆ : mouth directed obliquely ventrally, with a subglobular buccal capsule, the oral margin of which
is provided ventrally with teeth directed outwards.

Genus STRONGYLACANTHA Beneden, 1873.

Definition.—STRONGYLACANTHINÆ : mouth directed obliquely
ventrally, oval with long axis dorso-ventral ; from the ventral
margin of the mouth arise two strongly-curved teeth directed outwards and backwards ; the buccal cavity has thick chitinous
walls, is funnel-shaped, and is provided in its depth on the dorsal
wall with a lancet-shaped tooth directed forwards.   The œsophagus
is cylindrical and dilated posteriorly ; the excretory pore is very
far forward, just behind the mouth.   Male : bursal formula—
ventral ray cleft, externo-lateral and laterals arise from a common
trunk, medio-lateral and postero-lateral separated, externo-dorsal
arises separately from the dorsal, dorsal usually undivided, and
ending in six small branches, but may show various modifications ;
spicules fairly thick and equal, each bifurcated for its distal half.

   * Lane (1923) suggests a new subfamily *Agriostominæ* for this genus.

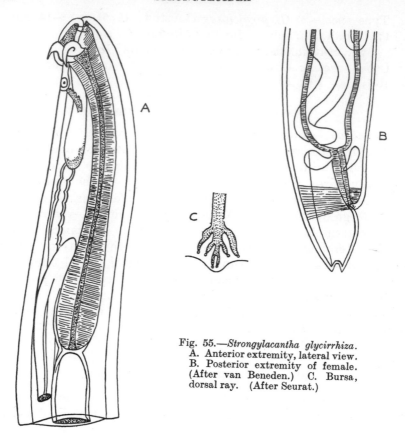

Fig. 55.—*Strongylacantha glycirrhiza.*
A. Anterior extremity, lateral view.
B. Posterior extremity of female.
(After van Beneden.)   C. Bursa,
dorsal ray.   (After Seurat.)

Female : posterior extremity narrows rapidly behind the anus and ends in two sharp points ; vulva in the posterior third of the body.   Parasites of bats.

Type species : *S. glycirrhiza* Beneden, 1873.   ♂ 2–3 mm., ♀ a little longer.   In bats.

Refs. 51, 558, 563.

Subfamily NECATORINÆ Lane, 1917.

Syn., *Bunostominæ** Looss, 1911.

Definition.—ANCYLOSTOMIDÆ : mouth directed antero-dorsally ; with a subglobular buccal capsule the oral margin of which is provided ventrally with semilunar plates.

---

* Owing to the difference of opinion which exists regarding the status of the genus *Bunostomum*, we adhere to the subfamily name *Necatorinæ*.

KEY TO GENERA.

Bursa symmetrical . . . 1
Bursa asymmetrical . . . 8
1. Intestinal diverticulum present . Grammocephalus, p. 102.
   Intestinal diverticulum absent . 2
2. Buccal capsule fissured, internal
   surface raised into a series of
   ridges . . . . . Bathmostomum, p. 104.
   Buccal capsule not fissured . . 3
3. Buccal capsule composed of a
   number of chitinous parts articulating with each other ; without
   lancets in depth of capsule . Arthrocephalus, p. 107.
   Buccal capsule continuous ; with
   lancets in depth of capsule . 4
4. With two pairs of lancets in depth
   of buccal capsule . . . 5
   With one pair of lancets in depth
   of buccal capsule . . . 7
5. Subdorsal and subventral lancets
   bi- or tri-cuspid . . . Tetragomphius, p. 105.
   Subdorsal and subventral lancets
   simple 6
6. Dorsal ray of bursa doubled . Necator, p. 97.
   Dorsal ray of bursa forked only at
   its extremity . . . . Brachyclonus, p. 99.
7. Dorsal lobe of bursa larger than
   lateral . . . . . Gaigeria, p. 101.
   Dorsal lobe of bursa much smaller
   than lateral . . . . Uncinaria, p. 101.
8. Both lateral and dorsal lobes of
   bursa asymmetrical ; mouth cap-
   sule without lancets in depth . Monodontella, p. 109.
   Lateral lobes of bursa symmetrical,
   dorsal lobe asymmetrical ; mouth
   capsule with lancets in depth . Bunostomum, p. 107.

Genus NECATOR Stiles, 1903.

Syn., ? *Eumonodontus* Railliet and Henry, 1910.
     ? *Monodontus* Molin, 1861, in part.

Definition.—NECATORINÆ : anterior extremity bent dorsally ;
buccal capsule subglobular with semilunar ventral cutting plates

at the oral margin, and in its depth two triangular subventral lancets, and two subdorsal (lateral) lancets ; duct of the dorsal œsophageal gland opens on the end of a cone projecting into the buccal cavity.   Male : bursa symmetrical ; with the following formula—ventral ray cleft, externo-lateral and laterals arise from a common trunk, medio-lateral and postero-lateral close together,

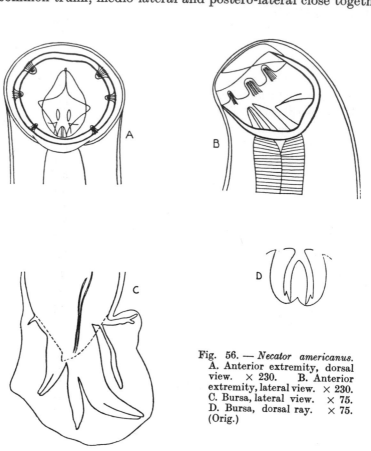

Fig. 56. — *Necator americanus.* A. Anterior extremity, dorsal view.   × 230.   B. Anterior extremity, lateral view. × 230. C. Bursa, lateral view.   × 75. D. Bursa, dorsal ray.   × 75. (Orig.)

externo-dorsal narrowed at its base and arises from a common trunk with the dorsal, dorsal doubled, each branch being bidigitate ; spicules equal and one of them barbed at the tip; gubernaculum absent.   Female : vulva near the middle of the body.   Parasites of man, chimpanzee, and pig.

Type species : *N. americanus* (Stiles, 1902).   ♂ 8 mm., ♀ 10 mm. In man and pig.

Syn., *N. suillus* Ackert and Payne, 1922.

Other species :

N. *exilidens* Looss, 1912.   In chimpanzee.

Syn., N. *africanus* Looss, 1911, not Harris, 1910.

N. *congolensis* Gedoelst, 1916.   In chimpanzee.

Refs. 1, 80, 188, 198, 199, 261, 360, 426, 458.

Genus EUMONODONTUS * Railliet and Henry, 1910.

Syn., *Monodontus* Molin, 1861 ; not *Monodonta* Lamarck, 1799.

Definition.—NECATORINÆ : this genus was erected by Railliet and Henry for the species *Monodontus semicircularis* Molin, 1861, about which little is known.   It differs from *Monodontus* in that the externo-dorsal ray is symmetrical.   According to Molin's drawing the dorsal ray is deeply divided and each branch is bidigitate.   The vulva is a little behind the middle of the body. Parasites of pigs.

Type species : E. *semicircularis* (Molin, 1861).   ♂ 6·5–8·5 mm., ♀ 9 mm.   In *Dicotyles torquatus.*

Refs. 80, 261, 360, 426, 458, 597.

Genus BRACHYCLONUS Railliet and Henry, 1910.

Definition.—NECATORINÆ : anterior extremity bent dorsally ; buccal capsule subglobular with semi-lunar ventral cutting plates

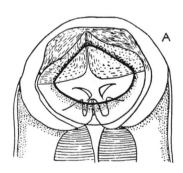

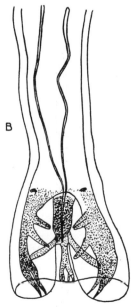

Fig. 57.—*Brachyclonus indicus.* A. Anterior extremity, dorsal view.   × 190. B. Bursa, dorsal view.   × 44. (After Khalil.)

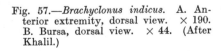

* Possibly the genus is identical with *Necator* which has been found in Brazilian pigs.

at the oral margin, and in its depth two subventral and two subdorsal lancets ; dorsal cone present.   Male : bursal formula differs
from that of *Necator* in that the dorsal ray is not doubled but is

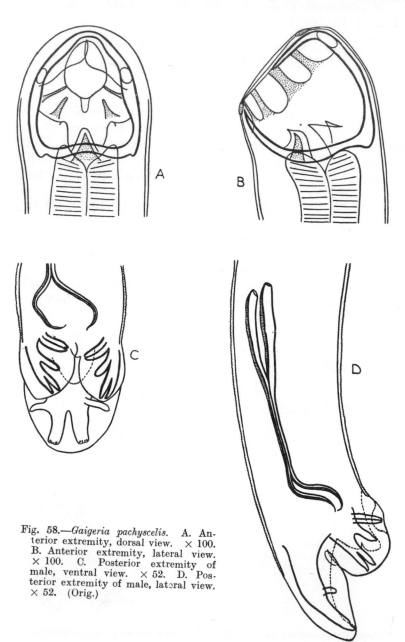

Fig. 58.—*Gaigeria pachyscelis*.   A. Anterior extremity, dorsal view.   × 100.
B. Anterior extremity, lateral view.
× 100.   C. Posterior extremity of
male, ventral view.   × 52.   D. Posterior extremity of male, lateral view.
× 52.   (Orig.)

forked in its distal portion, the externo-dorsal ray is not narrowed at its base, and the common trunk of the dorsal and externo-dorsal rays is long ; spicules equal and not barbed at the tips ; gubernaculum absent. Female : vulva in the anterior third of the body. Parasites of tapirs.

Type species : *B. indicus* Railliet and Henry, 1910. ♂ 12·5 mm., ♀ 12·15 mm. In *Tapirus indicus.*

Refs. 249, 261, 426.

Genus GAIGERIA Railliet and Henry, 1910.

Definition.—NECATORINÆ : anterior extremity bent dorsally ; buccal capsule infundibular with two ventral semilunar cutting plates at the oral margin, and in its depth two subventral lancets on the anterior edge of which is a small tubercle : dorsal cone short and sharp. Male : bursa consists of a very large dorsal, and two smaller lateral lobes which are joined together ventrally ; the dorsal lobe is separated from the lateral lobes ; with the following formula—ventral ray cleft, externo-lateral and laterals arise from a common trunk, the externo-lateral is short and blunt, the medio-lateral and postero-lateral are joined in their proximal two-thirds and diverge distally, externo-dorsal arises from a common trunk with the dorsal, dorsal bifurcated almost to its base, each branch being large, blunt, and terminating in three digitations. Female : vulva a little in front of the middle of the body. Parasites of ruminants.

Type species : *G. pachyscelis* Railliet and Henry, 1910. ♂ 11–12 mm., ♀ 15–17 mm. In sheep, goats, and ? cattle.

Refs. 82, 147, 151, 261, 426.

Genus UNCINARIA Froelich, 1789.

Syn., *Dochmius* Duj., 1845.
Dochmoides Cameron, 1924.

Definition.—NECATORINÆ : anterior extremity bent dorsally ; buccal capsule infundibular with two semilunar ventral cutting plates at its oral margin, and in its depth two subventral lancets ; dorsal cone absent. Male : bursa with two large lateral lobes and a small dorsal lobe ; with the following formula—ventral ray cleft, externo-lateral and laterals arise from a common trunk, medio-lateral and postero-lateral separated, externo-dorsal arises from a common trunk with the dorsal, dorsal forked in its distal portion, each branch being bidigitate or tridigitate ; spicules equal ; gubernaculum absent ? Female : vulva at the junction of the

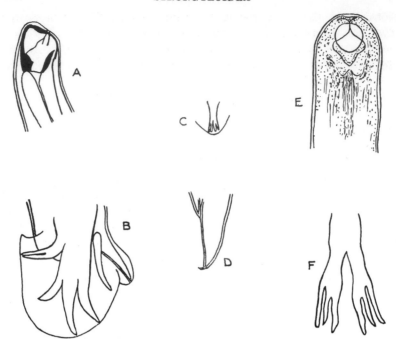

Fig. 59.—*Uncinaria criniformis.* A. Anterior extremity, lateral view.
× 120. B. Bursa, lateral view. × 120. C. Dorsal ray. × 120.
D. Tail of female. × 120. (After Ransom.)
    Uncinaria stenocephala. E. Anterior extremity, dorsal view. F.
Bursa, dorsal ray. (After Yorke and Blacklock.)

middle and posterior thirds of body. Parasites of carnivora and
the domesticated pig.

Type species : *U. criniformis* (Gœze, 1782). ♂ 5·5 mm.,
♀ 7·5 mm. In *Meles taxus.*

Syn., *Ascaris criniformis* Gœze, 1782.
    Dochmius criniformis (Gœze, 1782) Duj., 1845.

Other species : *U. stenocephala* (Railliet, 1884). In dog, fox,
cat, and pig.

Syn., *Dochmius stenocephalus* Railliet, 1884.
    U. polaris Looss, 1911.
    Dochmoides stenocephala (Railliet, 1884) Cameron, 1924.

Refs. 83, 131, 138, 146, 186, 209, 261, 337, 341, 395, 462.

Genus **GRAMMOCEPHALUS** Railliet and Henry, 1910.

Definition.—NECATORINÆ : anterior extremity bent dorsally ;
buccal capsule infundibular with two semilunar ventral cutting
plates at the oral margin, and in its depth one pair of triangular

lateral, and one of subventral, lancets ; dorsal cone present. From the dorsal wall of the gut, close to its union with the œsophagus, runs forward a long diverticulum. Male : bursal formula —ventral rays cleft to base, externo-lateral and laterals arise from

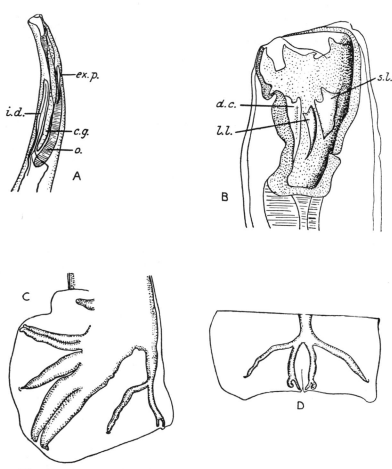

Fig. 60.—*Grammocephalus clathratus.* A. Anterior extremity, lateral view. *ex.p*, excretory pore ; *c.g*, cephalic glands ; *o*, œsophagus ; *i.d*, intestinal diverticulum. × 13. B. Head, lateral view ; *d.c*, dorsal cone ; *l.l*, lateral lancets ; *s.l*, subventral lancets. × 100. C. Bursa, lateral view. × 30. D. Bursa, dorsal ray. × 30. (After Lane.)

a common trunk, medio-lateral and postero-lateral close together, externo-dorsal arises from a common trunk with the dorsal, dorsal doubled, each limb being bidigitate ; spicules strong and alate ; gubernaculum absent. Female : vulva near middle of body ; uteri divergent. Parasites of elephants and rhinoceroses.

Type species : *G. clathratus* (Baird, 1868). ♂ 45 mm., ♀ 36 mm.
In African elephant.

Syn., *Sclerostoma clathratum* Baird, 1868.

    Strongylus clathratus (Baird, 1868) Cobbold, 1882.

Other species :

    G. varedatus Lane, 1921. In Indian elephant.

      Syn., *G. clathratus* (Baird, 1868) of Railliet and Henry, 1910.

    G. intermedius Neveu-Lemaire, 1924. In *Rhinoceros bicornis.*

Refs. 7, 30, 251, 261, 264, 371, 426.

Genus BATHMOSTOMUM Railliet and Henry, 1909.

Definition.—NECATORINÆ : anterior extremity bent dorsally ;
buccal capsule infundibular, with two semilunar ventral cutting

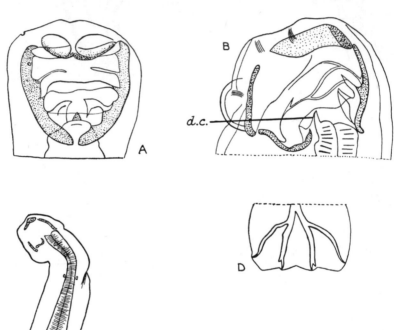

Fig. 61.—*Bathmostomum sangeri.* A. Head,
ventral view. × 126. B. Head, lateral
view. *d.c*, dorsal cone. × 126. C. Anterior extremity, lateral view. × 34.
D. Dorsal ray. × 60. (After Lane.)

plates at its oral margin ; the wall of the capsule is fissured on its
dorsal and lateral aspects and its internal surface is raised into a
series of circular ridges or lamellæ; subdorsal lancets are not present

in the depth of the capsule, but possibly there is a pair of subventral lancets in connection with a complete shelf which appears
to encircle the whole base of the cavity ; dorsal cone very small.
Male : bursal formula differs from that of *Necator,* in that the
dorsal ray is bifurcate beyond the point of origin of the externo-
dorsals, which consequently arise from the branches of the dorsal
ray ; spicules stout and equal ; gubernaculum absent. Female :
vulva a little in front of the middle of the body.

Type species : *B. sangeri* (Cobbold, 1879). ♂ 15–16 mm.,
♀ 20 mm. In *Elephas indicus.*

Syn., *Dochmius sangeri* Cobbold, 1879.

Uncinaria sangeri (Cobbold, 1879) Railliet, 1897.

Uncinaria os-papillatum Piana and Stazzi, 1900.

Refs. 103, 251, 261, 264, 392, 420, 426.

Genus TETRAGOMPHIUS Baylis and Daubney, 1923.

Definition.—NECATORINÆ : anterior extremity bent dorsally,
neck long and tapering ; buccal capsule cup-shaped, less elongated

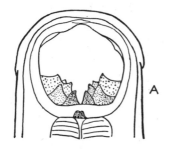

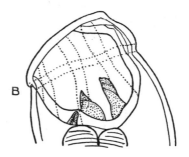

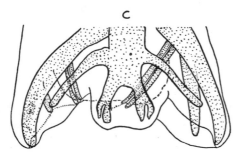

Fig. 62.—*Tetragomphius procyonis.*
A. Head, dorsal view.   × 315.
B. Head, lateral view.   × 315.
C. Bursa, dorsal view.   × 260.
(After Baylis and Daubney.)

than in *Uncinaria,* with poorly-developed ventral semilunar
cutting plates at the oral margin ; in its depth are two pairs of

lancets, the subdorsal being bi-cuspid and the subventral bi- or tri-digitate, usually the latter ; the dorsal cone is represented by a blunt tubercle. Male : bursa short and stunted ; with the following formula—ventral ray cleft, externo-lateral and laterals arise from a common trunk, medio-lateral and postero-lateral separated, externo-dorsal and dorsal arising from a common trunk, dorsal very thick and deeply divided almost to the point of origin of the externo-dorsal rays, each branch being bidigitate ; spicules filiform and extremely long. Female : vulva in the posterior fourth of the body.

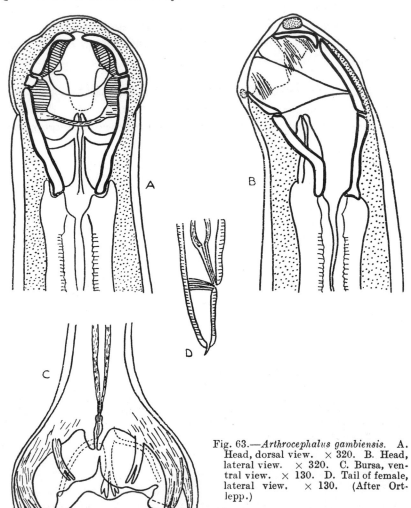

Fig. 63.—*Arthrocephalus gambiensis.* A. Head, dorsal view. × 320. B. Head, lateral view. × 320. C. Bursa, ventral view. × 130. D. Tail of female, lateral view. × 130. (After Ortlepp.)

Type species :   *T. procyonis* Baylis and Daubney,   1923.
♂ 13–15 mm., ♀ 15–20 mm.   In *Procyon* sp. (Raccoon).
Refs. 43, 45.

Genus ARTHROCEPHALUS Ortlepp, 1925.

Definition.—NECATORINÆ :   anterior extremity bent dorsally.
The buccal capsule is composed of a number of chitinous parts
articulating with each other : there are six of these ; the largest
is a complete funnel-shaped tube and forms the base of the capsule ; a single oval plate forms the antero-ventral wall of the
capsule, and on either side of this plate are two additional plates
forming respectively the dorso-lateral and the ventro-lateral
walls of the capsule ; the two ventro-lateral plates do not meet
along the mid-ventral line, but are separated by a V-shaped space.
The oral margin of the capsule is armed with two thin semilunar
cutting plates arising from the anterior edge of the ventro-lateral
plates ; dorsal cone well-developed, but lancets and teeth are
not present in the depth of the capsule.   Male : bursa with large
lateral lobes and a small dorsal lobe ; with the following formula :
ventral ray cleft, externo-lateral and laterals arise from a common
trunk, externo-dorsal arising from a common trunk with the dorsal,
dorsal bifurcated distally, each branch being tridigitate ; spicules
equal, thin, and filiform ; gubernaculum present.   Female : tail
conical and ends in a small spike ; vulva at the junction of the
middle and posterior thirds of the body.   Oviparous, eggs oval,
thin-shelled and contain a morula at deposition.   Parasites of
mongoose.

Type species : *A. gambiensis* Ortlepp, 1925.   ♂ 5–6 mm.,
♀ 7–9 mm.   In the African mongoose.
Ref. 381b.

Genus BUNOSTOMUM Railliet, 1902.

Syn., *Monodontus* Molin, 1861, in part.
       Bustomum Lane, 1917.

Definition.—NECATORINÆ :   anterior extremity bent dorsally ;
buccal capsule infundibular with two semilunar ventral cutting
plates at its oral margin, and in its depth two small lancets near
the opening of the œsophagus, and sometimes also a smaller pair
of subventral lancets is found in the lateral walls of the capsule ;
dorsal cone well-developed.   Male : lateral lobes of bursa continuous ventrally, dorsal lobe slightly-developed and asymmetrical ;
with the following formula—ventral, externo-lateral and lateral
rays arise from a large common trunk, ventral ray cleft, postero-

lateral and medio-lateral are fused in their proximal portions and
separated distally, externo-dorsal arising at different levels from
a common trunk with the dorsal ; dorsal bifurcate to a varying

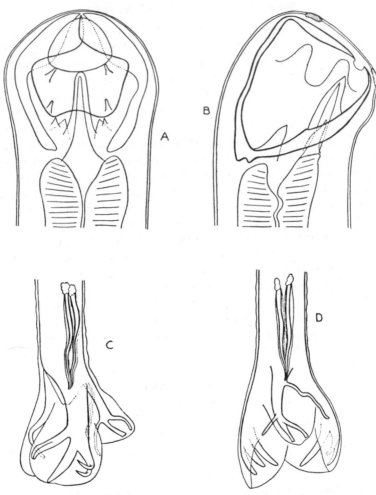

Fig. 64.—*Bunostomum trigonocephalum*. A. Anterior extremity, dorsal
   view. × 215. B. Anterior extremity, lateral view. × 215. C.
   Posterior extremity of male, lateral view. × 46. D. Posterior
   extremity of male, dorsal view. × 56. (Orig.)

degree, each branch being bidigitate or tridigitate ; spicules equal ;
gubernaculum absent. Female : vulva in front of the middle of
the body. Parasites of herbivora.

   Type species : *B. trigonocephalum* (Rud., 1808). ♂ 12–17 mm.,
♀ 19–26 mm. In sheep, goat, and ox.

Syn., *Strongylus trigonocephalus* Rud., 1808.

Sclerostoma hypostomum (Rud., 1819) Duj., 1845.

Monodontus wedlii Molin, 1861.

Dochmius cernuus (Crep., 1829) Baillet, 1868.

Uncinaria cernua (Crep., 1829) Railliet, 1885.

Monodontus trigonocephalus (Rud., 1809) Railliet, 1902.

Bunostomum kashinathi Lane, 1917.

Other species : *B. phlebotomum* (Railliet, 1900). In cattle and sheep.

Syn., *Strongylus radiatus* Rud., 1803, of Schneider, 1866.

Bunostomum radiatum (Rud. of Schneider, 1866) Linstow, 1906.

Bustomum phlebotomum (Railliet, 1900) Lane, 1917.

? *B. longecirratum* (Linst., 1879). In the yak.

? *B. foliatum* (Cobbold, 1882). In elephants.

Syn., *Uncinaria sangeri* Aless., 1905, not Railliet, 1897.

Refs. 80, 261, 401, 402, 426, 458, 597.

Genus MONODONTELLA n. g.

Definition.—NECATORINÆ : anterior extremity bent dorsally ; buccal capsule infundibular with two semilunar ventral cutting plates at its oral margin and with a very well-marked dorsal cone, but without lancets in its depth : on each side of the capsule are the broad bands of pulp of the head papillæ ; œsophagus club-shaped, cervical papillæ at the level of the nerve ring. Male : bursa markedly asymmetrical, the right lateral lobe being distinctly larger than the left ; the lateral lobes meet ventrally, and the dorsal lobe is broad and much shorter than the laterals and not sharply marked off ; with the following formula—on the right side the ventro-ventral and latero-ventral rays are completely fused and long and slender, the externo-lateral and laterals are fused into a large single ray, which is divided only at its extremity, the dorsal branch being broad and the ventral smaller and subdivided into two digitations, the externo-dorsal arises separately from the dorsal and is long and delicate ; on the left side the ventral, externo-lateral, laterals, and externo-dorsal rays all arise from a common trunk, the ventral is completely fused into a single ray, the medio-lateral and postero-lateral are quite separate and the externo-dorsal is fused with the postero-lateral for about half its length ; the dorsal ray commences as a thick trunk, and then breaks up into a short median stem with two longer lateral branches on each side, those on the left side being

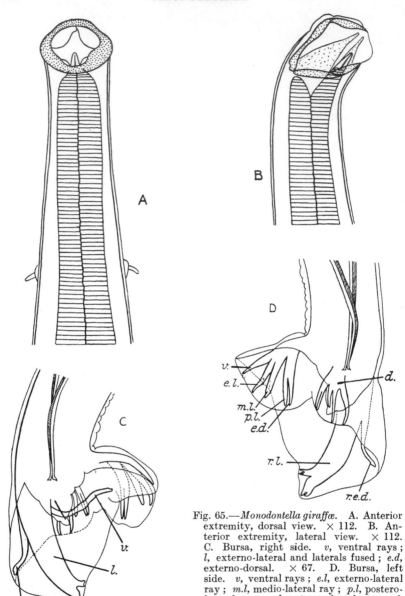

Fig. 65.—*Monodontella giraffæ*. A. Anterior extremity, dorsal view. × 112. B. Anterior extremity, lateral view. × 112. C. Bursa, right side. *v*, ventral rays; *l*, externo-lateral and laterals fused; *e.d*, externo-dorsal. × 67. D. Bursa, left side. *v*, ventral rays; *e.l*, externo-lateral ray; *m.l*, medio-lateral ray; *p.l*, postero-lateral ray; *e.d*, externo-dorsal ray; *r.l*, right lateral rays fused; *r.e.d*, right externo-dorsal ray. × 67. (Orig.)

more or less fused, whilst those on the right are clearly separate; spicules equal, alate and fused distally, with barbed tips. Female: posterior extremity conical; vulva slightly in front of the middle of the body, uteri divergent. Oviparous. Parasites of giraffes.

Type species : * *M. giraffæ* n. sp. ♂ 14–16 mm., ♀ 18–20 mm. In the giraffe.

FAMILY DIAPHANOCEPHALIDÆ TRAVASSOS, 1919.

Definition.—STRONGYLOIDEA : buccal capsule bivalvular and strongly compressed laterally. Parasites of stomach and intestine of snakes.

KEY TO GENERA.

1. With two chitinous ledges in lateral walls of capsule, and with delicate chitinous processes projecting into the capsule from the ventral cuticular pad. . Diaphanocephalus, p. 111.

   With only one chitinous ledge in lateral walls of capsule, and without delicate chitinous processes projecting into the capsule from the ventral cuticular pad . 2

2. With a distinct corona radiata, and with three teeth in œsophageal funnel . . . Occipitodontus, p. 114.

   Without a corona radiata, and without teeth in œsophageal funnel . . . . . Kalicephalus, p. 113.

Genus DIAPHANOCEPHALUS Diesing, 1851.

Definition.—DIAPHANOCEPHALIDÆ : anterior extremity obliquely truncated, so that the mouth opens slightly dorsally ; buccal capsule compressed laterally and consisting of two valves each with a much thickened base ; on the axial surface of each valve are two ledges projecting inwards, an anterior running parallel with the oral margin, and a posterior which has the shape of an arc when viewed laterally, the terminations of each posterior ledge rest on a thickened cuticular pad situated between the junctions of the buccal valves ; from the ventral cuticular pad two membranous cuticular processes project into the mouth cavity : on

---

* *Monodontella giraffæ* n. sp. Length of male 14–16 mm., female 18–20 mm. Length of œsophagus in female about 1·4 mm. Cervical papillæ are about 530–540 μ from the anterior extremity. Buccal capsule about 200–220 μ in depth and about 150 μ in greatest diameter at the oral margin. Spicules 700–750 μ in length, equal, winged, and fused distally, with barbed tips. In the female the anus is about 230–240 μ from the tip of the tail, and the vulva is just in front of the middle of the body.

the outer surface of each valve are three parenchymatous bands
arising from a basal collar, these terminate as the head papillæ.
The duct of the dorsal œsophageal gland projects well into the
mouth cavity. Male : bursa short and campanulate, its depth
being about the same on its dorsal and ventral aspects, there is
only a slight indication of a dorsal lobe ; with the following
formula—ventral rays cleft, externo-lateral and laterals arise

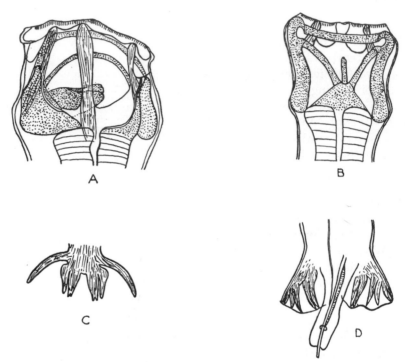

Fig. 66.—*Diaphanocephalus galeatus.* A. Head, lateral view. × 94. B.
Head, dorso-ventral view. × 94. C. Bursa, dorsal ray. × 80. D.
Bursa, ventral view. × 80. (After Ortlepp.)

from a common trunk, medio- and postero-lateral separated,
externo-dorsal arises from a common trunk with the dorsal, which
is very short and thick, and almost immediately divides into two
branches, which again immediately subdivide, the inner of the
two subdivisions being bifid at its extremity ; genital cone is very
long and protrudes beyond the bursa, the anogenital orifice is
situated on its ventral surface some distance in front of its tip ;
spicules equal ? ; gubernaculum present ; there is a dorsal hump
anterior to the bursa. Female : tail short and pointed ; vulva in
the posterior fourth of the worm. Oviparous. Parasites of snakes.

Type species : *D. galeatus* (Rud., 1819). ♂ and ♀ about 4 mm.
In intestine of *Podinema teguixin*.

Syn., *Strongylus galeatus* Rud., 1819.

Diaphanocephalus strongyloides Dies., 1851.

Refs. 42, 119, 123, 360, 381, 405, 477, 573.

Genus KALICEPHALUS Molin, 1861.

Syn., *Diaphanocephalus* Diesing, 1851, in part.

Definition.—DIAPHANOCEPHALIDÆ : head and buccal capsule
closely resembling those of *Diaphanocephalus*, but differing in the
absence of the second chitinous ledge in the lateral walls of the

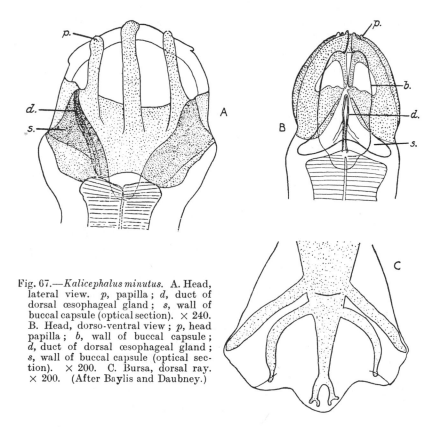

Fig. 67.—*Kalicephalus minutus*. A. Head,
lateral view. *p*, papilla ; *d*, duct of
dorsal œsophageal gland ; *s*, wall of
buccal capsule (optical section). × 240.
B. Head, dorso-ventral view ; *p*, head
papilla ; *b*, wall of buccal capsule ;
d, duct of dorsal œsophageal gland ;
s, wall of buccal capsule (optical section). × 200. C. Bursa, dorsal ray.
× 200. (After Baylis and Daubney.)

capsule, and in the absence of the two delicate chitinous projections into the mouth from the ventral chitinous mass. Male :
bursa definitely trilobed ; bursal formula as in *Diaphanocephalus*,
but the externo-dorsal ray arises higher up the common trunk,

with the result that the dorsal ray is longer ; genital cone usually long, but not so long as in *Diaphanocephalus*, and the anogenital orifice is on the tip of the cone ; spicules equal and alate ; gubernaculum present. Female : posterior extremity long and conical ; vulva in the posterior part of the body ; uteri divergent or convergent. Oviparous. Parasites of snakes.

Type species : *K. mucronatus* Molin, 1861. ♂ 9 mm., ♀ 15–30 mm. In *Crotalus horridus*.

Other species :

> *K. appendiculatus* Molin, 1861.   In *Ophis* spp., *Coluber* sp., *Leptophis* sp., etc.
>
> *K. boæ* (R. Blanchard, 1886).   In *Boa constrictor*.
>
> *K. bothropis* Molin, 1861.   In *Bothrops* sp.
>
> *K. brevipenis* Molin, 1861.   In *Ophis* sp. and *Dryophis* sp.
>
> *K. colubri* Ortlepp, 1923.   In Colubrine snake.
>
> *K. coronellæ* Ortlepp, 1923.   In *Coronella triangulum*.
>
> *K. costatus* (Rud., 1819).   In *Hylophis* sp., *Lachesis* sp., etc.
> Syn., *Diaphanocephalus costatus* (Rud., 1819) Dies., 1851.
>
> *K. ersiliæ* (Stoss., 1896).   In *Python molurus*.
>
> *K. indicus* Ortlepp, 1923.   In *Zamenis* sp. and *Tropidonotus* sp.
>
> *K. inermis* Molin, 1861.   In *Bothrops* sp. and *Crotalus horridus*.
>
> *K. micrurus* (Daubney, 1923).   In *Macrelaps* sp.
>
> *K. minutus* (Baylis and Daubney, 1922).   In *Naja* sp., *Bungarus* sp.
>
> *K. nigeriensis* Ortlepp, 1923.   In Nigerian snake.
>
> *K. obliquus* (Daubney, 1923).   In *Bitis gabonica*, etc.
>
> *K. parvus* Ortlepp, 1923.   In *Coronella getula*.
>
> *K. philodryadus* Ortlepp, 1923.   In *Philodryas serra*.
>
> *K. simus* (Daubney, 1923).   In Black mamba.
>
> *K. strumosus* Molin, 1861.   In *Coluber lichtensteinii*.
>
> *K. subulatus* Molin, 1861.   In *Boa constrictor*.
>
> *K. vallei* (Stoss., 1895).   In *Vipera ammodytes*.
>
> *K. viperæ* (Rud., 1819).   In *Vipera redii*.
>
> *K. willeyi* Linstow, 1904 (not 1908).   In *Vipera russelli* and *Coluber helena*.

N.B.—Probably many of the above are synonymous.

Refs. 42, 119, 123, 325, 328, 330, 360, 381, 420, 477, 573.

Genus OCCIPITODONTUS Ortlepp, 1923.

Definition.—DIAPHANOCEPHALIDÆ : closely related to *Kalicephalus*, but differing in the presence of a distinct corona radiata, and three pointed teeth in the œsophageal funnel.

Type species : *O. fimbriatus* Ortlepp, 1923. ♂ 10·5–11·5 mm., ♀ 15–17 mm. In *Bungarus fasciatus*, *Coluber* sp., *Vipera* sp., etc.

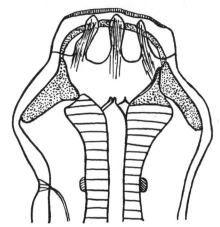

Fig. 68.—*Occipitodontus fimbriatus*. Anterior extremity, lateral view. × 110. (After Ortlepp.)

Syn., *Kalicephalus willeyi* Linstow, 1908 (not 1904).

Diaphanocephalus willeyi (Linstow) Baylis and Daubney, 1922.

Diaphanocephalus willeyi (Linstow) Daubney, 1923.

Refs. 42, 119, 330, 381.

Family TRICHOSTRONGYLIDÆ Leiper, 1912.

Definition.—Strongyloidea : body more or less filiform, mouth simple directed straight forwards ; buccal capsule usually absent or rudimentary, occasionally relatively well-developed, without anterior cutting organs or corona radiata. Bursa copulatrix with well-developed lateral lobes, dorsal lobe either not differentiated or very small ; near the cloaca is often to be found a supporting structure of variable form known as the " telamon." Parasites in the alimentary canal of vertebrates.

KEY TO SUBFAMILIES.

1. Genitalia of female single . Heligmosominæ, p. 140.
   Genitalia of female double . . 2
2. Buccal capsule relatively large . Amidostominæ, p. 152.
   Buccal capsule rudimentary or
       absent . . . . . Trichostrongylinæ, p. 116.
3. *Trichostrongylidæ* insufficiently known, p. 151.

Subfamily TRICHOSTRONGYLINÆ Leiper, 1908.

Definition.—TRICHOSTRONGYLIDÆ : more or less filiform worms ; buccal capsule rudimentary or absent. Spicules either long and filiform, or short and stout with crests and protuberances. Female with double genitalia.

KEY TO GENERA.

1. Head with umbellate membrane thickened at its edges . . Histiostrongylus, p. 132.
   Head without umbellate membrane 2
2. Spicules short and stout with crests and protuberances . 3
   Spicules long and filiform . . 14
3. Dorsal lobe of bursa asymmetrical Hæmonchus, p. 122.
   Dorsal lobe of bursa symmetrical 4
4. Accessory bursal membrane present . . . . . Ostertagia, p. 124.
   Accessory bursal membrane absent 5
5. Ventro-ventral and latero-ventral rays of bursa practically of equal size 6
   Ventro-ventral ray of bursa much smaller than the latero-ventral 10
6. Externo-lateral ray very short, about half the length of the other lateral rays . . . Molineus, p. 125.
   Externo-lateral ray about same length as the other lateral rays 7
7. Gubernaculum absent ; ventro-ventral and latero-ventral rays closely approximated for their whole length as also are the medio- and postero-lateral rays Oswaldocruzia, p. 126.
   Gubernaculum present ; ventro-ventral and latero-ventral rays definitely separated as also are the medio- and postero-lateral 8
8. Ventro-ventral and latero-ventral rays widely divergent at the tips, prebursal papillæ absent . Trichohelix, p. 121.

Ventro-ventral and latero-ventral rays not widely divergent at tips, prebursal papillæ present . 9

9. Dorsal ray bifurcate for half its length . . . . . Ornithostrongylus, p. 127.

Dorsal ray undivided except at its tip . . . . . Hyostrongylus, p. 120.

10. Gubernaculum absent . . 11

Gubernaculum present . . 13

11. Ventro-ventral and latero-ventral rays approximating at their tips ; spicules cleft distally and ending in two barbed processes . . . . Obeliscoides, p. 129.

Ventro-ventral and latero-ventral rays not approximating at their tips ; spicules not cleft distally . 12

12. Cervical papillæ present and pre-bursal papillæ large . . Travassosius, p. 130.

Cervical papillæ absent and pre-bursal papillæ absent . . Cooperia, p. 131.

13. Dorsal ray bifurcate at its extremity, each limb being bi-digitate . . . . Trichostrongylus, p. 118.

Dorsal ray bifurcate in its distal portion each limb giving off two lateral branches the first of which may, however, arise from the undivided trunk . Libyostrongylus, p. 119.

14. Vulva in anterior fourth of body . Nematodirella, p. 140.

Vulva in posterior part of body . 15

15. Bursa with asymmetrical lateral lobes . . . . . Austrostrongylus, p. 137.

Bursa with symmetrical lateral lobes 16

16. Spicules with multiple tips . Graphidium, p. 134.

Spicules with simple tips . . 17

17. Ventro-ventral and latero-ventral rays equal and parallel . . Nematodirus, p. 135.

Ventro-ventral and latero-ventral rays widely divergent, the ventro-ventral being much smaller than the latero-ventral 18

18. Cervical papillæ present, vulva
    close to anus   .   .   .   Mecistocirrus, p. 138.
Cervical papillæ absent, vulva
    not close to anus .   .   .   Graphidioides, p. 139.

Genus TRICHOSTRONGYLUS Looss, 1905.

Definition.—TRICHOSTRONGYLINÆ : head small (usually about 10 μ in diameter) ; mouth with three small lips ; buccal cavity not well defined ; cervical papillæ absent. Male : bursa with

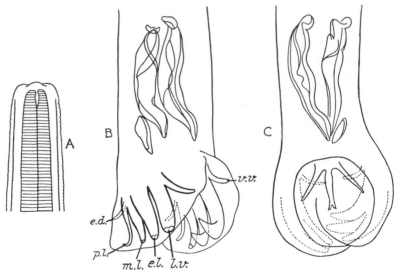

Fig. 69.—*Trichostrongylus retortæformis.* A. Anterior extremity, ventral view. × 900. B. Bursa, lateral view. *v.v,* ventro-ventral ray ; *l.v,* latero-ventral ray ; *e.l,* externo-lateral ray ; *m.l,* medio-lateral ray ; *p.l,* postero-lateral ray ; *e.d,* externo-dorsal ray. × 260. C. Bursa, dorsal view. × 260. (Orig.)

large lateral lobes, dorsal lobe either not differentiated or very slightly so ; with the following formula—ventro-ventral and latero-ventral rays widely separated, the ventro-ventral being much thinner and smaller than the latero-ventral, externo-lateral, medio-lateral, and postero-lateral arise separately, externo-dorsal arises from the base of the dorsal, dorsal bifurcate near its extremity, each branch being bidigitate ; spicules short, twisted and spoon- or spatula-shaped, the proximal end is thickened with a knob or disc-like process, toward the distal end a more or less prominent angular projection is usually present giving the point of the spicules a hooked or barbed appearance ; gubernaculum present, elongate and boat- or shoe-shaped in profile ; prebursal papillæ small. Female : vulva in the posterior half of the body, slit-like or crescentic, surrounded by somewhat protruding chitinous lips ; postanal portion of body of female relatively short, with a pair of small caudal papillæ near the tip. Oviparous. Parasites of mammals and more rarely of birds.

Type species : *T. retortæformis* (Zeder, 1800). ♂ 5–7 mm., ♀ 7–9 mm. In *Lepus timidus* and *Lepus cuniculus*.

Syn., *Strongylus retortæformis* Zeder, 1800.

Other species :

T. affinis Graybill, 1924. In rabbit.

T. axei (Cobbold, 1879). In equines, etc.

T. calcaratus Ransom, 1911. In *Sylvilagus floridanus*.

T. capricola Ransom, 1907. In goat, sheep, and antelope.

T. colubriformis (Giles, 1892). In sheep.

T. delicatus Hall, 1916. In *Sciurus aberti mimus*.

T. extenuatus (Railliet, 1898). In cattle, sheep, goat, antelope, and deer.

> Syn., *Strongylus gracilis* McFadyean, 1896, not Leuck., 1842.

T. falculatus Ransom, 1911. In *Capra hircus*.

T. fiberius Barker and Noyes, 1915. In *Fiber zibethicus*.

T. instabilis (Railliet, 1893). In sheep, gazelle, camel, baboon, man, goat, deer, etc.

> Syn., *Strongylus subtilis* Looss, 1895.

T. orientalis Jimbo, 1914. In man.

T. pergracilis (Cobbold, 1873). In *Lagopus scoticus*.

T. pigmentatus (Linstow, 1904). *Lepus nigricollis*.

T. probolurus (Railliet, 1896). In *Camelus dromedarius*.

T. rugatus Monn'g, 1925. In sheep.

T. tenuis (Mehl., 1846). In *Anser* spp., etc.

T. vitrinus Looss, 1905. In sheep, camel, man, and goat.

Refs. 203, 205, 245, 275, 290, 343, 363a, 458, 460, 642.

Genus LIBYOSTRONGYLUS* Lane, 1923.

Definition.—TRICHOSTRONGYLINÆ : cephalic cuticle sometimes inflated, buccal cavity minute. Male : bursa with large lateral lobes elongated dorsally to form sometimes a small dorsal lobe ; with the following formula—ventro-ventral and latero-ventral rays widely separate, the ventro-ventral being much smaller and thinner than the latero-ventral, the externo-lateral, medio-lateral, and postero-lateral arise separately, the externo-dorsal arises

---

* This genus resembles *Trichostrongylus* very closely, and we are doubtful whether it should be separated from it.

from the base of the dorsal and is short, not reaching the bursal margin, dorsal bifurcate in its distal portion, and giving off two lateral branches, the first of which may arise from the undivided trunk ; prebursal papillæ present ; spicules equal, stout, slightly curved, and giving off a dorsal spine distally ; gubernaculum imperfectly chitinized. Female : vulva in the posterior fifth of the body. Oviparous. Parasites of mammals and birds.

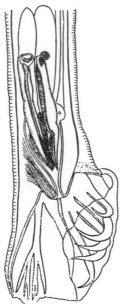

Fig. 70.—*Libyostrongylus douglassii*. Posterior extremity of male, ventral view. × 166. (After Theiler and Robertson.)

Type species : *L. douglassii* (Cobbold, 1882). ♂ 4·2 mm., ♀ 5·1 mm. In *Struthio camelus*.

Syn., *Strongylus douglassii* Cobbold, 1882.

Strongylus douglasi Gedoelst, 1911.

Trichostrongylus douglasi (Cobbold, 1882) Theiler and Robertson, 1915.

Ornithostrongylus douglasi (Cobbold, 1882) Travassos, 1918.

Other species : *L. hebrenicutus* Lane, 1923.   In gorilla.
Refs. 104, 268, 614, 642.

Genus HYOSTRONGYLUS Hall, 1921.

Definition.—TRICHOSTRONGYLINÆ :   head   small ;   cervical papillæ present.   Male : bursa with a small dorsal lobe and well-developed lateral lobes ; with the following formula—ventro-ventral and latero-ventral rays diverge slightly, but the latero-ventral, which is a little larger than the ventro-ventral, bends back near its extremity to end close to the ventro-ventral, externo-lateral lies close to the medio-lateral, they diverge only at their tips ;   postero-lateral widely separated from the medio-lateral, externo-dorsal arises separately from the dorsal and is short, dorsal bifurcate near the tip with two small branches arising from the common trunk ; spicules equal, short, tapering to a point with a wavy ridge running the length of the spicule and supporting a curved membranous portion which terminates in a second point ; gubernaculum long, narrow, and partly chitinized ; ventral to the

gubernaculum is a transparent structure known as the telamon ;
prebursal papillæ present.   Female : vulva in the posterior sixth
of the worm.   Oviparous.   Parasites of pigs.

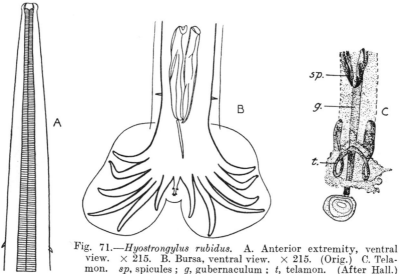

Fig. 71.—*Hyostrongylus rubidus.* A. Anterior extremity, ventral
view. × 215. B. Bursa, ventral view. × 215. (Orig.) C. Telamon. *sp*, spicules ; *g*, gubernaculum ; *t*, telamon. (After Hall.)

Type species : *H. rubidus* (Hassall and Stiles, 1892). ♂ 4–5 mm.,
♀ 5–8 mm.   In pigs.
   Syn., *Strongylus rubidus* Hassall and Stiles, 1892.
          Ostertagia rubida (Hassall and Stiles, 1892) Travassos,
          1918.
          Strongylus attenuatus Molin, 1860, not Leidy, 1856.
   Refs. 193, 207, 211, 271, 359, 642.

Genus TRICHOHELIX Ortlepp, 1922.

Definition.—TRICHOSTRONGYLINÆ : body spirally coiled ; head
round and thick (35 μ in diameter). Cuticle of head inflated in the
form of a vesicular swelling limited behind by a deep constriction
encircling the neck, the rest of the cuticle strikingly inflated, and
showing marked transverse striations only on the anterior half of
the ventral surface, longitudinal striations faint ; lateral alæ
absent ; cervical papillæ absent.   Male : bursa indistinctly trilobed ; with the following formula—ventro-ventral and latero-
ventral rays of about the same size but very divergent, externo-
lateral separate from the other lateral rays which are close together,
externo-dorsal arises from a common trunk with the dorsal, dorsal
bifurcate, each branch tridigitate ; prebursal papillæ absent ;

spicules straight, of medium size, equal and branched at their distal extremities ; gubernaculum present.   Female : vulva slightly in front of the anus ; uteri parallel. Oviparous, eggs with thin shell.   Parasites of the armadillos.

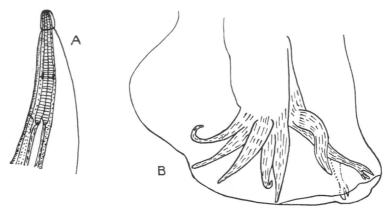

Fig. 72.—*Trichohelix tuberculata*. A. Anterior extremity, dorso-ventral view.   × 68.   B. Bursa, lateral view.   × 230.   (After Ortlepp.)

Type species : *T. tuberculata* (Parona and Stoss., 1901). ♂ 6·6 mm., ♀ 8·75 mm.   In the armadillo.

Syn., *Œsophagostomum tuberculatum* Parona and Stoss., 1901. Refs. 376, 388.

Genus HÆMONCHUS Cobb, 1898.

Syn., ? *Abomesi* Simmonds, 1881.

Definition.—TRICHOSTRONGYLINÆ : head relatively large (less than 50 μ in diameter), lips inconspicuous, buccal cavity small, with a slender tooth or lancet originating from the dorsal side of its base ; cervical papillæ prominent. Male : bursa with large lateral lobes and a small asymmetrical dorsal lobe ; with the following formula—ventro-ventral and latero-ventral rays fused proximally and separated distally, externo-lateral separate from the other lateral rays, externo-dorsal arises separately from the dorsal and is long and thin, dorsal bifurcate, each limb being bidigitate, it takes origin from the left side near the left externo-dorsal ; spicules relatively short (less than 1 mm. long) ; gubernaculum present. Female : vulva in the posterior part of the body and covered by a prominent flap projecting caudally. Oviparous. Parasites of ruminants.

Type species : *H. contortus* (Rudolphi, 1803).   ♂ 10–20 mm., ♀ 18–30 mm.   In sheep, goat, mouse, man, etc.

Syn., *Strongylus contortus* Rud., 1803.

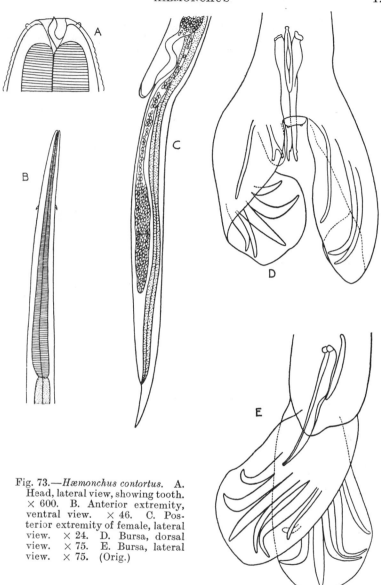

Fig. 73.—*Hæmonchus contortus.* A. Head, lateral view, showing tooth. × 600. B. Anterior extremity, ventral view. × 46. C. Posterior extremity of female, lateral view. × 24. D. Bursa, dorsal view. × 75. E. Bursa, lateral view. × 75. (Orig.)

Other species :

H. bispinosus (Molin, 1860).   In *Mazama nana.*

H. cervinus Baylis and Daubney, 1922.   In *Cervus axis.*

H. longistipes Railliet and Henry, 1909.   In camel.

H. lunatus Travassos, 1914.   In *Bos taurus.*

H. similis Travassos, 1914.   In *Bos taurus.*

Refs. 42, 67, 97, 419, 455, 458, 642, 653.

Genus OSTERTAGIA Ransom, 1907.

Definition.—TRICHOSTRONGYLINÆ : head less than 25 μ in diameter with a small buccal cavity ; cervical papillæ present. Male : bursa with two lateral lobes united by a small median lobe ; with the following formula—ventro-ventral and latero-ventral rays close together, externo-lateral separate from the other laterals,

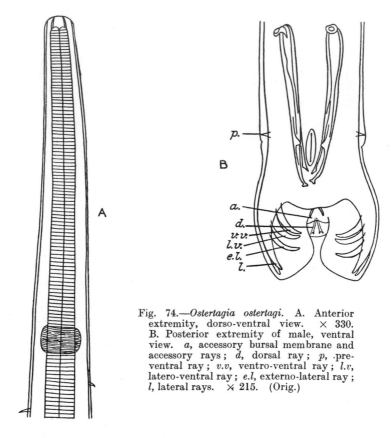

Fig. 74.—*Ostertagia ostertagi.* A. Anterior extremity, dorso-ventral view. × 330. B. Posterior extremity of male, ventral view. *a,* accessory bursal membrane and accessory rays ; *d,* dorsal ray ; *p,* pre-ventral ray ; *v.v,* ventro-ventral ray ; *l.v,* latero-ventral ray ; *e.l,* externo-lateral ray ; *l,* lateral rays. × 215. (Orig.)

externo-dorsal arises separately from the dorsal, dorsal bifurcate distally, each branch giving off one or two short lateral branches ; within the bursa, towards its dorsal surface, there is an accessory bursal membrane with the free posterior edge supported by two slender diverging rays ; spicules short, equal and ending in two or three processes ; gubernaculum present or absent ; prebursal papillæ present. Female : vulva in the posterior fifth of the worm. Oviparous. Parasites of mammals.

Type species : *O. ostertagi* (Stiles, 1892). ♂ 6·5–7·5 mm., ♀ 8·3–9·2 mm. In cattle and sheep (in nodules in stomach and also free in stomach).

Syn., *Strongylus ostertagi* Stiles, 1892.

Strongylus convolutus Ostertag, 1890.

Strongylus cervicornis McFadyean, 1897, in part.

Strongylus harkeri Stödter, 1901, in part.

Other species :

O. asymmetrica Ware, 1925. In *Cervus dama*.

O. bisonis Chapin, 1925. In *Bison bison*.

O. brigantiaca Blanchard, 1909. In the chamois.

O. bullosa Ransom and Hall, 1912. In *Ovis aries*.

O. callis (Travassos, 1914). In *Didelphys aurita*.

O. circumcincta (Stadelmann, 1894). In sheep, goat, and antelope.

Syn., *Strongylus vicarius* Stadelmann, 1894.

Strongylus cervicornis McFadyean, 1897, in part.

O. marshalli Ransom, 1907. In sheep.

O. mentulata Railliet and Henry, 1909. In camels.

O. occidentalis Ransom, 1907. In sheep.

O. tricuspis Marotel, 1912. In sheep.

O. trifida Cuillé, Marotel, and Panisset, 1911. In sheep.

O. trifurcata Ransom, 1907. In sheep and goat.

Refs. 59, 93b, 344a, 455, 458, 592a, 642, 663a.

Genus MOLINEUS Cameron, 1923.

Definition.—TRICHOSTRONGYLINÆ : head enlarged owing to inflation of the cephalic cuticle, which is transversely striated, elsewhere the cuticle exhibits twelve to fourteen longitudinal striations ; cervical papillæ absent. Male : bursa not distinctly divided into three lobes ; with the following formula—ventro-ventral and latero-ventral rays about equal, long and parallel, but slightly separated distally, externo-lateral very short, medio-lateral and postero-lateral long and parallel, externo-dorsal arises from a common trunk with the dorsal and is very short, reaching only about half-way to the edge of the bursa, dorsal bifurcate, each branch being tridigitate ; spicules short and slightly curved, the double points are directed posteriorly, the posterior point of each spicule is much the larger and seems to be formed of two smaller points fused together, the cephalic end of the spicules is broad and cup-shaped ; gubernaculum an elongated oval in shape ; pre-bursal papillæ absent. Female : vulva in the posterior fourth of the body ; posterior extremity bluntly rounded and from it projects a terminal spine. Oviparous. Parasites of mammals.

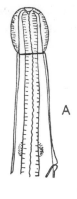

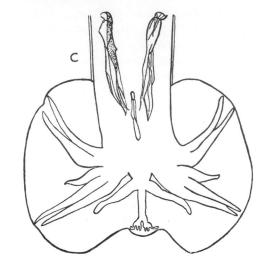

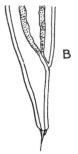

Fig. 75.—*Molineus felineus.* A. Anterior extremity, lateral view. × 220. B. Posterior extremity of female. × 220. C.
Bursa, dorsal view. × 220. (After
Cameron.)

Type species : *M. felineus* Cameron, 1923. ♂ 4·75 mm.,
♀ 5·25 mm. In *Felis yaguarundi.*

Other species :

    M. torulosus (Molin, 1861). In *Cebus capucinus* and *Saimiris
sciurea.*

        Syn., *Strongylus torulosus* Molin, 1861.

        Oswaldocruzia wisei Philpot, 1922.

        Trichostrongylus torulosus (Molin, 1861) Trav., 1922.

Refs. 79, 360, 390.

Genus OSWALDOCRUZIA Travassos, 1917.

Definition.—TRICHOSTRONGYLINÆ : head relatively large, over
50 μ in diameter, the cephalic cuticle being thickened and transversely striated. Male : bursa with the following formula—
ventro-ventral and latero-ventral rays close together and approximately equal, externo-lateral isolated and of about the same
length as the other rays, other laterals close together, externo-
dorsal arises from the base of the dorsal, dorsal very thick and
undivided except at its tip, where it ends in a number of digita-

tions ; spicules end in a number of processes ; gubernaculum absent. Female : vulva in posterior part of body. Parasites of reptiles and batrachians.

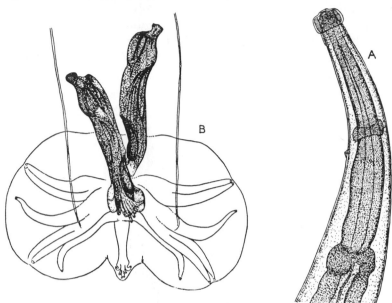

Fig. 76.—*Oswaldocruzia subauricularis.* A. Anterior extremity, lateral view. × 120. B. Posterior extremity of male, dorsal view. × 180. (After Travassos.)

Type species : *O. subauricularis* (Rudolphi, 1819). ♂ 6–7 mm., ♀ 10–11 mm. In *Bufo* spp., *Ceratophrys* sp.

Syn., *Strongylus subauricularis* Rud., 1819.

Other species :

O. bialata (Molin, 1861). In *Rana esculenta.*

O. denudata (Rud., 1819). In *Tropidonotus tesselatus.*

O. dispar (Duj., 1845). In *Anguis fragilis.*

O. filiformis (Gœze, 1782) Trav., 1917. In toads, frogs, lizards, etc.

Syn., *Strongylus auricularis* Zeder, 1800.

O. leidyi Travassos, 1917. In *Cistudo carolina.*

Syn., *Strongylus auricularis* Leidy, 1856, not Zeder, 1800.

O. subventricosa (Schneider, 1866). In *Ceratophrys cornuta.*

Refs. 477, 630, 642.

Genus ORNITHOSTRONGYLUS Travassos, 1914.

Syn., *Cephalostrongylus* Irwin-Smith, 1920.

Definition.—TRICHOSTRONGYLINÆ : cephalic cuticle inflated, buccal cavity with a reduced chitinous armature. Male : bursa with large lateral lobes, dorsal lobe very small; with the following formula—ventro-ventral and latero-ventral rays close together and about equal, externo-lateral close to medio-lateral proximally but diverging distally, medio-lateral and postero-lateral separated, externo-dorsal arises from the base of the dorsal, dorsal bifurcate and each branch bidigitate; prebursal papillæ present; spicules equal and end in three points; gubernaculum (telamon ?) elongate

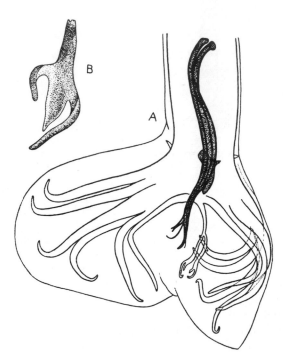

Fig. 77.—*Ornithostrongylus fariai.* A. Posterior extremity of male. × 190. (After Travassos.)
O. quadriradiatus. B. Telamon. × 470. (After Stephenson.)

with two lateral processes directed forwards almost forming a ring. Female : vulva in posterior half of body. Oviparous. Parasites of birds.

Type species : *O. fariai* Travassos, 1914. ♂ 9–10 mm., ♀ 17–20 mm. In *Leptoptila rufaxila.*

Other species :

O. hastatus (Linstow, 1905). In *Lyrurus tetrix.*

? *O. papillatus* (Linstow, 1882). In *Otis tarda.*

O. quadriradiatus (Stevenson, 1904). In *Columba* sp.

Syn., *Strongylus quadriradiatus* Stevenson, 1904.

Cephalostrongylus quadriradiatus (Stevenson, 1904)
Irwin-Smith, 1920.

Refs. 207, 238, 623, 642.

Genus OBELISCOIDES Graybill, 1924.

Syn., *Obeliscus* Graybill, 1923, preoccupied.

Definition.—TRICHOSTRONGYLINÆ : mouth simple, buccal capsule absent, cervical papillæ present. Male : bursa with two large

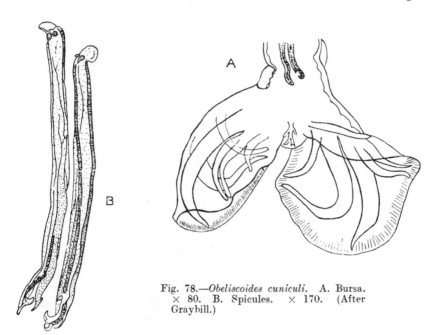

Fig. 78.—*Obeliscoides cuniculi.* A. Bursa.
× 80. B. Spicules. × 170. (After
Graybill.)

lateral lobes and a small well-defined dorsal lobe; with the following
formula—ventro-ventral widely divergent from and much smaller
than the latero-ventral ray, the two rays approximate, however,
at their tips, externo-lateral large and separated from the other
laterals, which are small and lie close together, externo-dorsal
small and slightly curved, dorsal bifurcated, each limb being
bidigitate, and from the common trunk is given off a lateral branch
on each side ; prebursal papillæ present ; spicules fairly short,
stout, cleft distally and ending in two barbed processes ; gubernaculum absent. Female : vulva in posterior fourth of body.
Oviparous. Parasites of rabbits.

Type species : *O. cuniculi* (Graybill, 1923). ♂ 10–14 mm., ♀ 15–18·5 mm. In rabbits.

Syn., *Obeliscus cuniculi* Graybill, 1923.

Refs. 201, 202.

Genus TRAVASSOSIUS Khalil, 1922.

Definition.—TRICHOSTRONGYLINÆ : slender worms slightly reddish in colour ; head about 30 μ in diameter, mouth with three lips ; cuticle of head region transversely striated, elsewhere

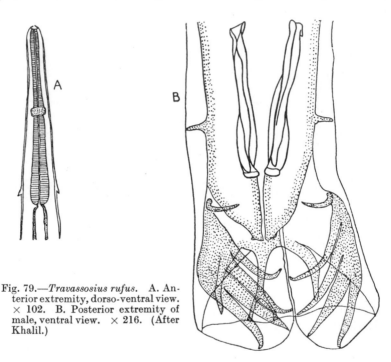

Fig. 79.—*Travassosius rufus.* A. Anterior extremity, dorso-ventral view. × 102. B. Posterior extremity of male, ventral view. × 216. (After Khalil.)

longitudinally striated ; cervical papillæ prominent. Male : bursa with large lateral lobes and with a small dorsal lobe ; with the following formula—ventro-ventral and latero-ventral rays widely separated, the ventro-ventral being much smaller than the latero-ventral, externo-lateral and the other laterals lie close together, externo-dorsal arises from the base of the dorsal, dorsal bifurcated in its distal third, each branch ending in two digitations ; spicules short and twisted with a knob-like caudal end ; gubernaculum absent ; prebursal papillæ large and conspicuous. Female : vulva in the posterior half of the body ; uteri divergent, Oviparous. Parasites of beavers,

Type species : *T. rufus* Khalil, 1922. ♂ 12 mm., ♀ 13 mm. In the beaver.

Other species : *T. americanus* Chapin, 1925. In *Castor canadensis*. Refs. 93b, 250.

Genus COOPERIA Ransom, 1907.

Definition.—TRICHOSTRONGYLINÆ : head relatively thick (25 μ or more in diameter), without well-marked lips or papillæ ; cuticle

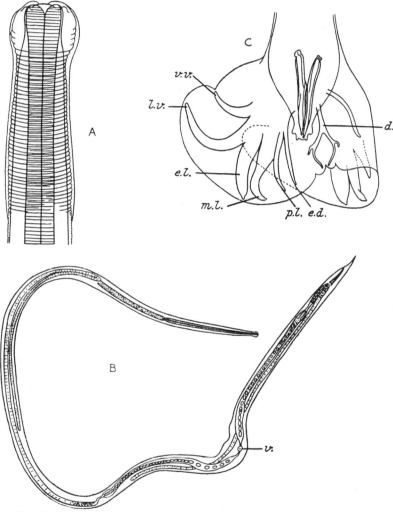

Fig. 80.—*Cooperia oncophora.* A. Anterior extremity, ventral view. × 330. B. Female. *v,* vulva. × 24. C. Bursa, dorso-lateral view. *v.v,* ventro-ventral ray ; *l.v,* latero-ventral ray ; *e.l,* externo-lateral ray ; *m.l,* medio-lateral ray ; *p.l,* postero-lateral ray ; *e.d,* externo-dorsal ray ; *d,* dorsal ray. × 75. (Orig.)

of head region transversely striated and often dilated, giving the head a swollen or bulbous appearance, cuticle of remainder of body with fourteen to sixteen longitudinal ridges ; buccal cavity small ; cervical papillæ absent. Male : bursa with two large lateral lobes and a small dorsal lobe ; with the following formula—ventro-ventral and latero-ventral rays widely separated, the ventro-ventral being much thinner and smaller than the latero-ventral, externo-lateral and other laterals separate, externo-dorsal arises from the base of the dorsal, dorsal ray divided about its mid-point into two branches, which together form a lyre- or horseshoe-shaped structure, from each branch near its origin a lateral twig is given off ; spicules short with simple points ; gubernaculum absent ; prebursal papillæ absent. Female : vulva in the posterior fourth of the body. Oviparous. Parasites of mammals.

Type species : C. curticei (Railliet, 1893).   ♂ 4·6–5·4 mm., ♀ 5·8–6·2 mm. In sheep and goat.

Syn., *Strongylus curticii* Giles, 1892.

Strongylus ventricosus Rud., 1809, of Curtice, 1890 :

Other species :

C. alata Railliet and Henry, 1909.   In monkeys.

C. bisonis Cram, 1925.   In *Bison bison*.

C. macieli (Travassos, 1915).   In *Tatus novemcinctus*.

C. oncophora (Railliet, 1898).   In cattle and sheep.

Syn., *Strongylus ventricosus* Rud., 1809, in part.

C. pectinata Ransom, 1907.   In cattle.

C. punctata (Linst., in Schnyder, 1907).   In cattle.

Refs. 111c, 182, 419, 457, 458, 642.

Genus HISTIOSTRONGYLUS Molin, 1861.

Definition.—TRICHOSTRONGYLINÆ : anterior extremity dilated and with an umbellate membrane sustained by large spines (Molin), or thickened towards the periphery and having a spinous appearance under a low magnification (Travassos) ; mouth small and triangular. Male : bursa with large lateral lobes widely separated ventrally, and with a small dorsal lobe ; with the following formula —ventro-ventral and latero-ventral rays widely separate and about equal, externo-lateral separated from the other lateral rays, externo-dorsal arises from the base of the dorsal, dorsal bifurcate for about half its length ; spicules equal ; gubernaculum present. Female : the posterior extremity ends in a spinous process, and there are two similar processes situated subventrally near the end of the body (Molin), but according to Travassos the posterior extremity of the female is provided with three strong spines, one dorsal and two subventral, between which the atrophied

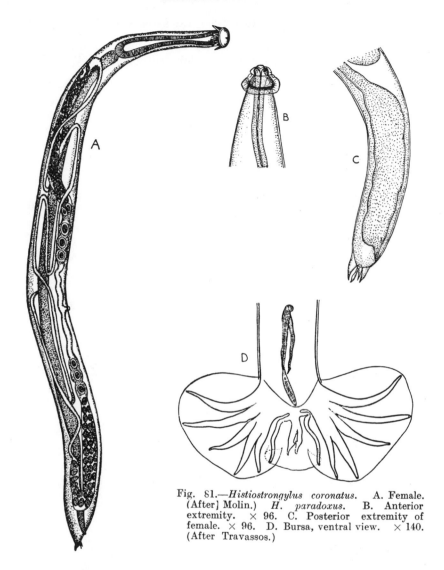

Fig. 81.—*Histiostrongylus coronatus.* A. Female. (After] Molin.) *H. paradoxus.* B. Anterior extremity. × 96. C. Posterior extremity of female. × 96. D. Bursa, ventral view. × 140. (After Travassos.)

tail is found ; vulva in the posterior part of the body. Parasites of Chiroptera.

Type species : *H. coronatus* Molin, 1861. ♂ 9 mm., ♀ 13 mm. In *Phyllostoma discolor.*

Other species :

    H. paradoxus Travassos, 1918. In *Mollossidæ.*

    H. tipula (v. Beneden, 1873). In bats.

Refs. 51, 360, 633, 642.

Genus GRAPHIDIUM Railliet and Henry, 1909.

Definition.—TRICHOSTRONGYLINÆ : head small ; mouth relatively large ; cuticle with numerous longitudinal striæ ; cervical

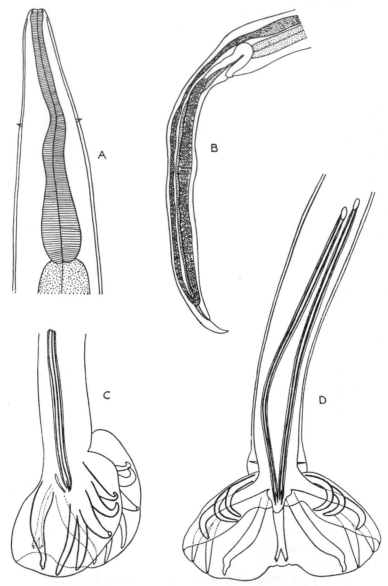

Fig. 82.—*Graphidium strigosum.* A. Anterior extremity, ventral view. × 75.
B. Posterior extremity of female, lateral view. × 28. C. Bursa, semi-
lateral view. × 46. D. Bursa, ventral view. × 46. (Orig.)

papillæ present. Male : bursa with well-developed lateral lobes and a small or indefinite dorsal lobe ; with the following formula— ventro-ventral and latero-ventral rays definitely separated, the ventro-ventral being smaller than the latero-ventral, the externo-lateral is about twice the thickness of the other rays, and is directed slightly anteriorly, medio-lateral and postero-lateral separate, externo-dorsal arises from a common trunk with the dorsal, dorsal bifurcate at the tip and each branch bidigitate ; spicules equal, long and filiform, each consisting of two chitinous rods joined by a membrane, the tips are multiple and very complicated ; gubernaculum colourless, but well-defined and situated close to the cloaca ; prebursal papillæ present. Female : vulva in the posterior third of the body, which narrows abruptly behind it. Oviparous. Parasites of the stomach and intestine of rodents.

Type species : *G. strigosum* (Dujardin, 1845). ♂ 8–16 mm., ♀ 11–20 mm. In *Lepus europæus*, etc.

Syn., *Strongylus strigosus* Duj., 1845.

Strongylus retortæformis Bremser, 1811, not Zeder, 1800.

Spiroptera leporum Moniez, 1880.

Strongylus blasii v. Linst., 1887.

Refs. 77, 79, 131, 205, 419, 642.

Genus NEMATODIRUS Ransom, 1907.

Definition.—TRICHOSTRONGYLINÆ : body capillary, attenuated anteriorly ; mouth simple surrounded by six papillæ ; cephalic cuticle dilated and transversely striated, body with eighteen distinct longitudinal striations ; cervical papillæ absent. Male : bursa with two large lateral lobes, dorsal lobe small or indefinite ; with the following formula—ventro-ventral and latero-ventral rays very close and parallel, externo-lateral separate from the other laterals, which are close together and parallel, externo-dorsal arises from the base of the dorsal ray, dorsal rays completely doubled with extremities bi- or tri-digitate ; spicules relatively large, filiform, and united by a membrane either throughout or only at their tips, which are simple ; gubernaculum absent. Female : vulva in the posterior third or fourth of the body ; tail conical and truncate, generally provided with a pointed process. Oviparous. Parasitic in the stomach and small intestine of mammals.

Type species : *N. filicollis* (Rudolphi, 1802). ♂ 10–15 mm., ♀ 15–20 mm. In sheep, goat, cattle, etc.

Syn., *Ascaris filicollis* Rud., 1802.

Other species :
>
> *N. abnormalis* May, 1920.   In sheep and goats.
> *N. dromedarii* May, 1920.   In dromedary.

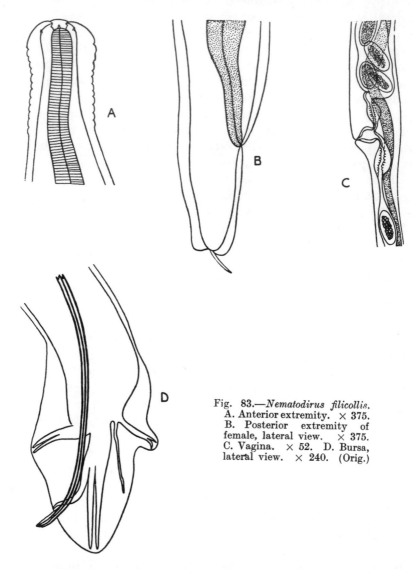

Fig. 83.—*Nematodirus filicollis.*
A. Anterior extremity. × 375.
B. Posterior extremity of
female, lateral view.   × 375.
C. Vagina. × 52. D. Bursa,
lateral view.   × 240. (Orig.)

N. furcatus May, 1920.   In sheep.
N. helvetianus May, 1920.   In cattle.
N. hopkeni Leiper, 1910.   In hippopotamus.
N. leporis Chandler, 1924.   In domesticated rabbit.

N. mauritanicus Maupas and Seurat, 1912. In dromedary.

N. molini (Railliet, 1898) Travassos, 1918. In *Tayassus* spp.

N. neotoma Hall, 1916. In *Neotoma* sp.

N. roscidus Railliet, 1911. In *Cervus* sp.

N. spathiger (Railliet, 1896). In camel, sheep, cattle, goat, antelope, etc.

N. weinbergi Railliet and Henry, 1909. In *Anthropopithecus troglodytes*.

Refs. 59, 60, 67, 90, 348, 350, 433, 455, 458, 642.

Genus AUSTROSTRONGYLUS Chandler, 1924.

Definition.—TRICHOSTRONGYLINÆ : body slender of nearly uniform diameter ; cervical cuticle dilated and smooth ; body with six or eight longitudinal ridges ; mouth cavity relatively

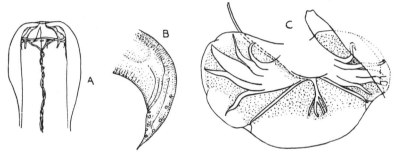

Fig. 84.—*Austrostrongylus macropodis.* A. Head. × 330. B. Posterior extremity of female, lateral view. × 130. C. Bursa. × 130. (After Chandler.)

conspicuous and chitinized, with a relatively large dorsal tooth in its depth, and a smaller perforated ventral tooth. Male : bursa with large lateral lobes, the left lobe being smaller than the right ; ventro-ventral and latero-ventral rays widely separate and of almost equal size, externo-lateral close to the medio-lateral, medio-lateral and postero-lateral widely divergent ; on the right side the externo-lateral is much broader than the other lateral rays, whereas on the left side it is of about the same size as the other lateral rays ; the externo-dorsal arises from the root of the dorsal ray and is longer on the right side than on the left, dorsal bifurcate in about its distal third, and a lateral branch is given off on each side just above the point of bifurcation ; spicules slender with single points and apparently united by a membrane ; gubernaculum present. Female : posterior extremity tapers rapidly behind the anus to end in a fine point ; vulva some distance in front of the anus. Oviparous. Parasites of marsupials.

Type species : *A. macropodis* Chandler, 1924. ♂ 4·5–5 mm., ♀ 6·4–9·5 mm. In *Macropus bennetti*.

Ref. 88.

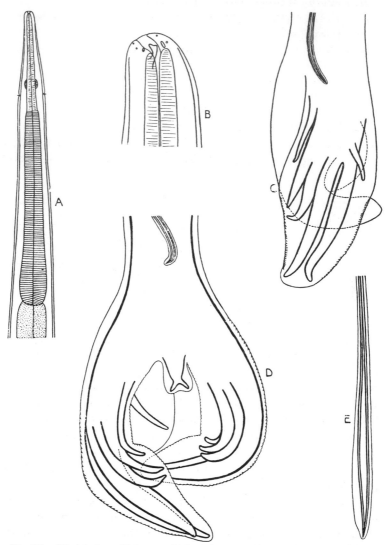

Fig. 85.—*Mecistocirrus digitatus*. A. Anterior extremity, ventral view. × 46. B. Head, lateral view, showing tooth. × 330. C. Bursa, lateral view. × 46. D. Bursa, dorsal view. × 46. E. Ends of spicules. × 215. (Orig.)

Genus MECISTOCIRRUS (Railliet and Henry, 1912) Neveu-Lemaire, 1914.

Definition.—TRICHOSTRONGYLINÆ : body attenuated anteriorly, head small with six small papillæ, mouth subterminal opening slightly dorsally, with a large buccal tooth ; cuticle with fine transverse striations and about thirty longitudinal striæ ; cervical papillæ present. Male : bursa with two large lateral lobes, and a small symmetrical dorsal lobe ; with the following formula—ventro-ventral and latero-ventral rays widely separate, the ventro-ventral being much smaller than the latero-ventral, which is very large, externo-lateral as large as the latero-ventral and close to it, these two being far larger than any of the other rays, medio-lateral and postero-lateral small and close together, externo-dorsal very slender and arises separately from the dorsal, dorsal short and bifurcated, each division ending in three papillæ ; spicules very long, slender, and united for almost their entire length, tips simple ; gubernaculum absent ; prebursal papillæ present. Female : vulva close to the anus, tail conical. Oviparous.

Type species : *M. digitatus* (v. Linstow, 1906). ♂ 16–24 mm. ♀ 19–29 mm. In bovines, pig, sheep, and man.

Syn., *Strongylus digitatus* Linst., 1906.
Strongylus fordii Daniels, 1908.
Strongylus gibsoni Stephens, 1909.
Nematodirus digitatus (Linst.) Railliet and Henry, 1909.
Mecistocirrus fordi (Daniels) Neveu-Lemaire, 1914.
Mecistocirrus tagumai Morishita, 1922.
Refs. 79, 116, 284, 328, 350, 369, 433, 589, 642.

Genus GRAPHIDIOIDES Cameron, 1923.

Definition.—Resembling *Graphidium*, but differing in the following particulars—cervical papillæ absent, ventro-ventral and

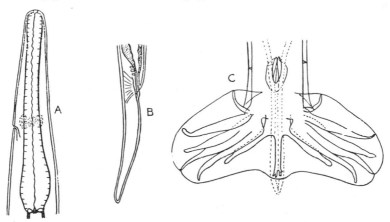

Fig. 86.—*Graphidioides affinis*. A. Anterior extremity, lateral view. × 100. B. Posterior extremity of female, lateral view. × 50. C. Bursa, dorsal view. × 50. (After Cameron.)

latero-ventral rays of bursa widely divergent ; the ventro-ventral being much smaller than the latero-ventral ; spicules long and filiform, each consisting of two chitinized rods joined near their tips, which are simple, from the median side of each spicule project two membranes, which anastomose near the termination of the spicules, so that these are virtually joined together ; gubernaculum situated at some distance from the genital cone, it consists of a broad base with raised lateral ridges, and a double central keel. In the female the body narrows abruptly behind the anus instead of behind the vulva.   Parasites of rodents.

Type species :   *G. affinis* (Mégnin, 1895).   ♂ 9–17 mm., ♀ 16–21 mm.   In *Dolichotis magellineus.*

Syn., *Strongylus affinis* Mégnin, 1895.
Strongylus rectus Linstow, 1906.

Other species :

G. rudicaudatus (Railliet and Henry, 1909).   In *Viscacia viscacia.*

Syn., *Graphidium rudicaudatum* Railliet and Henry, 1909.
Refs. 79, 84a, 419, 642.

Genus NEMATODIRELLA n. g.

Syn., *Microcephalus* Romanovitch, 1915, preoccupied.

Definition.—TRICHOSTRONGYLINÆ : body attenuated anteriorly, the cephalic extremity vesicular and 60 μ broad.   Head with two large lateral and four smaller submedian papillæ, cuticle marked by about forty longitudinal striations.   There is no buccal cavity, the mouth opening directly into the œsophagus.   Male : small bilobed bursa ; with the following formula—ventro-ventral and latero-ventral rays small, externo-lateral large and arising from a common trunk with the other laterals ; spicules equal and very long, measuring nearly half the length of the worm.   Female : anterior quarter of the body fiiliform, then suddenly enlarging, from which point it gradually attenuates towards the posterior extremity ; tail short and blunt ; vulva situated on an eminence at the end of the anterior fourth of the body.   Oviparous.

Type species :   *N. longispiculata* nom. nov.   ♂ 20–25 mm., ♀ 45–50 mm.   In *Tarandus rangifer.*

Syn., *Microcephalus longissime spiculatus* Romanovitch, 1915.
Ref. 471.

Subfamily HELIGMOSOMINÆ Travassos, 1914.

Definition.—TRICHOSTRONGYLIDÆ : buccal capsule absent or rudimentary ; female with single genitalia.

KEY TO GENERA.

1. Lateral lobes of bursa and rays
markedly asymmetrical   .   Nippostrongylus, p. 147.
Lateral lobes of bursa and rays
approximately symmetrical . 2

2. Tail of female ends in three or
more cusps ; vulva not close
to anus   .   .   .   .   Ollulanus, p. 148.
Tail of female not ending in
three cusps ; vulva close to
anus   3

3. Body not coiled in a permanent
spiral   4
Body coiled in a permanent spiral 6

4. Dorsal ray completely doubled . Heligmostrongylus, p. 144.
Dorsal ray only forked at its
extremity   5

5. Cervical cuticle studded with
papillæ ; dorsal ray very large Impalaia, p. 143.
Cervical cuticle not studded with
papillæ ; dorsal ray relatively
small .   .   .   .   .   Heligmosomum, p. 142.

6. Dorsal ray very short, not
approaching bursal margin   .   7
Dorsal ray long, almost reaching
bursal margin .   .   .   8

7. Dorsal ray divided only at its
extremity ; prebursal papillæ
present ; gubernaculum absent Heligmosomoides, p. 146.
Dorsal ray completely doubled ;
prebursal papillæ absent ;
gubernaculum present   .   .   Nematospira, p. 147.

8. Dorsal ray forked near its extremity ; ventro-ventral and
latero - ventral completely
separate, as also are the medio-
lateral and postero-lateral   . Viannaia, p. 149.
Dorsal ray split for more than
half its length ; ventro-ventral
and latero-ventral fused proximally, as also are the medio-
lateral and postero-lateral   . Viannella, p. 150.

Genus HELIGMOSOMUM Railliet and Henry, 1909.

Definition.—HELIGMOSOMINÆ : body not spirally rolled ; cuticle with marked transverse and longitudinal striations, of which some (the dorsal and sometimes the ventral) are very prominent, constituting true longitudinal alæ ; cephalic cuticle inflated. Male : bursa well-developed ; with the following formula—ventro-ventral and latero-ventral rays widely separate, about equal in size, and directed forward, externo-lateral, medio-lateral, and postero-lateral divergent and relatively large, externo-dorsal arising from a common trunk with the dorsal and very thin, dorsal ray small and ends in four branches, of which the two internal are bifid ; spicules relatively long, thin and equal ; gubernaculum absent or rudimentary. Female : vulva just in front of the anus. Parasites of the stomach and intestine of rodents and marsupials.

Fig. 87. — *Heligmosomum braziliense.* Posterior extremity of male. × 85. (After Travassos.)

Type species : *H. costellatum* (Dujardin, 1845). ♂ 11 mm., ♀ 17 mm. In *Microtus arvalis.*

Syn., *Strongylus costellatus* Duj., 1845.

Other species :

H. aculeatum Travassos, 1917. In *Muridæ.*

H. agoutii Neiva, Cunha, and Travassos, 1914. In *Dasyprocta agouti.*

H. alpha Travassos, 1918. In *Muridæ.*

H. beta Travassos, 1918. In *Muridæ.*

H. braziliense Travassos, 1914. In *Mus* sp.

H. cristatum Gedoelst, 1917. In *Sciurus prevosti.*

H. delta Travassos, 1918. In *Muridæ.*

H. didelphe (Travassos, 1914). In *Didelphys* sp.

H. elegans Travassos, 1921. In *Cœndu villosus.*

H. gamma Travassos, 1918. In *Mesomys guira.*

H. gracile (Leuckart, 1842). In *Myoxus glis.*

H. læve (Duj., 1845). In *Dipodilla* sp., *Pitymys* sp., *Apodemus* sp.

H. minutum (Duj., 1845). In *Microtus* sp., etc.

H. nematodiriformis Travassos, 1918. In *Muridæ*.

H. vexillatum Hall, 1916. In *Thomomys fossor*.

Refs. 131, 152, 205, 368, 419, 524a, 623, 642.

Genus IMPALAIA Monnig, 1924.

Definition.—HELIGMOSOMINÆ : body filiform, not spirally rolled, cuticle with well-marked longitudinal striations, cephalic

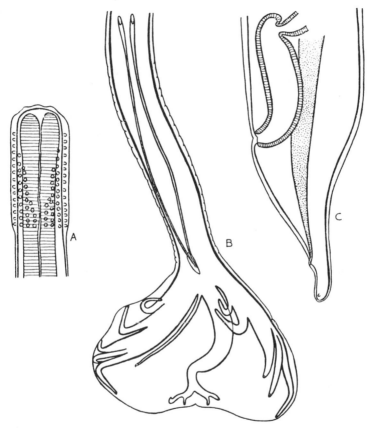

Fig. 88.—*Impalaia tuberculata*. A. Anterior extremity. × 330. B. Posterior extremity of male, dorsal view. × 215. C. Posterior extremity of female, lateral view. × 76. (Orig.)

and cervical cuticle slightly inflated, and cervical cuticle studded with small papillæ. Male : bursa with well-developed lateral lobes, and having the following formula—ventro-ventral and latero-ventral rays separate and directed forwards, externo-lateral and laterals arise from a common trunk, the postero-lateral being directed posteriorly and much longer than the medio-lateral,

externo-dorsal arises from the base of the dorsal ray and is long
and thin, dorsal ray very large and thick proximally, tapering
distally, and bifurcate near its extremity, each branch being
bidigitate ; spicules long and filiform ; gubernaculum present.
Female : tail narrows abruptly behind the vulva and ends in a
short conical process ; anus near the tip of the tail.

Type species : *I. tuberculata* Monnig, 1924. ♂ 8 mm., ♀ 17 mm.
In *Aepyceros melampus*.

Refs. 362, 363.

Genus HELIGMOSTRONGYLUS Travassos, 1917.

Definition.—HELIGMOSOMINÆ : body filiform, not spirally rolled ;
cuticle with fine transverse striations and marked longitudinal

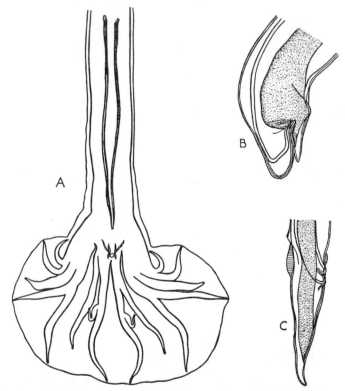

Fig. 89.—*Heligmostrongylus sedecimradiatus.* A. Posterior extremity of male,
dorsal view. × 90. B. Posterior extremity of old female. × 150.
C. Posterior extremity of young female. × 150. (After Travassos.)

striations, of which the dorsal is in the form of a flange extending
from the cephalic cuticular dilatation almost to the posterior

extremity. Male : bursa well-developed ; with the following
formula—ventro-ventral and latero-ventral rays united in their
proximal third, the distal portions being widely separate and
directed forwards, medio-lateral and postero-lateral united in
their proximal third and widely separated distally, the dorsal is
completely doubled and very long, each branch giving off near its
base the externo-dorsal, and further down a short lateral branch ;
spicules long and delicate ; gubernaculum consists of a central
piece with a number of branches. Female : vulva near anus, and
almost always with a ventral process, which may extend even as
far as the end of the tail. Parasites of rodents.

Type species : *H. sedecimradiatus* (Linst., 1899). ♂ 8–10 mm.,
♀ 14–16 mm. In *Agouti paca*.

Syn., *Strongylus sedecimradiatus* Linstow, 1899.

Refs. 318, 628, 642.

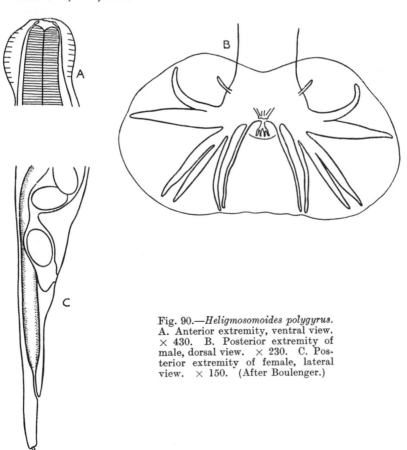

Fig. 90.—*Heligmosomoides polygyrus.*
A. Anterior extremity, ventral view.
× 430. B. Posterior extremity of
male, dorsal view. × 230. C. Posterior extremity of female, lateral
view. × 150. (After Boulenger.)

Genus HELIGMOSOMOIDES Hall, 1916.

Definition.—HELIGMOSOMINÆ : body spirally rolled, head small ; cephalic cuticle inflated, usually asymmetrically developed and showing transverse striations ; the rest of the body covered by faint transverse striations, and numerous distinct longitudinal ridges separated by similar fine striations ; cervical papillæ absent or minute. Male : bursa well-developed indistinctly trilobed, with the following formula—ventro-ventral and latero-ventral rays widely separate and divergent, externo-lateral and lateral rays arising from a common trunk and clearly separated, externo-dorsal long, slender, and arises separately from the dorsal, dorsal slender, very short, and dividing into four branches ; prebursal papillæ well-developed ; spicules simple and filiform ; gubernaculum absent. Female : posterior extremity conical and ending in a pointed spike ; vulva close to anus ; ovejector well-developed

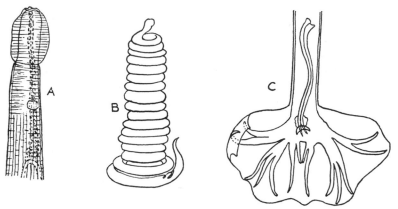

Fig. 91.—*Nematospira turgida.* A. Anterior extremity. × 115. B. Female. × 17. C. Posterior extremity of male, ventral view. × 85. (After Walton.)

and muscular. Oviparous, eggs small and oval, shells thin and rugose. Parasites of rodents.

Type species : *H. polygyrus* (Duj., 1845). ♂ 4–5·3 mm., ♀ 6–10 mm. In *Microtus arvalis.*

Syn., *Strongylus polygyrus* Duj., 1845.

Heligmosomum polygyrum (Duj., 1845) Railliet and Henry, 1909.

Viannaia polygyra (Duj., 1845) Hall, 1916.

Heligmosomoides linstowi Hall, 1916.

Refs. 70, 131, 205, 312, 642

Genus NEMATOSPIRA Walton, 1923.

Definition.—HELIGMOSOMINÆ : closely resembling *Heligmoso-moides*, but differing in the absence of prebursal papillæ, the presence of a gubernaculum, and the fact that the dorsal ray is completely doubled. Parasites of rodents.

Type species : *N. turgida* Walton, 1923. ♂ 4–6 mm., ♀ 12–15 mm. In *Microtus arvalis*.

Ref. 659.

Genus NIPPOSTRONGYLUS Lane, 1923.

Definition.—HELIGMOSOMINÆ : very delicate worms, mouth simple ; with a small oral cavity ; head small with the cephalic cuticle slightly inflated. Male : bursa markedly asymmetrical, large and somewhat inrolled ; with the following formula—the

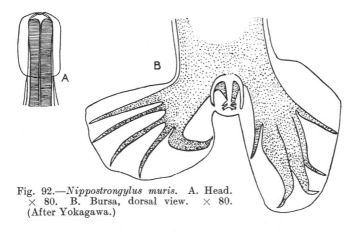

Fig. 92.—*Nippostrongylus muris.* A. Head.
× 80. B. Bursa, dorsal view. × 80.
(After Yokagawa.)

rays of the left side differ greatly from those of the right side ; on the left side the ventro-ventral and latero-ventral rays are parallel, long and thin, the externo-lateral and the medio-lateral are also long and thin, whilst the postero-lateral is thick, and towards its extremity curves dorsally to end in a conical tip ; on the right side the ventro-ventral is delicate and widely separated from the latero-ventral, which is also thin, but lies close to the externo-lateral except at its tip, the externo-lateral and medio-lateral are thick and lie close together, but diverge at their extremities, the postero-lateral is small and delicate ; the externo-dorsal may arise at slightly different levels from a common trunk with the dorsal, dorsal bifurcate near its tip, each limb ending in two or three digitations ; spicules equal, long and filiform

with sickle-shaped extremities ; gubernaculum present. Female :
vulva close to the anus. Oviparous. Parasites of rodents.

  Type species : *N. muris* (Yokogawa, 1920). ♂ 3–4 mm.,
♀ 4–6 mm. In rats.

  Syn., *Heligmosomum muris* Yokogawa, 1920.

  Refs. 268, 668.

Genus OLLULANUS Leuckart, 1865.

 Definition.—HELIGMOSOMINÆ : minute worms, generally found
with the head coiled on itself ; buccal cavity small without teeth,
cutting plates or similar structures ; the cavity is formed by a
reflection of the cuticle and in optical section is almost spherical ;
œsophagus only slightly swollen posteriorly ; cervical papillæ

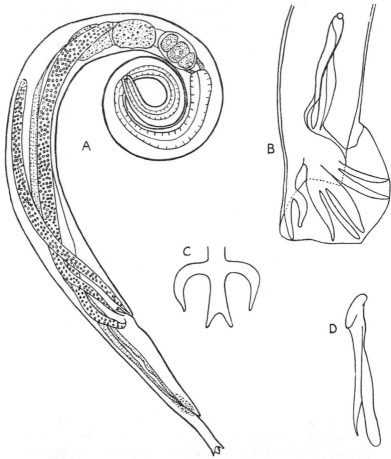

Fig. 93.—*Ollulanus tricuspis*. A. Female. × 288. B. Posterior extremity
of male. × 600. C. Dorsal ray of bursa. × 880. D. Spicule. × 800.
(After Cameron.)

large and situated at the posterior portion of the œsophagus.
Male : bursa undivided and open only on the ventral surface ;
with the following formula—ventro-ventral and latero-ventral
rays separate and about the same size, externo-lateral thick and
arises from a common trunk with the laterals, externo-dorsal arises
from a common trunk with the dorsal, dorsal thick and bifurcated
near the tip ; prebursal rays absent ; spicules equal, short, and
bifurcated, one limb being sharp and the other rounded ; gubernaculum absent. Female : the posterior extremity ends typically
in three cusps, but occasionally one or two small extra cusps may
be present ; vulva prominent, situated about the beginning of the
posterior fifth of the worm ; vagina short ; uterus single ; ovary
single. Oviparous, the eggs
being large and granular. Parasites of cats.

Type species : *O. tricuspis*
Leuckart, 1865. ♂ 0·7–0·8 mm.,
♀ 0·8–1 mm. In cats.

Refs. 81, 205, 299, 405.

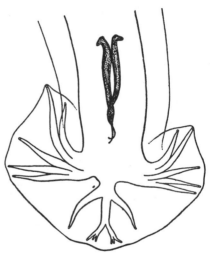

Genus VIANNAIA Travassos, 1914.

Definition.—HELIGMOSO-
MINÆ : body spirally coiled ;
cuticle with slight transverse
striations, but without longitudinal striations, and enormously thickened, especially in
the male ; cephalic cuticle inflated. Male: bursa with lateral
lobes generally slightly unequal ; with the following

Fig. 94.—*Viannaia viannai.* Posterior extremity of male, dorsal view. × 270.
(After Travassos.)

formula—ventro-ventral and latero-ventral rays separated slightly
and directed forwards, externo-lateral and laterals separate,
externo-dorsal arises from a common trunk with the dorsal, dorsal
bifurcated near its extremity, the branches may be digitate ;
spicules short, about equal ; gubernaculum, when present, is
indistinct. Female : vulva near the anus. Parasites in intestine
of marsupials, edentata, insectivora, and rodents.

Type species : *V. viannai* Travassos, 1914. In *Didelphys aurita.*
♂ 3·2 mm., ♀ 5·2 mm.

Other species :

V. conspicua Travassos, 1914. In *Didelphys opossum.*

V. depressa (Duj., 1845). In *Sorex* spp. and *Crocidura* sp.

V. hamata Travassos, 1914.   In *Didelphys aurita*.

V. linstowi Travassos, 1918.   In *Talpa europæa*.

V. minuscula Travassos, 1915.   In *Tamandua* sp. and *Myrmecophaga* sp.

V. pudica Travassos, 1921.   In *Dasyprocta agouti*.

V. pusilla Travassos, 1914.   In *Didelphys aurita*.

V. saimiris Cameron, 1923.   In *Saimiris sciurea*.

Refs. 79, 131, 205, 623, 642.

Genus VIANNELLA Travassos, 1918.

Definition.—HELIGMOSOMINÆ :   closely   resembles   *Viannaia*
except in the following points—ventro-ventral and latero-ventral
rays fused proximally and diverging distally, medio-lateral and

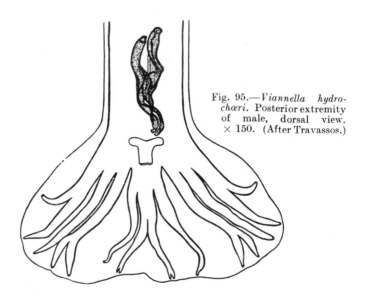

Fig. 95.—*Viannella hydrochœri.* Posterior extremity
of male, dorsal view.
× 150. (After Travassos.)

postero-lateral fused proximally and diverging distally, dorsal
bifurcated for more than half its length.   Parasites of small intestine
of rodents.

Type species :   *V. hydrochæri* (Travassos, 1914).   ♂ 1·9 mm.,
♀ 2·3–2·4 mm.   In *Hydrochœrus capibara*.

Syn., *Viannaia hydrochœri* Travassos, 1914.

Other species :   *V. fariai* (Travassos, 1915).   In *Silvilagus
brasiliensis*.

V. viscaciæ Goodey, 1925.   In *Viscacia viscacia*.

Refs. 195b, 205, 623, 633, 642.

TRICHOSTRONGYLIDÆ incompletely known.
Genus WARRENIUS Hall, 1916.

Definition.—TRICHOSTRONGYLIDÆ : subfamily ? Cuticle of head inflated ; a unilateral cervical wing present. Male : bursa with two large lateral lobes and a small but distinct dorsal lobe ; with the following formula—ventro-ventral and latero-ventral rays fused proximally diverging distally, externo-lateral arises from a

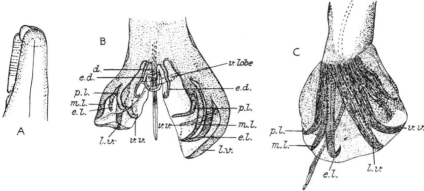

Fig. 96.—*Warrenius quadrivittati.* A. Head. × 200. B. Bursa, dorsal view. *d,* dorsal ray ; *e.d,* externo-dorsal ray ; *p.l,* postero-lateral ray ; *m.l,* medio-lateral ray ; *e.l,* externo-lateral ray ; *l.v,* latero-ventral ray ; *v.v,* ventro-ventral ray ; *v, lobe,* ventral lobe of bursa. C. Bursa, lateral view. (After Hall.)

common trunk with the other laterals, medio-lateral and postero-lateral fused proximally, externo-dorsal is long and wavy, dorsal bifurcates near its extremity, each branch gives off a short lateral twig ; spicules long and narrow. Female : unknown.

Type species : *W. quadrivittati* Hall, 1916. ♂ 6·2 mm., ♀ ? In *Eutamias quadrivittatus.*

Other species : * *W. bifurcatus* Sleggs, 1925. In *Citellus richardsonii.*

Refs. 205, 582b, 642.

Genus CITELLINEMA Hall, 1916.

Definition.—TRICHOSTRONGYLIDÆ : subfamily ? Head surrounded by a collar which forms the external limit of a depression around the head anteriorly. Male : bursa with two large lateral lobes ; with the following formula—ventro-ventral, latero-ventral, and externo-lateral rays arise from a common trunk, medio-lateral and postero-lateral separate, dorsal not distinguishable in the one specimen available ; spicules bifurcate for nearly their whole length. Female : unknown.

---

* As this species has double female genitalia, the genus belongs to the *Trichostrongylinæ.*

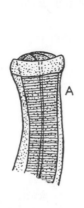

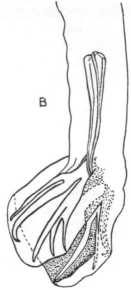

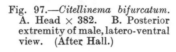

Fig. 97.—*Citellinema bifurcatum.*
A. Head × 382.   B. Posterior
extremity of male, latero-ventral
view.   (After Hall.)

Type species : *C. bifurcatum* Hall, 1916.   ♂ 6·8 mm., ♀ ?   In
Citellus elegans.

Refs. 205, 642.

Subfamily AMIDOSTOMINÆ Travassos, 1919.

Definition.—TRICHOSTRONGYLIDÆ : with buccal capsule relatively well-developed, but without a corona radiata or anterior
cutting organs.   Spicules short and divided distally into two or
three processes.   Female with double genitalia.

KEY TO GENERA.

1. Buccal capsule without teeth in its
     depth, head with prominent
     posteriorly directed papillæ   .   Epomidiostomum, p. 155.
   Buccal capsule with a pointed tooth
     or teeth in its depth, head with-
     out posteriorly directed papillæ   2
2. Ventro-ventral and latero-ventral
     rays widely separated ; medio-
     lateral   and   postero-lateral
     separate   .   .   .   .   Amidostomum, p. 153.
   Ventro-ventral and latero-ventral
     rays close together ; medio-
     lateral and postero-lateral fused
     proximally   .   .   .   .   Amphibiophilus, p. 154.

Genus AMIDOSTOMUM Railliet and Henry, 1909.

Definition.—AMIDOSTOMINÆ : mouth directed straight forwards ; buccal capsule subglobular, furnished in its depth with a sharp tooth or teeth ; œsophagus presenting in its lumen three axial chitinous plates extending practically its whole length.   Male : lateral lobes of bursa much longer than the dorsal lobe ; with the following formula—ventro-ventral and latero-ventral rays widely

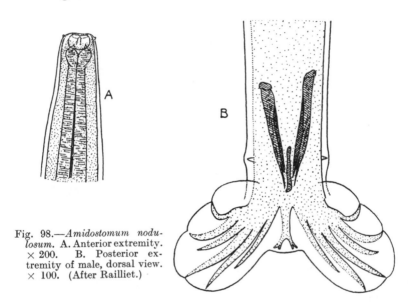

Fig. 98.—*Amidostomum nodulosum.* A. Anterior extremity. × 200.   B.   Posterior extremity of male, dorsal view. × 100. (After Railliet.)

separate, externo-lateral, medio-lateral and postero-lateral separate, externo-dorsal arises separately from the dorsal, is short, and does not reach the bursal margin, dorsal ray bifurcated near its extremity, each branch being bidigitate ; spicules equal, each divided for more than half its length ; gubernaculum present. Female : vulva in the posterior fifth of the body ; tail digitiform. Parasites of the gizzard of birds.

Type species : *A. nodulosum* (Rud., 1803).   ♂ 10–17 mm., ♀ 12–24 mm.   In *Anser domestica.*

Syn., *Strongylus nodulosus* Rud., 1803.

Strongylus nodularis Rud., 1809.

Strongylus anseris Zed., 1800, in part.

? *Strongylus acutus* Lundahl, 1848.

Ascaris mucronata Froel., 1791, not Schrank, 1780.

Strongylus mucronatus (Froel., 1791) Railliet, 1893.

Strongylus monodon Linstow, 1882.

Amidostomum anseris (Zeder, 1800) Railliet and Henry,
1909, in part.

Other species :

A. chevreuxi Seurat, 1918.   In *Himantopus himantopus.*

A. fulicæ (Rud., 1819).   In *Fulica atra.*

A. henryi Skrjabin, 1915.   In *Vanellus cristatus.*

A. raillieti Skrjabin, 1915.   In *Fulica atra.*

Refs. 150, 398, 420, 476, 550, 551, 572, 636, 681.

Genus AMPHIBIOPHILUS Skrjabin, 1916.

Definition.—AMIDOSTOMINÆ : mouth directed straight forwards,
buccal capsule resembles that of *Amidostomum*, in its depth is a
long triangular denticle directed forwards ; narrow cervical and

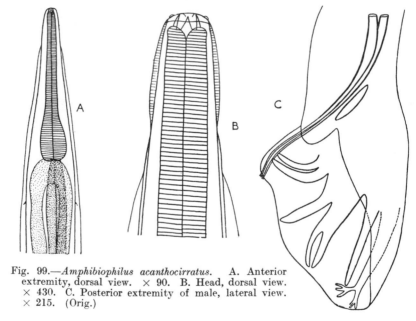

Fig. 99.—*Amphibiophilus acanthocirratus.*   A. Anterior
extremity, dorsal view.   × 90.   B. Head, dorsal view.
× 430.   C. Posterior extremity of male, lateral view.
× 215.   (Orig.)

well-developed lateral flanges present.   Male : bursal formula—
ventro-ventral and latero-ventral rays fused proximally, externo-
lateral arises from a common trunk with the other laterals, medio-
lateral and postero-lateral fused proximally, externo-dorsal arises
from a common trunk with the dorsal, dorsal bifurcated, each
branch tridigitate ; spicules equal and bifurcate at distal extremity ;
gubernaculum present.   Female : posterior extremity conical ;
vulva in the posterior third of the body.   Parasites of the intestine
of frogs.

Type species :   *A. acanthocirratus* Skrjabin, 1916.   ♂ 7 mm.,
♀ 11–12 mm.   In frogs.
Ref. 573.

Genus EPOMIDIOSTOMUM Skrjabin, 1916.

Definition.—AMIDOSTOMINÆ : mouth directed straight forwards,
on the dorsal and ventral surfaces of the head is a pair of posteriorly
directed nodules (epaulettes) with blunt extremities, on each side
is a pair of lateral papillæ ; buccal capsule short, limited to the
cephalic region ; three axially arranged chitinous lamellæ within
the œsophagus.   Male : bursa with two lateral lobes and a smaller

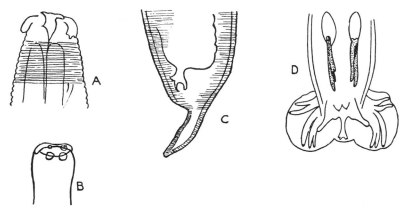

Fig. 100.—*Epomidiostomum uncinatum.* A. Head, showing lappets. B. Head,
showing papillæ. C. Posterior extremity of female, lateral view. D. Posterior extremity of male, dorsal view.   (After Skrjabin.)

dorsal lobe ; with the following formula—ventro-ventral and latero-
ventral rays parallel, externo-lateral ray close to the other lateral
rays, medio-lateral and postero-lateral fused proximally, externo-
dorsal ray short, thick, and arising at the base of the dorsal, dorsal
bifurcated at its tip, each branch bidigitate ; in addition there are
two large sessile papillæ on the posterior lip of the cloaca ; spicules
short, equal, and terminating in three branches ; gubernaculum
absent.   Female : body narrows rapidly behind the anus and ends
in a long digitiform tail bearing about its posterior third two
distinct caudal pores ; vulva behind the middle of the body.
Oviparous.   Parasites of the gizzard wall of birds.

Type species :   *E. uncinatum* (Lundhal, 1848).   ♂ 7 mm.,
♀ 11·5 mm.   In *Anas* spp.

Syn., *Strongylus uncinatus* Lundhal, 1848.

Epomidiostomum anatinum Skrjabin, 1916.

Other species :

E. orispinum (Molin, 1861). In *Anas* spp.
Syn., *Strongylus orispinus* Molin, 1861.
    Strongylus anseris Zeder, 1800, in part.
Refs. 360, 551, 572, 681.

Family SYNGAMIDÆ Leiper, 1912.

Definition.—STRONGYLOIDEA : with a well-developed chitinous buccal capsule, the oral margin of which is not supplied with teeth or other cutting organs, but is thickened to form a prominent chitinous rim. Parasites of respiratory system.

Genus SYNGAMUS Siebold, 1836.

Syn., *Cyathostoma* E. Blanchard, 1849.

Definition.—SYNGAMIDÆ : with a well-developed buccal capsule provided at its surface with a large chitinous ring, and in its depth with a variable number (usually six) of small triangular teeth ; with two lateral and four submedian head papillæ. The males are

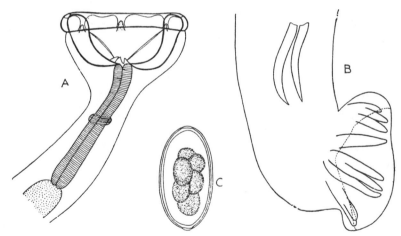

Fig. 101.—*Syngamus trachea.* A. Anterior extremity, lateral view. × 42.
B. Posterior extremity of male, lateral view. × 67. C. Egg. × 300.
(Orig.)

much smaller than the females to which they are permanently coupled. Male : bursa short ; with the following formula—ventral ray cleft, externo-lateral arising separately from the other laterals, but lying close to them, medio-lateral and postero-lateral lying close together and parallel, externo-lateral arises separately from the dorsal, dorsal bifurcated for about half its length or more, each branch usually bi- or tri-digitate ; spicules equal, lightly chitinized, usually fairly stout, and short ; gubernaculum absent. Female : posterior extremity conical ; vulva in the anterior part of the body ; uteri parallel. Oviparous, eggs of very characteristic shape slightly flattened on one side. Parasites of the respiratory tract of birds and mammals.

Type species : *S. trachea* (Montagu, 1811). ♂ 2·6 mm., ♀ 5-20 mm. In *Gallus* sp., *Pavo* sp., *Phasianus* sp., *Meleagris* sp., *Anser* sp., *Corvus* spp., etc.

   Syn., *Fasciola trachea* Montagu, 1811.
         Syngamus trachealis Sieb., 1836.
         Strongylus pictus Creplin, 1849.
         Syngamus bifurcatus Theobald, 1896.]
         Syngamus mucronatus Schlotthauber, 1860.
         Syngamus primitivus Molin, 1861.
         Syngamus sclerostomum Molin, 1861.

Other species :
   S. americanus (Chapin, 1925). In *Buteo borealis.*
   S. boularti Mégnin, 1844. In *Casuarius galeatus.*
   S. bronchialis Muehlig, 1884. In *Anser* sp.
   S. cœlebs Schlotthauber, 1860. In *Falco lagopus.*
   S. coscorobæ (Chapin, 1925). In *Coscoroba coscoroba.*
   S. dispar (Dies., 1851). In *Felis concolor.*
   S. gracilis Chapin, 1925. In *Corvus brachyrhynchos.*
   S. hippopotami Gedoelst, 1924. In *Hippopotamus* sp.
   S. kingi Leiper, 1913. In *Homo sapiens.*
   S. lari (E. Blanchard, 1849). In *Larus* sp.
      Syn., *Cyathostoma lari* Blanchard, 1849.
   S. laryngeus Railliet, 1899. In cattle.
   S. microspiculum Skrjabin, 1915. In *Phalacrocorax* sp.
   S. nasicola Linstow, 1899. In *Capra* sp., *Cervus* sp.
   S. parvus Chapin, 1925. In *Nucifraga caryocatactes.*
   S. pugionatus Schlotthauber, 1860. In *Corvus* sp., *Sturnus* sp.
   S. tadornæ (Chatin, 1874). In *Tadorna* sp.
   S. variegatus (Creplin, 1849). In *Ciconia* sp.

Chapin (1925) in a recent paper has separated the genus *Cyathostoma* Blanchard, 1849, from *Syngamus* Siebold, 1836, on the following grounds. In *Syngamus* the buccal capsule is provided with eight or nine teeth in its depth, the bursa is thick-walled, the rays short and thick, and the spicules small to very small ; in *Cyathostoma* the buccal capsule has six or seven teeth in its depth, the bursa is of the usual strongyliform type, the rays are slender and the spicules long and filiform. He includes the following species in *Cyathostoma*—*lari*, *americanum*, *boularti*, *bronchialis*, *coscorobæ*, *tadornæ*, and *variegatum*.

Refs. 55, 93a, 291, 351, 380, 403, 572.

FAMILY METASTRONGYLIDÆ LEIPER, 1908.

Definition.—STRONGYLOIDEA : body generally filiform, mouth directed straight forwards, simple, with or without a very feeble buccal capsule. Bursa copulatrix well-developed with more or less typical rays. Parasites of respiratory and circulatory systems of mammals.

Subfamily METASTRONGYLINÆ Leiper, 1908.

Definition.—METASTRONGYLIDÆ : with the characters of the family.

KEY TO GENERA.

1. Cuticle armed with a series of rings
    of minute spines along whole or
    part of the body   .   .   .   Crenosoma, p. 165.
   Cuticle not armed with spines   .   2
2. Dorsal ray of bursa thick and un-
    divided except at its extremity .   3
   Dorsal ray doubled, each limb being
    thin   5
3. Posterior extremity of male rein-
    forced by a chitinous arc .   .   Synthetocaulus, p. 162.
   Posterior extremity of male not
    reinforced by a chitinous arc   .   4
4. Externo-lateral ray fused with the
    medio-lateral   except   at   tip ;
    gubernaculum present   .   .   Troglostrongylus, p. 164.
   Externo-lateral ray separate from
    medio-lateral, gubernaculum ab-
    sent   .   .   .   .   .   Hæmostrongylus, p. 164.
5. Dorsal rays simple at extremity,
    spicules long and thin   .   .   Metastrongylus, p. 158.
   Dorsal rays bilobed or trilobed at
    extremity,   spicules   short   and
    thick   .   .   .   .   .   Dictyocaulus, p. 161.

Genus METASTRONGYLUS Molin, 1861.

Definition.—METASTRONGYLINÆ :   body   filiform ;   cuticle smooth ; mouth bounded by two lateral trilobed lips, the median lobes being the largest ; buccal cavity very small ; œsophagus slightly club-shaped posteriorly ; excretory pore just behind the nerve ring. Male : bursa with large lateral lobes and a very small dorsal lobe ; with the following formula—ventro-ventral and latero-ventral rays definitely separated from each other, externo-lateral large and arises separately from the other laterals, medio-

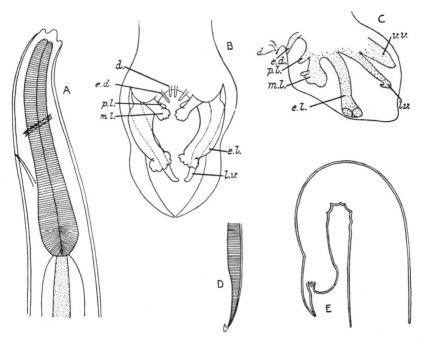

Fig. 102.—*Metastrongylus* (*Metastrongylus*) *salmi*. A. Anterior extremity, lateral view. × 90. B. Bursa, dorsal view. *d*, dorsal ray ; *e.d*, externo-dorsal ray ; *p.l*, postero-lateral ray ; *m.l*, medio-lateral ray ; *e.l*, externo-lateral ray ; *l.v*, latero-ventral ray. × 90. (Orig.). *Metastrongylus* (*Metastrongylus*) *elongatus*. C. Bursa, lateral view. *d*, dorsal ray ; *e.d*, externo-dorsal ray ; *p.l*, postero-lateral ray ; *m.l*, medio-lateral ray ; *e.l*, externo-lateral ray ; *l.v*, latero-ventral ray ; *v.v*, ventro-ventral ray. (After Stephens. D. End of spicule. × 75. E. Posterior extremity of female, lateral view. × 75. (After Gedoelst.)

lateral large, and the postero-lateral is represented by a small branch arising from it, externo-dorsal small, thin, and arising separately from the dorsal, dorsal doubled, small, and thin ; spicules long and delicate with a transversely striated wing ; gubernaculum present or absent. Female : posterior extremity straight or bent upon itself, narrows suddenly behind the anus and ends as a conical tail ; vulva near anus ; uteri parallel. Oviparous. Parasites of bronchi of pigs.

Type species : *M. elongatus* (Duj., 1845). ♂ 16–18 mm., ♀ 39–42 mm. In the pig.

Syn., *Strongylus elongatus* Duj., 1845.

Ascaris apri Gmelin, 1790, in part.

Strongylus suis Rudolphi, 1809, in part.

Strongylus paradoxus Mehlis, 1831, in part.

Strongylus longevaginatus Dies., 1851.

Other species :

M. pudendotectus Wostokow, 1905. In the pig.

Syn., *M. brevivaginatus* Railliet and Henry, 1907.

M. salmi Gedoelst, 1923. In the pig.

Gedoelst (1923) has subdivided the genus into the following subgenera :—

Subgenus METASTRONGYLUS (Molin, 1861) Gedoelst, 1923.

Definition.—The bursa is small, its axis is more or less parallel to that of the worm, and its wall is thickened in its distal half ; the latero-ventral ray is bent dorsally at its extremity and the externo-lateral is more or less lobulated at its extremity ; the spicules terminate in a single barb ; the posterior extremity of the female is bent upon itself, and is without a cuticular dilatation covering the orifices of the vulva and anus. Contains the species *elongatus* and *salmi*.

Subgenus CHŒROSTRONGYLUS Gedoelst, 1923.

Definition.—The bursa is voluminous, its axis is at right angles to that of the worm, and its wall is not thickened in its distal half ; the latero.

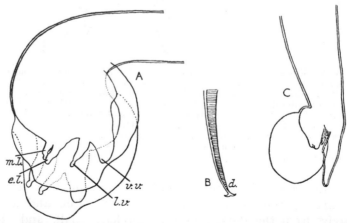

Fig. 103.—*Metastrongylus* (*Chœrostrongylus*) *pudendotectus*. A. Posterior extremity of male, lateral view. *m.l*, medio-lateral ray ; *e.l*, externo-lateral ray ; *l.v*, latero-ventral ray ; *v.v*, ventro-ventral ray ; × 75. B. End of spicule. × 75. C. Posterior extremity of female, lateral view. × 75. (After Gedoelst.)

ventral ray is straight at its extremity and the externo-lateral is not lobulated at its extremity ; the spicules terminate in a double barb ; the posterior extremity of the female is straight, and presents a cuticular dilatation covering the orifices of the vulva and anus. Contains the species *pudendotectus* (*brevivaginatus*).

Refs. 123, 131, 159, 185, 291, 351a, 360, 417, 432, 476, 582, 590, 667.

Genus DICTYOCAULUS Railliet and Henry, 1907.

Definition.—METASTRONGYLINÆ : body filiform ; mouth surrounded by four small lips, the dorsal and ventral a little larger

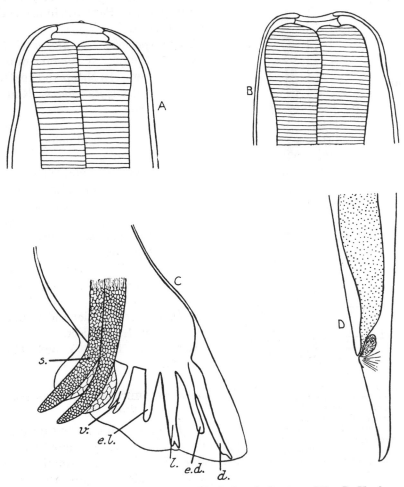

Fig. 104.—*Dictyocaulus filaria.* A. Head, dorsal view. × 256. B. Head, lateral view. × 256. C. Posterior extremity of male, lateral view. *s,* spicule ; *v,* ventral rays ; *e.l,* externo-lateral ray ; *l,* medio-lateral and postero-lateral rays fused ; *e.d,* externo-dorsal ray ; *d,* left branch of dorsal ray. × 90. D. Posterior extremity of female, lateral view. × 56. (Orig.)

than the lateral ; there is a very small buccal capsule about twice as broad as it is deep, the posterior portion of which is surrounded by a thick chitinous ring. Male : bursal formula—ventral ray-cleft, externo-lateral arises separately from the other laterals, medio-lateral and postero-lateral fused except at their tips, externo-dorsal arises separately from the dorsal, dorsal doubled and bilobed or trilobed at its extremity ; spicules equal, short, and stout ; gubernaculum present. Female : vulva near the middle of the body. Oviparous or viviparous. Parasitic in bronchi of herbivora.

Type species : D. filaria (Rudolphi, 1809). ♂ 30–80 mm., ♀ 50–100 mm. In sheep and goats.

Syn., Strongylus filaria Rud., 1809.

Other species :

D. arnfieldi (Cobbold, 1884). In Equidæ.

D. hadweni Chapin, 1925. In Bison bison, Alce americanus, Cervus canadensis.

D. viviparus (Bloch, 1782). In Bovidæ, rarely in Equidæ.

Syn., D. micrurus (Mehl., 1831). In ox, goat, deer.

D. nœrneri Railliet and Henry, 1907. In deer.

Refs. 93b, 117, 360, 398, 417, 476, 493.

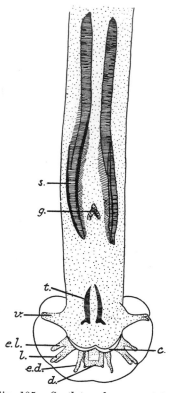

Fig. 105.—Synthetocaulus commutatus. Posterior extremity of male, ventral view. v, ventral rays ; e.l, externo-lateral ray ; l, medio-lateral and postero-lateral rays fused ; e.d, externo-dorsal ray ; d, dorsal ray ; s, spicule ; g, gubernaculum ; c, chitinous arc ; t, telamon. × 200. (After Railliet.)

Genus SYNTHETOCAULUS Railliet and Henry, 1907.

Definition.—METASTRONGY-LINÆ : body capillary, mouth with three lips, and six small head papillæ. Male : posterior extremity of body reinforced by a chitinous arc ; bursal formula—ventral ray cleft at its extremity, externo-lateral and other laterals arise from a common trunk, medio-lateral and postero-lateral fused for about half their length, externo-dorsal arising separately from the dorsal, dorsal a single thick trunk ending in a few short digitations ; spicules equal, fairly stout, and striate or pectinate ; gubernaculum present, and in addition, more posteriorly two parallel chitinous structures (telamon). Female : vulva a little in front of the anus. Oviparous, eggs unsegmented when deposited. Parasites of the respiratory system of rodents, carnivora, and ungulates.

Type species : *S. commutatus* (Dies., 1851). ♂ 18–33 mm., ♀ 28–58 mm. In *Lepus* sp.

Syn., *Strongylus commutatus* Diesing, 1851.

Filaria pulmonalis Froelich, 1802, in part.

Filaria leporis pulmonalis Froel., 1802, Rud., 1819.

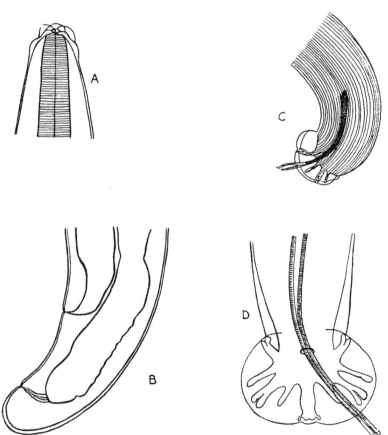

Fig. 106.—*Hæmostrongylus vasorum.* A. Anterior extremity. × 144. B. Posterior extremity of female, lateral view. × 144. (After Railliet and Henry.) C. Posterior extremity of male, lateral view. × 80. (After Railliet.) *Hæmostrongylus subcrenatus.* D. Posterior extremity of male, ventral view. × 204. (After Railliet and Henry.)

Other species :

   S. abstrusus (Railliet, 1898). In cat.

   S. capillaris (Mueller, 1889). In sheep and goats.

   S. linearis Marotel, 1913. In sheep.

   S. ocreatus Railliet and Henry, 1907. In sheep.

   S. rufescens (Leuckart, 1865). In sheep, goat, and rabbit.

   S. sagittatus (Mueller, 1890). In *Cervidæ*.

   S. unciphorus Railliet and Henry, 1907. In goat and sheep.

Refs. 139, 205, 207, 403, 417.

Genus HÆMOSTRONGYLUS Railliet and Henry, 1907.

Definition.—METASTRONGYLINÆ : body not capillary, mouth with six small lips or papillæ, buccal capsule absent. Male : bursal formula—ventral ray cleft at its extremity, externo-lateral arises separately from the other laterals, medio-lateral and postero-lateral fused for the greater part of their length, externo-dorsal arising separately from the dorsal, dorsal a single large thick trunk ending in a few short digitations ; spicules equal, long, and delicate ; gubernaculum absent. Female : vulva behind the middle of the body. Oviparous or viviparous. Parasites of circulatory or respiratory systems of carnivora.

Type species : *H. vasorum* (Baillet, 1866). ♂ 14–18 mm., ♀ 18–21 mm. In heart, pulmonary arteries, and eye of dog.

   Syn., *Strongylus vasorum* Baillet, 1866.

Other species : *H. subcrenatus* Railliet and Henry, 1913. In *Felis pardus*.

Refs. 4a, 398, 417, 438, 439.

Genus TROGLOSTRONGYLUS Vevers, 1922.

Definition.—METASTRONGYLINÆ : body filiform, mouth with two inconspicuous lips each having two minute papillæ ; cuticle with fine longitudinal striations. Male : bursal formula—externo-lateral and medio-lateral rays fused, postero-lateral separated from the medio-lateral, externo-dorsal arises separately from the dorsal, dorsal single and broad owing to the fusion of all its elements ; spicules long and equal, tesselated throughout, and carrying pectinate lamellæ along their inner edges, each ends in a palmate expansion the fingers of which are webbed, with a cuticular expansion which bears minute spines ; gubernaculum dagger-shaped. Female : vulva just behind the middle of the body. Oviparous. Parasites of carnivora.

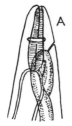

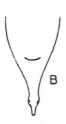

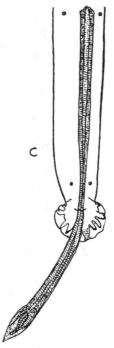

Fig. 107. — *Troglostrongylus troglostrongylus.*
A. Anterior extremity, lateral view. × 44.
B. Posterior extremity of female, ventral
view. × 44. C. Posterior extremity of
male, ventral view. × 44. (After
Vevers.)

Type species : *T. troglostrongylus* Vevers, 1922. In frontal sinus
of *Felis bengalensis.*

Ref. 656.

Genus CRENOSOMA Molin, 1861.

Definition.—METASTRONGYLINÆ : cuticle armed along the
whole, or only the anterior part, of the body with a series of rings
composed of minute spines ; mouth circular, buccal capsule very
small. Male : bursa consisting of two large lateral lobes and a
dorsal lobe ; bursal formula—ventro-ventral and latero-ventral
rays parallel, externo-lateral arises separately from the other
laterals, medio-lateral and postero-lateral lying close together and
parallel, externo-dorsal arises separately from the dorsal, the
dorsal undivided except at its tip where it ends in a number of
minute digitations ; spicules equal and fairly long ; gubernaculum
present. Female : vulva near the middle of the body ; posterior
extremity of female tapers rapidly to a blunt point ; tail furnished
with two small lateral papillæ. Viviparous. Parasites of carnivora
and insectivora.

Type species : *C. striatum* (Zeder, 1800). ♂ 5–7 mm., ♀ 12–13 mm.
In bronchi of *Erinaceus europæus.*

Syn., *Strongylus striatus* Zeder, 1800.

Fig. 108.—*Crenosoma striatum.*
A. Male. (After Molin.) B.
Bursa, expanded.   × 90.
(After Schneider.)

Other species :

    C. decoratum (Creplin, 1847).   In bronchi of *Canis vulpes.*
    Syn., *Strongylus decoratus* Creplin, 1847.
        Crenosoma semiarmatum Molin, 1861.
Refs. 115, 123, 131, 360, 403, 419, 480, 603, 681.

FAMILY PSEUDALIIDÆ RAILLIET, 1916.

Definition.—STRONGYLOIDEA : with a rudimentary bursa consisting of a cuticular prolongation supported by a few atypical rays.

Subfamily PSEUDALIINÆ Railliet and Henry, 1909.

Definition.—PSEUDALIIDÆ : with the characters of the family.

KEY TO GENERA.

1. Bursa consists of two elongated lateral
    lobes ; posterior end of female bent
    dorsally and conical.   .   .   . Pseudalius, p. 168.

Bursa not consisting of two elongated
    lateral lobes ; posterior end of female
    truncate   2

2. With a definite shallow buccal cap-
    sule   .   .   .   .   .   Stenurus, p. 168.
    Without a definite buccal capsule   .   3

3. With a prebursal sucker-like organ   .   Torynurus, p. 171.
    Without a prebursal sucker-like organ .   Halocercus, p. 171.

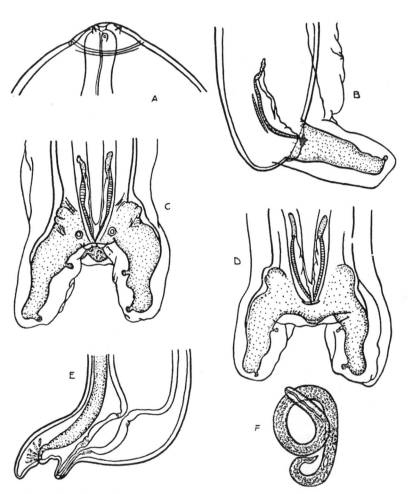

Fig. 109.—*Pseudalius inflexus.* A. Anterior extremity of female, lateral
view. × 120. B. Posterior extremity of male, lateral view. × 110.
C. Posterior extremity of male, ventral view. × 110. D. Posterior
extremity of male, dorsal view. × 110. E. Posterior extremity of
female, lateral view. × 30. F. Embryo from uterus. × 260.
(After Baylis and Daubney.)

Genus PSEUDALIUS Dujardin, 1845.

Definition.—PSEUDALIINÆ : body relatively thick anteriorly, tapering posteriorly, especially in the male ; head bluntly conical ; mouth very small and circular, without a buccal capsule ; cuticle with an annular fold slightly behind the anterior end, the head being to some extent retractile. Male : bursa reduced to two elongated lateral lobes projecting ventrally almost at right angles to the longitudinal axis of the body and each containing a lateral ray, bearing on its inner surface two papillary terminations, one near the extremity and one near the base ; these lobes are joined dorsally by a flange of cuticle in the middle of which there is a slight indication of a dorsal lobe ; spicules short, membranous, folded and not fused at the tips ; gubernaculum present. Female : posterior extremity bent dorsally in front of the vulva, which is near the anus at the extremity of a tubular outgrowth. Viviparous. Parasites of bronchi, blood-vessels, and heart of porpoises.

Type species : *P. inflexus* (Rud., 1809). ♂ 120–140 mm., ♀ 120–160 mm. In *Phocæna phocæna.*

Syn., *Strongylus inflexus* Rud., 1809, not *Stenurus inflexus* Duj., 1845.

Strongylus major Raspail, 1829.

P. filum Dujardin, 1845.

Prosthecosacter inflexus (Rud., 1809) Dies., 1851.

Pseudalius inflexus (Rud., 1809) Schneider, 1866.

Refs. 45a, 48, 98, 103, 123, 131, 253a, 253b, 253c, 360, 405, 419, 435, 480.

Genus STENURUS Dujardin, 1845.

Syn., *Phururus* Leuckart, 1848.

Prosthecosacter Diesing, 1851.

Definition.—PSEUDALIINÆ : body relatively stout anteriorly, tapering posteriorly ; with a shallow buccal capsule ; the cuticular lining of the œsophagus is thickened for some distance at the anterior end forming an œsophageal funnel. Male : bursa well-developed and more or less divided into a dorsal lobe and a pair of lateral lobes ; each of the latter contains a lateral ray with a trilobate extremity and a single papillary termination on its inner surface, and also a ventral ray with a single termination ; the dorsal ray is relatively elongated and has a pair of ventral terminations near its tip ; spicules broad, membranous, folded, and fused at their tips ; gubernaculum present. Female : posterior extremity truncate with a small terminal button situated dorsally ;

vulva with a cuticular process on its anterior lip and situated near the anus which is subterminal. Viviparous. Parasites of bronchi,

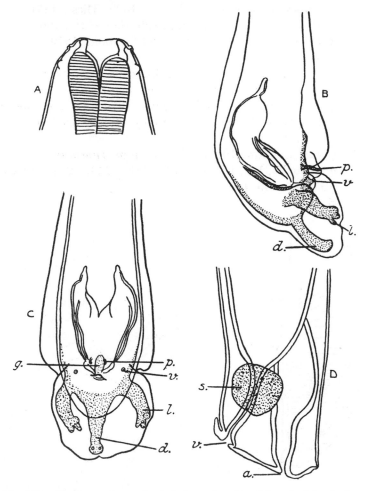

Fig. 110.—*Stenurus minor*. A. Anterior extremity of female, lateral view. × 200. B. Posterior extremity of male, lateral view. *p*, prebursal ray; *v*, ventral ray; *l*, lateral ray; *d*, dorsal ray. × 200. C. Posterior extremity of male, ventral view. *p*, prebursal ray; *v*, ventral ray; *l*, lateral ray; *d*, dorsal ray; *g*, gubernaculum. D. Posterior extremity of female, lateral view. *s*, sphincter; *v*, vulva; *a*, anus. × 200. (After Baylis and Daubney.)

tympanic cavity, and blood-vessels of whales, porpoises, and dolphins.

Type species : *S. minor* (Kuhn, 1829). ♂ 21 mm., ♀ 26 mm. In *Phocæna phocæna*.

Syn., *Strongylus minor* Kuhn, 1829.
  Stenurus inflexus Dujardin, 1845, not *Strongylus inflexus*
    Rud., 1809.
  Prosthecosacter minor (Kuhn, 1829) Dies., 1851.
  Pseudalius minor (Kuhn, 1829) Schneider, 1866.
  Pharurus minor (Kuhn, 1829) Cobbold, 1879.

Other species :
  S. alatus (Leuckart, 1848).   In *Monodon monoceros.*
  S. arcticus (Cobb, 1888).   In *Beluga leucas.*
    Syn., *Strongylus pallasii* Beneden, 1870.   [Nomen nudum.]
  S. globicephalæ Baylis and Daubney, 1925.   In *Globicephala
    melæna.*
  S. ovatus (Linstow, 1910).   In *Tursiops truncatus.*

Refs. 45a, 48, 98, 103, 123, 125, 131, 253a, 253b, 253c, 297, 360,
  405, 419, 435, 480.

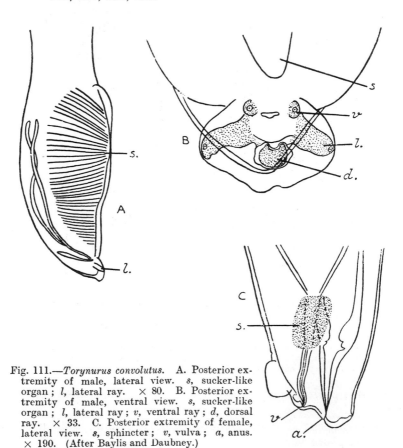

Fig. 111.—*Torynurus convolutus.* A. Posterior extremity of male, lateral view. *s*, sucker-like organ ; *l*, lateral ray. × 80. B. Posterior extremity of male, ventral view. *s*, sucker-like organ ; *l*, lateral ray ; *v*, ventral ray ; *d*, dorsal ray. × 33. C. Posterior extremity of female, lateral view. *s*, sphincter ; *v*, vulva ; *a*, anus. × 190. (After Baylis and Daubney.)

Genus TORYNURUS Baylis and Daubney, 1925.

Definition.—PSEUDALIINÆ : without a buccal capsule, but cuticle slightly thickened where it is invaginated to form the mouth. Male : posterior extremity thickened and terminating in a bursa which is ventrally placed and roughly circular in outline and not clearly divided into lobes ; bursa with a pair of large lateral rays and a short dorsal ray ; ventrally, in front of the bursa, there is an area surrounded by a free cuticular border and containing an elongated, median, muscular, sucker-like organ ; spicules slender, with membranous alæ extending for a considerable part of their length, and filiform unfused tips ; gubernaculum present. Female : posterior extremity truncate resembling that of *Stenurus* Parasites of bronchi and pulmonary blood-vessels of porpoises and whales.

Type species : *T. convolutus* (Kuhn, 1829). ♂ 38 mm., ♀ 45 mm. In *Phocæna phocæna* and *Globicephala melæna*.

Syn., *Strongylus convolutus* Kuhn, 1829.
Prosthecosacter convolutus (Kuhn, 1829) Dies., 1851.
Prosthecosacter convolutus (Kuhn, 1829) Cobbold, 1864.
Pseudalius convolutus (Kuhn, 1829) Schneider, 1866.
? *Pseudalius bicostatus* Linstow, 1906.
Refs. 45a, 98, 123, 253c, 480.

Genus HALOCERCUS Baylis and Daubney, 1925.

Definition.—PSEUDALIINÆ : mouth small with a slight cuticular invagination. Male : posterior end somewhat conical furnished in the genotype with a very much reduced ventrally-placed bursa not clearly divided into lobes ; bursal rays extremely thick and short ; spicules relatively long and slender, tubular proximally and alate distally, not fused at the tips ; gubernaculum feebly-developed. Female : posterior extremity truncate or obliquely conical ; vulva near the anus, without definite cuticular swellings. Viviparous. Parasites of bronchi of dolphins.

Type species : *H. delphini* Baylis and Daubney, 1925. ♂ 50–65 mm., ♀ 60–90 mm. In *Delphinus delphis*.

Other species :
H. gymnurus (Railliet, 1899). In *Phoca vitulina*.
Syn., *Pseudalius gymnurus*.
H. inflexocaudatus (von Siebold, 1842). In *Phocæna phocæna*.
Syn., *Filaria inflexocaudata* von Siebold, 1842.

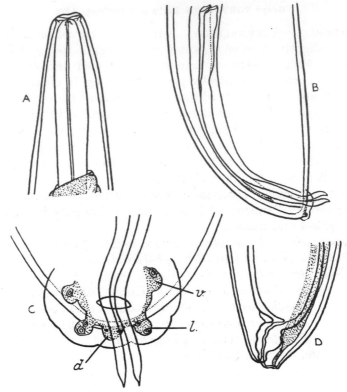

Fig. 112.—*Halocercus delphini.* A. Anterior extremity of female, lateral
 view. × 260. B. Posterior extremity of male, lateral view. × 100.
 C. Posterior extremity of male, ventral view. *v*, ventral ray ; *l*, lateral
 ray ; *d*, dorsal ray. × 260. D. Posterior extremity of female, lateral
 view. × 100. (After Baylis and Daubney.)

H. lagenorhynchi Baylis and Daubney, 1925. In *Lagenorhynchus albirostris.*

Ref. 45a.

STRONGYLOIDEA insufficiently known.

Genus DELETROCEPHALUS Diesing, 1851.

Definition.—STRONGYLOIDEA : head compressed laterally with
six head papillæ, mouth directed straight forward, elliptical with
longest diameter dorso-ventral ; buccal capsule globular, the oral
margin being provided with six radially striated membranous
expansions ; the wall of the capsule is supported by six longitudinal ribs. At the bottom of the capsule are twelve small teeth
of which two, at the base of the duct of the dorsal œsophageal
gland, are a little larger than the rest. From the anterior end of
the œsophagus there arise solid dorsal and ventral bulgings

immediately behind the mouth capsule. Male : bursal formula—
ventral ray cleft, externo-lateral arising from a common trunk
with the other laterals, externo-dorsal arising from common trunk
with the dorsal, dorsal forked at its extremity, each branch giving
off immediately three delicate sub-branches ; spicules long and

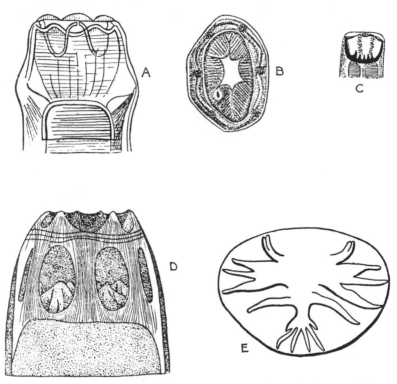

Fig. 113.—*Deletrocephalus dimidiatus*. A. Head, lateral view. × 90.
B. Head, end-on view. (After Schneider.) C. Head. (After Railliet
and Henry.) D. Head. (After Diesing.) E. Bursa. × 160. (After
Schneider.)

delicate. Female : vulva near anus and covered by a cuticular
expansion. Eggs with thin shell. Parasites of ostriches.

Type species : *D. dimidiatus* Dies., 1851. ♂ 11–18 mm.,
♀ 17–24 mm. In *Rhea americana*.

Refs. 123, 124, 360, 405, 420, 431, 435, 480.

Genus GLOBOCEPHALOIDES * n. g.

Definition. — STRONGYLOIDEA ? delicate worms, anterior
extremity bent dorsally, cuticle with prominent transverse

* This genus is possibly related to *Globocephalus*, but in the absence of the male,
it is impossible to determine its exact position.

striations especially anteriorly ; buccal capsule large and subglobular ; duct of dorsal œsophageal gland does not project into
mouth capsule ; there is a prominent triangular subventral tooth
in the depth of the capsule ; mouth opening circular, without a
corona radiata ; œsophagus slightly club-shaped posteriorly.
Male : unknown. Female : posterior extremity tapers regularly
behind the anus to end in a conical tail ; vulva situated about

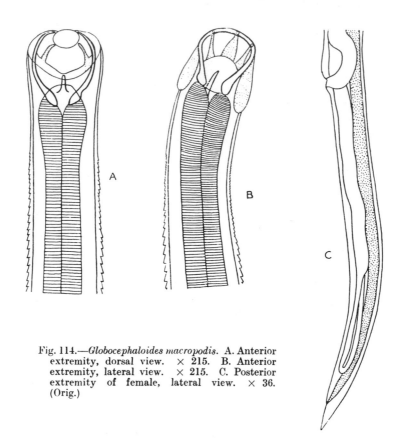

Fig. 114.—*Globocephaloides macropodis.* A. Anterior
extremity, dorsal view. × 215. B. Anterior
extremity, lateral view. × 215. C. Posterior
extremity of female, lateral view. × 36.
(Orig.)

the commencement of the posterior fourth of the worm ; vagina
short ; uteri divergent. Oviparous. Parasites of marsupials.

Type species : *G. *macropodis* n. sp. ♂ ? ♀ about 9 mm. In
Macropus sp.

---

* *Globocephaloides macropodis* n. sp. : the material available consisted of a single
female which is about 9 mm. in length, the buccal capsule is about 400 μ in depth, the
length of œsophagus is about 900 μ, the anus is about 180 μ from the tip of the tail,
and the vulva about 2·3 mm. in front of the anus.

Genus CLOACINA Linstow, 1898.

Definition.—STRONGYLOIDEA : cuticle thick and transversely striated, anterior extremity domed ; mouth directed straight forwards and bounded by six rounded lips, a dorsal, ventral, and four submedian, the last bearing long head papillæ. At the base of the lips is a strong chitinous ring [? buccal capsule] with an undulating anterior border. Mouth opening leads into a long cylindrical vestibule ; œsophagus narrow anteriorly and enlarges posteriorly. Male : bursa apparently closed ventrally ; with the

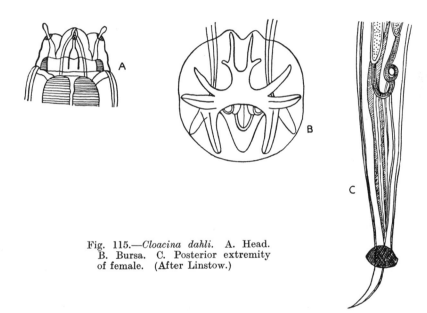

Fig. 115.—*Cloacina dahli.* A. Head. B. Bursa. C. Posterior extremity of female. (After Linstow.)

following formula *—ventral ray cleft, externo-lateral separate from the other laterals, medio-lateral and postero-lateral fused, externo-dorsal arises separately from the dorsal, dorsal divided for about half its length, the two branches being widely separated and parallel, and each giving off a short accessory branch near its point of origin ; spicules very long ; gubernaculum ? Female : posterior extremity narrowing suddenly behind the anus to end in a sharply-pointed tail ; vulva very close to anus (Linstow was of the opinion that the vagina and rectum opened into a common cloaca, but Railliet and Henry, who have studied the worm, state that this is not the case). Female genitalia doubled. Oviparous.

* Linstow appears to have figured the bursa upside down,

Type species : *C. dahli* Linstow, 1898. ♂ 9 mm., ♀ 15 mm. In *Macropus browni*.

Refs. 317, 435, 440, 636.

Genus ZONIOLAIMUS Cobb, 1898.

Definition.—Cobb, who erected this genus, gave no description of it beyond the drawings, which are here reproduced, and his formula, giving some information regarding the size and position of certain of the organs.

Fig. 116. — *Zoniolaimus setifera.* A. Head. B. Anterior extremity, lateral view. C. Head, end-on view. D. Posterior extremity of male. E. Bursa. (After Cobb.)

Type species : *Z. setifera* Cobb, 1898. ♂ 7·5 mm., ♀ ? In *Macropus* sp.

Other species : *Z. brevicaudatus* Cobb, 1898. In *Macropus* sp.

Refs. 97, 440.

Railliet and Henry (1913) state that *Zoniolaimus* is synonymous with *Cloacina*, apparently on the grounds that both came from marsupials, and that the bursal formula is the same in both instances. Examination of the drawings given by Linstow, and by Cobb, causes one to doubt the accuracy of this assumption, the more especially as we have found in *Macropus* spp. a number of worms belonging to obviously different genera and all having approximately the same bursal formula. Whether either *Cloacina* or *Zoniolaimus* is identical with one of the genera described by us from *Macropus* species, it is impossible to state, in view of the inadequacy (or inaccuracy) of the descriptions of Linstow and Cobb. Travassos (1919) erected a family *Cloacinidæ* for the genus *Cloacina* on the assumptions that the buccal capsule was absent, and that there was a cloaca in both sexes.   As both these assumptions are probably incorrect, there is no justification for this family.

Superfamily DIOCTOPHYMOIDEA Railliet, 1916.

Definition.—EUNEMATODA : medium to large worms ; œsophagus without a posterior bulb. Male : with a closed, bell-shaped, muscular bursa copulatrix, not supported by rays ; spicule single. Female : with one ovary.

Family DIOCTOPHYMIDÆ Railliet, 1915.

Syn., *Eustrongylidæ* Leiper, 1908.
Eustrongylididæ Leiper, 1912.

Definition.—DIOCTOPHYMOIDEA : medium to large worms ; mouth without lips, but surrounded by six, twelve (or eighteen), papillæ arranged in one or two circles ; cuticle coarsely striated with or without spines ; vestibule short and thin-walled ; œsophagus fairly long without a posterior bulb ; nerve ring situated very anteriorly ; excretory organs apparently absent. Male : bursa closed and bell-shaped, with muscular walls and without rays ; with a single large spicule. Female : vulva near the anus, or in the anterior part of the body ; vagina very long. Eggs with thick shell, their poles modified, and the surface covered with depressions. Parasites of mammals and birds.

KEY TO GENERA.

1. Head and anterior part of body armed
   with spines . . . . Hystrichis, p. 180.
   Head and anterior portion of body
   smooth 2
2. Head papillæ six in one circle ; vulva
   anterior . . . . . Dioctophyme, p. 177.
   Head papillæ twelve (or eighteen)
   arranged in two circles ; vulva near
   anus . . . . . . Eustrongylides, p. 178.

Genus DIOCTOPHYME Collet-Meygret, 1802.

Syn., *Eustrongylus* Diesing, 1851.

Definition.—DIOCTOPHYMIDÆ : head not particularly swollen, mouth simple without lips, but surrounded with a circle of six papillæ ; cuticle transversely striated without spines ; œsophagus long and narrow, slightly dilated posteriorly. Male : bursa copulatrix bell-shaped, muscular, and not supported by rays ; spicule single and long. Female : tail blunt ; anus terminal ; vulva in the anterior part of the body ; one ovary. Oviparous, eggs ellipsoidal, brown in colour, shell thick and covered by small depressions except at the poles which are homogeneous, they contain a segmented ovum at the time of deposition. Parasites of kidneys and peritoneal cavity, and rarely of liver, pleura, and heart, of mammals.

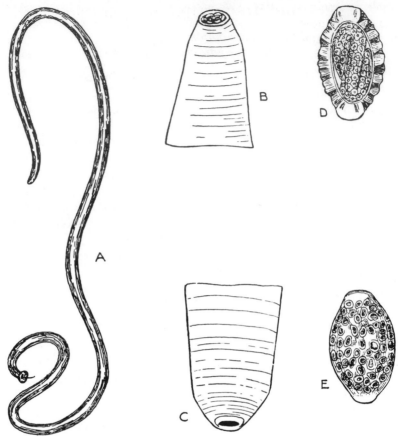

Fig. 117.—*Dioctophyme renale.* A. Male. × 1. (After Railliet.) B. Head.
C. Posterior extremity of female. (After Riley and Chandler.) D. Egg,
optical section. × 390. E. Egg, superficial view. × 390. (After
Balbiani.)

Type species : *D. renale* (Goeze, 1782). ♂ 140–400 mm.,
♀ 200–1,000 mm. In many mammals.

    Syn., *Ascaris renalis* Goeze, 1782.
           Ascaris visceralis Gmelin, 1790.
           Strongylus gigas Rudolphi, 1802.
           Eustrongylus gigas (Rud., 1802) Dies., 1851.
Refs. 8, 107, 123, 244, 319, 360, 361, 398, 466.

Genus EUSTRONGYLIDES Jaegerskiöld, 1909.

Definition.—DIOCTOPHYMIDÆ : head not particularly swollen ;
mouth simple, and with twelve (or eighteen) papillæ arranged in
two circles (always two lateral and four submedian in each circle) ;

cuticle coarsely striated, but without spines ; œsophagus very long and without any particular swelling. Male : bursa closed, the form varying in different species, but always bell-shaped and muscular, without rays ; spicule very long. Female : posterior extremity stumpy ; anus terminal ; vulva very close to anus. Parasites of glands of fore-stomach of aquatic birds.

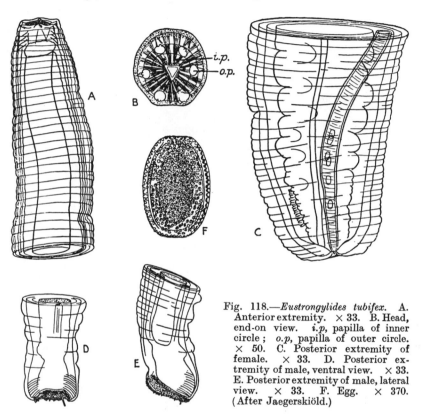

Fig. 118.—*Eustrongylides tubifex.* A. Anterior extremity. × 33. B. Head, end-on view. *i.p*, papilla of inner circle ; *o.p*, papilla of outer circle. × 50. C. Posterior extremity of female. × 33. D. Posterior extremity of male, ventral view. × 33. E. Posterior extremity of male, lateral view. × 33. F. Egg. × 370. (After Jaegerskiöld.)

Type species : *E. tubifex* (Nitzsch, 1819). ♂ 34 mm., ♀ 35–44 mm. In *Colymbus* spp., *Podiceps* sp., *Alca* sp., etc.

Syn., *Strongylus tubifex* Nitzsch of Rud., 1819, restricted.
　　　Eustrongylus tubifex Nitzsch of Diesing, 1851, restricted.
　　　Hystrichis tubifex Nitzsch of Molin, 1861, restricted.
　　　Hystrichis elegans Olfers of Railliet, 1895, in part.

Other species :

E. africanus Jaegerskiöld, 1909. In *Leptoptilus* sp., *Ardea* sp., *Pelecanus* sp., *Anhinga* sp.

E. elegans (Olfers, 1816). In *Alca* sp., *Colymbus* sp., *Harelda* sp., etc.

E. excisus Jaegerskiöld, 1909.   In *Phalacrocorax* spp.

E. ignotus Jaegerskiöld, 1909.   In *Ardea* sp., *Botaurus* sp.,
   ? *Anhinga* sp.

E. papillosus (Rud., 1802).   In *Nucifraga caryocatactes.*

E. perpapillatus Jaegerskiöld, 1909.   In *Herodias* sp., *Ardea* sp.
Refs. 244, 374, 572.

Genus HYSTRICHIS Dujardin, 1845.

Definition.—DIOCTOPHYMIDÆ : head more or less swollen, often
almost spherical, mouth simple, with six relatively small papillæ
in a circle (two lateral and four submedian); cuticle striated ;

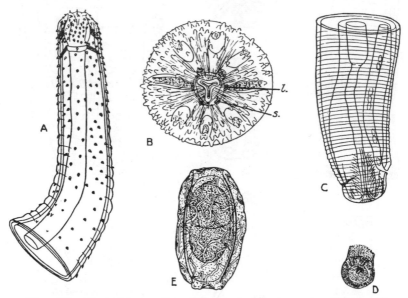

Fig. 119.—*Hystrichis acanthocephalicus.* A. Anterior extremity.   × 33.
B. Head, end-on view.   *l*, lateral papilla ;   *s*, submedian papilla.
× 100.   C. Posterior extremity of female.   × 33.   D. Posterior
extremity of male, end-on view.   × 33.   E. Egg.   × 370. (After
Jaegerskiöld.)

head, usually the anterior part of the body, and sometimes the
whole body, armed with spines ; œsophagus long without a
posterior swelling.   Male : bursa more or less bell-shaped ; spicule
very long.   Female : posterior end stumpy ; anus terminal ;
vulva very close to anus.   Parasites of the glands of the proventriculus of aquatic birds.

Type species : *H. tricolor* Duj., 1845.   ♂ ? ♀ 27 mm.   In ducks.

* Dujardin, who erected the genus *Hystrichis*, described one species *H. tricolor*
from ducks, but, as the precise host is not mentioned, as the description of the species
is rather vague, and as the types are no longer available, Jaegerskiöld erroneously
decided to cite *H. acanthocephalicus* as the type of the genus.

Syn., *Eustrongylus tubifex* Nitzsch of Dies., 1851, in part.
   Spiroptera tricolor Duj., of Dies., 1851.
   Hystrichis tubifex Nitzsch of Molin, 1861, in part.
   Hystrichis tubifex Nitzsch of Linstow, 1900, in part.
Other species :
   H. acanthocephalicus Molin, 1861.   In *Ibis* spp., *Phimosus* sp.
   H. coronatus Molin, 1861.   In *Mergus* sp.
   H. neglectus Jaegerskiöld, 1909.   In *Numenius* sp., *Querquedula* sp.
   H. orispinus Molin, 1858.   In *Ibis* sp.
   H. pachicephalus Molin, 1861.   In *Cygnus olor*.
   H. varispinosus Jaegerskiöld, 1909.   In *Mergus* sp.
   H. wedlii Linstow, 1879.   In *Fulica atra*.
Refs. 131, 244, 319, 360.

Superfamily OXYUROIDEA Railliet, 1916.

Definition.—EUNEMATODA : œsophagus with a posterior bulbar enlargement : intestine without diverticula (except in *Cruziidæ*) ; caudal extremity of females usually prolonged into a finely-pointed tail.

KEY TO FAMILIES.

1. Females with single genitalia (one ovary)   Atractidæ, p. 243.
   Females with double genitalia (two ovaries).   2
2. With intestinal diverticulum   .   .   Cruziidæ, p. 242.
   Without intestinal diverticulum .   .   3
3. Males without any special development of ventral precloacal musculature   .   Oxyuridæ, p. 182.
   Males with precloacal musculature strongly - developed usually in the form of a sucker or pseudosucker   .   4
4. Males with a definite circular precloacal sucker with a chitinous rim   .   .   Heterakidæ, p. 214.
   Males without a definite circular precloacal sucker with a chitinous rim, but with well-developed precloacal musculature usually forming an elongate sucker or pseudosucker   .   .   5
5. Mouth with lips inconspicuous or absent ; vestibule cylindrical with three triangular teeth at its base.   Parasites of warm-blooded animals   .   .   .   Subuluridæ, p. 225.

Mouth with three well-developed lips,
sometimes armed ; vestibule without
teeth at its base. Parasites of cold-
blooded animals . . . . Kathlaniidæ, p. 234.
6. *Oxyuroidea* insufficiently known, p. 253.

FAMILY OXYURIDÆ COBBOLD, 1864.

Definition.—OXYUROIDEA : medium or small worms, mouth
variable ; œsophagus terminated by a bulb, often clearly separated ;
intestine simple without a diverticulum. Male : without a preanal
sucker or any special development of precloacal muscles ; spicule
single, or two equal spicules ; gubernaculum present or absent.
Female : tail usually long and subulate ; two ovaries ; vulva
situated generally in the anterior part of the body, but sometimes
posteriorly even as far back as the region of the anus. Usually
oviparous, rarely viviparous. Eggs ellipsoidal, generally rather
large and asymmetrical.

KEY TO SUBFAMILIES.

Male with a single spicule . . 1
Males with two spicules . . . 2
1. With a gubernaculum . . . Syphaciinæ, p. 194.
   Without a gubernaculum. . . Oxyurinæ, p. 182.
2. Spicules equal, gubernaculum present Cosmocercinæ, p. 205.
   Spicules equal, gubernaculum absent. Oxysomatiinæ, p. 203.
3. *Oxyuridæ* of uncertain position, p. 211.

Subfamily OXYURINÆ Hall, 1916.

Definition.—OXYURIDÆ : male with a single spicule (rarely
imperfectly chitinised or even absent), gubernaculum absent.

KEY TO GENERA.

Mouth a dorso-ventral slit with two
   lateral lips 1
Mouth more or less circular . . 2
1. Œsophagus divided into two parts . Ozolaimus, p. 191.
   Œsophagus not divided into two parts Macracis, p. 191.
2. Vestibule with a chitinous armature . 3
   Vestibule unarmed or absent . . 5

3. Vestibule with a complicated armature of chitinous bristles (and teeth
   in females) .   .   .   .   .   Oxyuris, p. 183.
   Vestibule armed with three teeth   .   4
4. Posterior extremity of male short and
   blunt, and with a row of transverse
   comb-like crests on ventral surface.
   Tail of old females without circular
   cuticular thickenings   .   .   .   Dermatoxys, p. 189.
   Posterior extremity of male long and
   pointed, comb-like crests absent.
   Tail of old females with circular
   cuticular thickenings   .   .   .   Passalurus, p. 185.
5. With prominent cephalic lateral cuti-
   cular expansions   6
   Without prominent cephalic lateral
   cuticular expansions   .   .   .   7
6. Tail of male truncate, spicule present   Enterobius, p. 186.
   Tail of male conical, spicule absent   Aspiculuris, p. 188.
7. With a circumoral membrane sup-
   ported by prominent papillæ, œso-
   phageal cavity unusually broad   .   Protozoophaga, p. 190.
   With three or six small lips, œsopha-
   geal cavity not unusually broad   .   8
8. Posterior extremity blunt with a long
   process arising from the mid-line
   dorsally; spicule short and acicular;
   vulva posterior to middle   .   .   Thelandros, p. 192.
   Posterior extremity of male prolonged
   as a subulate process, without a
   process arising from the mid-line
   dorsally ; spicule short and lightly
   chitinized ; vulva anterior to middle   Pharyngodon, p. 193.

Genus OXYURIS Rud., 1803.

Syn., *Lepturis* Schlotthauber, 1860.

Definition.—OXYURINÆ : mouth hexagonal ; cuticle without
cephalic vesicular expansions or lateral flanges ; vestibule short
with a complicated armature of chitinous bristles, and also of
teeth in the female ; œsophagus muscular, swollen in front, con-
tracted in the middle, then gradually enlarging again posteriorly
into a non-separated bulb containing a valvular apparatus. Male :

posterior extremity obliquely truncated immediately behind the
anus ; caudal alæ supported by a pair of preanal and a pair of
postanal costiform papillæ ; spicule needle-shaped ; gubernaculum

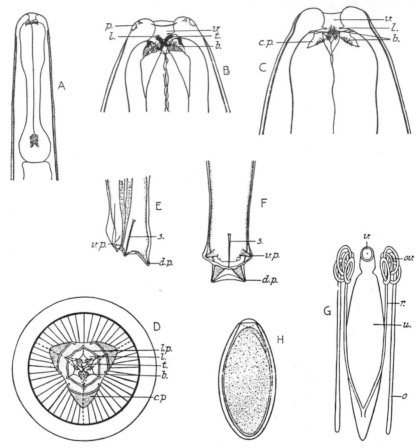

Fig. 120.—*Oxyuris equi.* A. Anterior extremity of female, dorsal view.
× 21. B. Head of female, dorsal view. *p*, head papillæ ; *v*, vestibule ;
l, ledge ; *t*, œsophageal tooth ; *b*, œsophageal bristles. × 40. C. Head
of male, dorsal view. *v*, vestibule ; *l*, ledge ; *b*, œsophageal bristles ;
c.p, chitinized pouch. × 64. D. Head of female, end-on view. *l.p*,
lip ; *l*, ledge ; *t*, œsophageal tooth ; *b*, œsophageal bristles ; *c.p*,
chitinized pouch. × 64. E. Posterior extremity of male, lateral
view. × 42. F. Posterior extremity of male, ventral view. *s*, spicule ;
v.p, subventral papilla ; *d.p*, dorsal papilla. × 40. G. Female
genitalia, diagram. *v*, vulva ; *o*, ovary ; *u*, uterus ; *r*, receptaculum
seminis ; *ov*, oviduct. H. Egg. × 280. (Orig.)

absent. Female : body narrows more or less suddenly behind the
anus and tapers regularly to the extremity or ends in a long whip-
like prolongation, the length of which varies according to the age

of the worm ; vulva in the anterior part of the body ; vagina
directed posteriorly, continuing as a single uterus which reaches
to the anterior part of the tail, where it receives the short canal
formed by the union of the two oviducts. Oviparous, eggs large,
asymmetrical, truncate at one pole, which is closed by a lenticular
operculum, and containing a tadpole-shaped larva at deposition.
Parasites of equines (and ? rodents).

Type species : *O. equi* (Schrank, 1788). ♂ 9–12 mm.,
♀ 40–150 mm. In equines.

Syn., *Trichocephalus equi* Schrank, 1788.
Oxyuris curvula Rudolphi, 1803.
Oxyuris mastigodes Nitzsch, 1857.
Lepturis curvula (Rud., 1803) Schlotthauber, 1860.

Other species :

O. poculum Linstow, 1904. In horses.

O. tenuicauda Linstow, 1901. In zebra.

? *O. triradiata* Hall, 1916. In *Ammospermophilus* sp. and
Callospermophilus sp.

Refs. 205, 320, 325, 407, 444, 476, 479, 481, 679.

Genus PASSALURUS Duj., 1845.

Definition.—OXYURINÆ : mouth simple, with four head papillæ,
cuticle without cephalic expansions, narrow lateral flanges present ;
vestibule short, with three teeth at its base surrounding the opening
of the œsophagus ; œsophagus club-shaped, with a posterior bulb
armed with a valvular apparatus and separated from the rest by
a constriction ; excretory pore behind the bulb. Male : tail very
long, the body first tapers gradually behind the anus, then
suddenly narrows and ends in a long fine process : narrow caudal
alæ limited to the broader portion of the tail, three pairs of large
contiguous sessile pericloacal papillæ, a pair of small sessile
papillæ immediately behind the anus and two pedunculated
papillæ at the base of the caudal point sustaining the alæ ; spicule
relatively short ; gubernaculum absent. Female : tail very
elongate, ending in a long thin process and moniliform in the
sub-terminal part in old females ; vulva not salient, in the
anterior fifth of the body ; uteri parallel. Oviparous. Parasites
of rodents.

Type species : *P. ambiguus* (Rudolphi, 1819). ♂ 5 mm.,
♀ 10–11 mm. In *Lepus* spp.

Syn., *Oxyuris ambigua* Rud., 1819.

Refs. 131, 205, 318, 444, 477, 525.

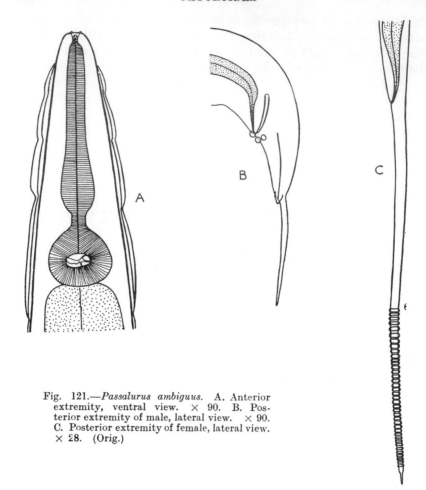

Fig. 121.—*Passalurus ambiguus.* A. Anterior
extremity, ventral view. × 90. B. Posterior extremity of male, lateral view.   × 90.
C. Posterior extremity of female, lateral view.
× 28. (Orig.)

Genus ENTEROBIUS Leach, 1853.

Syn., *Oxyurias* Stiles, 1905.
    Fusarella Seurat, 1916.
    Lumbriculus Aldrovande.—Blanchard, 1889.

Definition.—OXYURINÆ : mouth with three lips ; cuticle with
two vesicular cephalic expansions, very narrow lateral flanges
present arising shortly behind the nerve ring and extending
almost to the anus in the female ; vestibule absent ; œsophagus
club-shaped, follwed by a bulb containing a valvular apparatus
and separated from the rest by a constriction ; excretory pore
opens behind the œsophageal bulb. Male : tail sharply truncate
a little behind the cloaca ; caudal alæ supported in front by a

pair of pedunculated preanal papillæ and posteriorly by two large papillæ inserted at the extremity of the tail, two pairs of postanal sessile papillæ ; spicule relatively long ; gubernaculum absent. Female : tail conical and relatively short ; vulva not salient, in the anterior third of the body ; ovejector very short, forming with

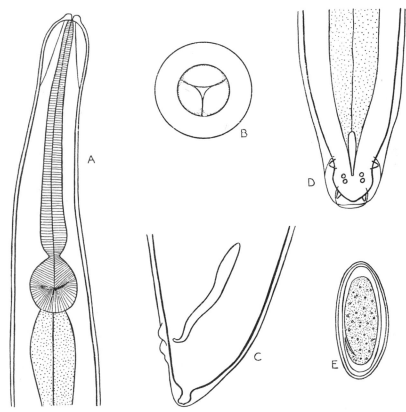

Fig. 122.—*Enterobius vermicularis*. A. Anterior extremity, ventral view. × 75. B. Head, end-on view. × 215. C. Posterior extremity of male, lateral view. × 450. D. Posterior extremity of male, ventral view. × 215. E. Egg. × 430. (Orig.)

the first part of the vagina a pyriform reservoir ; vagina very short ; uteri parallel. Oviparous. Parasites of man and monkeys.

Type species : *E. vermicularis* (Linn., 1758). ♂ 3·5 mm.. ♀ 10 mm. In man.

Syn., *Ascaris vermicularis* Linn., 1758.

Oxyuris vermicularis (Linn., 1758) Bremser, 1819.

Oxyurias vermicularis (Linn., 1758) Stiles, 1905.

Fusarella vermicularis (Linn., 1758) Seurat, 1916.

Other species :

E. *anthropopetheci* (Gedoelst, 1916). In chimpanzee.

E. *bipapillatus* (Gedoelst, 1916). In monkey.

E. *minutus* (Schneider, 1866). In *Cebus* sp.

Refs. 5, 55a, 151, 444, 525, 599, 646, 679.

Genus ASPICULURIS Schulz, 1924.

Definition.—OXYURINÆ : mouth with three lips ; cuticle transversely striated with broad cervical alæ terminating abruptly

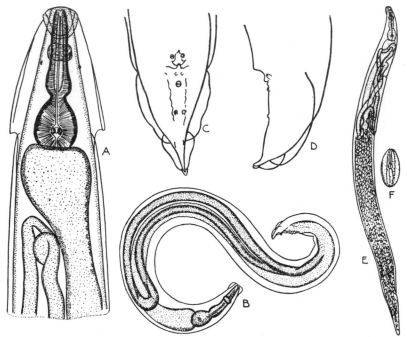

Fig. 123.—*Aspiculuris tetraptera.* A. Anterior extremity, ventral view. B. Male. C. Tail of male, ventral view. D. Tail of male, lateral view. E. Female, lateral view. F. Egg. (After Schulz.)

behind at the level of the œsophageal bulb, from which level narrow lateral flanges run to the posterior end of the worm ; œsophagus somewhat club-shaped and terminating posteriorly in a well-developed bulb containing a valvular apparatus and separated from the rest of the œsophagus by a constriction. Male : tail conical, with caudal alæ divided transversely into three portions of which the anterior is the largest ; with one pair of preanal papillæ and several pairs of postanal papillæ ; spicule and gubernaculum apparently absent. Female : tail conical ;

vulva in front of the middle of the body.   Oviparous.   Parasites
of rodents.

Type species :   *A. tetraptera* (Nitzsch, 1821).   ♂ 2–2·6 mm.,
♀ 2·6–4·75 mm.   In *Mus musculus, Cricetus* spp., etc.

Syn., *Ascaris tetraptera* Nitzsch, 1821.

Refs. 215, 311, 374, 478a, 481a.

Genus DERMATOXYS Schneider, 1866.

Definition.—OXYURINÆ :   mouth with three lips, each bearing
two papillæ ;   cuticle with cervical alæ extending from the head to

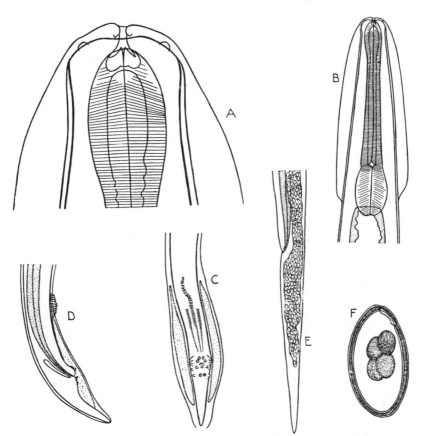

Fig. 124.—*Dermatoxys veligera.* A. Head, ventral view.   × 160.   B. Anterior
extremity, ventral view.   × 35.   C. Posterior extremity of male, ventral
view.   × 35.   D. Posterior extremity of male, lateral view.   × 35.
E. Posterior extremity of female, lateral view.   × 35.   F. Egg.   × 250.
(Orig.)

about the end cf the œsophagus ;   vestibule short, provided with
three teeth ; œsophagus dilated into a bulb-like swelling posteriorly,

with or without a valvular apparatus, the bulb may or may not be separated from the rest by a constriction. Male : tail short and ends in a blunt point, with a curving longitudinal row of transverse comb-like crests on the ventral surface in front of the cloaca ; caudal alæ very long and well-developed, with a number of large papillæ close to the anus and about two pairs of postanal papillæ ; spicule very short ; gubernaculum absent. Female : tail long and gradually tapering ; vulva in front of the middle of the body ; ovaries massive, deeply coloured, in the anterior part of the body, and communicating by narrow oviducts with the long receptacula which unite in the vicinity of the anus to form the single uterus which extends anteriorly to the vagina. Oviparous, eggs asymmetrical with thick shells and a plug at one pole. Parasites of rodents.

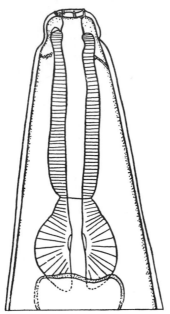

Type species : *D. veligera* (Rudolphi, 1819). ♂ 8 mm., ♀ 16 mm. In *Lepus* spp., *Sylvilagus* spp.

Syn., *Ascaris veligera* Rudolphi, 1819.

Other species :

D. getula Seurat, 1915. In *Xerus getulus*.

? *D. polyoon* (Linstow, 1909). In *Xerus setosus*.

Refs. 205, 444, 477, 480, 515, 518.

Fig. 125. — *Protozoophaga obesa.*
Anterior extremity of female.
× 40. (After Travassos.)

Genus PROTOZOOPHAGA Travassos, 1923.

Definition. — OXYURINÆ : exhibiting great sexual dimorphism, mouth large with four prominent papillæ in the male and six in the female supporting a circumoral membrane without definite lips ; œsophagus cylindrical with a large cavity, and followed by a bulb containing a valvular apparatus and separated from the rest by a constriction. Male : tail conical and alate with a terminal conical process, two pairs of large lateral papillæ, one adanal and the other postanal ; spicule single, slightly chitinized ; gubernaculum absent. Female : tail conical in young specimens and long and subulate in gravid worms ; vulva anterior, ovejector large. Oviparous. Parasites of rodents.

Type species : *P. obesa* (Diesing, 1851). ♂ 15 mm., ♀ 40 mm.
In *Hydrochœrus capibara.*
Syn., *Oxyuris obesa* Diesing, 1851.
Refs. 123, 205, 480, 646.

Genus OZOLAIMUS Duj., 1845.

Definition.—OXYURINÆ : mouth dorso-ventral with two lateral lips ; œsophagus very long and composed of two sections in tandem of which the first is shorter and thicker and dilates into a fusiform swelling before entering the second, which is thin and almost filiform and is followed by a bulb ; the intestine is dilated at its origin. Male : posterior extremity obliquely truncate, with a short blunt tail ; spicule long and straight.   Female : tail straight and gradually attenuating ; anus near the extremity ; vulva salient and situated in the posterior fourth of the body.   Parasites of reptiles.

Type species : *O. megatyphlon* (Rud., 1819).
♂ 5 mm., ♀ 7–8 mm.   In *Iguana tuberculata.*
Syn., *Ascaris megatyphlon* Rud., 1819.
Other species : *O. cirratus* (Linstow, 1906).
In *Iguana tuberculata.*
Refs. 131, 436, 444, 477, 480.

Fig.   126. — *Ozolaimus megatyphlon.* Posterior extremity of male, lateral view. × 90. (After Schneider.)

Genus MACRACIS Gedoelst, 1916.

Definition.—OXYURINÆ : closely resembling *Ozolaimus*, mouth dorso-ventral, two lateral lips ; œsophagus very long (nearly half the length of the worm) and narrow, not divided into anterior and posterior portions, but ending in a well-marked bulb.   Male : posterior extremity obliquely truncate, with a short blunt tail ; spicule long and straight.   Female : tail short and blunt ; vulva in the posterior third of the body.   Parasites of reptiles.

Type species : *Macracis monhystera* (Linstow, 1902). ♂ 7·1 mm., ♀ 7·6 mm.   In *Iguana cornuta.*
Syn., *Oxyuris monhystera* Linstow, 1902.

Gedoelst erected this genus for *Oxy. monhystera* on the assumption that Linstow's statement, that the female genitalia were single,

is correct, but it was later shown (Rauther, 1918) that contrary
to the statement of Linstow the female genitalia are double.   The

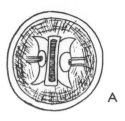

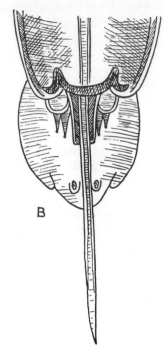

Fig. 127. — *Macracis monhystera.*
A. Head, end-on view. B. Posterior extremity of male, ventral
view. (After Linstow.)

chief difference between *Macracis* and *Ozolaimus* appears to lie in
the structure of the œsophagus.

Refs. 151, 155, 323, 464.

Genus THELANDROS Wedl, 1862.

Definition.—OXYURINÆ : mouth bounded by six (three bilobed)
lips, buccal margin carrying six sessile papillæ corresponding to
the lips ; lateral flanges sometimes present ; vestibule short ;
œsophagus with a posterior bulb. Male : posterior extremity
truncate ; caudal alæ absent ; one pair of large pedunculated
preanal papillæ and two pairs of postanal papillæ of which the
more posterior pair is situated on a process arising from the mid-
line dorsally in front of the anus and prolonged posteriorly as a
kind of short conical tail ; spicule short, acicular ; gubernaculum
absent. Female : vulva behind the middle of the body with
slightly projecting lips. Oviparous. Parasites of reptiles.

Type species : *T. alatus* Wedl, 1862. ♂ 2·5–4 mm., ♀ 5–9 mm.
In *Uromastix* spp.

Syn., *Oxyuris uromasticola* Galeb, 1889.

Other species :

T. bulbosus (Linstow, 1899).   In *Chalcides* sp., *Scincus* sp.

T. cinctus (Linstow, 1897).   In *Agama stellio*.

T. echinatus (Rud., 1819).   In Gecko, etc.

T. micipsæ Seurat, 1917.   In *Chalcides micipsæ*.

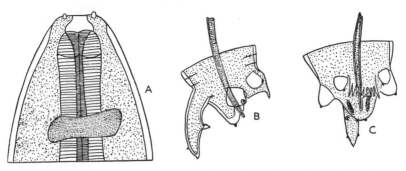

Fig. 128.—*Thelandros alatus*. A. Head. B. Posterior extremity of male, lateral view. C. Posterior extremity of male, ventral view. (After Seurat.)

T. numidicus Seurat, 1918.   In tortoises.

T. scleratus Travassos, 1923.   In *Tropidurus* spp.

Refs. 34, 149, 486, 524, 541, 552, 647, 664.

Genus PHARYNGODON Diesing, 1861.

Definition.—OXYURINÆ : mouth with three small lips ; cuticle with or without lateral flanges ; vestibule absent ; œsophagus with a posterior globular bulb containing a valvular apparatus and separated from the rest by a slight constriction ; excretory pore behind the œsophageal bulb. Posterior extremity of the body in both sexes obliquely truncate ventrally at the level of the cloaca, rounded and prolonged as a long subulate tail, provided with spines or smooth. Male : with caudal alæ which may be continuous with the lateral flanges ; one pair of preanal and two of pedunculated postanal papillæ, the cloaca is at the end of the body just before commencement of subulate tail ; spicule imperfectly chitinized or even absent. Female : anus near the end of the body shortly before the commencement of the subulate tail ; vulva near the middle of the body or anterior to this. Oviparous, eggs very elongate and oval. Parasites of reptiles, and ? amphibia.

Type species : *P. spinicauda* (Duj., 1845). ♂ 3 mm., ♀ 3–5 mm. In *Lacerta muralis, Tejus* sp., *Triton* sp.

Syn., *Oxyuris spinicauda* Duj., 1845.

Ascaris acanthura Diesing, 1851.

Pharyngodon acanthurus Diesing, 1861, in part.

Other species :
>   P. *auziensis* Seurat, 1917.   In *Scincus* sp., *Cerastes* sp.
>   P. *extenuatus* (Rud., 1819).   In *Lacerta* sp.
>   Syn., P. *acanthurus* Dies., 1861, in part.
>   P. *hindlei* Thapar, 1925.   In *Tiligua senicordis*.
>   P. *inermicauda* Baylis, 1923.   In *Tarentola annularis*.

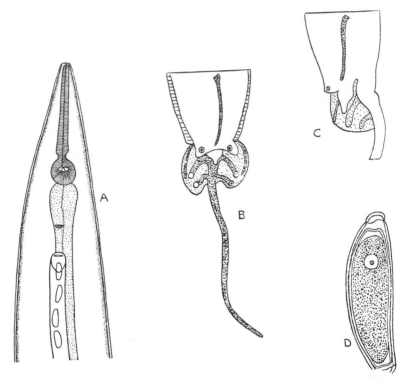

Fig. 129.—*Pharyngodon spinicauda*. A. Anterior extremity of female.   × 56. (Orig.)   B. Posterior extremity of male, ventral view.   × 276.   C. Posterior extremity of male, lateral view.   × 276.   D. Egg.   × 276.   (After Seurat.)

>   P. *lævicauda* (Seurat, 1914).   In *Scincus* sp., etc.
>   P. *megalocerca* (Skrjabin, 1916).   In *Geckonidæ*.
>   P. *mamillatus* (Linstow, 1897).   In *Plestiodon* sp., etc.
>   P. *tectipenis* Gedoelst, 1919.   In a grey lizard.
Refs. 34, 123, 125, 131, 153, 444, 508, 541, 573, 613c.

Subfamily SYPHACIINÆ Railliet, 1916.

Definition.—OXYURIDÆ : males with a single spicule, and a gubernaculum.

KEY TO GENERA.

Vulva posterior to middle of body . 1
Vulva anterior to middle of body . 4
1. Posterior extremity of male short and
    truncate . . . . . Tachygonetria, p. 198.
    Posterior extremity of male prolonged
    dorsally into a conical process . 2
2. Male with broad caudal alæ . . Alæuris, p. 203.
    Male with caudal alæ very narrow or
    absent 3
3. With teeth and spherical knobs at an-
    terior end of œsophagus ; with only
    one uterus . . . . . Veversia, p. 201.
    Without teeth and knobs at anterior
    end of œsophagus ; with two uteri . Mehdiella, p. 200.
4. Posterior extremity of male rounded
    with a short sharp spike . . Trypanoxyuris, p. 198.
    Posterior extremity of male prolonged
    as a subulate process . . . 5
5. Male with cuticular " mamelons " . Syphacia, p. 195.
    Male without cuticular "mamelons". Wellcomia, p. 196.

Genus SYPHACIA Seurat, 1916.

Definition.—SYPHACIINÆ : mouth bounded by three lips ; small cervical alæ present ; vestibule absent ; œsophagus club-shaped with a posterior bulb containing a valvular apparatus and separated from the rest by a constriction. Male : with two or three cuticular "mamelons" on the ventral surface ; posterior extremity bent ventrally, body cut away ventrally behind the cloaca and then suddenly narrows and ends in a long pointed tail ; narrow caudal alæ present limited to the first part of the tail ; two pairs of preanal papillæ and one pair of postanal pedunculated papillæ supporting the alæ behind ; spicule relatively long and very obvious ; gubernaculum directed transversely. Female : tail long and pointed ; vulva in the anterior region of the body, behind the excretory pore, and communicating by a short vagina, fre-quently protruded, with a cuticle-lined ovejector remarkable for the thickness of its muscle coat ; uterus single, very long ; receptacula seminis parallel and narrow ; two ovaries. Oviparous. Parasites of rodents and man.

Type species : *S. obvelata* (Rud., 1802). ♂ 1·3 mm., ♀ 3·5–5·7 mm. In mice, rats, and man.

Syn., *Ascaris obvelata* Rud., 1802.
   Oxyuris stroma Linstow, 1884.
Other species :
   S. bonnei Thiel, 1925.   In *Mycetes seniculus*.

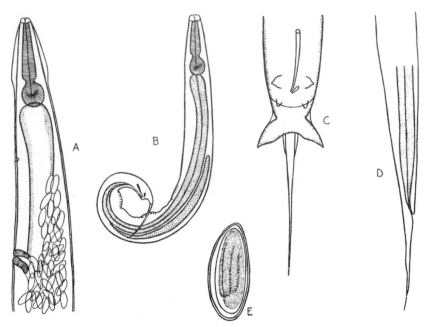

Fig. 130.—*Syphacia obvelata*. A. Anterior extremity of female, lateral view.
× 330. B. Male, lateral view. × 75. C. Posterior extremity of male,
ventral view. × 330. D. Posterior extremity of female, lateral view.
× 215. E. Egg. × 150. (Orig.)

   S. pallaryi (Seurat, 1915).   In *Xerus getulus*.
   S. stossichi (Setti, 1897).   In *Hystrix cristata*.
Refs. 205, 444, 465, 481a, 482, 515, 525, 616a, 646.

Genus WELLCOMIA Sambon, 1907.

Definition.—SYPHACIINÆ : mouth with three broad lips ;
cervical alæ may or may not be present ; œsophagus club-shaped
followed by a spherical bulb with a valvular apparatus. Male :
without cuticular "mamelons" on the ventral surface ; posterior
extremity tightly coiled spirally, tail narrows suddenly a little
behind the cloaca and ends in a long pointed process ; just before
the narrowing there is a pair of highly-developed postanal papillæ
supporting membranous expansions stretching from them to the

adanal papillæ ; spicule single, feebly chitinized ; gubernaculum flask-shaped. Female : tail long and tapering gradually to a point, and sometimes with cuticular markings ; vulva in front of the

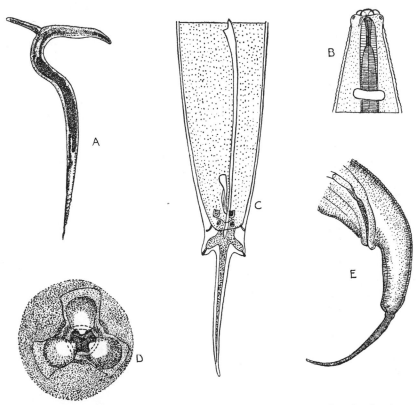

Fig. 131.—*Wellcomia mitchelli*. A. Female, lateral view. (After Sambon.) *W. hilgerti*. B. Anterior extremity, ventral view. × 175. C. Posterior extremity of male, ventral view. × 175. (After Seurat.) *W. evoluta*. D. Head, end-on view. × 225. E. Posterior extremity of female. (After Hall.)

middle of the body, and through it the vagina is extruded. Oviparous. Parasites of rodents.

Type species : *W. mitchelli* Sambon, 1907. ♂ 12 mm., ♀ 15 mm. In Cape jumping hare.

Other species :

W. decorata Travassos, 1923.   In *Cœndu brandti*.

W. evoluta (Linstow, 1899).   In *Acanthion brachyura*, etc.

W. hilgerti (Seurat, 1914).   In *Ctenodactylus gundi*.

W. samboni Baylis, 1922.   In the hairy porcupine.

Refs. 31, 205, 318, 444, 478, 519, 524, 646.

Genus TRYPANOXYURIS Vevers, 1923.

Definition.—Syphaciinæ : mouth with two inconspicuous lips ; small cervical alæ present ; vestibule absent ; œsophagus with a very distinct bulb. Male : posterior end terminates abruptly in a rounded extremity in the centre of which is a short sharp spike ; there are five pairs of papillæ—two preanal and three postanal, the larger pair of preanals carry out a cuticular expansion which surrounds the tail ; spicule relatively short and straight ; gubernaculum annular. Female : tail tapers gradually and ends in a

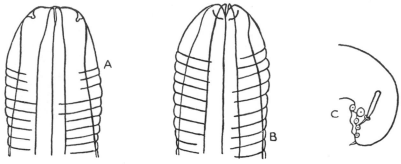

Fig. 132.—*Trypanoxyuris trypanuris.* A. Head, dorsal view. × 160. B. Head, lateral view. × 160. C. Posterior extremity of male, lateral view. × 160. (After Vevers.)

blunt point ; vulva near the junction of the anterior and middle thirds of the body. Oviparous. Parasites of monkeys.

Type species : *T. trypanuris* Vevers, 1923. ♂ 2 mm., ♀ 6·7 mm. In *Pithecia monachus,* " Hura monkey."

Ref. 657.

Genus TACHYGONETRIA Wedl, 1862.

Syn., *Paracis* Railliet and Henry, 1916.

Definition.—Syphaciinæ : mouth surrounded by six small lips ; cuticle finely striated transversely and sometimes provided with delicate hairs ; lateral flanges absent ; vestibule short ; œsophagus usually very long and followed by a bulb with a valvular apparatus. Male : posterior extremity sharply cut away ventrally at the level of the cloaca, and terminates as a short truncated tail having a trapezoidal form, bearing a pair of lateral papillæ at the two angles of the truncated extremity ; in addition there are three pairs of papillæ grouped around the cloaca—one pair of preanal, one of voluminous latero-ventral postanal and one of small adanal papillæ ; spicule short and of variable form : gubernaculum in the form of an open **V**. Female : tail conical and relatively short ; vulva behind the middle of the body ; uteri parallel. Usually oviparous, the eggs being few in number and segmented at deposition ; rarely viviparous. Parasites of cæcum of herbivorous reptiles.

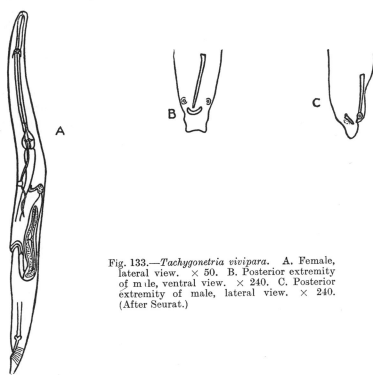

Fig. 133.—*Tachygonetria vivipara*. A. Female, lateral view. × 50. B. Posterior extremity of m le, ventral view. × 240. C. Posterior extremity of male, lateral view. × 240. (After Seurat.)

Type species : *T. vivipara* Wedl, 1862. ♂ 1·5 mm., ♀ 2–2·5 mm. In *Uromastix* spp.

Other species :

T. conica (Drasche, 1884). In *Testudo græca*, etc.

T. dentata (Drasche, 1884). In *Testudo græca*, etc.

T. jugurthæ Seurat, 1918. In tortoises.

T. lambdiensis Seurat, 1918. In tortoises.

T. longicollis (Schneider, 1866). In *Testudo græca*, etc.
      Syn., *Paracis longicollis* (Schneider, 1866) Railliet and
            Henry, 1916.

T. macrolaimus (Linstow, 1899). In *Testudo pardalis*.

T. massinissæ Seurat, 1918. In tortoises.

T. microlaimus (Linstow, 1899). In *Testudo pardalis*.

T. nicollei Seurat, 1918. In tortoises.

T. numidica Seurat, 1918.   In tortoises.

T. paronai (Linstow, 1893).   In *Macroscincus coctæi*.

T. pusilla Seurat, 1918.   In tortoises.

   Syn., *Oxyuris longicollis* Drasche, 1883, not Schneider, 1866.

T. setosa Seurat, 1918.   In tortoises.

T. stylosa Thapar, 1925.   In *Testudo ibera*.

T. weissi Seurat, 1918.   In tortoises.

Refs. 34, 444, 480, 486, 524, 552, 613c, 664.

Genus MEHDIELLA Seurat, 1918.

Definition.—SYPHACIINÆ : mouth surrounded by three lips which may be bilobed; cuticle thick, transversely striated, with or without bristles ; vestibule short, œsophagus cylindrical

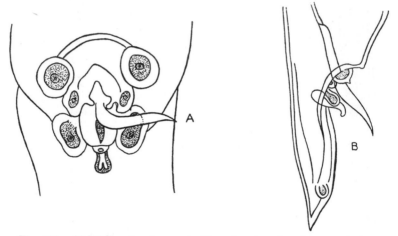

Fig. 134.—*Mehdiella microstoma.*   A. Cloacal region of male, ventral view. × 528.   B. Posterior extremity of male, lateral view.   × 220.   (After Drasche.)

followed by a bulb.   Male : body sharply cut away ventrally at the level of the cloaca, terminating dorsally as a long conical tail bearing a pair of voluminous papillæ towards its posterior third ; in addition there are three pairs of pericloacal papillæ—one pair of preanal, and one pair of latero-ventral voluminous papillæ, and one pair of small adanal papillæ ; caudal alæ narrow ; spicule short and acicular ; gubernaculum in the form of an open V. Female : tail conical and relatively short ; vulva a little distance behind the middle of the body ; with two uteri.   Oviparous, eggs large, numerous, ellipsoidal and segmented at deposition. Parasites of herbivorous reptiles.

Type species : *M. microstoma* (Drasche, 1884). ♂ 5·4 mm.
♀ 7·6 mm. In *Testudo græca*, etc.

Syn., *Oxyuris microstoma* Drasche, 1884.
Oxyuris robusta Drasche, 1884.
Oxyuris draschei Stossich, 1898.

Other species :

M. uncinata (Drasche, 1884). In *Testudo græca*.

Syn., *Oxyuris uncinata* Drasche, 1884.
Oxyuris inflata Drasche, 1884, not Linstow, 1883.
Oxyuris albanica Stossich, 1898.

Refs. 34, 129, 552.

Genus VEVERSIA Thapar, 1925.

Definition.—SYPHACIINÆ : mouth surrounded by three conical
lips ; buccal cavity small and armed in its depth with small teeth,

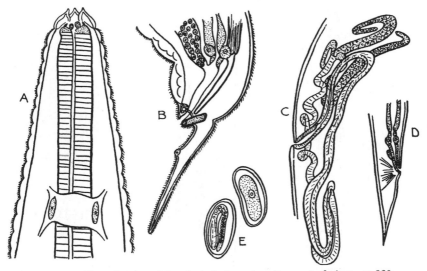

Fig. 135.—*Veversia tuberculata*. A. Anterior extremity, ventral view. × 320.
B. Posterior extremity of male, lateral view. × 215. C. Femal‧
genitalia. × 46. D. Tail of female, lateral view. × 46. E. Eggs.
× 135. (After Thapar.)

and granular knob-like outgrowths arising from the anterior end
of the œsophagus ; cuticle thick, transversely striated and
furnished in both sexes with thick hairs ; lateral areas well-
developed, and each bears a pair of thick flanges running parallel
to each other along the entire length of the body ; œsophagus
elongated, with a posterior bulb, provided with a denticular

apparatus, and separated by a constriction from the rest of the œsophagus ; excretory pore behind the œsophageal bulb. Male : body cut away ventrally behind the cloaca and ends in a long narrow tail ; in front of the tail the cuticle is inflated to form lateral alæ, but caudal alæ are absent ; with one pair of preanal papillæ and two of postanal, one of which is on the tail ; spicule relatively long, stout, and slightly curved ; gubernaculum present. Female : tail elongated, conical, and pointed ; vulva behind the middle of the body ; ovejector very long ; uterus single, dividing anteriorly into two short oviducts leading into the ovaries which are massive and club-shaped. Oviparous, eggs bean-shaped and embryonated *in utero*. Parasites of reptiles.

Type species : *V. tuberculata* (Linstow, 1904). ♂ 2–3 mm., ♀ 3–4 mm. In *Trachysaurus rugosus*.

Syn., *Oxyuris tuberculata* Linstow, 1904.

Refs. 326, 613c.

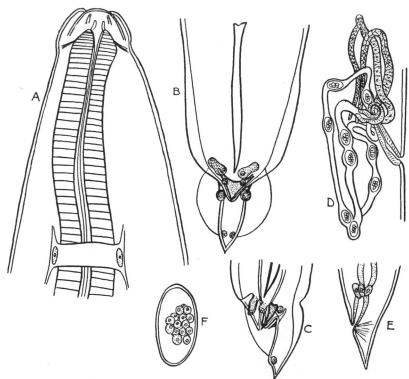

Fig. 136.—*Alæuris alæuris*. A. Anterior extremity, dorsal view. × 320. B. Posterior extremity of male, ventral view. × 215. C. Posterior extremity of male, lateral view. × 215. D. Female genitalia. × 29. E. Tail of female. × 46. F. Egg. × 135. (After Thapar.)

Genus ALÆURIS Thapar, 1925.

Definition.—SYPHACIINÆ : mouth with three lips ; cuticle with lateral flanges ; œsophagus elongated and provided posteriorly with a bulb containing a valvular apparatus and separated from the rest of the œsophagus by a constriction. Male : body cut away ventrally behind the cloaca and ending as a conical tail provided with broad caudal alæ, with three pairs of circumanal papillæ and a pair of papillæ near the tip of the tail ; spicule very long, slender, and acicular ; gubernaculum present and V-shaped. Female : tail short and conical ; vulva behind the middle of the body ; ovejector long ; ovaries club-shaped. Oviparous. Parasites of reptiles.

Type species : *A. alæuris* Thapar, 1925. ♂ 4 mm., ♀ 4·5–6 mm. In *Testudo ibera.*

Other species : *A. iguanæ* Thapar, 1925. In *Iguana tuberculata.* Ref. 613c.

Subfamily OXYSOMATIINÆ Railliet, 1916.

Definition.—OXYURIDÆ : Male : with two equal spicules ; gubernaculum absent.

KEY TO GENERA.

Vestibulum present ; spicules short . Probstmayria, p. 204.
Vestibulum absent ; spicules long and
 winged . . . . . . Oxysomatium, p. 203

Genus OXYSOMATIUM Railliet and Henry, 1913.

Syn., *Oxysoma* Schneider, 1866, in part.

Definition.—OXYSOMATIINÆ : mouth with three small lips and ten head papillæ, the submedian being double ; lateral flanges absent ; vestibule absent ; œsophagus long with a posterior bulb. Male : tail tapering rapidly behind the anus to end in a sharp point ; caudal alæ absent ; three pairs of preanal, three of circumanal, and four of postanal papillæ ; spicules long, equal, and winged ; gubernaculum absent. Female : vulva behind the middle of the body. Parasites of amphibia.

Type species : *Oxysomatium longespiculum* Railliet and Henry, 1916. ♂ 3 mm., ♀ 5·5 mm. In frogs.

Fig. 137.—*Oxysomatium longe-spiculum.* A. Head. × 62. B. Posterior extremity of male, ventral view. × 62. (After Schneider.)

Syn., *Oxysoma brevicaudatum* Schneider, 1866, not *Fusaria brevicaudata* Zeder, 1800.

Refs. 405, 444, 445, 480, 681.

Genus PROBSTMAYRIA Ransom, 1907.

Definition.—OXYSOMATIINÆ : mouth small, surrounded by six insignificant lips ; cuticle without lateral flanges ; a cylindrical vestibule present ; œsophagus consisting of two tandem parts separated by a transverse groove, the posterior part terminates in a bulb furnished with a valvular apparatus. The tail in both sexes is long and pointed, the anus lying at the commencement of the tail some distance from the posterior extremity. Male : posterior extremity curved, but not spirally rolled ; caudal alæ absent ; about six pairs of postanal papillæ ; spicules almost equal ; gubernaculum absent. Female : vulva near the middle of the body ; the two uteri contain eggs and free embryos. Viviparous. Parasites of equines.

Type species : *P. vivipara* (Probstmayr, 1865). ♂ 2·7 mm., ♀ 2·7–3 mm. In intestine of equines.

Syn., *Oxyuris vivipara* Probstmayr, 1865.

Refs. 226, 456.

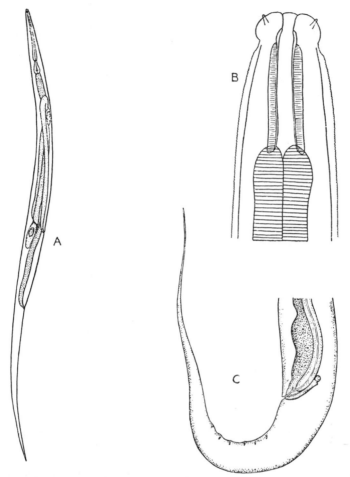

Fig. 138.—*Probstmayria vivipara.* A. Female, lateral view. × 45. B. Anterior extremity. × 900. (Orig.) C. Posterior extremity of male, lateral view. (After Ransom.)

Subfamily COSMOCERCINÆ Railliet, 1916.

Definition.—OXYURIDÆ : male with two equal spicules ; gubernaculum present.

KEY TO GENERA.

1. Posterior extremity of both sexes
   blunt and rounded . . . Amblyonema, p. 210.
   Posterior extremity of both sexes
   finely pointed 2
2. Males with plectanes . . . 3
   Males without plectanes . . . 4

3. Males with a pouch-shaped caudal ala
   on each side of cloaca .   .   .   Cosmocercella, p. 208.
   Males without pouch-shaped caudal
   alæ .   .   .   .   .   .   Cosmocerca, p. 206.

4. Males with very wide caudal alæ, and
   with only about three caudal
   papillæ .   .   .   .   .   Syphaciella, p. 209.
   Males with caudal alæ very narrow or
   absent, and with about twelve
   caudal papillæ .   .   .   .   Aplectana, p. 208.

Genus COSMOCERCA Diesing, 1861.

Syn., *Nematoxys* Schneider, 1866.
Ananconus Railliet and Henry, 1916.

Definition.—COSMOCERCINÆ : mouth with three small lips ;
cuticle of male ornamented on the ventral surface with two or

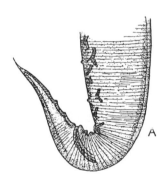

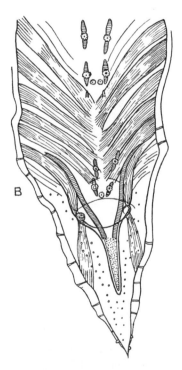

Fig. 139.—*Cosmocerca ornata.* A. Posterior extremity of male, lateral view. × 112. (After Dujardin.) *C. commutata.* B. Posterior extremity of male, ventral view. × 132. (After Drasche.)

four rows, each consisting of thirteen or fourteen plectanes, of which
two or three are postanal ; lateral flanges absent ; œsophagus
cylindrical followed by a bulb separated from the rest by a con-

striction. Male : posterior extremity bent ventrally and rapidly narrowing behind the anus, it may or may not end in three points ; spicules equal ; gubernaculum present. Female : posterior extremity terminating in a long delicate process which may or may not end in three fine points ; vulva in front of the middle of the body. Viviparous. Parasites of amphibia.

Type species : *C. trispinosa* Railliet and Henry, 1916. ♂ 3–4 mm., ♀ 4–5 mm. In intestine and lung of *Triton alpestris*.

Syn., *Oxyuris ornata* Walter, 1856, not Duj., 1845.

C. ornata Dies., 1861.

Other species :

C. ornata (Duj., 1845). In *Rana esculenta* and *Rana temporaria*.

Syn., *Oxyuris ornata* Duj., 1845.

C. commutata (Dies., 1851). In *Bufo viridis*.

Syn., *Ascaris commutata* Dies., 1851.

Nematoxys ornatus Dujardin of Schneider, 1866.

Ananconus commutatus (Dies., 1851) Railliet and Henry, 1916.

Refs. 123, 128, 131, 444, 445, 480.

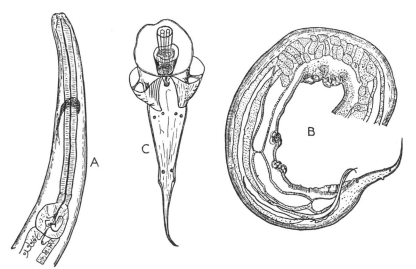

Fig. 140.—*Cosmocercella haberi*. A. Anterior extremity. B. Posterior extremity of male, lateral view. C. Posterior extremity of male, ventral view. (After Steiner.)

* The literature dealing with this genus is very complicated, but so far as it is possible to ascertain, there appear to be three species, viz., *C. trispinosa*, having four rows of plectanes and a trifid tail, *C. ornata*, having four rows of plectanes and a simple tail, and *C. commutata*, having two rows of plectanes and a simple tail.

Genus COSMOCERCELLA Steiner, 1924.

Definition.—COSMOCERCINÆ : mouth with three lips, with six labial and four head papillæ ; cuticle of male ornamented on the ventral surface with two rows of plectanes, and with a short pouch-shaped caudal ala on each side of the cloaca ; lateral flanges present ; œsophagus cylindrical and followed by a bulb containing a valvular apparatus.　Male : posterior extremity bent ventrally, rapidly narrows behind the cloaca and ends in a finely-pointed tail ; pre- and post-anal papillæ present ; spicules long and equal ; gubernaculum present.　Female : posterior extremity terminating in a long conical process ; vulva near the middle of the body.　Viviparous.　Parasites of amphibia.

Type species : *C. haberi* Steiner, 1924.　♂ 1·7 mm., ♀ 1·9 mm. In the Carolina tree frog *Hyla carolinensis.*
Ref. 588.

Genus APLECTANA Railliet and Henry, 1916.

Syn., *Aplecta* Railliet and Henry, 1916, preoccupied.
Nematoxys Schneider, 1866, in part.

Definition.—COSMOCERCINÆ : mouth with three lips ; cuticle smooth without plectanes ; lateral flanges present ; vestibule present with three small teeth ; œsophagus cylindrical and divided indistinctly into two parts, a short anterior part or pharynx and a longer posterior part followed by a bulb separated from the rest by a constriction ; excretory pore in front of the bulb.　Male : posterior extremity bent ventrally, rapidly narrowing behind the anus and ending in a pointed tail ; very narrow caudal alæ sometimes present ; on each side is a row of about twelve papillæ, of which three to five are behind the anus ; spicules equal and not winged ; gubernaculum present.　Female : posterior extremity conical and pointed ;′ vulva near the middle of the body.　Oviparous or viviparous.　Parasites of the intestine of amphibia and reptiles.

Type species : *A. acuminata* (Schrank, 1788).　♀ 5–7 mm.　In *Rana esculenta,* etc.
　　Syn., *Ascaris acuminata* Schrank, 1788.
　　　　Nematoxys commutatus Schneider, 1866, not Diesing, 1851.
Other species :
　　A. brevicaudata (Zeder, 1800).　In *Bufo* spp., *Rana* spp.
　　　Syn., *Fusaria brevicaudata* Zeder, 1800, not *Oxysoma brevicaudatum* Schneider, 1866.

A. contorta (Linstow, 1906).   In *Bufo vulgaris*.

A. dogieli (Skrjabin, 1916).   In *Bufonidæ*.

? *A. fœcunda* (Rud., 1819).   In *Rana cornuta, Hyla* sp.

A. linstowi nom. nov.   In *Bufo viridis*.

   Syn., *Nematoxys unguiculatus* Linstow, 1906.

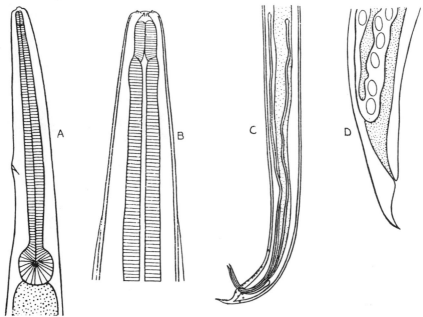

Fig. 141.—*Aplectana brevicaudata*.   A. Anterior extremity, lateral view.
× 75.   B. Anterior extremity, ventral view.   × 215.   C. Posterior
extremity of male, lateral view.   × 46.   D. Posterior extremity of female.
× 75.   (Orig.)

A. membranosa (Schneider, 1866).   In *Rana* sp., *Leptodactylus ocellatus*.

A. perezi (Gendre, 1911).   In *Chamæleon gracilis*.

A. pusilla Miranda, 1924.   In *Amphisbæna* sp.

A. unguiculata (Rudolphi, 1819) Miranda, 1924.   In *Amphisbæna* sp.

Refs. 166, 352, 444, 445, 480, 481, 573, 681.

Genus SYPHACIELLA Monnig, 1924.

Definition.—COSMOCERCINÆ : mouth with three distinct bilobed lips each bearing two projecting papillæ ; vestibule present containing triangular teeth arising from the end of the œsophagus ; lateral flanges present : œsophagus slightly enlarged posteriorly, and followed by a bulb containing a valvular apparatus and separated from the rest by a constriction.   Male : posterior extremity tapers rapidly behind the cloaca and is prolonged into a finely-pointed tail ; broad caudal alæ not supported by pedunculated papillæ ; on each side of the cloaca are three small sessile papillæ ; spicules finely chitinized and difficult to see ; gubernaculum distinct.   Female : posterior extremity prolonged into

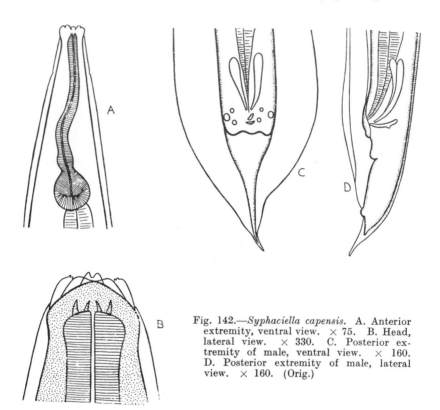

Fig. 142.—*Syphaciella capensis*. A. Anterior extremity, ventral view. × 75. B. Head, lateral view. × 330. C. Posterior extremity of male, ventral view. × 160. D. Posterior extremity of male, lateral view. × 160. (Orig.)

a delicate tail ; vulva with prominent lips situated anteriorly. Oviparous, eggs oval with a plug at one pole and with a thick striated shell.   Parasites of birds.

Type species : *S. capensis* Monnig, 1924.   ♂ 4·5 mm., ♀ 5–6 mm. In *Pteroclurus namaqua, Pterocles bicinctus*.

Refs. 362, 363.

Genus AMBLYONEMA Linstow, 1898.

Definition.—COSMOCERCINÆ : mouth with three lips ; cuticle with narrow lateral flanges ; vestibule short with three teeth ; œsophagus cylindrical with a posterior bulb, and followed by a

larger bulb separated from the rest by a constriction. Male :
posterior extremity rounded ; caudal alæ absent ; three pairs of
preanal and one pair of postanal papillæ ; spicules equal, relatively
short, stout, and winged ; gubernaculum present. Female : tail

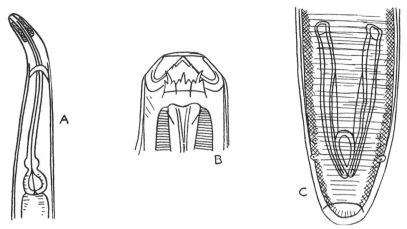

Fig. 143.—*Amblyonema terdentatum*. A. Anterior extremity. B. Head,
ventral view. C. Posterior extremity of male, ventral view. (After
Linstow.)

relatively short and rounded ; vulva behind the middle of the
body. Oviparous. Parasites of fishes.

Type species : *A. terdentatum* Linstow, 1898. ♂ 8 mm., ♀ 10·4
mm. In *Ceratodus forsteri* (the Australian lung fish).

Refs. 316, 444, 445.

OXYURIDÆ of uncertain position.

Genus DERMATOPALLARYA Skrjabin, 1924.

Definition.—OXYURIDÆ : mouth with three lips ; with a
definite buccal cavity ; cuticle with well-developed asymmetrical
cervical alæ terminating near the posterior end of the œsophagus ;
œsophagus cylindrical with a posterior bulb containing a valvular
apparatus. Male : tail conical with broad caudal alæ ; in front
of the cloaca is an S-shaped comb-like crest consisting of separate
chitinous plates, and in front of this are two median ventral
combs or " mamelons " ; spicule ? ; gubernaculum ? Female :
body tapers regularly behind the anus to end in a conical tail ;
vulva in front of the middle of the body. Oviparous. Parasites of
rodents.

Type species : *D. baylisi* Skrjabin, 1924. ♂ 5·24 mm., ♀ 11·4 mm. In *Spermophilopsis lep:odactylus*.

Skrjabin considers that this genus occupies an intermediate position between *Dermatoxys* and *Syphacia*, but as the spicules

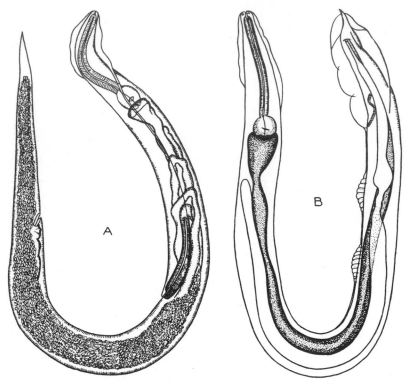

Fig. 144.—*Dermatopallarya baylisi*. A. Female. B. Male. (After Skrjabin.)

and gubernaculum could not be properly examined in the specimens available, it is impossible to place the genus in its subfamily.
Ref. 582a.

Genus ODONTOGETON Allgén, 1921.

Definition.—OXYURIDÆ: mouth situated in a shallow depression; the anterior extremity is furnished with a cuticular hood which bears internally the teeth of the buccal cavity and externally a crown of powerful posteriorly directed hooks. Œsophagus with a posterior bulb provided with a valvular apparatus; excretory pore slightly in front of the œsophageal bulb. Male: precloacal muscles well-developed; with one pair of preanal and three of postanal papillæ; spicules long, equal

and powerful ; gubernaculum ?   Female : with double genitalia ;
vulva a litt'e behind middle of body.   Parasites of warthogs.

Type species : *O. phacochœri* Allgén, 1921.   ♂ and ♀ 4–6 mm.
In *Phacochœrus æthiopicus.*

Ref. 3b.

Genus OXYASCARIS Travassos, 1920.

Definition.—OXYURIDÆ : marked sexual dimorphism, females
much larger than the males.   Meromyarian ; mouth with three

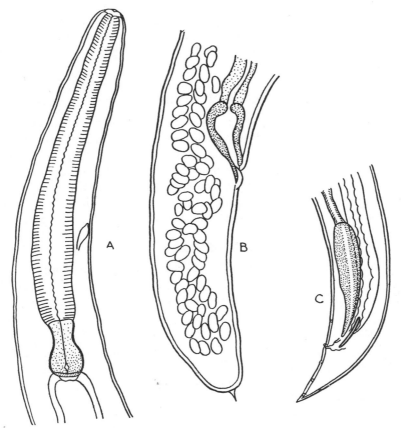

Fig. 145.—*Oxyascaris oxyascaris.* A. Anterior extremity, lateral view.   × 64.
B. Tail of female, lateral view.   × 64.   C. Tail of male, lateral view.
× 100.   (After Travassos.)

small lips ; œsophagus without a definite bulb, but differentiated
posteriorly into a ventriculus ; intestine terminates in a large
strongly chitinized piriform dilatation.   Male : tail conical,
caudal alæ absent, with a few pairs of pre- and post-anal papillæ ;
spicules subequal and lightly chitinized ; gubernaculum ? Female :

tail digitiform and ending in a short, sharply conical process ;
vulva a little in front of middle of body ; anus some distance in
front of the posterior extremity of the body, the uterus extending
backwards beyond it.   Oviparous, eggs *in utero* embryonated.
Parasites of reptiles and amphibia.

Type species : *O. oxyascaris* Travassos, 1920.   ♂ 5·6 mm.,
♀ 14–17 mm.   In *Drymobius bifossatus*.

Other species : *O. similis* Travassos, 1920.   In *Leptodactylus
ocellatus, Bufo* sp.

Travassos (1920) considers that this genus occupies a position
intermediate between the *Ascaroidea* and *Oxyuroidea*, and creates
for it a new family, *Oxyascaridæ* Travassos, 1920.

Refs. 639a, 647a.

Family HETERAKIDÆ Railliet and Henry, 1914.

Definition.—OXYUROIDEA : medium or small worms ; mouth
with three well-defined lips ; vestibule absent ; œsophagus with
a short narrow anterior portion (pharynx) and a long posterior
part ending in a bulb ; intestine simple without a diverticulum.
Male : with a definite circular preanal sucker, with a chitinous
rim ; spicules equal or unequal.   Female : tail elongate ; two
ovaries ; vulva usually near the middle of the body.   Oviparous.

Subfamily HETERAKINÆ Railliet and Henry, 1912.

Definition.—HETERAKIDÆ : with characters of the family.

KEY TO GENERA.

With cervical cordons .	.	. 1
Without cervical cordons	.	. 2
1. Males with caudal alæ .	.	. Pseudaspidodera, p. 220.
Males without caudal alæ	.	. Aspidodera, p. 219.
2. Males with large caudal alæ supported by pedunculated papillæ.		3
Males with caudal alæ absent or narrow, and not supported by pedunculated papillæ	.	. 6
3. Caudal alæ short and broad, posterior extremity of male truncate, sucker close to cloaca	.	. Strongyluris p. 221.
Caudal alæ longer and narrower, posterior extremity of male conical, sucker not so close to cloaca .		4

4. Spicules unequal . . . Heterakis, p. 215.
  Spicules equal 5
5. Preanal sucker pedunculated . Ganguleterakis, p. 218.
  Preanal sucker sessile . . . Gireterakis, p. 219.
6. Gubernaculum absent . . . Africana, p. 225.
  Gubernaculum present . . . 7
7. Parasites of warm-blooded animals Paraspidodera, p. 221.
  Parasites of cold-blooded animals . Spinicauda, p. 223.

Genus HETERAKIS Duj., 1845.

Definition.—HETERAKINÆ : cuticle usually with lateral flanges ; œsophagus with a short narrow anterior portion (pharynx) and with

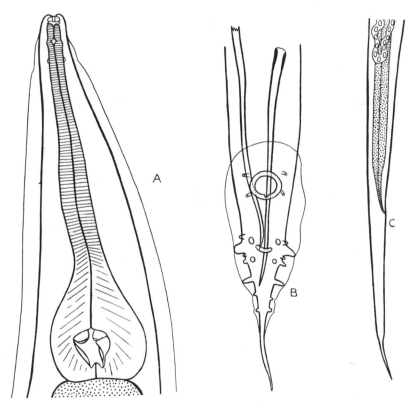

Fig. 146.—*Heterakis vesicularis.* A. Anterior extremity, dorsal view. × 90. B. Posterior extremity of male, ventral view. × 90. C. Posterior extremity of female, lateral view. × 46. (Orig.)

a long broader posterior portion ending in a well-developed bulb containing a valvular apparatus. Male : caudal alæ well-developed supported by about ten to fifteen pairs of costiform papillæ ;

spicules equal or unequal ; gubernaculum absent.   Female :
vulva near the middle of the body, or in front of it ; uteri opposed.
Oviparous, eggs with a thick shell and with a clear granulation at
one pole.   Parasites of birds and mammals.

Type species :   *H. vesicularis* (Frölich, 1791) Duj., 1845.
♂ 8–10 mm., ♀ 11–13 mm.   In fowls and ducks.

    Syn., *Ascaris papillosa* Bloch, 1782, in part.
          Ascaris vesicularis Frölich, 1791.

Other species :

H. alata Schneider, 1866.   In *Tinamus* sp.

H. arquata Schneider, 1866.   In *Cypturus* sp., *Tinamus* sp.

H. bancrofti Johnston, 1912.   In *Catheturus lathami.*

H. beramporia Lane, 1914.   In domesticated fowls.

H. bosia Lane, 1914.   In *Ceriornis satyra.*

H. brevispiculum Gendre, 1911.   In *Numida meleagris,
    Gallus* sp.

H. caudata Linstow, 1906.   In *Lampronessa sponsa.*

H. chenonettæ Johnston, 1912.   In *Chenonetta jubata.*

H. circumvallata Linst., 1906.   In *Cygnus atratus.*

H. dahomensis Gendre, 1911.   In *Cricetomys gambianus.*

H. dispar (Schrank, 1790).   In geese.

H. fariai Travassos, 1913.   In *Odontophorus capueira.*

H. girardi (Lane, 1917).   In birds and the Bengal porcupine.
    Syn., *Gireterakis girardi* Lane, 1917.

H. hamulus Linst., 1906.   In *Pavo spicifer.*

H. interlabiata Ortlepp, 1923.   In *Rhizothera longirostris.*

H. isolonche Linstow, 1906.   In *Thaumalea* sp., *Lophophorus*
    sp., *Tragopan* sp.

H. longecaudata Linstow, 1879.   In *Megacephalon* sp., etc.

H. macroura Linst., 1883.   In *Megaloperdix nigelii.*

H. monticelliana Stossich, 1892.   In *Otis tarda.*
    Syn., *H. stylosa* Linstow, 1907.

H. nattereri Travassos, 1923.   In *Crax blumenbachi.*

H. paradoxa Linst., 1906.   In *Didelphys dorsigera.*

H. psophiæ Travassos, 1913.   In *Psophia viridis.*

H. putaustralis Lane, 1914.   In domesticated fowl.

H. spumosa Schneider, 1866.   In *Mus decumanus.*
    Syn., *Ganguleterakis gangula* Lane, 1914.

H. tenuicauda Linstow, 1883.   In *Ammoperdix griseogularis.*
    Syn., *H. numidæ* Leiper, 1908.

H. valvata Schneider, 1866.   In *Crypturus cupreus.*

Refs. 72, 131, 205, 256, 260, 262, 275, 379, 436, 441, 546, 601,
    620, 647.

Lane (1914, and 1917) divided the genus *Heterakis* into the following three genera.

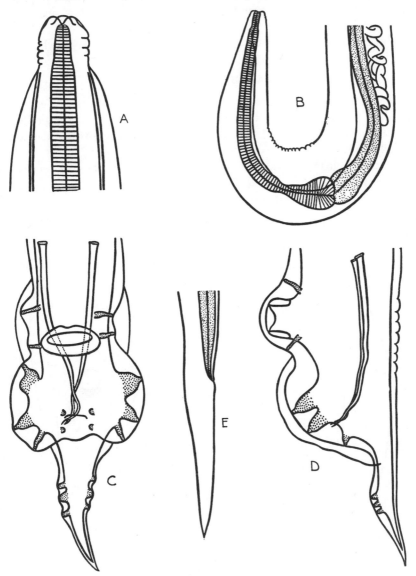

Fig. 147.—*Ganguleterakis spumosa*. A. Anterior extremity, dorsal view. × 180. B. Anterior extremity, lateral view. × 76. C. Posterior extremity of male, ventral view. × 180. D. Posterior extremity of male, lateral view. × 180. E. Posterior extremity of female, lateral view. × 76. (Orig.)

Genus HETERAKIS Duj., 1845, restr. Lane, 1914.

Definition.—HETERAKIS s. l. with twelve pairs of caudal papillæ in the male ; spicules unequal and dissimilar ; vulva near the middle of the body.

Type species : *H. vesicularis* (Frölich, 1791). In fowls and ducks.

Genus GANGULETERAKIS Lane, 1914.

Definition.—HETERAKIS s. l. with only ten pairs of caudal papillæ in the male ; spicules equal and similar ; sucker pedunculated, and the tail of the male with a great ventral cuticular thickening.

Type species : *G. spumosa* (Schneider, 1866). In *Mus decumanus.*

Syn., *Heterakis spumosa* Schneider, 1866.

Ganguleterakis gangula Lane, 1914.

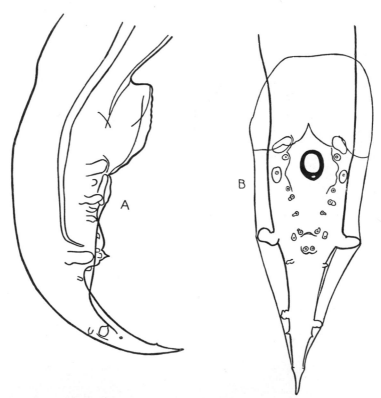

Fig. 148.—*Gireterakis girardi.* A. Posterior extremity of male, lateral view. × 65. B. Posterior extremity of male, ventral view. × 65. (After Lane.)

Genus GIRETERAKIS Lane, 1917.

Definition.—HETERAKIS s. l. with fifteen pairs of caudal papillæ in the male ; spicules equal and similar ; vulva at the junction of the middle and anterior thirds of the body.

Type species : *G. girardi* Lane, 1917. In *Hystrix bengalensis.*

If it is found desirable to subdivide the genus on the question of equality and inequality of the length of the spicules, then many of the species commonly placed in *Heterakis* must be transferred to one or other of Lane's genera, *e.g.*, *dahomensis*, *brevispiculum*, *psophiæ*, *interlabiata*, *tenuicauda*, *arquata*, etc.

Genus ASPIDODERA Railliet and Henry, 1912.

Syn., *Aspidocephalus* Diesing, 1851, preoccupied.

Definition.—HETERAKINÆ : cuticle with cervical cordons describing six longitudinal loops, three of the anterior limbs being

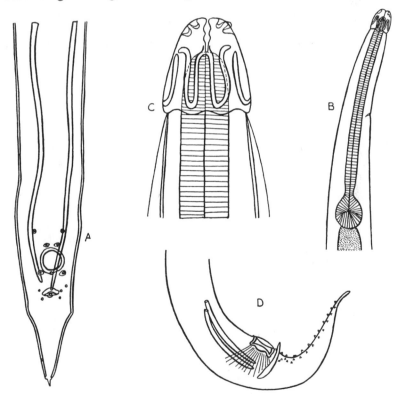

Fig. 149.—*Aspidodera scoleciformis.* A. Posterior extremity of male, ventral view. (After Travassos.)
    A. fasciata. B. Anterior extremity, lateral view. × 46. C. Head, ventral view. × 215. D. Posterior extremity of male, lateral view. × 75. (Orig.)

prolonged as a canal to open into each interlabial space; lateral flanges small. Male: caudal alæ absent; spicules equal; gubernaculum present. Female: vulva near the middle of the body; uteri opposed. Oviparous, eggs with a thin shell, containing an unsegmented ovum. Parasites of S. American marsupials and edentata.

Type species: *A. scoleciformis* (Diesing, 1851). ♂ 10 mm., ♀ 12 mm. In *Cabassus* spp., *Dasypus* spp., *Didelphys* spp., etc.

Syn., *Aspidocephalus scoleciformis* Dies., 1851.

Other species:

A. binansata Railliet and Henry, 1913. In *Dasypus villosus*.

A. fasciata (Schneider, 1866). In *Tatus* sp. and *Tolypeutes* sp.

A. raillieti Travassos, 1913. In *Didelphys aurita*.

A. subulata (Molin, 1860). In *Didelphys nudicaudata*.

Refs. 123, 260, 436, 480, 620, 621.

Genus PSEUDASPIDODERA Baylis and Daubney, 1922.

Definition.—HETERAKINÆ: occupies an intermediate position between the genera *Heterakis* and *Aspidodera*. It has cervical cordons similar to, but rather less highly-developed than those of,

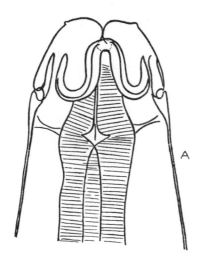
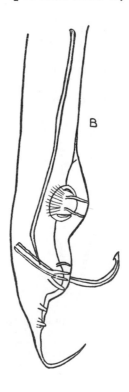

Fig. 150.—*Pseudaspidodera pavonis.* A. Anterior extremity, lateral view. × 360. B. Posterior extremity of male, lateral view. × 120. (After Baylis and Daubney.)

Aspidodera, while in the male, caudal alæ are present, with long costiform papillæ like those of *Heterakis* in shape and development; spicules very unequal ; gubernaculum absent.

Type species : *P. pavonis* Baylis and Daubney, 1922. ♂ 6 mm., ♀ 7 mm. In the pea fowl.

Ref. 42.

Genus PARASPIDODERA Travassos, 1914.

Definition.—HETERAKINÆ: closely resembles *Aspidodera,* except that the cervical cordons are absent. Male : caudal alæ absent ;

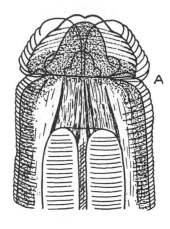

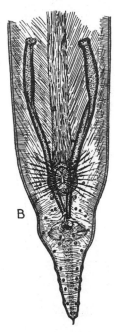

Fig. 151.—*Paraspidodera uncinata.* A. Anterior extremity, dorsal view. B. Posterior extremity of male, ventral view. (After Travassos.)

spicules almost equal ; gubernaculum present. Female : vulva in front of the middle of the body. Parasites of rodents.

Type species : *P. uncinata* (Rud., 1819) of Travassos, 1914. ♂ 11 mm., ♀ 16 mm. In *Agouti paca, Cavia* spp.

Syn., *Ascaris uncinata* Rud., 1819, of Travassos, 1914.

Refs. 477, 621.

Genus STRONGYLURIS Müller, 1894.

Definition.—HETERAKINÆ : cuticle generally furnished with small papillæ, especially in the anterior part ; œsophagus divided into a narrow anterior portion (pharynx) and a wider posterior portion ending in a bulb. Male : posterior extremity truncated ;

sucker relatively near the anus ; caudal alæ short and broad, supported by very thick pedunculated papillæ ; spicules equal, long, and thin ; gubernaculum absent. Female : vulva behind the middle of the body ; uteri opposed. Oviparous, eggs ellipsoidal

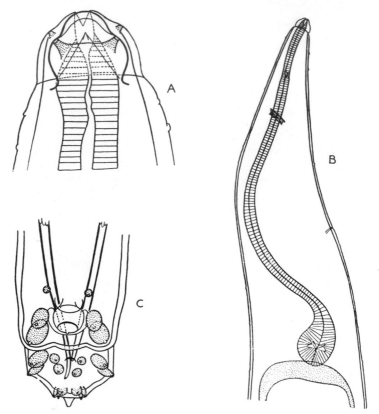

Fig. 152.—*Strongyluris brevicaudata*. A. Head, dorsal view.   × 330. B. Anterior extremity, lateral view. × 46. C. Posterior extremity of male, ventral view. × 90. (Orig.)

with a thick shell, containing an embryo at deposition. Parasites of reptiles.

Type species : *S. brevicaudata* Müller, 1894. ♂ 6–9 mm. ♀ 7·12 mm. In *Agama colonorum*.

Other species :

    * *S. calotis* Baylis and Daubney, 1923. In *Calotes nigrilabris*.

    * *S. chamæleonis* Baylis and Daubney, 1922. In *Chamæleon vulgaris*.

   * According to Taylor (1924), these worms are probably identical with *S. brevicaudata*.

* *S. elegans* (Gendre, 1909).   In *Chamæleon gracilis*.

S. gigas Spaul, 1923.   In *Agama distanti*.

* *S. ornata* (Linstow, 1897).   In *Stellio vulgaris*.

S. oscari Travassos, 1923.   In *Tropidurus* sp.

S. paronai (Stossich, 1902).   In *Amphibolurus muricatus*.

* *S. streptœsophageus* Connal, 1912.   In *Agama colonorum*.

Refs. 164, 260, 364, 573, 587, 610, 620, 621, 637.

Genus SPINICAUDA † Travassos, 1920.

Syn., *Sonsinia* Baylis and Daubney, 1922.

Definition.—HETERAKINÆ: closely   resembles   *Strongyluris*, except that the tail of both sexes is long and subulate, and in the

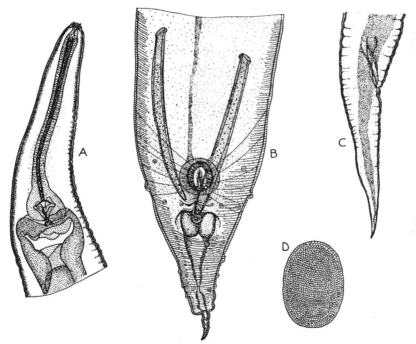

Fig. 153.—*Spinicauda spinicauda*.   A. Anterior extremity.   B. Posterior extremity of male, ventral view.   C. Posterior extremity of female, lateral view.   D. Egg.   (After Travassos.)

---

* According to Taylor (1924), these worms are probably identical with *S. brevicaudata*.

† Travassos (1919) suggested a subfamily *Spinicaudinæ* to include the genera *Spinicauda*, *Strongyluris*, and *Africana*.   So far as we can ascertain the only justification for this is the fact that these are all parasites of cold-blooded animals.   There do not appear to be any morphological characters whereby one can distinguish the *Spinicaudinæ* from the *Heterakinæ*, and in point of fact the genus *Spinicauda* seems to be indistinguishable from *Paraspidodera*.

male the caudal alæ are absent or rudimentary ; the papillæ are sessile ; the spicules are short and subequal ; a gubernaculum is present : in the female the vulva is near the middle of the body. Oviparous, eggs with a thick, often rugose, shell.   Parasites of reptiles.

Type species :   *S. spinicauda* (Olfers, 1819).   ♂ 5–7 mm., ♀ 5–7 mm. In *Lacerta teguixin, Ctenodon* sp., etc.

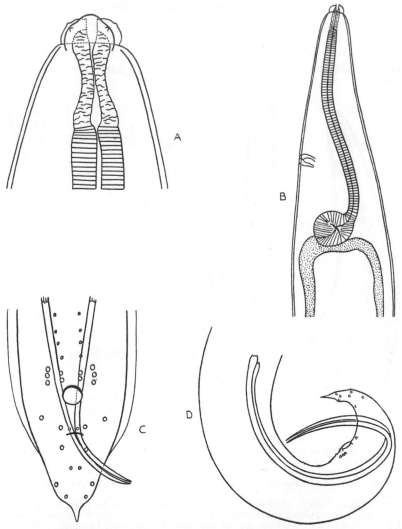

Fig. 154.—*Africana africana.* A. Anterior extremity, dorsal view. × 330. B. Anterior extremity, lateral view. × 75. C. Posterior extremity of male, ventral view. × 75. D. Posterior extremity of male, lateral view. × 75. (Orig.)

Other species :
  S. campanula (Linstow, 1899).   In *Agama* sp.
  S. wosiensis (Seurat, 1917).   In *Gingylus ocellatus.*
  S. sonsinoi (Linstow, 1894).   In *Gingylus* sp., *Lacerta* sp. and
       Chamæleon sp.
     Syn., *Sonsinia sonsinoi* (Linstow, 1904) Baylis and Daub-
          ney, 1922.
Refs. 42, 636, 637.

Genus AFRICANA Travassos, 1920.

Definition.—HETERAKINÆ : resembles *Strongyluris*, except that
the caudal alæ are narrow and the papillæ are sessile ; the spicules
are long and thin, equal or unequal ; gubernaculum absent.
Female : vulva in front of the middle of the body.   Parasites of
reptiles.
  Type species : *A. africana* (Gendre, 1909).   ♂ 4·5–5 mm.,
♀ 3·1–5·77 mm.   In *Cinixys belliana.*
  Syn., *Heterakis africana* Gendre, 1909.
  Other species :
  A. acuticeps (Gedoelst, 1916).   In *Chamæleon* spp.
  A. brodeni (Gedoelst, 1916).   In *Chamæleon* sp.
Refs. 151, 163, 610, 637.

FAMILY SUBULURIDÆ n. f.

Definition.—OXYUROIDEA : medium or small worms ; mouth
with lips inconspicuous or absent ; vestibule present, usually with
teeth in its depth ; œsophagus with a posterior bulb ; intestine
simple.   Male : precloacal muscles well-developed and usually
forming an elongate sucker, or pseudosucker, without a chitinous
rim ; spicules usually two, equal or unequal, rarely one or even
none ; gubernaculum usually present.   Female : with the
posterior extremity pointed ; vulva variable in position.   Parasites of warm-blooded animals.

KEY TO SUBFAMILIES.

Œsophagus very short and thick, the
  anterior portion being only about
  the same length as the posterior
  bulb   .   .   .   .   .   Hoplodontophorinæ, p. 233.

Œsophagus much longer, the anterior
  portion being many times the
  length of the posterior bulb   .   Subulurinæ, p. 226.

Subfamily SUBULURINÆ Travassos, 1914.

Definition.—SUBULURIDÆ : vestibule usually cylindrical with
three triangular teeth in its depth ; œsophagus relatively long,
with a posterior bulb. Male : with precloacal muscles usually
forming an elongate sucker or pseudosucker. Parasites of birds
and mammals.

KEY TO GENERA.

1. Males without spicules or guber-
     naculum   .   .   .   .   .   Heteroxynema, p. 231.
   Males with one spicule and a guber-
     naculum   .   .   .   .   .   Oxynema, p. 230.
   Males with two spicules and a guber-
     naculum   2
2. Males with preanal sucker represented
     by a cuticular prominence, and with
     large caudal alæ : vulva near anus.   Maupasina, p. 232.
   Males with preanal sucker of usual
     type, and with rudimentary caudal
     alæ : vulva near middle of body   .   3
3. Preanal sucker oval, surrounded by a
     rim of cuticular trabeculæ   .   .   Numidica, p. 229.
   Preanal sucker fusiform without cuti-
     cular trabeculæ   4
4. Vestibule clearly divided into two
     parts and strongly chitinized   .   Allodapa, p. 228.
   Vestibule not so clearly divided into
     two parts and lightly chitinized   .   Subulura, p. 226.

Genus SUBULURA Molin, 1860.

Definition.—SUBULURINÆ : mouth elongate dorso-ventrally ;
lateral flanges usually present ; vestibule with a very thin chitinous lining and not clearly divided into two parts, at the base are
three large strongly chitinized teeth with sharp points ; œsophagus
dilated posteriorly and followed by a bulb. Male : preanal sucker
fusiform, and some distance in front of the cloaca ; caudal alæ
slightly-developed or absent ; a longitudinal row of papillæ, up to
eleven in number, on each side ; spicules equal or unequal ; gubernaculum present. Female : vulva near the middle of the body ;

uteri divergent. Oviparous, eggs subglobular, with a thin shell, and frequently embryonated at time of deposition. Parasites of birds, and mammals, *e.g.*, primates, lemurs, carnivora, and rodents.

Type species : *S. acutissima* Molin, 1860. ♂ 7 mm., ♀ 12 mm. In *Strix* and *Cuculus* sp.

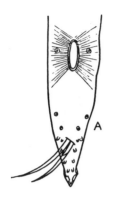
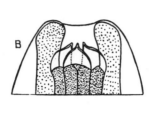
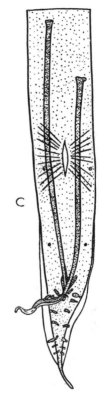

Fig. 155.—*Subulura acutissima*. A. Posterior extremity of male, ventral view. × 50. (After Drasche.)
    S. forcipata. B. Head, lateral view. × 145. C. Posterior extremity of male, ventral view. × 50. (After Seurat.)

Other species :
? *S. acuticauda* (Linstow, 1901) Railliet and Henry, 1913. In *Numida* sp.
S. andersoni (Cobbold, 1876). In *Sciurus* sp.
? *S. anulata* (Molin, 1860) Travassos, 1913. In *Ophis saurocephalus*.
S. bentocruzi Barreto, 1919. In *Trogon* sp.
S. carlosi Barreto, 1919. In *Piaya cayanna*.
S. curvata (Linstow, 1883). In *Perdix græca, Caccabis* sp.
S. differens (Sonsino, 1890). In *Gallus* sp., etc.
S. distans (Rud., 1809). In *Cercopithecus* spp.

S. forcipata (Rud., 1819). In *Coccyzus* spp., *Cuculus* sp., *Diplopterus* sp., etc.

S. galloperdicis Baylis and Daubney, 1922. In *Galloperdix spadicea.*

? *S. gracilis* (Linst., 1899) Railliet and Henry, 1913. In *Francolinus* sp.

S. halli Barreto, 1917. In *Tetrax* sp.

S. jacchi (Marcel, 1857). In *Callithrix* spp.

S. lutzi Barreto, 1918. In *Strix* sp.

? *S. macronis* (Stewart, 1914) Barreto, 1917. In *Macrones aor.*

S. olympioi Barreto, 1918. In *Crypturus* sp., etc.

S. otolicni (van Beneden, 1890). In *Galago* sp.

Syn., *S. loveridgei* Baylis, 1920. In *Mungos fasciatus.*

S. papillosa (Molin, 1860). In *Corvus cajanus, Cyanocorax* sp.

? *S. perarmata* (Ratzel, 1868) Railliet and Henry, 1913. In *Tarsius* sp.

S. pigmentata Gedoelst, 1917. In *Sciurus* sp.

S. plotina Baylis, 1919. In *Plotus rufus.*

S. poculum (Linstow, 1909). In *Francolinus* sp.

S. reclinata (Rud., 1819). In *Crotophaga* spp.

S. recurvata (Linstow, 1901). In *Eurystomus* sp.

S. rima (Linstow, 1906). In *Otis haubara*, etc.

S. rimula (Linstow, 1903). In *Centropus sinensis.*

S. sarasinorum (Meyer 1896). In *Loris gracilis.*

S. schebeni (Linstow, 1909). In *Cynictis* sp.

S. seurati Barreto, 1917. In *Caccabis* spp.

S. similis (Gendre, 1909). In *Centropus* sp., *Coracias* sp., etc.

S. strongylina (Rud., 1819). In *Crypturus* spp., *Bucco* spp. *Tinamus* sp., etc.

S. subulata (Rud., 1819). In *Caprimulgus* spp.

S. travassosi Barreto, 1919. In *Bucco* spp., etc.

S. trogoni Barreto, 1919. In *Trogon viridis.*

S. uncinata (Rud. 1819) of Hall, 1916. In *Cavia aperea, Cavia paca.*

Refs. 15, 26, 42, 72, 205, 256, 359, 500, 620.

Genus ALLODAPA Diesing, 1861.

Definition.—SUBULURINÆ : closely resembling *Subulura*, and, according to Seurat, differing only in that its vestibule is heavily chitinized and clearly divided into two parts. Barreto (1917 and 1919), however, holds thàt this difference is merely specific, and that *Allodapa* is synonymous with *Subulura.*

Type species : *Allodapa allodapa* (Creplin, 1853). ♂ 4–10 mm.,
♀ 12–14 mm. In *Dicholophus cristatus, Cariama cristata.*
Syn., *Oxyuris allodapa* Creplin, 1853.
Allodapa typica Dies., 1861.
Heterakis suctoria Molin, 1860, in part.

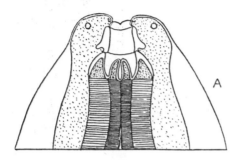
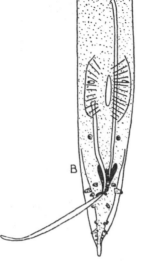

Fig. 156.—*Allodapa allodapa.* A. Head,
ventral view. × 216. B. Posterior
extremity of male, ventral view.
× 48. (After Seurat.)

Other species :
A. *elongata* Seurat, 1914. In *Dipodilla campestris.*
A. *leprincei* (Gendre, 1909). In *Caprimulgus* sp.
A. *noctuæ* Seurat, 1914. In little owls.
A. *suctoria* (Molin, 1860, in part, Drasche, 1883). In fowls,
etc.
Refs. 12, 205, 500, 501, 510.

Genus NUMIDICA Barreto, 1917.

Definition.—SUBULURINÆ : mouth bounded laterally by two
indistinct lips each bearing three papillæ ; lateral cephalic alæ
absent ; vestibule with thick chitinous walls clearly divided into
two parts, the posterior of which contains three teeth at the
entrance to the œsophagus ; œsophagus with a slight club-shaped
swelling posteriorly, and followed by a bulb separated from the
rest by a constriction. Male : preanal sucker modified, being
represented by an elliptical area surrounded by a margin of
cuticular trabeculæ ; caudal alæ very small ; ten pairs of genital
papillæ ; spicules unequal, the right strongly chitinized and the
left so lightly chitinized as to be scarcely visible ; gubernaculum

narrow and strongly chitinized. Female : vulva about the junction of the anterior and middle thirds of the body ; uteri divergent. Oviparous. Parasites of carnivora.

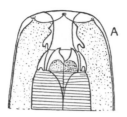

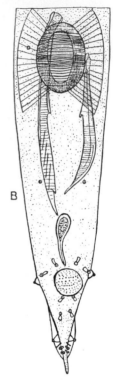

Fig. 157.—*Numidica numidica.*
A. Head. B. Posterior extremity of male, ventral view. (After Seurat.)

Type species : *N. numidica* (Seurat, 1915). ♂ 13·5–18 mm., ♀ 25 mm. In Algerian fox.

Syn., *Allodapa numidica* Seurat, 1915.

Refs. 15, 519.

Genus OXYNEMA Linstow, 1899.

Definition.—SUBULURINÆ : mouth with rudimentary lips and six cephalic papillæ ; vestibule large, cylindrical, with three teeth in its lower part ; œsophagus followed by a bulb. Male : caudal alæ very narrow ; ten or eleven pairs of caudal papillæ ; spicule single ; gubernaculum present. Female : vulva near the middle of the body. Oviparous. Parasites of carnivora and rodents.

Type species : *O. crassispiculum* (Sonsino, 1889). ♂ 12 mm., ♀ 18 mm. In *Vulpes* spp.

Syn., *Heterakis crassispiculum* Sonsino, 1889.

Oxynema rectum Linstow, 1899.

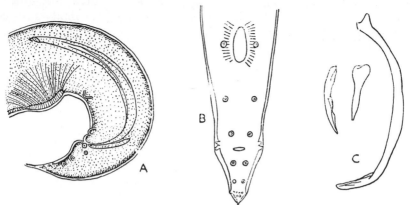

Fig. 158.—*Oxynema crassispiculum*. A. Posterior extremity of male, lateral
view. (After Linstow.)
   O. boueti. B. Posterior extremity of male, ventral view. C. Spicule
and gubernaculum. (After Gendre.)

Other species :
   O. boueti (Gendre, 1911).   In *Xerus erythropus*.
      Syn., *Heterakis boueti* Gendre, 1911.
         ? *Ascaris uncinata* Rud., 1819.
   Refs. 13, 15, 165, 205, 318, 585.

Genus HETEROXYNEMA Hall, 1916.

Definition.—SUBULURINÆ : mouth with three lips ; well-
developed cervical alæ present ; vestibule shallow ; teeth, if
present, feebly-developed ; œsophagus with a posterior bulb.
Male : tail straight and conical ; preanal sucker fusiform with

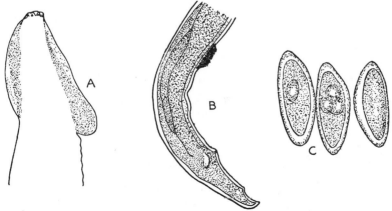

Fig. 159.—*Heteroxynema cucullatum*. A. Anterior extremity, ventral view.
 × 48. B. Posterior extremity of male, lateral view.   × 72. C. Eggs.
 × 260. (After Hall.)

lateral cuticular membranes ; caudal alæ very narrow ; spicules absent ; gubernaculum absent. Female : vulva at the junction of the anterior and middle thirds of the body. Oviparous.

Type species : *H. cucullatum* Hall, 1916. ♂ 2·8 mm., ♀ 4–8 mm. In *Eutamias amœnus operarius.*

Refs. 15, 205.

Genus MAUPASINA Seurat, 1913.

Syn., *Maupasiella* Seurat, 1913, preoccupied.

Definition.—SUBULURINÆ : mouth with two lateral indistinct lips ; cervical alæ absent ; vestibule clearly divided into two

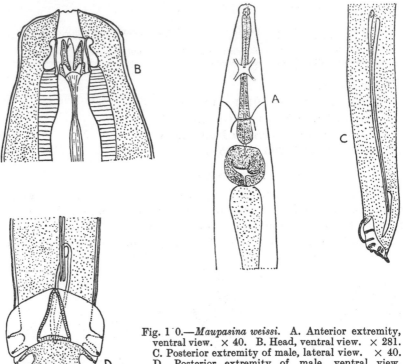

Fig. 1·0.—*Maupasina weissi.* A. Anterior extremity, ventral view. × 40. B. Head, ventral view. × 281. C. Posterior extremity of male, lateral view. × 40. D. Posterior extremity of male, ventral view. × 90. (After Seurat.)

portions, of which the posterior is occupied by three tricuspid teeth ; œsophagus dilated posteriorly and followed by a bulb. Male : preanal sucker replaced by a vesicular prominence ; large caudal alæ supported by ten pairs of pedunculated papillæ ; spicules equal and very long ; gubernaculum long. Female : vulva near anus. Parasites of shrews.

Type species : *M. weissi* Seurat, 1913. ♂ 12·7 mm., ♀ 16–17 mm. In *Elephantulus deserti*.

Syn., *Maupasiella weissi* Seurat, 1913.

Refs. 205, 491, 494, 539.

Subfamily HOPLODONTOPHORINÆ n. sf.

Definition.—SUBULURIDÆ : vestibule shallow and armed with pointed teeth ; œsophagus very short and stout with a large posterior bulb.   Male : preanal sucker prominent, horseshoe-shaped with teeth in the gap between the limbs ; spicule single. Parasites of mammals.

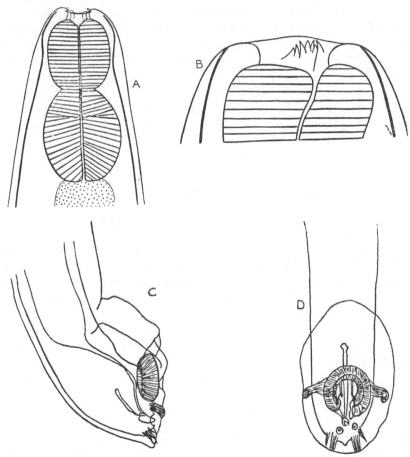

Fig. 161.—*Hoplodontophorus flagellum.*   A. Anterior extremity, ventral view.   × 56.   B. Anterior extremity, lateral view.   × 160.   (Orig.)   C. Posterior extremity of male, lateral view.   D. Posterior extremity of male, ventral view.   (After Turner.)

Genus HOPLODONTOPHORUS Turner, 1921.

Definition.—HOPLODONTOPHORINÆ : mouth elongate dorso-ventrally and surrounded by two larger lateral, and smaller dorsal, and ventral lips ; vestibule present and armed with about twelve teeth ; œsophagus very short and stout with a large posterior bulb containing a valvular apparatus. Male : preanal sucker horse-shoe-shaped, walls striated with the opening posteriorly, and containing two teeth with their points directed posteriorly ; posterior extremity surrounded by large alæ continuous anteriorly in front of the sucker and posteriorly behind the tip of the tail ; three pairs of pedunculated papillæ—one pair large and preanal, and the other two postanal and near the tip of the tail, and in addition, one pair of ventral sessile papillæ near the cloaca ; the tail ends in a short blunt point ; spicule single, fairly long, with the proximal end knob-like ; gubernaculum present. Female : tail long and pointed ; vulva in the anterior third of the body. Oviparous, eggs flattened on one side. Parasites of Hyracoidea.

Type species : *H. flagellum* (Hemprich and Ehrenberg, 1828). ♂ 7·7–8·4 mm., ♀ 17–32 mm. In *Hyrax* sp.

Syn., *Oxyuris flagellum* Hemprich and Ehrenberg, 1828. Refs. 213, 362, 652.

FAMILY KATHLANIIDÆ (TRAVASSOS, 1918).

Syn., *Kathlanidæ* Travassos, 1918.

Definition.—OXYUROIDEA : mouth with three well-developed lips sometimes armed with teeth, vestibule without teeth in its depth ; œsophagus with a posterior bulb usually preceded by a definite swelling ; intestine simple. Male : with precloacal muscles well-developed and usually forming an elongate sucker without a chitinous rim. Female : with posterior extremity pointed ; vulva posterior to the middle of the body. Parasites of cold-blooded animals.

KEY TO SUBFAMILIES.

Lips armed with powerful teeth and lamellæ . . . . . . Cissophyllinæ, p. 241.
Lips not armed with powerful teeth and lamellæ . . . . . . Kathlaniinæ, p. 235.

Subfamily KATHLANIINÆ Lane, 1914.

Definition.—KATHLANIIDÆ : mouth with three distinct lips ; vestibule present ; œsophagus frequently with a short anterior portion (pharynx) and a larger posterior portion ending in a swelling, and followed by a bulb containing a valvular apparatus. Male : with strong oblique ventral muscles, usually forming a sucker or pseudosucker without a chitinous rim ; spicules equal or unequal ; gubernaculum present. Female : vulva in the posterior half of the body. Parasites of cold-blooded animals.

KEY TO GENERA.

With many subsidiary or intermediate
    lips 1
Without subsidiary or intermediate
    lips 2
1. Spicules extremely long, almost as long
    as the worm . . . . Tonaudia, p. 236.
    Spicules not extremely long . . Kathlania, p. 235.
2. Lips united to one another by a horse-
    shoe-shaped cuticular band, vesti-
    bule large and wide, pharynx absent Zanclophorus, p. 240.
    Lips not united by a horseshoe-shaped
    cuticular band, vestibule small,
    pharynx present . . . . Spironoura, p. 237.

Genus KATHLANIA Lane, 1914.

Syn., *Pseudoheterakis* Travassos, 1917.

Oxysoma Schneider, 1866, in part.

Definition.—KATHLANIINÆ : mouth with three main lips wider near their free ends ; between the dorsal and each subventral lip are four subsidiary lips, and between the subventral lips five subsidiary lips ; cuticle transversely striated with lateral flanges ; at the bottom of the buccal cavity are three tooth-like structures ; vestibule long and funnel-shaped ; œsophagus consists of a long cylindrical portion terminating in a swelling and followed by a bulb separated by a constriction. Male : tail long and pointed ; preanal sucker without a chitinous rim ; caudal alæ present ; three pairs of, and one single, preanal papillæ, and eight pairs of post- or ad-anal papillæ ; spicules equal, relatively short and stout ; gubernaculum present. Female : tail long and pointed ;

vulva posterior to the middle of the body. Oviparous. Parasites of turtles.

Type species : *K. leptura* (Rud. 1819). ♂ 13 mm., ♀ 15 mm. In *Chelone midas, Thalassochelys* sp.

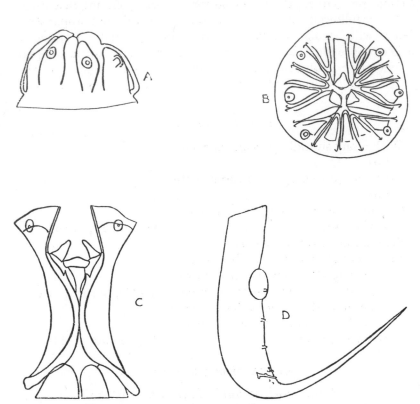

Fig. 162.—*Kathlania leptura*. A. Head, lateral view. × 190. B. Head, end-on view. × 190. C. Oral cavity and vestibule, dorsal view. × 190. D. Posterior extremity of male, lateral view. × 24. (After Clayton Lane.)

Syn., *Ascaris leptura* Rud., 1819.
   Oxysoma lepturum (Rud., 1819) Schneider, 1866.
   K. kathlena Lane, 1914.
   Pseudoheterakis leptura (Rud., 1819) Travassos, 1917.
Refs. 256, 260, 477, 480, 631, 632.

Genus TONAUDIA Travassos, 1919.

Definition.—KATHLANIINÆ : closely resembling *Kathlania*, but distinguished from it by the extraordinary length of the spicules,

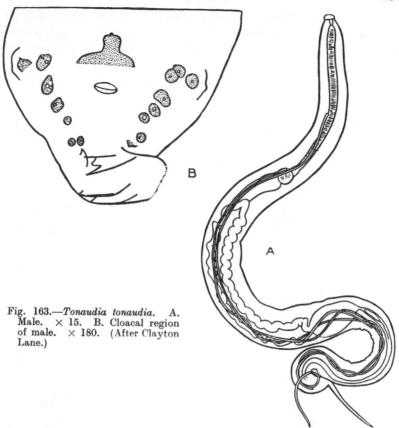

Fig. 163.—*Tonaudia tonaudia*. A.
Male. × 15. B. Cloacal region
of male. × 180. (After Clayton
Lane.)

which are very slender and reach from the mid-œsophageal region
to the cloaca.

Type species : *T. tonaudia* (Lane, 1914). ♂ 11·5 mm., ♀ 15 mm.
In *Chelone midas*.

Syn., *Kathlania tonaudia* Lane, 1914.

Refs. 256, 636.

Genus SPIRONOURA Leidy, 1856.

Syn., *Spirura* Diesing, 1861, not Blanchard, 1849.
Falcaustra Lane, 1915.
Florencioia Travassos, 1919.
Spectatus Travassos, 1923.

Definition.—KATHLANIINÆ : mouth with three lips, each
bearing two outer and two inner papillæ ; cuticle smooth ; lateral
flanges absent ; vestibule present and surrounded anteriorly by
a ring of thickened cuticle ; œsophagus with a short anterior
portion (pharynx) and a long posterior portion ending in an hour-

glass-shaped posterior bulb separated from the rest by a constriction. Posterior extremity of both sexes tapering and pointed. Male : preanal muscles well-developed, so as frequently to form a sucker-like organ ; caudal alæ absent ; three pairs of preanal, and seven or nine pairs of postanal papillæ, and an unpaired

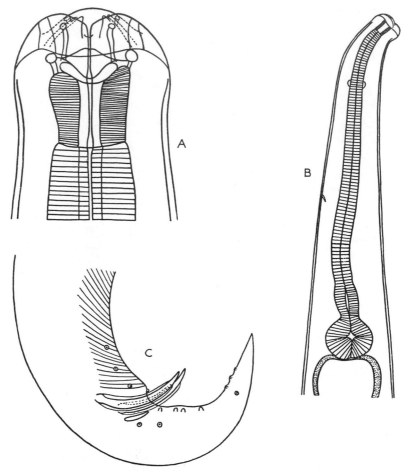

Fig. 164.—*Spironoura congolense.* A. Head, ventral view. × 215. B. Anterior extremity, lateral view. × 38. C. Posterior extremity of male, lateral view. × 46. (Orig.)

median precloacal papilla ; spicules equal and compressed laterally ; gubernaculum usually present, sometimes imperfectly chitinized or even absent. Female : vulva towards the posterior third of the body ; uteri opposed. Oviparous. Parasites of tortoises, snakes, and fishes.

Type species : *S. gracile* Leidy, 1856.   ♂ 8 mm., ♀ 16 mm. In *Emys serrata*.

Other species :

S. affine Leidy, 1856.   In *Cistudo carolina*.
  Syn., *Falcaustra chapini* Boulenger, 1923.
S. araxiana (Massino, 1924).   In *Emys orbicularis*.
S. armenica (Massino, 1924).   In *Emys orbicularis*.
S. barbi (Baylis and Daubney, 1922).   In *Barbus tor*.
S. congolense Taylor, 1925.   In fresh-water fish.
S. falcatum (Linstow, 1906).   In *Nicoria trijuga*.
  Syn., *Falcaustra falcata* (Linstow, 1906) Lane, 1915.
    Oxysoma falcata Linstow, 1906.
S. kachugæ (Stewart, 1914).   In *Kachuga lineata*.
  Syn., *Oxysoma kachugæ* Stewart, 1914.
S. lambdiense (Seurat, 1918).   In *Clemmys leprosa*.
S. leptocephalum (Baylis and Daubney, 1922).   In *Barbus tor*.
S. masculum (Rud., 1819).   In *Drymobius bifossalus* and *Coluber* sp.
  Syn., *Ascaris mascula* Rud., 1819.
    Florencioia mascula (Rud., 1819) Travassos, 1919.
S. nitidum (Travassos, 1919).   In *Cobra* sp.
  Syn., *Florencioia nitida* Travassos, 1919.
S. siamense (Baylis, 1920).   In *Hieremys annandalei*.
S. spectatum (Travassos, 1923).   In *Piaractus brachypomus*.
  Syn., *Spectatus spectatus* Travassos, 1923.
S. stewarti (Baylis and Daubney, 1922).   In *Kachuga* sp. and *Hardella* sp.
S. testudinis (Baylis and Daubney, 1922).   In *Testudo elongata*.

Travassos has added the following two genera to his family *Kathlaniidæ* :—

Genus FLORENCIOIA * Travassos, 1919.

Definition.—KATHLANIINÆ : mouth with three lips ; preanal sucker slightly-developed or rudimentary—sometimes four in number ; spicules short and curved ; gubernaculum slightly-developed. Containing the species : *mascula, nitida* and *siamensis*.

Genus SPECTATUS † Travassos, 1923.

Definition.—KATHLANIINÆ : mouth with six lips, each with a median papilla ; œsophagus without a clearly-defined second bulb ; preanal

* Travassos (1923) spells this genus *Florencoia*.
† In the same paper this genus is spelt *Spectalus, Spectatus,* and *Espectatus* : as all the figures are labelled *S. spectatus* we presume that the correct name of the genus is *Spectatus*.

sucker ellipsoidal ; spicules short and curved ; gubernaculum V-shaped ; tail conical in both sexes ; vulva median, ovejector long.   Containing the species *spectatus*.

Refs. 27, 42, 93, 258, 271, 272, 328, 347a, 444, 545, 640, 645.

We do not consider it possible to break up the genus *Spironoura*, syn., *Falcaustra*, in this manner and prefer to regard these genera as synonymous with *Spironoura*. The degree of development of the preanal sucker varies very considerably in the different members of this genus, as also does the second bulb on the œsophagus ; the six lips, each bearing a single papilla, of *Spectatus* can hardly be distinguished from the three bilobed lips, each bearing two papillæ, seen in such species as *Spironoura siamense*.

Genus ZANCLOPHORUS Baylis and Daubney, 1922.

Definition.—KATHLANIINÆ : mouth with three large lips, bordered internally by cuticular fringes and each carrying a pair

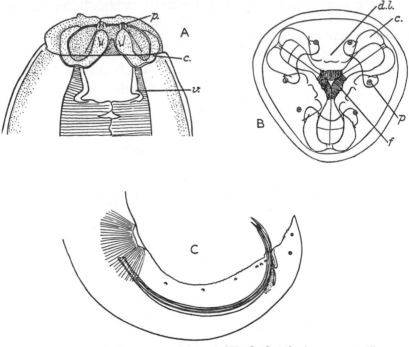

Fig. 165.—*Zanclophorus annandalei.* A. Head, dorsal view.   *p*, papilla ; *c*, cuticular support ; *v.* vestibule.   × 85.   B. Head, end-on view. *d.l*, dorsal lip ; *c*, cuticular support ; *p*, papilla ; *f*, fringe of lip. × 190. C. Posterior extremity of male.   × 26.   (Baylis and Daubney.)

of prominent papillæ ; there are three horseshoe-shaped cuticular supports uniting the adjacent portions of the lips ; vestibule well-developed ; œsophagus cylindrical ending in an hourglass-shaped bulb separated from the rest by a constriction. Male . tail conical ; preanal sucker present ; caudal alæ absent ; about ten pairs of caudal papillæ, of which four are postanal, and one unpaired papilla immediately in front of the cloaca ; spicules moderately long and equal ; gubernaculum large but incompletely chitinized. Female : tail conical ; vulva towards the posterior third of the body ; uteri opposed. Viviparous. Parasites of stomach and intestine of Chelonia.

Type species : *Z. annandalei* Baylis and Daubney, 1922. ♂ 15·5–16 mm., ♀ 15–17·5 mm. In *Testudo travancorica*.

Other species :

Z. ararath Massino, 1924. In *Emys orbicularis*.

Z. kempi Baylis and Daubney, 1922. In *Testudo elongata*. Refs. 42, 347a.

Subfamily CISSOPHYLLINÆ n. sf.

Definition.—KATHLANIIDÆ : mouth with three lips armed with powerful teeth and lamellæ. Male : preanal sucker without a chitinous rim. Parasites of reptiles.

Genus CISSOPHYLLUS Railliet and Henry, 1912.

Definition.—CISSOPHYLLINÆ : mouth elongate dorso-ventrally with three strongly-chitinized lips, the dorsal lip armed with a

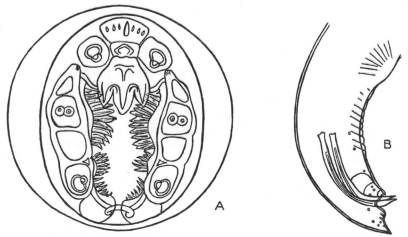

Fig. 166.—*Cissophyllus laverani.* A. Head, anterior view. × 120. B. Posterior extremity of male, lateral view. × 14. (After Railliet and Henry.)

powerful trilobed tooth, and the sub-ventral lips with numerous lamellæ directed towards the centre of the mouth ; œsophagus long, consisting of three parts, the first two distinguishable only by their degree of chitinization, whilst the third part is of a slightly greater diameter and terminates in a globular bulb containing a valvular apparatus. Male : tail short and conical ; preanal sucker oval without a chitinous rim ; caudal alæ absent ; six pairs of preanal and five pairs of postanal papillæ ; spicules long, stout, and equal ; gubernaculum present. Female : body attenuated suddenly behind the anus ; tail conical ; vulva in the posterior third of the body ; uteri parallel. Oviparous. Parasites of Chelonia.

Type species : *C. laverani* Railliet and Henry, 1912. ♂ 25–31 mm., ♀ 24–31 mm. In *Testudo emys*.

Other species :
? *C. penita* (Leidy, 1886) Barreto, 1917. In *Chrysemys scripta*, N. America.
? *C. roseus* (Leidy, 1851) Barreto, 1917. In *Testudo* spp.
Refs. 15, 436.

Family CRUZIIDÆ (Travassos, 1917).

Syn., *Cruzidæ* Travassos, 1917.

Definition.—OXYUROIDEA : mouth with three lips ; vestibule present ; œsophagus with a well-marked posterior bulb ; intestinal diverticulum present.

Genus CRUZIA Travassos, 1917.

Syn., *Oxysoma* Schneider, 1866, in part.

Definition.—CRUZIIDÆ : mouth with three lips ; well-marked chitinous vestibule armed with comb-like teeth ; œsophagus cylindrical enlarged posteriorly, and followed by a well-developed bulb separated from the rest and containing a valvular apparatus ; intestine with an anterior diverticulum. Male : posterior extremity conical ; caudal alæ very small or absent ; about nine pairs of papillæ, of which three are preanal, three adanal, and three postanal ; spicules sub-equal ; gubernaculum present. Female : posterior extremity tapering gradually behind the cloaca and ending in a fine point ; vulva near the middle of the body ; two ovaries. Oviparous, eggs with a thick rugose shell, containing an embryo when deposited. Parasites of marsupials.

Type species : *C. tentaculata* (Rud., 1819). ♂ 8–14 mm., ♀ 12–16 mm. In *Didelphys* spp.

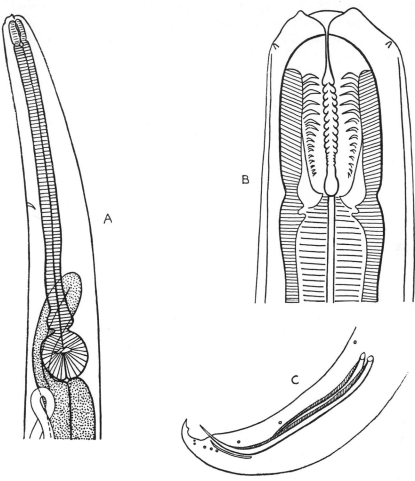

Fig. 167.—*Cruzia tentaculata*. A. Anterior extremity, lateral view. × 26. B. Anterior extremity, ventral view. × 240. C. Posterior extremity of male, lateral view. × 84. (Orig.)

Syn., *Ascaris tentaculata* Rud., 1819.

Oxysoma tentaculata (Rud., 1819) Schneider, 1866.

Refs. 480, 631, 643.

Family ATRACTIDÆ Travassos, 1919.

Definition.—OXYUROIDEA : small worms ; mouth variable ; œsophagus clearly divided into two parts, the posterior terminating in a bulb* sometimes clearly separated ; intestine simple without

* In a few of the genera, viz., *Leiperenia*, *Cobboldina*, and *Monhysterides*, the bulbar enlargement at the end of the second part of the œsophagus is not very pronounced.

diverticula. Male : without a preanal sucker ; spicules equal or unequal ; gubernaculum present or absent. Female : tail pointed ; genitalia single (one ovary) ; vulva situated posteriorly. Viviparous.

KEY TO SUBFAMILIES.

1. Males with two equal spicules and
      without a gubernaculum   .   Labidurinæ, p. 247.
   Males with two unequal spicules   .   2
2. With a gubernaculum .   .   .   Atractinæ, p. 244.
   Without a gubernaculum   .   .   Crossocephalinæ, p. 250.

Subfamily ATRACTINÆ Railliet, 1917.

Definition.—ATRACTIDÆ : males with two unequal spicules, and a gubernaculum.

KEY TO GENERA.

Mouth with six lips, anterior part of œsophagus longer than posterior ; parasites
   of reptiles .   .   .   .   .   .   Atractis, p. 244.
Mouth with more than six lips, anterior
   part of œsophagus shorter than pos-
   terior ; parasites of mammals   .   .   Leiperenia, p. 246.

Genus ATRACTIS Duj., 1845.

Definition.—ATRACTINÆ : body cylindrical ; mouth with six lips ; vestibule absent ; œsophagus divided into two parts, the first (longer) part thick and muscular with rounded extremities and the lumen strongly chitinized, the second part is less chitinized, narrow, and terminates in a bulb provided with a valvular apparatus. Male : posterior extremity curved spirally, tail conical ; caudal alæ absent ; there are a number of preanal and postanal papillæ ; spicules unequal ; gubernaculum present. Female : straight or bowed ; tail long and pointed ; vulva near anus. Viviparous. Parasites of lizards and tortoises.

   Type species : *A. dactyluris* (Rud., 1819) Dujardin, 1845.

      ♂ 2 mm., ♀ 5–6 mm. In *Testudo græca*, etc.

   Syn., *Ascaris dactyluris* Rudolphi, 1819.

   Other species :

   A. fasciolata Gendre, 1909. In *Cinixys belliana.*

A. hystrix (Dies., 1851).   In *Podocnemis erythrocephalus.*

A. kachugæ Stewart, 1914.   In *Kachuga lineata.*

A. opeatura Leidy, 1891.   In *Cyclura bæolopha.*

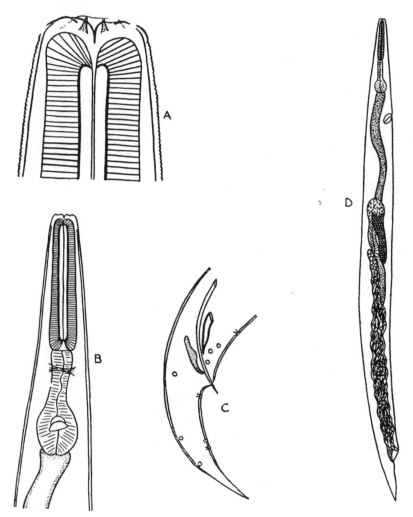

Fig. 163.—*Atractis dactyluris.* A. Head, ven'ral view. × 400. B. Anterior
extremity, ventral view. × 9J. C. Tail of male, lateral view. × 9J.
D. Female. × 28. (Orig.)

A. ortleppi Thapar, 1925.   In *Podocnemis unifilis.*

A. perarmata Linstow, 1910.   In *Cinixys belliana.*

Refs. 42, 129, 131, 151, 155, 162, 210, 313, 323, 407, 436, 591,
613c, 636.

Genus LEIPERENIA Khalil, 1922.

Definition.—ATRACTINÆ : mouth surrounded by more than six lips ; cervical alæ present ; vestibule absent ; anterior portion of œsophagus shorter than the posterior, which is slightly swollen

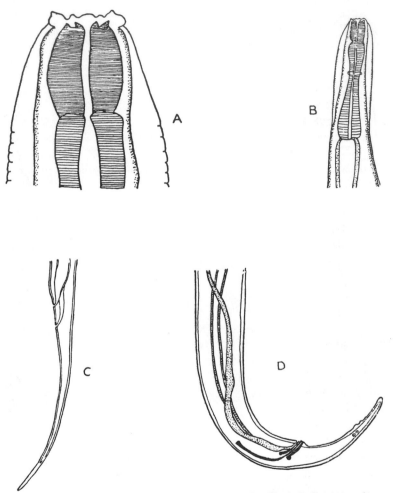

Fig. 169.—*Leiperenia leiperi.* A. Head. × 180. B. Anterior extremity. C. Posterior extremity of female. × 60. D. Posterior extremity of male. × 60. (After Khalil.)

posteriorly. Male : tail incurved, long, and pointed ; caudal alæ absent ; four postanal papillæ ; spicules unequal ; gubernaculum present. Female : tail long and pointed ; vulva near anus. Viviparous. Parasites of elephants.

Type species : *L. leiperi* Khalil, 1922. ♂ 3·8 mm., ♀ 3·9 mm.
In African elephant.

Other species : *L. galebi* Khalil, 1922. In Indian elephant.
Refs. 247, 251.

Subfamily LABIDURINÆ * n. sf.

Definition.—ATRACTIDÆ : males with two equal spicules, and
without a gubernaculum.

KEY TO GENERA.

1. Females with a cloaca   .   .   .   Rondonia, p. 248.
    Females with vulva opening separately
        from anus   2
2. Mouth with three prominent lips, of
        which the two subventral are provided
        with a posterior fringe   .   .   .   Labiduris, p. 247.
    Mouth hexagonal with six small lips   .   Cyrtosomum, p. 249.

Genus LABIDURIS Schneider, 1866.

Definition.—LABIDURINÆ : mouth with three prominent lips, one
dorsal and two subventral, the subventral are separated from the
dorsal by relatively shallow notches, but from one another by a
cleft extending to their bases, the median free edges are curved,
overlap each other, and are fringed posteriorly ; vestibule short ;
œsophagus consists of two parts, the posterior ending in a bulb,
this is followed by a post-œsophageal bulb containing a valvular
apparatus. Male : with a prominent posteriorly directed horn-
like process on each side of the cloaca, and a little further back
two large papillæ, in addition there are three or four pairs of preanal papillæ, and a similar number of postanal papillæ ; the body
ends in a conical pointed tail of varying length in different species ;
spicules equal ; gubernaculum absent. Females : tail long and
conical ; vulva near anus. Viviparous. Parasites of tortoises.

Type species : *L. gulosa* (Rud., 1819). ♂ 6 mm., ♀ 8–12 mm.
In *Testudo* spp., etc.

Syn., *Ascaris gulosa* Rud., 1819.

Other species :

L. africana Gedoelst, 1916.   In *Cinixys erosa.*

†*L. zschokkei* Linstow, 1899.   In *Testudo tabulata.*

Refs. 92, 151, 155, 318, 477, 480, 613c.

---

* Thapar (1925) has created a new family *Labiduridæ* for the genus *Labiduris.*
† Chapin (1924) considers that *L. zschokkei* is synonymous with *L. gulosa,* but
Thapar (1925) holds that they are distinct species, and that *L. africana* Gedoelst 1916,
is identical with *L. zschokkei.*

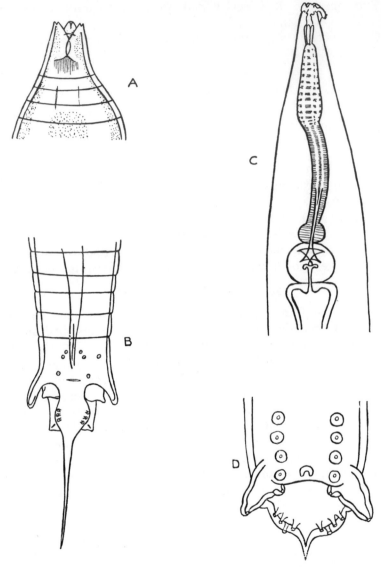

Fig. 170.—*Labiduris gulosa*. A. Head, ventral view. × 130. B. Posterior extremity of male, ventral view. × 98. (After Schneider.) *Labiduris africana*. C. Anterior extremity, lateral view. D. Posterior extremity of male, ventral view. (After Gedoelst.)

Genus RONDONIA Travassos, 1919.

Definition.—LABIDURINÆ : insufficiently defined ; œsophagus swollen posteriorly and followed by a bulb. Male : spicules sub-

equal. Female : genitalia single ; vulva opening with the anus
in a cloaca. Viviparous. Parasites of fishes.

Type species : *R. rondoni* Travassos, 1919. In *Piaractus
brachypomus*.

Ref. 636, 645.

Genus CYRTOSOMUM Gedoelst, 1919.

Definition.—LABIDURINÆ : mouth small and hexagonal with
the greatest diameter dorso-ventral, surrounded by six insignificant
lips, each with one papilla ; lateral flanges absent ; œsophagus

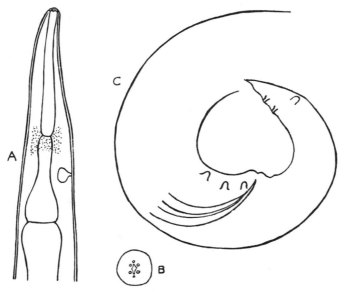

Fig. 171.—*Cyrtosomum scelopori.* A. Anterior extremity, lateral view.
B. Head, end-on view. C. Posterior extremity of male, lateral view.
(After Gedoelst.)

composed of two parts separated by a transverse groove, the
posterior part terminates in a bulb furnished with a valvular
apparatus, and is not followed by a separate bulb. The tail of
both sexes is relatively short, conical, and ends in a sharp point.
Male : posterior portion rolled in a spiral ; caudal alæ absent ;
about three pairs of preanal papillæ and the same number of
postanal papillæ ; spicules equal and pointed ; gubernaculum
absent. Female : vulva a little in front of the anus. Viviparous.

Type species : *C. scelopori* Gedoelst, 1919. ♂ 2·4 mm., ♀ 2·3–
2·7 mm. In *Sceloporus undulatus.*

Ref. 155.

Subfamily CROSSOCEPHALINÆ n. sf.

Definition.—ATRACTIDÆ : males with two unequal spicules, and no gubernaculum.

KEY TO GENERA

1. Parasites of fishes . . . . Monhysterides, p. 252.
Parasites of mammals . . . 2
2. Mouth with three pairs of pectinated
laminæ . . . . . Crossocephalus, p. 250.
Mouth with cuticular collar and no
laminæ . . . . . Cobboldina, p. 250.

Genus CROSSOCEPHALUS Railliet, 1909.

Syn., *Pterocephalus* Linstow, 1899, preoccupied.

Definition.—CROSSOCEPHALINÆ : mouth with three lips ; head with numerous papillæ ; œsophagus consists of two parts, the anterior end being furnished with three pairs of pectinated laminæ capable of eversion, the posterior terminating in a subglobular bulb not followed by a separate bulb. Male : posterior extremity spiral ; tail conical ; caudal alæ absent ; three pairs of preanal and five pairs of postanal papillæ ; spicules unequal ; gubernaculum absent. Female : tail long and sharply pointed ; vulva near anus. Viviparous. Parasites of zebras and rhinoceroses.

Type species : *C. viviparus* (Linstow, 1899). ♂ 7–8·5 mm., ♀ 7·5–9·5 mm. In intestine of zebra.

Syn., *Pterocephalus viviparus* Linstow, 1899.
C. zebræ Yorke and Southwell, 1920.

Other species :
C. brevicaudatus Baylis and Daubney, 1923. In *Rhinoceros indicus.*
C. longicaudatus Baylis, 1919. In *Rhinoceros sumatrensis.*

Refs. 23, 43, 151, 318, 402ʌ, 615, 680.

Genus COBBOLDINA Leiper, 1911.

Syn., *Cobboldia* Leiper, 1910, preoccupied.

Definition.—CROSSOCEPHALINÆ : mouth with a cuticular collar prolonged laterally into two triangular flaps, the collar is supported by four papillæ, the lateral pair being twice the length of the median pair ; œsophagus divided into two parts, the posterior

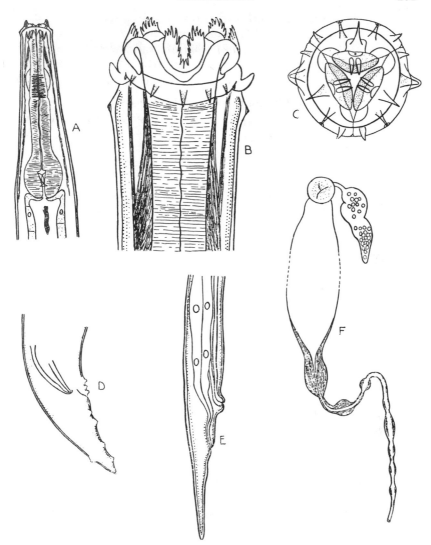

Fig. 172.—*Crossocephalus viviparus*. A. Anterior extremity, ventral view.
× 35.   B. Head, dorsal view.   × 200.   C. Head, end-on view.   × 200.
D. Posterior extremity of male.   × 72.   E. Posterior extremity of
female.   × 60.   F. Diagram of female genitalia. (After Yorke and
Southwell.)

becoming bulbous at its extremity and not followed by a separate
bulb.   Tail of both sexes long and pointed.   Male : posterior
extremity spirally coiled ; five circumanal and four postanal
papillæ ; spicules unequal ; gubernaculum absent.   Female : vulva
close to anus.   Viviparous.   Parasites of the hippopotamus.

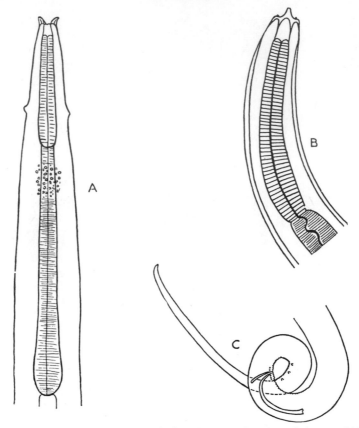

Fig. 173.—*Cobboldina vivipara*.   A. Anterior extremity, ventral view.   × 160.
B. Anterior extremity, lateral view.   × 260.   C. Posterior extremity of
male, lateral view.   × 90.   (Orig.)

Type species : *C. vivipara* (Leiper, 1910). ♂ 4 mm., ♀ 4·3 mm.
In hippopotamus.

Syn., *Cobboldia vivipara* Leiper, 1910.

Refs. 155, 279, 286.

Genus MONHYSTERIDES Baylis and Daubney, 1922.

Definition.—CROSSOCEPHALINÆ : mouth surrounded by six
small nodules ; œsophagus divided into two parts, the posterior
becoming bulbous at its extremity and not followed by a separate
bulb.   Tail of both sexes long and pointed.   Male : posterior
extremity spirally coiled ; nine pairs of caudal papillæ, of which
four are preanal and five postanal ; spicules unequal ; gubernaculum absent.   Female : vulva close to anus.   Viviparous.
Parasites of fishes.

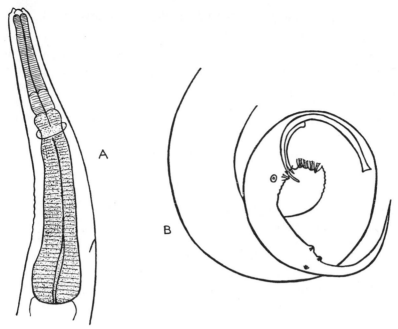

Fig. 174.—*Monhysterides piscicola*. A. Anterior extremity, lateral view. × 150. B. Posterior extremity of male. × 210. (After Baylis and Daubney.)

Type species : *M. piscicola* Baylis and Daubney, 1922. ♂ 3·5–4 mm., ♀ 3·7–4·4 mm. In *Barbus tor*.

Ref. 42.

OXYUROIDEA insufficiently known.

Genus STENODES Duj., 1845.

Definition.—OXYUROIDEA : slender, filiform worms ; head small, trŭncated ; mouth circular in the middle of a small chitinous disc, or small buccal capsule ; cuticle transversely striated with small lateral flanges ; œsophagus slightly enlarged posteriorly, followed by a bulb containing a valvular apparatus, and clearly separated from the rest of the œsophagus. Male : posterior extremity bent ventrally ending in a fine point ; anus a little distance from tip of tail ; two pairs of small suckers in front of the anus ; spicules equal, long, and filiform. Female : tail terminating in a very fine point ; vulva in the anterior third of the body. Eggs globular, thin-shelled, containing larvæ.

Type species : *S. acus* Duj., 1845. ♂ 16·5 mm., ♀ 25 mm. From an exotic mammal.

Ref. 131.

Superfamily ASCAROIDEA Railliet and Henry, 1915.

Definition.—EUNEMATODA : usually fairly large and stout ; head bilobed or trilobed ; œsophagus frequently more or less enlarged posteriorly, but without a definite spherical posterior bulb containing a valvular apparatus (except in *Dujardinia*, where there is a small unarmed bulb), with or without a posterior ventriculus, or diverticula ; intestine with or without diverticula. Spicules equal or unequal. Females not much larger than the males. Sometimes an intermediate host is required.

KEY TO FAMILIES.

Alimentary canal simple, without a post-
 œsophageal ventriculus, or œsophageal
 or intestinal diverticula   .   .   .   Ascaridæ, p. 254.
Alimentary canal not simple, with a post-
 œsophageal ventriculus, and/or œso-
 phageal or intestinal diverticula   .   Heterocheilidæ, p. 268.
ASCAROIDEA insufficiently known, p. 287.

FAMILY ASCARIDÆ BAIRD, 1853.

Definition.—ASCAROIDEA : head consisting of three prominent lips (or lobes) surrounding the mouth and supplied with papillæ, the dorsal lip being median and the other two submedian ; or with three main lips and three relatively prominent or inconspicuous lips (interlabia) ; without a chitinous buccal capsule or vestibule. Intestine simple, without a post-œsophageal ventriculus, or œso-phageal or intestinal diverticula (occasionally in *Polydelphis* there is a rudimentary intestinal cæcum). Male : usually without caudal alæ ; two spicules usually equal or subequal ; gubernaculum some-times present : rarely with a precloacal sucker. Female : caudal extremity usually terminating conically and fairly abruptly ; vulva usually in front of middle of body. Oviparous.

KEY TO SUBFAMILIES.

Males without a precloacal sucker   .   .   Ascarinæ, p. 254.
Males with a precloacal sucker   .   .   Ascaridiinæ, p. 266.

Subfamily ASCARINÆ (Railliet and Henry, 1912) Travassos, 1913.

Syn., *Askarinæ* Railliet and Henry, 1912.

Definition.—ASCARIDÆ : males without a precloacal sucker.

KEY TO GENERA.

Interlabia present . . .	1
Interlabia absent . . .	4

1. Males with wide caudal alæ ; only four pairs of preanal papillæ ; gubernaculum present . . Trispiculascaris, p. 263.

Males with caudal alæ narrow or absent ; numerous preanal papillæ ; gubernaculum absent . 2

2. Behind lips is a cuticular ring from which interlabia arise . . Lagochilascaris, p. 260.

Cuticular ring absent . . . 3

3. Lips with a deep groove extending more or less horizontally round their inner surfaces . . . Parascaris, p. 261.

Lips without the above character . Ophidascaris, p. 262.

4. Females with more than two uterine tubes 5

Females with only two uterine tubes 6

5. With four uterine tubes . . Polydelphis, p. 265.

With six uterine tubes . . Hexametra, p. 266.

6. Males with wide caudal alæ ; preanal papillæ few in number and pedunculated . . . . Orneoascaris, p. 264.

Males without, or with narrow, caudal alæ ; preanal papillæ numerous 7

7. Cervical alæ absent . . . Ascaris, p. 255.

Cervical alæ present . . . 8

8. Tail of male probular ; spicules winged ; egg shell with mosaic marking . . . . . ' Toxocara, p. 257.

Tail of male not probular ; spicules not winged ; egg shell smooth . Toxascaris, p. 258.

Genus ASCARIS Linnæus, 1758.

Syn., *Fusaria* Zeder, 1800.

Stomachida Pereboom, 1780.

Lombricoïdes Mérat, 1821.

Definition.—ASCARINÆ : lips with dentigerous ridges ; interlabia absent ; cervical alæ absent. Male : tail conical without caudal alæ ; with numerous preanal papillæ and few postanal papillæ ; spicules equal, not winged ; gubernaculum absent.

Female : vulva anterior to the middle of the body ; vagina directed backwards ; two uterine tubes. Oviparous, eggs with a thick smooth shell surrounded by an albuminous coat with a coarsely granular surface, and containing an unsegmented ovum when deposited. Parasites of mammals.

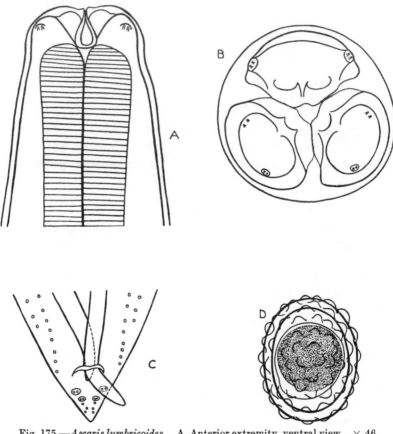

Fig. 175.—*Ascaris lumbricoides*. A. Anterior extremity, ventral view. × 46. B. Head, end-on view. × 56. C. Posterior extremity of male, ventral view. × 45. D. Egg. × 500. (Orig.)

Type species : *A. lumbricoides* Linnæus, 1758. ♂ 150–250 mm., ♀ 200–400 mm. In man, monkey, squirrel, and pig.

    Syn., *Fusaria lumbricoides* (Linn., 1758).

        Stomachida pereboomii Gœze, 1782.

        Lombricoides vulgaris Mérat, 1821.

        A. suum Gœze, 1782.

        A. suilla Duj., 1845.

       ? *A. texana* Smith and Goeth, 1904.

Other species :

A. *columnaris* (Leidy, 1856).   In *Mephitis* sp.

A. *dasypodina* Baylis, 1922.   In armadillo.

*A. *ovis* Rud., 1819.   In sheep.

A. *phacochœri* Gedoelst, 1916.   In *Phacochœrus africanus*.

†A. *vitulorum* Gœze, 1782.   In cattle.

Refs. 5, 28, 31, 42, 69, 196, 436, 597a, 602, 618, 620, 681.

Genus TOXOCARA Stiles, 1905.

Syn., *Belascaris* Leiper, 1907.

Definition.—ASCARINÆ : lips with pulp forming very distinctly two lateral lobes, separated by a deep sinus, and a single inter-

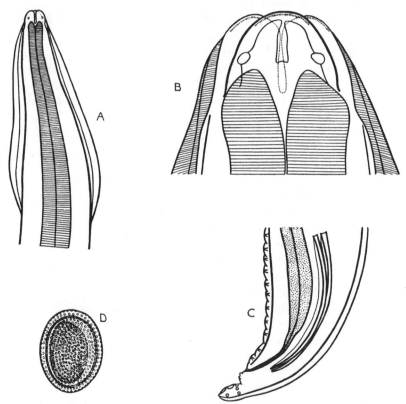

Fig. 176.—*Toxocara canis.*   A. Anterior extremity, ventral view.   × 28.
B. Head, dorsal view.   × 160.   C. Posterior extremity of male, lateral view.   × 56.   D. Egg.   × 250.   (Orig.)

---

* Probably identical with *A. lumbricoides.*

† In this species the œsophagus is modified posteriorly into a small almost globular ventriculus which is, however, not clearly constricted off from the muscular portion of the œsophagus.

mediate lobe, the lateral lobes contract anteriorly and terminate in a digitiform process the extremity of which is bent inwards towards that of the opposite side ; fine dentigerous ridges sometimes present ; interlabia absent ; cervical alæ present ; œsophagus with a distinct posterior muscular ventriculus. Male : posterior extremity probular ; caudal alæ absent ; a group of five papillæ on each side of the conical tail, a double subventral papilla on each side behind the cloaca and in front of the tail, and a row of about twenty preanal papillæ on each side ; spicules subequal and winged ; gubernaculum absent. Female : vulva in the anterior fourth of the body ; vagina directed backwards ; two uterine tubes. Oviparous, eggs with a corrugated shell. Parasites of carnivora and elephants.

Type species : *T. canis* (Werner, 1782). ♂ 50–90 mm., ♀ 50–170 mm. In dogs.

Syn., *Lumbricus canis* Werner, 1782.
Ascaris werneri Rud., 1793.
Ascaris marginata Rud., 1802.
Belascaris marginata (Rud., 1802) Railliet and Henry, 1911.

Other species :
T. crenulata (Bremser, 1824). In *Felis onça*.
T. lonchoptera (Dies., 1851). In elephants.
T. masculior (Railliet and Henry, 1911). In *Fennecus zerda*.
T. melis (Gedoelst, 1920). In the badger.
T. mystax (Zeder, 1800). In *Felis* spp.
Syn., *Fusaria mystax* Zeder, 1800.
Ascaris cati Schrank, 1788, in part.
Ascaris leptoptera Rud., 1809, in part.
Ascaris alata Bellingham, 1839.
Belascaris mystax (Zeder, 1800) Leiper, 1907.
T. vulpis (Frölich, 1789). In *Vulpes vulpes* [possibly identical with *T. canis*].
Syn., *T. triquetra* (Schrank, 1790).

Refs. 42, 251, 273, 430, 583, 596, 597a, 599, 609, 681.

Genus TOXASCARIS Leiper, 1907.

Definition.—ASCARINÆ : lips resembling those of *Toxocara*, but with the anterior lobules of pulp clearly separated from the lobes by a deep furrow and enlarged and bilobed at their extremity ; fine dentigerous ridges present ; interlabia absent ; cervical alæ present ; œsophagus without a posterior muscular ventriculus. Male : posterior extremity not probular but tapering gradually ;

caudal alæ absent ; a group of five postanal papillæ and a double
subventral papilla on each side behind the cloaca, and a row of
at least twenty-five simple preanal papillæ ; spicules subequal not
winged ; gubernaculum absent. Female : vulva towards the

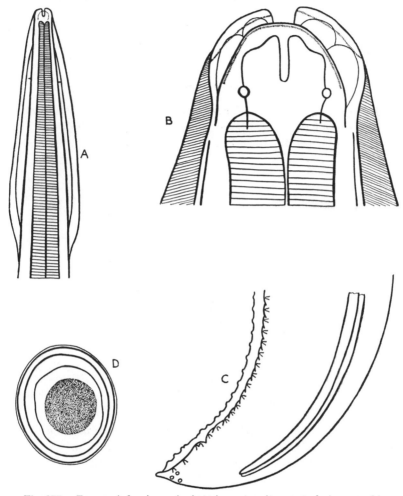

Fig. 177.—*Toxascaris leonina*. A. Anterior extremity, ventral view. × 24.
B. Head, dorsal view. × 215. C. Posterior extremity of male, lateral
view. × 75. D. Egg. × 350. (Orig.)

anterior third of the body ; vagina directed backwards ; two
uterine tubes. Oviparous, eggs with a thick smooth shell.
Parasites of carnivora.

Type species : *T. leonina* (Linstow, 1902). ♂ 20–70 mm.,
♀ 22–80 mm. In carnivora.

Syn., *Ascaris leonina* Linstow, 1902.
  Ascaris cati Schrank, 1788, in part.
  Ascaris leptoptera Rud., 1809, in part.
  Toxascaris limbata Railliet and Henry, 1911.
  Toxascaris marginata (Rud., 1802) of Leiper, 1907.
  Ascaris microptera (Rud., 1819).
Other species :
  T. transfuga (Rud., 1819).   In *Ursus* sp., etc.
Refs. 42, 273, 322, 430, 583, 597a, 609.

Genus LAGOCHILASCARIS Leiper, 1909.

Definition.—Ascarinæ : lips with a strongly-developed cuticular covering obscuring the pulp and separated off from the body by a deep groove behind which is a cuticular ring from which arise

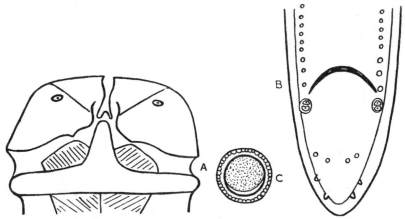

Fig. 178.—*Lagochilascaris minor.* A. Head, ventral view. *Lagochilascaris major.* B. Tail of male. C. Egg. (After Leiper.)

three subsidiary lips (interlabia), the inner surface of each of the main lips is split vertically, giving the appearance of hare-lips ; narrow lateral flanges extending the whole length of the body. Male : posterior extremity bluntly conical ; caudal alæ absent ; about five pairs of postanal papillæ, and at least twenty-four pairs of preanal papillæ ; spicules subequal not winged. Female : vulva slightly in front of the middle of the body ; vagina directed forwards ; two uterine tubes. Oviparous, eggs spherical, shells thick with mosaic markings. Parasites of carnivora.

Type species : *L. minor* Leiper, 1909. ♂ 9 mm., ♀ 15 mm. In subcutaneous abscess of man, normal site probably intestine of *Felis* spp.

Other species : *L. major* Leiper, 1910. In African lion.

                  L. turgida (Stoss., 1902). In *Didelphys crassi-caudata.*

Refs. 276, 280, 281, 291, 597a, 647a.

Genus PARASCARIS n. g.

Definition.—ASCARINÆ : lips quadrangular, the internal surface being provided with a transparent membrane bordered by

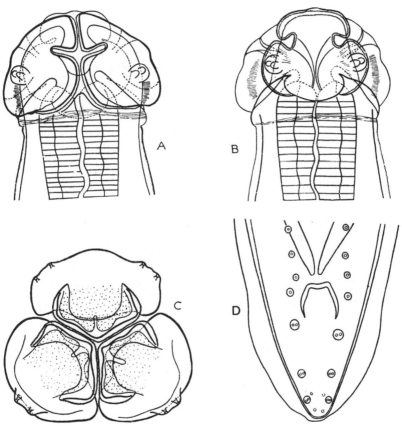

Fig. 179.—*Parascaris equorum.* A. Anterior extremity, ventral view. × 42. B. Anterior extremity, dorsal view. × 42. C. Head, end-on view. × 56. D. Posterior extremity of male, ventral view. × 35. (Orig.)

dentigerous ridges ; on the median surface of each lip is a deep fissure, which runs more or less horizontally round the internal surface of the lip, but is not continued over the external surface ; the dorsal lip bears two large double papillæ and each subventral lip one large double papilla ; small interlabia present ; cervical

alæ absent. Male : posterior extremity rounded or bluntly
conical ; small caudal alæ present ; about six pairs of postanal
papillæ and numerous preanal papillæ arranged in three longitudinal subventral rows on each side ; spicules equal and not
winged ; gubernaculum absent. Female : posterior extremity
rounded and ending in a short conical process ; vulva somewhat
posterior to the middle of the body. Oviparous, eggs finely
punctate.

Type species : *P. equorum* (Gœze, 1782). ♂ 15–27 cm.,
♀ 18–37 cm. In equines.

> Syn., *Ascaris equorum* Gœze, 1782.
> *Ascaris equi* Schrank, 1788.
> *Ascaris megalocephala* Cloquet, 1824.

Other species : ? *P. zebræ* (Skrjabin, 1916). In zebras.

> Syn.,* *Ascaris zebræ* Skrjabin, 1916.

Refs. 186, 481, 573.

Genus OPHIDASCARIS Baylis, 1921.

Definition.—ASCARINÆ : lips almost square, with more or less
rounded angles and about as broad as long ; dentigerous ridges

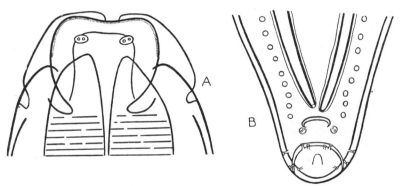

Fig. 180.—*Ophidascaris filaria.* A. Head, dorsal view. × 160. B. Posterior
extremity of male, ventral view. × 56. (Orig.)

present ; interlabia present ; from the interlabia deep transverse
grooves in the cuticle run partially round the bases of the main
lips ; genital tubes in both sexes usually confined to the posterior
region of the body, which often shows a fusiform thickening.
Male : tail bluntly conical ; caudal alæ absent or rudimentary ;
numerous preanal papillæ ; spicules equal or subequal ; gubernaculum absent. Female : vulva usually behind the middle of

---

* Possibly young forms of *P. equorum.*

the body ; vagina directed backwards ; two uterine tubes. Oviparous, eggs with a punctate shell. Parasites of snakes and lizards.

Type species : *O. filaria* (Duj., 1845). ♂ 110 mm., ♀ 170 mm. In *Python* sp. and *Varanus* sp.

Syn., *Ascaris filaria* Dujardin, 1845.

Ascaris rubicunda Schneider, 1866.

? *Ascaris infundibulicola* Linst., 1903.

Other species :

O. gestri (Parona, 1890). In *Tropidonotus* sp.

O. intorta (Gedoelst, 1916). In *Bitis* sp.

O. mombasica Baylis, 1921. In *Psammophis* sp.

O. naiæ (Gedoelst, 1916). In *Naja* sp.

O. obconica (Baird, 1860). In *Helicops* sp.

O. papillifera (Linstow, 1898). In snakes.

O. radiosa (Schneider, 1866). In *Bitis* sp.

O. solitaria (Linstow, 1903). In *Dipsadomorphus* sp.

Refs. 29, 131, 151, 324, 480, 597a.

Genus TRISPICULASCARIS Skrjabin, 1916.

Definition.—ASCARINÆ : lips prominent with auricular outgrowths at their sides and with dentate margins ; interlabia

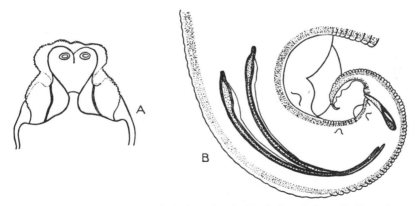

Fig. 181.—*Trispiculascaris trispiculascaris.* A. Head, dorsal view. B. Posterior extremity of male, lateral view. (After Skrjabin.)

present. Male : tail strongly bent with well-marked alæ ; preanal and postanal papillæ arranged in a row on each side and few in number ; spicules long, delicate, and equal ; gubernaculum present. Female : tail straight and conically pointed ; vulva in the anterior half of the body. Parasites of reptiles.

Type species : *T. trispiculascaris* Travassos, 1920. ♂ 6–8 mm., ♀ 13–28 mm. In crocodiles.

Syn., *T. helicina* (Molin, 1860), of Skrjabin, 1916.
Refs. 36, 42, 128, 573, 597a, 639.

Genus ORNEOASCARIS Skrjabin, 1916.

Definition.—ASCARINÆ : lips large and hexagonal with dentate margins ; interlabia absent ; œsophagus and intestine simple. Male : posterior extremity not strongly bent, the ventral surface

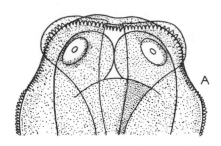

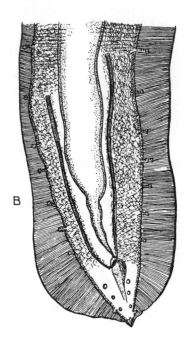

Fig. 182.—*Orneoascaris chrysanthemoides.* A. Head, dorsal view. B. Posterior extremity of male, ventral view. (After Skrjabin.)

of the tail is marked both in longitudinal and transverse directions with a series of furrows which form a fine mosaic network of stellate loops ; wide caudal alæ ; preanal papillæ few in number (about seven), pedunculated, and with their free ends exhibiting the appearance of a double flower ; postanal papillæ sessile ; spicules thin and equal ; gubernaculum absent. Female : tail bluntly rounded ; vulva in the anterior half of the body. Oviparous, eggs large and oval. Parasites of amphibia.

Type species : *O. chrysanthemoides* Skrjabin, 1916. ♂ 23–30 mm., ♀ 68·5–85 mm. In *Bufo* sp.

Refs. 573, 597a.

Genus **POLYDELPHIS** Duj., 1845.

Definition.—ASCARINÆ : lips oblong or more or less hexagonal, frequently longer than broad, with two papillæ (simple or double) on the dorsal and one on each subventral lip ; interlabia absent ; no groove at the base of the lips ; œsophagus short without a bulb or ventriculus ; a rudimentary intestinal cæcum sometimes

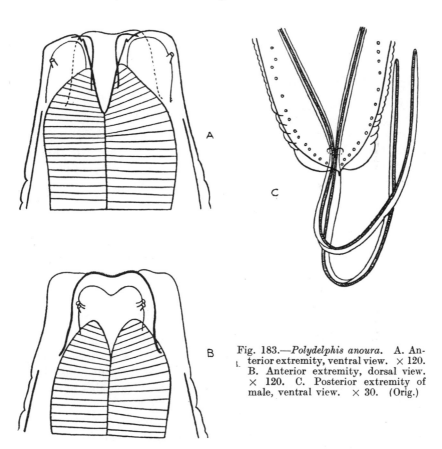

Fig. 183.—*Polydelphis anoura.* A. Anterior extremity, ventral view. × 120. B. Anterior extremity, dorsal view. × 120. C. Posterior extremity of male, ventral view. × 30. (Orig.)

present. Male : tail blunt ; spicules equal ; gubernaculum absent. Female : vulva usually in the anterior region of the body, rarely behind the middle ; vagina directed posteriorly ; four to six uterine tubes. Parasites of snakes and lizards.

Type species : *P. anoura* Duj., 1845. ♂ 116 mm., ♀ 144 mm. In *Python* spp., etc.

Syn., *Ascaris attenuata* Molin, 1858, of Linstow, 1899.

Ascaris attenuata Molin, 1858, of Stossich, 1896, in part.

Ascaris pythonis Retzius, 1830, of Railliet and Henry, 1910, in part.

Other species :

P. *attenuata* (Molin, 1858).   In *Python* spp., *Bitis* sp.

P. *boddaërtii* (Baird, 1860).   In *Drymobius boddaërti.*

P. *hexauterina* Skrjabin, 1916.   In *Bothrops* sp.

P. *hexametra* (Gedoelst, 1916).   In *Chamæleon dilepis.*

P. *oculata* (Linstow, 1899).   In *Python* sp.

P. *quadricornis* (Wedl, 1862).   In *Naja* spp., *Bitis* sp., etc.

P. *sewelli* Baylis and Daubney, 1922.   In *Cœlopeltis* sp.

P. *waterstoni* Baylis, 1921.   In *Zamenis* sp.

Refs. 29, 131, 355, 574, 597a, 636.

Genus HEXAMETRA Travassos, 1919.

Definition.—This genus was created for the members of the genus *Polydelphis* which contain six uterine branches.   If this be accepted, it would contain the species *hexametra, boddaërtii, quadricornis, sewelli, waterstoni,* and *hexauterina.*

Refs. 597a, 636.

Subfamily ASCARIDIINÆ Travassos, 1919.

Definition.—ASCARIDÆ : male with a precloacal sucker with a chitinous rim.

Genus ASCARIDIA Duj., 1845.

Syn. ? *Ascarida* Mueller, 1880.

Definition.—ASCARIDIINÆ :   generally with cuticular lateral flanges ; œsophagus club-shaped, but without a posterior bulb. Male :   preanal sucker slightly prominent with a chitinous rim ; caudal alæ narrow ; papillæ relatively large ; spicules equal or subequal ; gubernaculum absent.   Female :   vulva near the middle of the body ; uteri opposed.   Oviparous, eggs with a thick shell.   Parasites of birds and perhaps of reptiles and fishes.

Type species :   A. *hermaphrodita* (Frölich, 1789).   ♂ 52 mm., ♀ 63 mm.   In *Psittacus* sp.

Syn., *Ascaris hermaphrodita* Froel., 1789.

Fusaria truncata Zeder, 1803.

Other species :

A. *ægyptiaca* (Linst., 1902).   In *Ardea* sp.

A. *amblymoria* (Drasche, 1883).   In *Caprimulgus* sp.

Syn., *Heteracis amblymoria* Drasche, 1883.

A. *anseris* Schwartz, 1925.   In *Anser domesticus.*

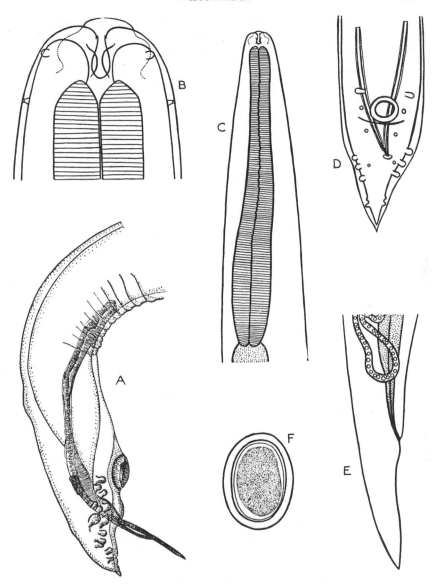

Fig. 184.—*Ascaridia hermaphrodita*. A. Posterior extremity of male, lateral
view. (After Skrjabin.) *Ascaridia perspicillum*. B. Head, ventral view.
× 96. C. Anterior extremity, ventral view. × 37. D. Posterior
extremity of male, ventral view. × 46. E. Posterior extremity of
female. × 23. F. Egg. × 333. (Orig.)

A. australis (Linst., 1898). In *Macropygia* sp.

A. borealis (Linst., 1884). In *Lagopus* sp.

A. brasiliana (Linst., 1899). In *Perdix* sp., *Rhynchotus* sp.

A. brasiliensis (Magalhães, 1892).   In *Gallus* sp.

A. brevicauda (Rátz, 1897).   In *Lucioperca* sp.

A. calcarata (Gendre, 1909).   In *Numida meleagris.*

A. catheturina (Johnst., 1912).   In *Talegallus* sp.

A. circularis (Linst., 1903).   In *Centropus* sp.

A. columbæ (Gmel., 1790.)   In *Columba* sp.

A. compar (Schrank, 1790).   In *Tetraonidæ* sp.

A. compressa (Schneid., 1866).   In *Gallus* sp.

A. cordata (Linst., 1906).   In *Callipepla squamata.*

A. cristata (Linst., 1901).   In *Balearica* sp.

A. cylindrica (Blome, 1909).   In *Tetrao* sp.

A. dolichocerca (Stoss., 1902).   In *Circus* sp.

A. fasciata Baylis, 1920.   In *Vinago delalandii.*

A. flexuosa (Schneid., 1866).   In *Crotalus* sp.

A. francolina (Linst., 1899).   In *Francolinus* sp.

A. granulosa (Linst., 1906).   In *Gallus* sp.

A. lineata (Schneid., 1866).   In *Anas* sp., *Gallus* sp.
   Syn., *A. hamia* Lane, 1914.

A. longecirrata (Linst., 1879).   In *Geopelia* sp.

A. maculosa (Rud., 1802).   In *Columba* sp., *Stictœnas* sp.,
   Vinago sp.

A. magalhãesi Trav., 1913.   In *Geotrygon* sp.

A. magnipapilla (Linst., 1906).   In *Lyrurus* sp.

A. orthocerca (Stoss., 1902).   In *Rhea* sp.

A. perspicillum (Rud., 1803).   In domestic fowl.
   Syn., *Ascaris inflexa* Zeder, 1800, of Rud., 1819.

A. pterophora (Crep., 1854).   In *Cariama* sp.

A. serrata (Schneid., 1866).   In *Penelope* sp.

A. strelnikowi Skrjabin, 1916.   In *Tinamus* sp.

A. stroma (Linst., 1899).   In *Grus* sp.

A. styphlocerca (Stoss., 1904).   In ducks.

A. trilabium (Linst., 1904).   In *Centropus* sp.

Refs. 26, 42, 72, 131, 441, 481c, 481e, 574, 620, 621, 636, 682.

FAMILY HETEROCHEILIDÆ RAILLIET AND HENRY, 1915.

Definition.—ASCAROIDEA : head consisting of three large lips ;
alimentary canal not simple. The œsophagus may or may not be
divided into an anterior muscular portion and a posterior ventriculus of different histological structure ; when the latter is
absent (and frequently when it is present) there is an anterior
cæcum springing from the intestine and lying alongside the
œsophagus ; a posterior cæcum or solid glandular appendix may

also be developed in connection with the ventricular portion of the œsophagus.

KEY TO SUBFAMILIES.

1. Cuticle without spines or other raised
      structures . . . . . Anisakinæ, p. 271.
   Cuticle with spines or other raised
      structures 2
2. Cuticle with annular thickenings
      spined posteriorly . . . Gœziinæ, p. 284.
   Cuticle without annular thickenings . 3
3. Behind lips is a collar consisting of a
      double row of fimbriæ . . . Crossophorinæ, p. 286.
   Behind lips is a cuticular swelling con-
      sisting of a series of longitudinal
      ribs . . . . . . Heterocheilinæ, p. 269.

Subfamily HETEROCHEILINÆ Railliet and Henry, 1912.

Definition.—HETEROCHEILIDÆ : behind the lips is a cuticular swelling consisting of a series of longitudinal ribs.

KEY TO GENERA.

Vulva near anus . . . . Heterocheilus, p. 269.
Vulva in front of middle of body . . Typhlophorus, p. 271.

Genus HETEROCHEILUS Diesing, 1839.

Syn., *Lobocephalus* Diesing, 1838. [nomen nudum.]

Definition.—HETEROCHEILINÆ : mouth surrounded by three prominent complex lips each of which sends a tongue-like prolongation backwards, these processes are united by membranes which are thrown into longitudinal folds ; œsophagus cylindrical slightly enlarged posteriorly ; from the anterior end of the intestine a long cæcum is directed forwards and reaches almost to the anterior end of the worm. Male : posterior extremity almost straight, conical, and ending in a sharp point ; three pairs of preanal and five pairs of postanal papillæ ; spicules equal, long, and winged. Female : posterior extremity long and conical ; vulva near anus. Oviparous, eggs oval and unsegmented when deposited. Parasites of Sirenia.

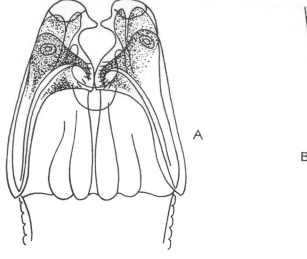
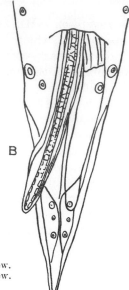

Fig. 185.—*Heterocheilus tunicatus.* A. Head, ventral view.
× 120. B. Posterior extremity of male, ventral view.
× 50. (After Drasche.)

Type species: *H. tunicatus* Diesing, 1839. ♂ 25–30 mm.,
♀ 25–37 mm. In *Manatus exunguis.*

Syn., *Lobocephalus heterolobus* Diesing, 1838. [nomen nudum
except for host.]

Refs. 28, 122, 128, 436.

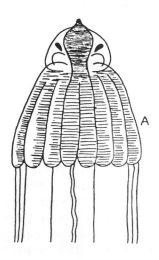
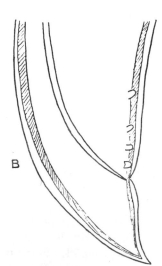

Fig. 186.—*Typhlophorus lamellaris.* A. Anterior extremity, dorsal view.
B. Posterior extremity of male, lateral view. (After Linstow.)

Genus TYPHLOPHORUS Linstow, 1906.

Definition.—HETEROCHEILINÆ : mouth with three triangular lips behind which is a cuticular thickening consisting of longitudinal ribs ; cuticle smooth with lateral flanges ; anterior cæcum from the intestine running right to the anterior end of the body. Male : four pairs of preanal papillæ ; spicules equal. Female : tail bent dorsally ; two rounded projections in front of the anus ; vulva just in front of the middle of the body. Oviparous, eggs with a thick shell.

Type species : *T. lamellaris* Linstow, 1906. ♂ 11 mm., ♀ 16 mm. In *Gavialis gangeticus.*

Refs. 28, 327, 436.

Subfamily ANISAKINÆ Railliet and Henry 1912.

Definition.—HETEROCHEILIDÆ : cuticle not provided with spines or other raised structures.

KEY TO GENERA.

Œsophagus with a posterior ventriculus ; intestinal cæcum present or absent	1
Œsophagus without a posterior ventriculus ; intestinal cæcum present	6
1. With an intestinal cæcum . .	2
Without an intestinal cæcum . .	4
2. With one œsophageal appendix .	3
With several œsophageal appendices	Multicæcum, p. 283.
Without an œsophageal appendix .	Porrocæcum, p. 279.
3. Lips with teeth ; interlabia absent ; collar round neck . . .	Clœoascaris, p. 283.
Lips without teeth ; interlabia present without cervical collar . .	Contracæcum, p. 281.
4. With œsophageal appendix . .	Raphidascaris, p. 274.
Without an œsophageal appendix .	5
5. Interlabia absent ; dentigerous ridges present	Anisakis, p. 272.
Interlabia present ; dentigerous ridges absent	Paranisakis, p. 274.

6. With a small muscular œsophageal
    bulb .   .   .   .   .   .   Dujardinia, p. 275.
    Without a muscular œsophageal bulb   7
7. With small interlabia   .   .   .   Amplicæcum, p. 278.
    Without small interlabia   .   .   Angusticæcum, p. 279.

Genus ANISAKIS Duj., 1845.

Syn., *Peritrachelius* Dies., 1851.
    Conocephalus Dies., 1861, not Thunb., 1812.

Definition.—ANISAKINÆ : interlabia absent ; dentigerous ridges present ; œsophagus with an anterior muscular portion and a posterior ventriculus, the latter being oblong or sigmoid in shape

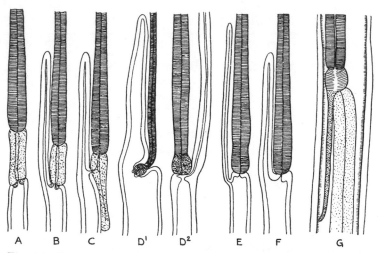

Fig. 187.—Diagram illustrating types of structures met with in the alimentary canal of various *Anisakinæ*. A. *Anisakis*. B. *Porrocæcum*. C. *Contracæcum*. D. *Dujardinia* (D¹, *D. helicina* ; D², *D. halicoris*). E. *Angusticæcum*. F. *Amplicæcum* (After Baylis.) G. *Raphidascaris*. (Orig.)

and clearly marked off from the muscular portion ; œsophageal appendix and intestinal cæcum absent. Male : spicules sometimes unequal. Female : vulva in front of the middle of the body. Parasites of marine mammals, and birds.

    Type species : *A. dussumierii* (van Ben., 1870). ♂ 79 mm., ♀ 70–100 mm. In dolphins.

    Syn., *Ascaris dussumierii* van Ben., 1870.

         A. simplex Duj., 1845, not *Ascaris simplex* Rud., 1809. Other species :

    A. diomedeæ (v. Linst., 1888). In *Diomedea* sp.

A. insignis (Dies., 1851). In *Delphinus amazonicus.*

Syn., *Peritrachelius insignis* Dies., 1851.

? *A. kükenthalii* (Cobb, 1888). In *Delphinapterus* sp.

A. patagonica (v. Linst., 1880). In *Phoca* sp.

A. physeteris Baylis, 1923. In *Physeter catodon.*

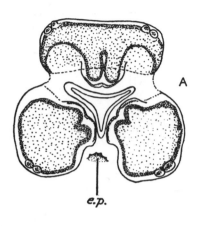

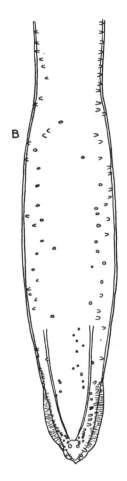

Fig. 188.—*Anisakis rosmari.* A. Head, end-on view. × 144. *e.p*, excretory pore. B. Posterior extremity of male, ventral view. × 200. (After Baylis.)

A. rosmari (Baylis, 1916). In walruses.

Syn., *Ascaris bicolor* Baird, 1868.

A. similis (Baird, 1853). In seals.

A. simplex (Rud., 1809). In *Balænoptera* sp., *Delphinus* sp.

A. typica (Dies., 1861). In *Delphinus* sp., *Phocæna* sp. and *Prodelphinus* sp.

Syn., *Conocephalus typicus* Dies., 1861.

Refs. 20, 28, 37, 49, 123, 125, 127, 128, 131, 436, 597a.

Genus PARANISAKIS Baylis, 1923.

Definition.—ANISAKINÆ : small interlabia present ; dentigerous ridges absent ; the muscular œsophagus is followed by an oval ventriculus ; œsophageal appendix and intestinal cæcum absent. Male : spicules subequal and alate ; gubernaculum massive. Female : vulva in front of the middle of the body. Oviparous, eggs lenticular, shells thin, contents unsegmented when deposited. Parasites of fishes.

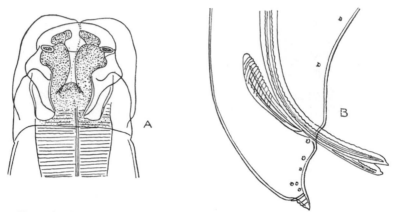

Fig. 189.—*Paranisakis squatinæ.* A. Anterior extremity dorsal view. × 130. B. Posterior extremity of male, lateral view. × 70. (After Baylis.)

Type species : *P. squatinæ* Baylis, 1923. ♂ up to 80 mm., ♀ up to 115 mm. In *Squatina squatina.*
Ref. 34.

Genus RAPHIDASCARIS Railliet and Henry, 1915.

Syn., *Hysterothylacium* Ward and Magath, 1916.

Definition.—ANISAKINÆ : interlabia absent ; dentigerous ridges absent ; lips with cuticular expansions, particularly well-developed on the subventral lips ; the dorsal lip has two papillæ and the subventral lips one each ; œsophagus with an anterior muscular portion and a small posterior ventriculus, from which springs a posterior appendix ; intestinal cæcum absent. Male : tail slightly curved ventrally, tapering to a point ; spicules equal and winged ; gubernaculum absent. Female : vulva in front of the middle of the body. Oviparous. Parasites of fishes.

Type species : *R. acus* (Bloch, 1779). ♂ 31 mm., ♀ 36·5 mm. In *Esox* sp.

Syn., *Ascaris acus* Bloch, 1779.

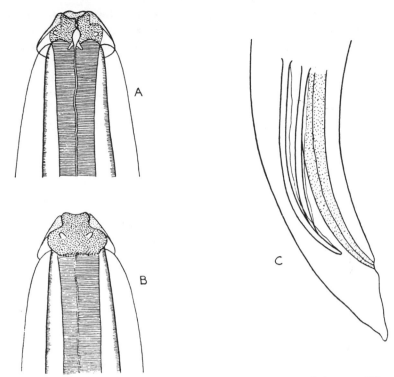

Fig. 190.—*Raphidascaris acus.* A. Anterior extremity, ventral view. × 115. B. Anterior extremity, dorsal view. × 115. C. Posterior extremity of male, lateral view. × 90. (Orig.)

Other species :

    R. brachyurus (Ward and Magath, 1916). In black bass.

    Syn., *Hysterothylacium brachyurum* Ward and Magath,1916.

    R. cayugensis Wigdor, 1918. In *Esox americanus.*

    Syn., *Hysterothylacium cayugensis* Wigdor, 1918.

Refs. 28, 57, 131, 442, 597a, 662, 666.

Genus DUJARDINIA Gedoelst, 1916.

Definition.—ANISAKINÆ : interlabia present with marked grooves running to the bases of the lips ; dentigerous ridges absent, but with the cuticle of their internal surfaces produced into large tooth-like structures apparently capable of being inter-locked ; these structures are carried by three main cuticular lobes on the anterior border of each lip ; œsophagus with a small spherical posterior bulb ; œsophageal appendix absent ; intestinal cæcum present. Male : caudal alæ present in the cloacal region ; caudal papillæ few ; spicules equal and slender ; gubernaculum usually present with an expanded and solid head, and tapering and hollow posteriorly. Female : vulva in the anterior half of the body opening into a muscular almost sucker-like atrium.

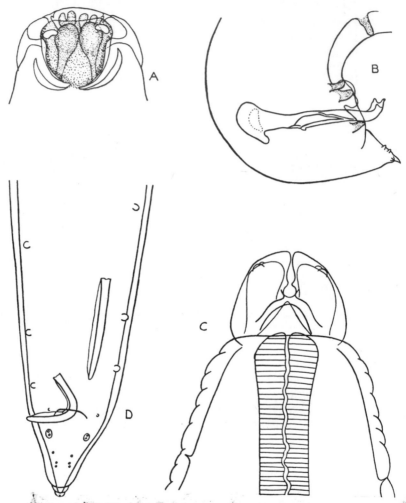

Fig. 191.—*Dujardinia helicina*. A. Head, dorsal view. × 133. B. Posterior extremity of male, lateral view. × 133. (After Baylis.) *Dujardinia halicoris*. C. Anterior extremity, ventral view. × 56. D. Posterior extremity of male, ventral view. × 18. (Orig.)

Oviparous, eggs subglobular with thin shells, unsegmented when deposited. Parasites of reptiles, fishes, and marine mammals.

Type species : *D. helicina* (Molin, 1860). ♂ about 18 mm. ♀ 34–40 mm. In *Crocodilus* spp.

Syn., *Ascaris helicina* Molin, 1860, not *Trispiculascaris heli-cina* (Molin, 1860) of Skrjabin, 1916.

Dujardinia dujardini Travassos, 1920.

Other species :

D. halicoris (Owen, 1833).   In *Halicore dugong.*

D. malapteruri Baylis, 1923.   In *Malpterurus electricus.*

? *D. nigra* (Gedoelst, 1916).   In *Crocodilus niloticus.*

D. woodlandi Baylis, 1923.   In *Gavialis gangeticus.*

Refs. 28, 36, 42, 128, 151, 359, 597a, 639.

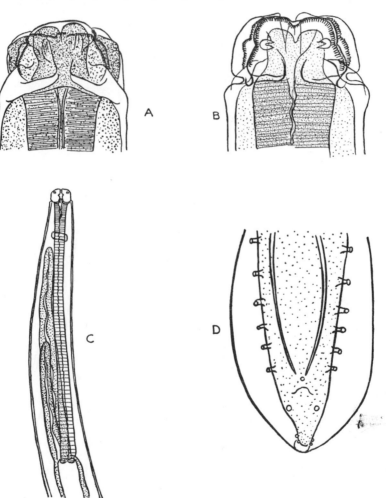

Fig. 192.—*Amplicæcum colurum.* Head, dorsal view. × 70. (After Baylis.)
Amplicæcum africanum. B. Head, dorsal view. × 26. C. Anterior extremity, lateral view. × 26. D. Posterior extremity of male, ventral view. × 70. (After Taylor.)

Genus AMPLICÆCUM Baylis, 1920.

Definition.—ANISAKINÆ : small interlabia present ; dentigerous ridges present ; œsophagus without a ventriculus or posterior bulb ; one (rarely two) intestinal cæcum present ; œsophageal appendix absent. Male : with a few postanal and a number of preanal papillæ ; spicules equal ; gubernaculum absent. Female : vulva in the anterior part of the body. Parasites of birds, amphibia, and reptiles.

Type species : *A. colurum* (Baylis, 1919). ♂ and ♀ 46 mm. In *Lophoaëtus occipitalis.*

Syn., *Ascaris colura* Baylis, 1919.

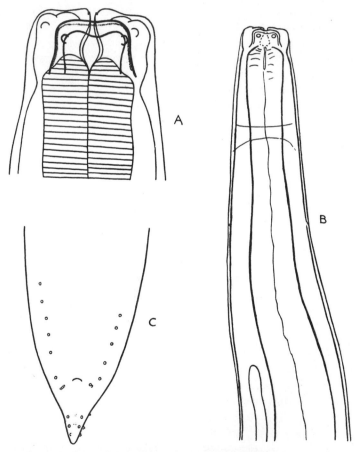

Fig. 193.—*Angusticæcum holopterum.* A. Head, dorsal view. × 84. B. Anterior extremity, dorsal view. × 33. C. Posterior extremity of male, ventral view. × 35. (Orig.)

Other species :

A. *africanum* Taylor, 1924. In *Bufo regularis.*

A. *gedoelsti* nom. nov. In a large toad.

    Syn., *Ascaris bufonis* Gedoelst, 1916, not Schrank, 1788, not Gmelin, 1790.

A. *involuta* (Gedoelst, 1916). In *Chamæleon dilepis.*

A. *varani* Baylis and Daubney, 1922. In *Varanus* sp.

Refs. 22, 28, 151, 597a, 610.

Genus ANGUSTICÆCUM Baylis, 1920.

Definition.—ANISAKINÆ : interlabia absent ; dentigerous ridges present ; œsophagus without a ventriculus or posterior bulb ; a long slender cæcum springs from the intestine a little behind its origin ; œsophageal appendix absent. Male : caudal alæ may or may not be present ; six or seven pairs of preanal papillæ and a variable number of postanal papillæ ; spicules equal ; gubernaculum absent. Female : vulva in the anterior part of the body. Parasites of reptiles and amphibia.

    Type species : A. *holopterum* (Rud., 1819). ♂ 85–95 mm., ♀ 126 mm. In *Testudo* spp.

    Syn., *Ascaris holoptera* Rud., 1819.

Other species :

A. *brevispiculum* Chapin, 1924. In *Testudo denticulata.*

A. *numidicum* (Seurat, 1917). In *Rana* sp.

    Syn., *Porrocæcum numidicum* Seurat, 1917.

Refs. 28, 92, 129, 131, 480, 537, 597a.

Genus PORROCÆCUM Railliet and Henry, 1912.

    Syn., *Terranova* Leiper and Atkinson, 1914.

    ? *Capsularia* Zeder, 1800 (*Agamonema*).

Definition.—ANISAKINÆ : interlabia (usually small) present in most cases ; dentigerous ridges present ; œsophagus with an anterior muscular portion and a posterior ventriculus of oblong shape ; the latter is short in the genotype but in the other species frequently long and bent at an angle so as to open into the intestine laterally ; intestinal cæcum present ; œsophageal appendix absent. Male : spicules equal ; gubernaculum usually absent. Female : vulva near the middle of the body. Oviparous. Parasites of birds, marine mammals, and fishes.

    Type species : P. *crassum* (Deslongchamps, 1824). ♂ (? Adult) 11·6 mm., ♀ 46–48 mm. In ducks.

Other species :

P. *americanum* Schwartz, 1925.   In *Scalopus aquaticus*.

P. *antarcticum* (Leiper and Atkinson, 1914).   In *Mustelus antarcticus*.

   Syn., *Terranova antarctica* Leiper and Atkinson, 1914.

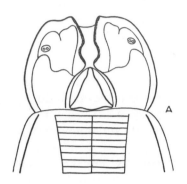
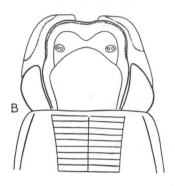

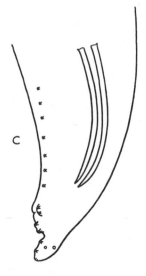

Fig. 194.—*Porrocæcum sulcatum*.   A. Anterior extremity, ventral view.   × 64.
B. Anterior extremity, dorsal view.
× 64.   C. Posterior extremity of male,
lateral view.   × 64.   (Orig.)

P .*angusticolle* (Molin, 1860).   In *Buteo* sp., *Archibuteo* sp.,
   Cirus sp., *Pernis* sp., *Milvus* sp., etc.

P. *crocodili* Taylor, 1924.   In crocodiles.

P. *decipiens* (Krabbe, 1878).   In seals.   Larval form probably
   Ascaris capsularia Rud., 1802;   so *Capsularia salaris*
   (Gmel., 1790) Zeder, 1880.

P. depressum (Zed., 1800).   In *Falco* sp., etc.

P. encapsulatum Schwartz, 1925.   In *Blarina brevicauda*.

P. ensicaudatum (Zed., 1800).   In *Turdus* sp., *Sturnus* sp.

P. pristis Baylis and Daubney, 1922.   In *Pristis* sp.

P. reticulatum (Linst., 1899).   In *Ardea* sp., *Nycticorax* sp.
 Syn., *Ascaris ardeæ* Smith, Fox, and White, 1908.

P. semiteres (Zed., 1800).   In *Vanellus*, etc.

P. serpentulus (Rud., 1809).   In *Ardea* sp., *Grus* sp.

P. sulcatum (Rud., 1819).   In *Thalassochelys* sp., *Testudo* sp.,
 etc.

and probably also :

P. heteroura (Crepl., 1829).   In *Charadrius* sp., etc.

P. kirghisensis (Skrjabin, 1916).   In *Aguila imperialis*.

P. prælongum (Duj., 1845).   In *Colymbus* sp.

P. spirale (Rud., 1795).   In owls.

Refs. 20, 28, 31, 131, 296, 436, 481d, 597a.

Genus CONTRACÆCUM Railliet and Henry, 1912.

Syn., *Kathleena* Leiper and Atkinson, 1914.

Definition.—ANISAKINÆ : interlabia present, usually very well-developed ;   dentigerous ridges absent ;   œsophagus with a

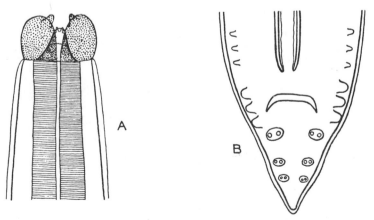

Fig. 195.—*Contracæcum spiculigerum*. A. Anterior extremity, ventral view.
 × 144.   B. Posterior extremity of male, semi-diagrammatic.   (Orig.)

reduced posterior ventriculus, giving off a solid posterior appendix ;
intestinal cæcum present.   Male : without definite caudal alæ ;
three or four pairs of postanal papillæ which may be doubled, and

numerous preanal papillæ ; spicules equal ; gubernaculum usually absent.   Female : vulva in the anterior part of the body.   Oviparous.   Parasites of fish-eating mammals and birds, and of fishes.

Type species : *C. spiculigerum* (Rud., 1809).   ♂ 32–36 mm., ♀ 30–44 mm.   In *Pelecanus* spp., *Phalacrocorax* sp.

Syn., *Ascaris spiculigera* Rud., 1809.

Other species :

C. aduncum (Rud., 1802).   In *Alosa* sp., *Clupea* sp.

C. andersoni Vevers, 1923.   In *Florida cærulea.*

C. auctum (Rud., 1802).   In *Blennius* sp., etc.

C. bidentatum (Linstow, 1899).   In *Acipenser ruthenus.*

C. clavatum (Rud., 1809).   In various fishes.

C. cornutum (Stossich, 1904).   In *Thynnus* sp.

C. engonium Baylis and Daubney, 1922.   In *Ciconia nigra.*

C. fabri (Rud., 1819).   In *Zeus faber.*

C. falcigerum (Railliet and Henry, 1907).   In seals.

C. filiforme (Stoss., 1904).   In *Uranoscopus scaber.*

C. haliaëti Baylis and Daubney, 1923.   In *Haliaëtus* sp.

Syn., *Ascaris aquillæ* Smith, Fox and White, 1908.

C. incurvum (Rud., 1819).   In *Xiphias gladius, Histiophorus gladius.*

C. lobulatum (Schneider, 1866).   In *Platanista* sp.

C. microcephalum (Rud., 1809).   In *Ardea* spp., etc.

Syn., *Kathleena arcuata* Gedoelst, 1916.

C. micropapillatum (Stossich, 1890).   In *Pelecanus* spp.

C. multipapillatum (Drasche, 1882).   In *Tantalus* sp.

C. nasutum (Schneider, 1866).   In *Pelecanus* sp.

C. osculatum (Rud., 1802).   In seals.

Syn., *Kathleena osculata* (Rud., 1802).

C. ovale (Linst., 1907).   In *Podiceps* sp.

C. phoxini (Linst., 1887).   In *Phoxinus lævis.*

C. punctatum (Gedoelst, 1916).   In *Pseudotantalus ibis.*

C. quadricuspe Walton, 1923.   In *Buforides* sp.

C. radiatum (Linst., 1906).   In seals.

C. rectangulum (Linstow, 1906).   In seals.

C. rigidum (Rud., 1809).   In *Lophius* sp.

C. rodhaini (Gedoelst, 1916).   In *Plotus rufus.*

C. rosarium (Connal, 1912).   In *Nycticorax griseus.*

C. schizothoracis Baylis and Daubney, 1922.   In *Schizothorax* sp.

C. scotti (Leiper and Atkinson, 1914).   In *Diomedea* sp.

C. stenocephalum (Railliet and Henry, 1907).   In *Stenorhynchus leptonyx* and *Leptonychotes* sp.

C. tricuspe (Gedoelst, 1916).   In heron, Indian darter.

C. turkestanicum Skrjabin, 1923.   In *Mergus merganser*.

Refs. 28, 34, 42, 151, 296, 328a, 436, 581, 583, 597a, 657, 659.

Genus CLŒOASCARIS Baylis, 1923.

Definition.—ANISAKINÆ : each lip is provided with a pair of large conical teeth on its inner surface ; interlabia absent : a collar-like fold of cuticle surrounds the neck, and between this and the bases of the lips is an area covered with small spines ; œsophagus with a small rounded ventriculus and also an œsophageal appendix ; intestinal cæcum present ; cervical papillæ prominent. Male: spicules short, slender, and equal. Female : vulva in the anterior half of the body. Oviparous, eggs oval, shells thin and granulated and containing an unsegmented ovum

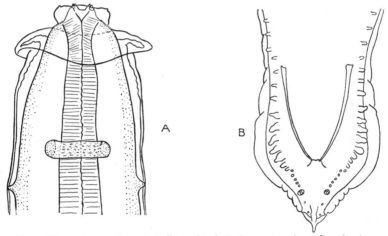

Fig. 196.—*Clœoascaris spinicollis*. A. Anterior extremity, dorsal view. × 70. B. Posterior extremity of male, ventral view. × 70. (After Baylis.)

at deposition.   Parasites of semiaquatic carnivorous land mammals.

Type species : *C. spinicollis* Baylis, 1923. ♂ 40 mm., ♀ 39 mm. In *Lutra* sp. and *Atilax* sp.

Ref. 38.

Genus MULTICÆCUM Baylis, 1923.

Definition.—ANISAKINÆ : small interlabia present with well-marked grooves running to the bases of the lips ; dentigerous ridges present ; œsophagus with a small posterior ventriculus from which arise two anterior and three posterior appendices ; intestinal cæcum present. Male : caudal alæ absent ; caudal papillæ few ; spicules equal ; gubernaculum present. Female : vulva near the middle of the body ; vagina directed posteriorly.

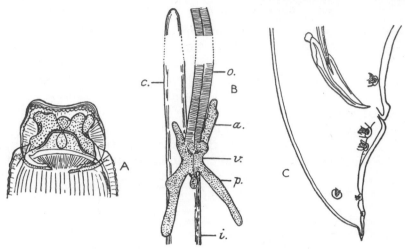

Fig. 197.—*Multicæcum agile.* A. Head, dorsal view. (After Wedl.) B. Intestinal and œsophageal diverticula. *c*, intestinal cæcum ; *i*, intestine ; *o*, œsophagus ; *v*, ventriculus ; *a*, anterior appendix ; *p*, posterior appendix. × 36. C. Posterior extremity of male, lateral view. × 150. (After Baylis.)

Oviparous, eggs oval with a thin shell, contents segmented when deposited. Parasites of crocodiles.

Type species : *M. agile* (Wedl, 1862). ♂ 34·6 mm., ♀ 31·6 mm. In *Crocodilus niloticus.*

Syn., *Ascaris agilis* Wedl, 1862.

Refs. 36, 664.

Subfamily GŒZIINÆ (Travassos, 1919) Baylis, 1920.

Syn., *Gœzinæ* Travassos, 1919.

Definition.—HETEROCHEILIDÆ : cuticle furnished with a series of circlets of spines.

Genus GŒZIA Zeder, 1800.

Syn., *Cochlus* Zeder, 1803.
     Prionoderma Rud., 1809, not Cuvier, 1817.
     Lecanocephalus Dies., 1839.

Definition.—GŒZIINÆ : cuticle presenting a series of rings provided posteriorly with spines directed backwards ; caudal extremity in each sex rounded and prolonged into an appendix more or less unarmed ; anterior extremity domed and separated from the rest of the body by a constriction ; œsophagus pestle-shaped and provided with a long glandular appendix directed posteriorly ; intestine generally bent at its origin, where it gives off a short cæcum directed anteriorly. Male : spicules subequal. Female : vulva a little in front of the middle of

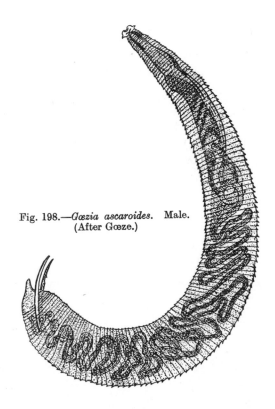

Fig. 198.—*Gœzia ascaroides*. Male.
(After Gœze.)

the body. Oviparous, eggs small and globular. Parasites of fishes.

Type species : *Gœzia ascaroides* (Gœze, 1782). ♂ and ♀ 25 mm. In *Silurus glanis*.

Syn., *Cucullanus ascaroides* Gœze, 1782.
Cochlus armatus Zeder, 1803.
Prionoderma ascaroides (Gœze, 1782) Rud., 1809.

Other species :
G. annulata (Molin, 1860). In *Labrax lupus*.
G. kollari (Molin, 1858). In *Chrysophrys aurata*.

G. spinulosa (Dies., 1839). In *Sudis gigas.*
Syn., *Lecanocephalus spinulosus* Dies., 1839.
Refs. 28, 122, 128, 186, 442, 476, 636, 681, 682.

Subfamily CROSSOPHORINÆ Baylis, 1920.

Definition.—HETEROCHEILIDÆ : behind the lips is a collar consisting of a double row of fimbriæ.

Genus CROSSOPHORUS Hemprich and Ehrenberg, 1828.

Definition.—CROSSOPHORINÆ : lips semicircular in outline, each provided with two papillæ and furnished near the outer edges of

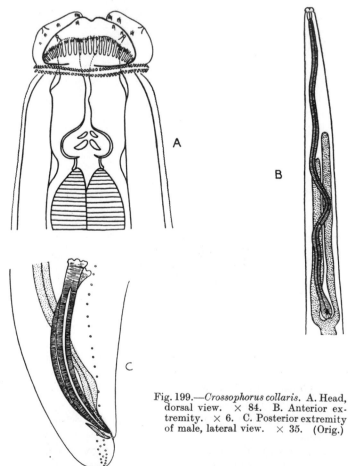

Fig. 199.—*Crossophorus collaris.* A. Head, dorsal view. × 84. B. Anterior extremity. × 6. C. Posterior extremity of male, lateral view. × 35. (Orig.)

its inner aspect with seven or eight groups of " combs " of pointed teeth forming an interrupted dentigerous ridge ; behind the three lips is a constriction occupied by a collar consisting of a double row of fimbriæ, these form in reality a single endless chain which doubles on itself at the base of each lip externally and passes round the base of the lip on its inner surface ; œsophagus very long and slender, enlarged posteriorly, the anterior portion contains an elaborate chitinous apparatus ; two intestinal cæca directed forwards from the commencement of the gut.   Male : tail blunt ; caudal papillæ arranged in two parallel rows on each side, each row consisting of nine postanal papillæ, whilst in front of the anus the inner row consists of about forty papillæ and the outer of only five ; spicules equal and alate ; gubernaculum present.   Female : tail conical ; vulva in the middle third of the body ; uteri opposed.   Oviparous, eggs oval with a moderately thick smooth shell.   Parasites of Hydracoidea.

Type species : *Crossophorus collaris* Hemprich and Ehrenberg, 1828.   ♂ 50–65 mm., ♀ 55–90 mm.   In *Hyrax*.

Syn., *Ascaris ferox* Hemprich and Ehrenberg, 1828.

Other species :   ? *Crossophorus tentaculatus* Hemprich and Ehrenberg, 1828.   In *Hyrax*.

Refs. 24, 28, 213, 370.

ASCAROIDEA insufficiently known.

Genus ACANTHOCHEILUS Molin, 1858.

Definition.—ANISAKINÆ ? :   insufficiently described ;   mouth with three lips, each having two pairs of small pointed teeth on

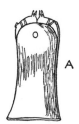 

Fig. 200.—*Acanthocheilus quadridentatus.*   A. Anterior extremity, dorsal view. B. Anterior extremity, end-on view.   (After Molin.)

its inner surface and a single papilla externally.   Female : vulva in the anterior part of the body.   Found in marine fishes.   Linton

(1900) described a worm from the stomach of the tiger shark which he named *Acanthocheilus nidifex :* this worm had an intestinal cæcum running forwards beside the œsophagus.

Type species : *A. quadridentatus* Molin, 1858. ♂ 23 mm., ♀ 8 (80 ?) mm. In *Mustelus plebejus.*

Other species :

A. bicuspis (Wedl, 1855). In *Scillium* sp., *Pristiurus* sp.

A. intermedius Oerley, 1885. In *Mustelus lævis.*

A. nidifex Linton, 1900. In *Galeocerdo tigrinus.*

Refs. 125, 333, 355.

Genus HELIGMUS Dujardin, 1845.

Definition.—ANISAKINÆ ? : body slightly attenuated towards the extremities, head rounded with three small lips each bearing a papilla ; œsophagus muscular and enlarged posteriorly, followed by a distinct ventriculous or ? bulb. Male : tail curved spirally, terminating sharply in a conical point ; anus on a prominent tubercle ; a double row of twelve or thirteen adanal papillæ ; spicule single, capable of being rolled into a loose helix in the interior, and consisting of a transversely striated tube formed of a transparent membrane. Female : vulva about the anterior third of the body. Parasites of fishes.

Type species : *H. longicirrus* Dujardin, 1845. ♂ 17 mm., ♀ 25·5 mm. In a fish, *Pleuronectes platessa,* from Rennes.

Ref. 131, 597a.

Superfamily SPIRUROIDEA Railliet & Henry, 1915.

Definition.—EUNEMATODA : usually more or less filiform worms ; mouth usually with two lips, but there may be four or six small lips, or rarely the lips may be inconspicuous or absent. Behind the buccal cavity, which is bounded by the lips, there is frequently a chitinous vestibule ; rarely the buccal cavity is large and chitinous ; œsophagus usually long, cylindrical, and divided into two parts, a shorter anterior muscular portion and a longer glandular posterior portion, rarely it is undivided and sometimes enlarged anteriorly or posteriorly ; intestine usually simple without diverticula. Male : spicules usually very unequal and dissimilar. Female : vulva usually near the middle of the body, sometimes posteriorly, and rarely in the œsophageal region. Parasites of the alimentary canal, respiratory system, or orbital, nasal or oral cavities of vertebrates.

KEY TO FAMILIES.

1. Sexual dimorphism marked, the female being greatly distended towards the middle of its length and fusiform in shape .   .   Tetrameridæ, p. 361.

    Sexual dimorphism not marked .   2

2. Head provided with more or less prominent appendages of diverse appearance .   .   .   .   Ancyracanthidæ, p. 364.

    Head without appendages .   .   3

3. With four highly specialized lips ; males always rolled about females, the posterior end of which is invaginated forming a sucker-like groove from which projects a chitinous hook.   .   Hedruridæ, p. 374.

    Without four highly specialized lips, etc.   4

4. With a large chitinous buccal capsule .   .   .   .   .   Camallanidæ, p. 376.

    Without a large chitinous buccal capsule   5

5. Head consisting of two large lateral lobes ; œsophagus muscular throughout, dilated anteriorly to form a pseudo-buccal capsule, and enlarged posteriorly   .   .   .   .   .   Cucullanidæ, p. 380.

    Head and œsophagus not exhibiting the above characters .   .   6

6. Anterior end of body with cuticular cordons   .   .   .   .   Acuariidæ, p. 326.

    Anterior end of body without cuticular cordons   .   .   .   7

7. Mouth with two large lateral trilobed lips, each having the cuticle of its inner surface thickened and raised into longitudinal tooth-like ridges meeting or interlocking with those of the opposite lip ; with a cuticular head bulb   .   .   .   .   Gnathostomidæ, p. 338.

Lips usually without the above
characters ; without a cuticular
head bulb   8
8. Cuticle armed with chitinous hook-
like spines arranged in longitudinal rows or in circles along
the whole, or the anterior por-
tion, of the body   .   .   .   Rictulariidæ, p. 343.
Cuticle not armed with chitinous
hook-like spines   .   .   .   9
9. Cuticle with numerous longitudinal
dark bands ; œsophagus short,
entirely muscular, and some-
what enlarged posteriorly   .   Seuratidæ, p. 349.
Cuticle without longitudinal dark
bands ; œsophagus without the
above characters   .   .   .   10
10. Mouth with large simple triangular
lateral lips armed with one or
more teeth ; usually with a large
cephalic   collarette ;   usually
without a vestibule. Males with
large caudal alæ supported by
long costiform papillæ   .   .   Physalopteridæ, p. 351
Lips, if present, without the above
characters ; cephalic collarette
absent ; vestibule almost always
present. Males with or without
caudal alæ   11
11. Males with broad caudal alæ, and
usually with four pairs (rarely
more) of large preanal papillæ
which   are   almost   invariably
pedunculated   .   .   .   Spiruridæ, p. 290.
Males with or without caudal alæ,
preanal papillæ sessile, usually
numerous, and arranged in a
linear row   .   .   .   .   Thelaziidæ, p. 316.
12. SPIRUROIDEA insufficiently known, p. 385.

FAMILY SPIRURIDÆ OERLEY, 1885.

Definition.—SPIRUROIDEA : mouth usually with trilobed lateral
lips, occasionally small dorsal and ventral lips may also be present,

or definite lips absent. Behind the mouth cavity bounded by the lips there is usually a more or less cylindrical, chitinized vestibule ; œsophagus long and cylindrical, and divided into a short anterior muscular portion, and a longer glandular part ; cervical papillæ, usually at least one, in front of the nerve ring ; lateral flanges present or absent. Male : caudal alæ well-developed and supported by pedunculated papillæ, of which there are almost always four preanal pairs. Female : vulva usually near the middle of the body ; oviparous. Parasites of œsophagus, stomach, and intestine of vertebrates.

KEY TO SUBFAMILIES.

1. Cephalic and œsophageal regions ornamented with cuticular plaques . . . . . Gongyloneminæ, p. 312.
   Cephalic and œsophageal regions not ornamented with cuticular plaques 2
2. Vestibule with ring-like or spiral thickenings . . . . Arduenninæ, p. 306.
   Vestibule without ring-like or spiral thickenings 3
3. Lips large and distinctly trilobed with cuticle of inner surface thickened and tending to inter-lock with that of opposite lip . Spiroxyinæ, p. 302.
   Lips indefinite or, if present, with-out the above characters . . Spirurinæ, p. 291.

Subfamily SPIRURINÆ Railliet, 1915.

Definition.—SPIRURIDÆ : mouth with or without definite lips vestibule without ring-like or spiral thickenings ; cephalic and œsophageal regions not ornamented with cuticular tubercles.

KEY TO GENERA.

1. Cuticle with a ventral prominence or boss in anterior region of body . Spirura, p. 292.
   Cuticle without a ventral boss . . 2
2. Vestibule infundibular with six radially arranged triangular chitinous plates Cylicospirura, p. 294
   Vestibule without six radially arranged triangular chitinous plates . . 3

3. Mouth hexagonal, without definite lips; pulp of cephalic papillæ very large, prominent, and sending a branch inwards to small subsidiary papillæ situated just within the mouth aperture . . . . . Spirocerca, p. 295.

    Mouth with definite lips; cephalic papillæ without the above characters 4

4. Lateral lips each bear externally two small triangular membranous alæ . Hadjelia, p. 301.

    Lateral lips without membranous alæ . 5

5. Dorsal and ventral lips deeply notched; vestibule with very delicate walls; uteri parallel . . . . Cyrnea, p. 299.

    Dorsal and ventral lips not deeply notched; vestibule with heavily-chitinized walls; uteri divergent . 6

6. Left spicule longer than right, with one or two pairs of pedunculated postanal papillæ; eggs without polar filaments; parasites of mammals and birds . . . . . . Habronema, p. 296.

    Right spicule longer than left; with four pairs of pedunculated postanal papillæ; eggs with polar filaments; parasites of fishes . . . . Metabronema, p. 299.

Genus SPIRURA Blanchard, 1849.

Syn., *Spiroptera* Rud., 1819, in part.

Definition.—SPIRURINÆ: posterior part of body decidedly thicker than the anterior, more or less spirally twisted; cuticle with fine transverse striations and with a prominent ventral hump or boss about 2 mm. from the anterior extremity, lateral flanges absent; mouth elongated dorso-ventrally, surrounded by the chitinous prolongation of the vestibule, which is everted and thickened dorsally and ventrally; just outside this are two small trilobed lateral lips each having a lateral and two submedian head papillæ, but without teeth on their inner surface; vestibule well-marked, wide, and cylindrical when seen laterally, but much narrower and funnel-shaped when viewed dorsally or ventrally; œsophagus very long, cylindrical, and indistinctly divided into two parts, a very short anterior and a long slightly wider posterior portion. Excretory pore just behind the first portion of the œsophagus. Male : posterior extremity conical with large caudal alæ, uniting behind the tip of the tail, supported by four pairs of pedunculated preanal papillæ, a single unpaired papilla immediately in front of the cloaca and two or three pairs of pedunculated postanal papillæ—one pair immediately behind the cloaca and the others some distance posteriorly—and in addition there are

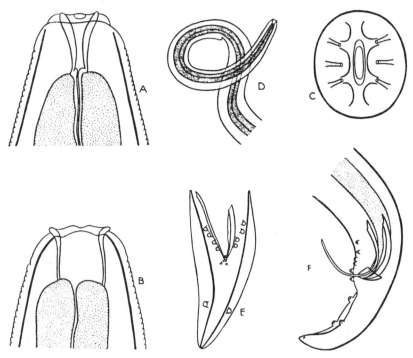

Fig. 201.—*Spirura talpæ*. A. Head, ventral view. × 300. B. Head, lateral view. × 300. C. Head, end-on view. × 300. D. Anterior extremity, lateral view showing ventral boss. × 32. E. Posterior extremity of male, ventral view. × 64. F. Posterior extremity of male, lateral view. × 64. (Orig.)

one or two pairs of small papillæ near the tip of the tail ; spicules unequal and dissimilar, the right being longer and narrower, and the left broader and winged ; gubernaculum present. Female : posterior extremity conical and rounded ; vulva behind the middle of the body about three-fifths of the length of the worm from the anterior extremity. Oviparous, eggs with a thick shell containing an embryo when deposited. Parasites of insectivora and carnivora.

Type species : *S. talpæ* (Gmelin, 1790). ♂ 10–20 mm.,
♀ 20–32 mm. In *Talpa europæa.*

Syn., *Ascaris talpæ* Gmelin, 1790.

Ascaris strumosa Froelich, 1791.

Fusaria convoluta Zeder, 1803.

Spiroptera strumosa (Froelich, 1791) Rud., 1819.

Filaria strumosa (Froelich, 1791) Schneider, 1866.

Other species :

S. rothschildi Seurat, 1915. In *Elephantulus deserti.*

Syn., *S. gastrophila* Seurat, 1913, not Mueller, 1894.

S. rytipleurites (Deslongchamps, 1824). In cat, fox, and
hedgehog.

Syn., *Filaria rytipleurites* Deslongchamps, 1824.

Filaria gastrophila Mueller, 1894.

Refs. 55, 205, 483, 485, 489, 511, 524, 535.

Genus CYLICOSPIRURA Vevers, 1922.

Definition.—SPIRURINÆ : mouth circular without definite lips,
with six small head papillæ ; vestibule deep, infundibular, and

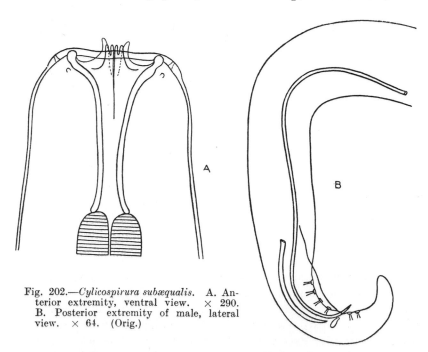

Fig. 202.—*Cylicospirura subæqualis.* A. Anterior extremity, ventral view. × 290.
B. Posterior extremity of male, lateral
view. × 64. (Orig.)

provided with six triangular chitinous plates arranged radially,
the internal free end of each of which terminates in a bicuspid

tooth, which projects slightly beyond the entrance to the mouth capsule ; œsophagus very long and divided into two portions, the anterior being much shorter than the posterior. Male : posterior extremity twisted spirally ; narrow symmetrical caudal alæ ; four pairs of preanal and two of postanal papillæ ; spicules very unequal ; gubernaculum present. Female : vulva in the anterior half of the body. Ovoviviparous. Parasites of carnivora.

Type species : *C. subæqualis* (Molin, 1860). ♂ 22·5 mm., ♀ 19–21 mm. In *Felis* spp.

Syn., *Spiroptera subæqualis* Molin, 1860.

Refs. 128, 358, 490, 656.

Genus SPIROCERCA Railliet and Henry, 1911.

Definition.—SPIRURINÆ : without definite lips, mouth hexagonal with long axis dorso-ventral, leading into a vestibule with

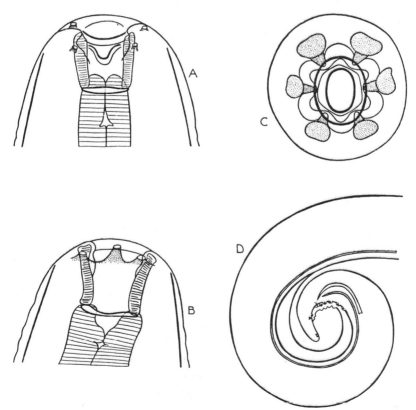

Fig. 203.—*Spirocerca sanguinolenta.* A. Head, ventral view. × 140. B. Head, lateral view. × 140. C. Head, end-on view. × 140. D. Posterior extremity of male, lateral view. × 24. (Orig.)

cuticular walls of considerable thickness, which is expanded anteriorly with its edges folded inwards and is narrower posteriorly. The border of the mouth is surrounded by six masses of dense parenchyma, which are the pulps of the cephalic papillæ, each pulp mass sends a branch inwards to a small subsidiary papilla situated in the wall of the vestibule just within the mouth aperture —these are " the teeth " described by Railliet and Henry (1911) ; œsophagus divided into two portions, a shorter narrow muscular anterior portion and a longer wide glandular posterior portion ; cervical papillæ at the level of the nerve ring. Male : tail spiral ; caudal alæ present ; four pairs of pedunculated preanal papillæ and a single large median papilla on the anterior lip of the cloacal aperture, two pairs of postanal pedunculated papillæ and a group of five pairs of minute papillæ near the tip of the tail ; spicules very unequal ; a rudimentary accessory piece is present. Female : tail blunt, with a pair of almost terminal papillæ ; vulva anterior, near the posterior end of the œsophagus ; uteri parallel. Oviparous, eggs cylindrical with thick shells, containing embryos when deposited. Parasites in tumours of the œsophagus, stomach, aorta, and lungs of carnivora.

Type species : *S. sanguinolenta* (Rud., 1819). ♂ 40–50 mm., ♀ 70–80 mm. In dog, jackal, and fox.

Syn., *Spiroptera sanguinolenta* Rud., 1819.

Refs. 33, 432, 477, 490, 496, 552.

Genus HABRONEMA Dies., 1861.

Syn., *Dermofilaria* Rivolta, 1884.

Definition.—SPIRURINÆ : mouth with two lateral lips usually trilobed and without teeth, sometimes dorsal and ventral lips in addition ; cuticular flange may be present on one or both sides of the body ; cervical papillæ in front of the nerve ring ; vestibule well-developed, strongly chitinized and cylindrical or funnel-shaped ; œsophagus consists of two parts, the anterior part being the shorter. Male : tail spirally coiled ; large caudal alæ present ; four pairs of pedunculated preanal papillæ and one or two pairs of postanal papillæ, with two or three pairs of small papillæ near the tip of the tail ; spicules very unequal, the left being the longer ; gubernaculum present. Female : posterior extremity conical ; vulva near the middle of the body ; uteri divergent. Oviparous, eggs oval, with thin or thick shells, containing embryos at deposition. Parasites of the stomach of mammals and birds.

Type species : *H. muscæ* (Carter, 1861). ♂ 8–14 mm., ♀ 13–22 mm. In equines.

Syn., *Filaria muscæ* Carter, 1861.

Other species :

H. chevreuxi Seurat, 1913. In *Felis ocreata*.

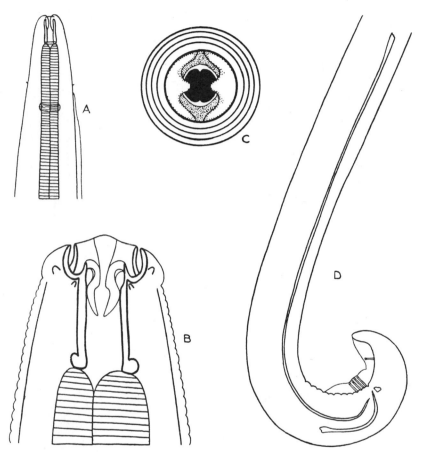

Fig. 204.—*Habronema muscæ.* A. Anterior extremity, ventral view. × 90.
B. Head, lateral view. × 400. C. Head, end-on view. × 480. D.
Posterior extremity of male, lateral view. × 56. (Orig.)

H. colaptes Walton, 1923. In *Colaptes* sp.

H. ficheuri Seurat, 1916. In *Bubulcus lucidus*.

H. grimaldiæ Seurat, 1915. In *Vulpes atlantica*.

H. incertum (Smith, 1908). In parrakeets.

H. leptopterum (Rud., 1819). In *Falco buteo, Accipiter nisus*.

H. mansioni Seurat, 1914. In *Buteo vulgaris*.

H. megastoma (Rud., 1819).   In equines.
 Syn., *Spiroptera megastoma* Rud., 1819.
   Dermofilaria irritans Rivolta, 1884.
H. microstoma (Schneider, 1866).   In equines.
H. monopterum Gendre, 1923.   In nocturnal birds of prey.
H. nouveli Seurat, 1915.   In *Genetta* sp.
H. seurati Skrjabin, 1917.   In *Falco* sp.
H. spinosum Gendre, 1923.   In *Falco tinnunculus*.

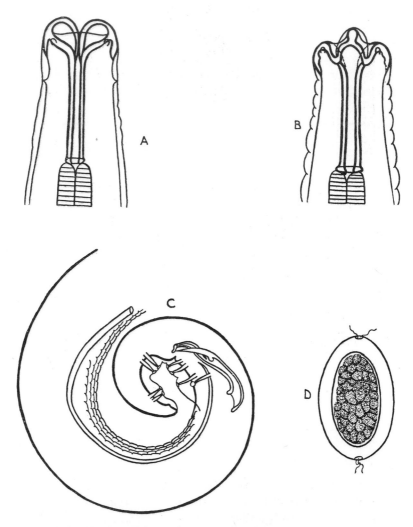

Fig. 205.—*Metabronema magnum*. A. Head, ventral view.   × 115.
B. Head, lateral view.   × 115.   C. Tail of male, lateral view.   × 56.
D. Egg.   × 900.   (Orig.)

*H. *tulostoma* (Hemp. and Ehrenb., in Schneider, 1866).   In vultures.

H. *unilaterale* (Molin, 1860) Seurat, 1914.   In *Neophron percnopterus.*

H. *zebræ* Theiler, 1923.   In zebra.

Refs. 125, 181, 443a, 459, 467, 472a, 490, 497, 499, 511, 524, 555, 578, 583, 615, 659.

Genus METABRONEMA n. g.

Definition.—SPIRURINÆ : mouth with large lateral lips, and small median lips continuous with the lateral by means of a cuticular fold ; the whole head structure is strengthened with a chitinous support which is continuous with the chitinous wall of the vestibule ; cuticular flanges present on both sides of the body ; cervical papillæ situated far forwards slightly behind the lips ; vestibule thick-walled and cylindrical ; œsophagus consists of two parts.   Male : tail spirally coiled ; caudal alæ well-developed ; four pairs of pedunculated preanal papillæ and four pairs of pedunculated postanal papillæ, and a pair of large sessile papillæ near the tip of the tail ; spicules very unequal, the right being the larger ; gubernaculum present.   Female : tail conical ; vulva near the junction of the anterior and middle thirds of the body ; uteri divergent.   Oviparous, eggs thick-shelled with a small button-shaped structure at either end from each of which arise two very delicate filaments, they contain a morula when deposited.   Parasites of fishes.

Type species :   *M. magnum* (Taylor, 1925).   ♂ 23–25 mm., ♀ 19–94 mm.   In *Trochurus declivis*, and *Sparus* sp.

Syn., *Habronema magna* Taylor, 1925.

Ref. 611.

Genus CYRNEA Seurat, 1914.

Definition.—SPIRURINÆ :   mouth with two well-developed lateral lips, exhibiting dentiform thickenings internally, and dorsal and ventral lips with the free border deeply notched, each having a pair of submedian papillæ ; lateral flanges absent ; cervical papillæ far forward, anterior to œsophagus ; vestibule cylindrical and not strongly chitinized ; œsophagus long, divided into two parts, the anterior being the shorter.   Male : tail not inrolled ; well-developed, transversely striated caudal alæ ; with nine pairs of long pedunculated papillæ, of which three are preanal, and in addition a pair of very small preanal papillæ ; spicules very

---

* Possibly this species is synonymous with *H. unilaterale.*

unequal ; gubernaculum present. Female : tail conical, digitiform ; vulva near the middle of the body, or a little in front of
the anus ; uteri parallel. Oviparous, eggs with thick shells and
containing embryos. Parasites of birds.

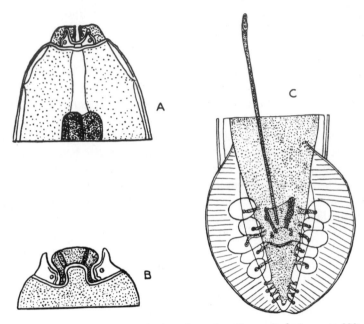

Fig. 206.—*Cyrnea eurycerca.* A. Anterior extremity, ventral view. × 230.
B. Anterior extremity, lateral view. × 230. C. Posterior extremity of
male, ventral view. × 150. (After Seurat.)

Type species : *C. eurycerca* Seurat, 1914. ♂ 7·6 mm., ♀ ? In
partridges.

Other species :

    C. bulbosa (Linstow, 1906).   In *Pavo* spp.

    C. excisa (Molin, 1860).   In *Ciconia* spp.

        Syn., *Spiroptera excisa* Molin, 1860.

            Physaloptera striata Linstow, 1883.

    C. ovata (Linstow, 1907).   In *Astur melanoleucus.*

        Syn., *Physaloptera ovata* Linstow, 1907.

    C. parroti Seurat, 1917.   In rock partridge.

    C. semilunaris (Molin, 1860).   In *Crotophaga major.*

        Syn., *Spiroptera semilunaris* Molin, 1860.

            Spiroptera lanceolata Molin, 1860.

Refs. 128, 358, 378, 497, 499, 504, 543.

Genus HADJELIA Seurat, 1916.

Syn., *Gilsonia* Gedoelst, 1919.

Definition.—SPIRURINÆ : mouth with two large lateral trilobed lips, without teeth on their inner surface, but with two small triangular wings or crests set obliquely on the external surface of each, and with small deeply-notched dorsal and ventral lips ;

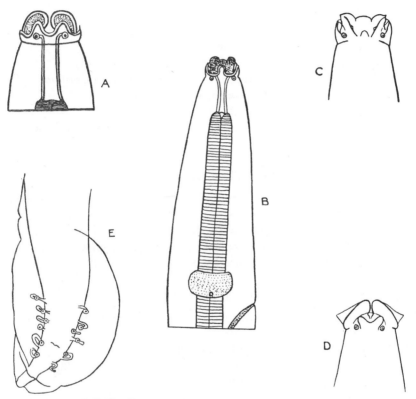

Fig. 207.—*Hadjelia lhuillieri.* A. Anterior extremity, ventral view. B. Anterior extremity, lateral view. (After Seurat.) *Hadjelia inermis.* C. Anterior extremity, lateral view. D. Anterior extremity, ventral view. E. Posterior extremity of male, ventral view. (After Gendre.)

lateral flanges absent ; mouth cavity leads into a cylindrical vestibule ; œsophagus divided into two parts, the anterior being the shorter. Male : posterior extremity conical and slightly coiled ; large caudal alæ ; four pairs of long pedunculated preanal papillæ, two pairs of long pedunculated postanal papillæ, and a pair of sessile papillæ near the tip of the tail ; spicules very unequal ; gubernaculum absent. Female : posterior extremity short, rounded and conical ; vulva in the anterior part of the body, in front of the posterior extremity of the œsophagus ; ovejector elongate ; uteri divergent. Oviparous, eggs with a thick smooth shell, slightly thickened at the poles, and containing an embryo at deposition. Parasites of the gizzard of birds.

Type species : *H. lhuillieri* Seurat, 1916. ♂ unknown, ♀ 18–22 mm. In *Caccabis petrosa*.

Other species :

> *H. inermis* (Gedoelst, 1919). In *Cranorrhinus corrugatus, Lophoceros* sp., *Irrisor* sp., *Oriolus* sp., *Halcyon* sp., etc. Syn., *Gilsonia inermis* Gedoelst, 1919.
>
> *H. parva* Gendre, 1923. In *Trachelotis senegalensis*.
>
> *H. truncata* (Creplin, 1825). In *Upupa* sp. and *Coracias* sp. Syn., *Spiroptera truncata* Creplin, 1825.

Refs. 112, 156, 179, 180, 533.

The genera *Cyrnea* and *Hadjelia* seem to be very closely allied to *Habronema*.

Subfamily SPIROXYINÆ Baylis and Lane, 1920.

Definition.—SPIRURIDÆ : mouth with large distinctly trilobed lips ; the cuticle of the inner surface is thickened and thrown into folds and tends to interlock with that of the outer lip ; vestibule present without ring-like or spiral thickenings ; cephalic and œsophageal regions not ornamented with cuticular plaques.

KEY TO GENERA.

1. Vestibule long and cylindrical . . Protospirura, p. 304.
   Vestibule short 2
2. Spicules subequal, gubernaculum absent . . . . . Spiroxys, p. 302.
   Spicules very unequal, gubernaculum present . . . . . Hartertia, p. 305.

Genus SPIROXYS Schneider, 1866.

Definition.—SPIROXYINÆ : mouth with two large distinctly trilobed lateral lips each having the cuticle of its inner surface thickened, tending to interlock with that of the opposite lip, and provided with teeth ; mouth cavity leads into a short vestibule ; œsophagus cylindrical and divided into an anterior muscular and a larger posterior glandular portion. Male : well-developed caudal alæ, and a preanal vesicular swelling, supported by nine pairs of pedunculated papillæ, of which three pairs are preanal, and in addition, there are two pairs of ventral sessile papillæ, one in front of, and one behind, the cloaca ; spicules delicate and sub-equal ; gubernaculum absent. Female : vulva near the middle

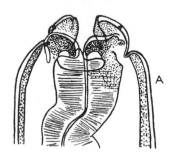

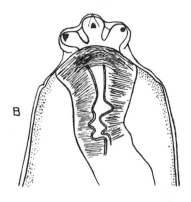

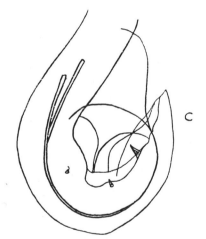

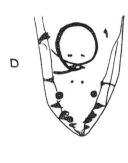

Fig. 208. *Spiroxys contorta*. A. Anterior extremity, ventral view. × 160. B. Anterior extremity, lateral view. × 160. C. Posterior extremity of male, lateral view. × 36. D. Posterior extremity of male, ventral view. × 48. (After Baylis and Lane.)

of the body ; vagina directed anteriorly ; uteri divergent. Oviparous, eggs with a thin colourless stippled shell, from which the unsegmented granular contents are separated by a space. Parasites of stomach wall of tortoises and ? snakes.

Type species : *S. contorta* (Rud., 1819). ♂ 15–25 mm., ♀ 20–30 mm. In *Emys* spp.

Syn., *Spiroptera contorta* Rud., 1819.

Other species :

S. annulata Baylis and Daubney, 1922.   In *Chitra indica*.

S. gangetica Baylis and Lane, 1920.   In *Trionyx gangeticus*.

? *S. constricta* (Leidy, 1856).   In *Tropidonotus* sp.

Refs. 42, 46, 271, 444, 477, 480, 545.

Genus PROTOSPIRURA Seurat, 1914.

Definition.—Spiroxyinæ : body regularly attenuated anteriorly, mouth with two large lateral trilobed lips each bearing three papillæ, each lobe is provided with teeth on its internal surface ;

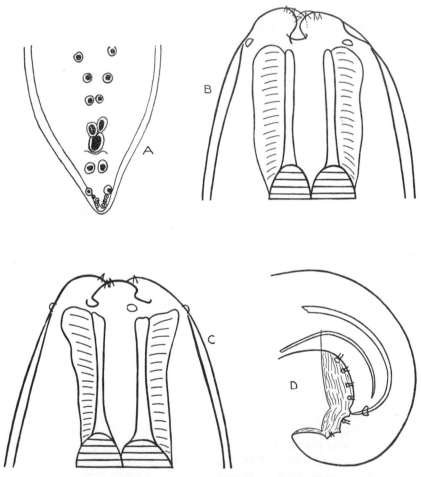

Fig. 209. *Protospirura numidica.* A. Posterior extremity of male, ventral view. (After Seurat.) *Protospirura ascaroidea.* B. Head, ventral view. × 160. C. Head, lateral view. × 160. D. Posterior extremity of male, lateral view. × 23. (Orig.)

cuticular lateral flanges absent ; cervical papillæ very anterior, in front of the nerve ring ; vestibule cylindrical and long ; œsophagus very long, divided into two parts. Male : posterior extremity spiral ; large cylindrical caudal alæ present ; four pairs of slightly pedunculated preanal papillæ and two pairs of large postanal papillæ, also three or four pairs of small papillæ near the tip of the tail; spicules unequal or subequal; gubernaculum present. Female : tail conical and very short ; vulva towards the middle of the body, or anterior to it ; ovejector relatively short and simple ; uteri divergent. Oviparous, eggs oval with a thick shell and containing an embryo when deposited. Parasites of mammals.

Type species : *P. numidica* Seurat, 1914. ♂ 22 mm., ♀ 35 mm. In *Felis ocreata.*

Other species :

P. ascaroidea Hall, 1916. In *Geomys breviceps.*

P. bonnei Ortlepp, 1924. In rats.

P. gracilis Cram, 1924. In cats.

P. guianensis Ortlepp, 1924. In Monki-monki.

P. labiodentata (Linstow, 1899). In *Mus navalis.*

P. muris (Gmelin, 1790). In *Mus decumanus.*

Syn., *Spiroptera obtusa* Rud., 1819.

P. muricola Gedoelst, 1916. In rats.

Refs. 111b, 205, 381a, 511, 514, 526.

Genus HARTERTIA Seurat, 1914.

Definition.—SPIROXYINÆ : mouth with two large lateral trilobed lips, with the cuticle of their inner surfaces thickened, bearing teeth, thrown into folds, and interlocking with those of the opposite side ; each lip is provided with a lateral and a pair of submedian papillæ ; lateral flanges very narrow and limited to the anterior part of the body ; cervical papillæ very anterior, just behind the lips ; mouth cavity followed by a short vestibule ; œsophagus divided into two parts, the anterior short and muscular. Male : posterior extremity straight ; large caudal alæ, with four pairs of pedunculated preanal and two pairs of pedunculated postanal papillæ, and four pairs of sessile papillæ near the tip of the tail ; spicules very unequal ; gubernaculum present. Female : posterior extremity conical and rounded at the tip ; vulva near the. middle of the body. Oviparous, eggs with a thick double shell with a very distinct vitelline membrane, containing a larva when deposited. Parasites of birds.

Type species : *H. obesa* Seurat, 1915. ♂ 23·5 mm., ♀ 40·8 mm. In *Caccabis petrosa spatzi.*

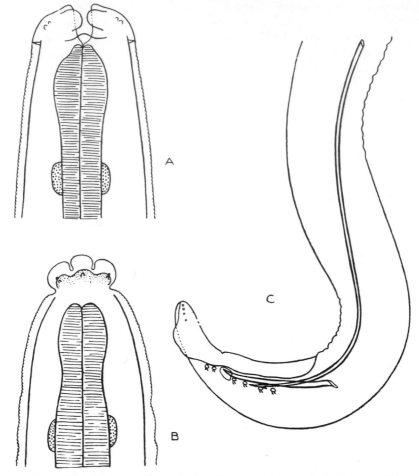

Fig. 210.—*Hartertia obesa*. A. Anterior extremity, ventral view. × 90.
B. Anterior extremity, lateral view. × 90. C. Posterior extremity of
male, lateral view. × 44. (Orig.)

Other species : *H. rotundata* (Linstow, 1883). In *Otis macquini*.
　Syn., *Filaria rotundata* Linstow, 1883.
Refs. 514, 524, 572.

Subfamily ARDUENNINÆ Railliet and Henry, 1911.

Definition.—SPIRURIDÆ : mouth with two lateral lips (Piana
states that in *Simondsia* they are dorso-ventral) ; vestibule large
and cylindrical, walls furnished with cuticular ridges in the form
of rings or spirals. Cephalic and œsophageal regions not ornamented with cuticular plaques.

KEY TO GENERA.

1. Prominent rosette-like excrescence
   towards posterior end of body of
   female containing uterus, which
   gives off many branches ter-
   minating blindly   .   .   .   Simondsia, p. 309.
   Female without the above   .   .   2
2. Vestibule with spiral twist or S-
   shaped bend   .   .   .   .   Streptopharagus, p. 311.
   Vestibule straight   .   .   .   3
3. Vestibule with spiral markings.
   Male with pericloacal crown   .   Arduenna, p. 307.
   Vestibule with transverse markings.
   Male without pericloacal crown .   Physocephalus, p. 308.

Genus ARDUENNA Railliet and Henry, 1911.

Definition.—ARDUENNINÆ : mouth with two lateral trilobed
lips, each bearing three papillæ externally, and a tooth on each

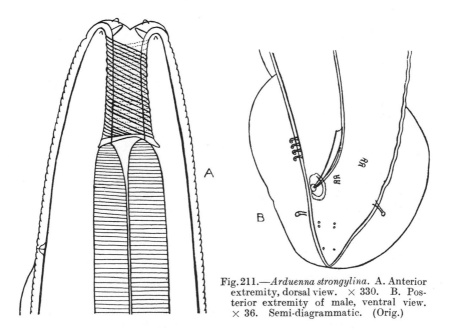

Fig. 211.—*Arduenna strongylina.* A. Anterior
extremity, dorsal view. × 330. B. Posterior extremity of male, ventral view.
× 36. Semi-diagrammatic. (Orig.)

side internally ; lateral flange on left side only ; cervical papillæ
asymmetrical, one in front of the nerve ring ; mouth followed by

a cylindrical vestibule with a stout wall showing spiral markings ; œsophagus long and divided into two parts, the anterior much the shorter. Male : tail inrolled ; large, asymmetrical caudal alæ present ; cloaca surrounded by a serrate pericloacal crown ; four pairs of pedunculated preanal papillæ, one pair of pedunculated postanal, and one or two pairs of sessile papillæ near the tip of the tail ; spicules very unequal and dissimilar ; gubernaculum absent. Female : vulva in front of the middle of the body. Oviparous, eggs ellipsoidal with a thick shell, and containing an embryo at deposition. Parasites of stomach of pigs.

Type species : *A. strongylina* (Rud., 1819). ♂ 10–13 mm., ♀ 15–20 mm. In pigs.

Syn., *Spiroptera strongylina* Rud., 1819.

Other species : *A. dentata* (Linstow, 1904). In pigs.

Refs. 325, 432, 477.

Genus PHYSOCEPHALUS Dies., 1861.

Syn., *Leiuris* Leuck., 1850, preoccupied.

Definition.—ARDUENNINÆ : mouth with two lateral trilobed lips, each bearing three papillæ externally, but without teeth internally ; cervical cuticle inflated ; a triple cuticular flange on each side ; cervical papillæ asymmetrical, one in front of the nerve ring ; vestibule cylindrical with ring-like thickenings of the walls ; œsophagus long and divided into two parts, the anterior much the shorter. Male : tail inrolled ; caudal alæ present ; four pairs of pedunculated preanal papillæ, four pairs of very small papillæ near the tip of the tail ; spicules very unequal ; gubernaculum present ; no pericloacal crown. Female : vulva usually behind the middle of the body. Oviparous, eggs subcylindrical with a thick shell, containing an embryo at deposition. Parasites of stomach of pigs, dromedary, donkey, etc.

Type species : *P. sexalatus* (Molin, 1860). ♂ 7–13 mm., ♀ 10–12 mm. In pig.

Syn., *Spiroptera sexalata* Molin, 1860.

Other species :

    P. cristatus (Seurat, 1912) Railliet, 1915. In the dromedary and ass.

      Syn., *Spiroptera sexalata* var. *cristata* Seurat, 1912.

    P. gracilis (Rud., 1819). In *Bradypus tridactylus*.

    P. leptocephalus (Rud., 1819). In *Bradypus tridactylus*.

      Syn., *Leiuris leptocephalus* (Rud., 1819).

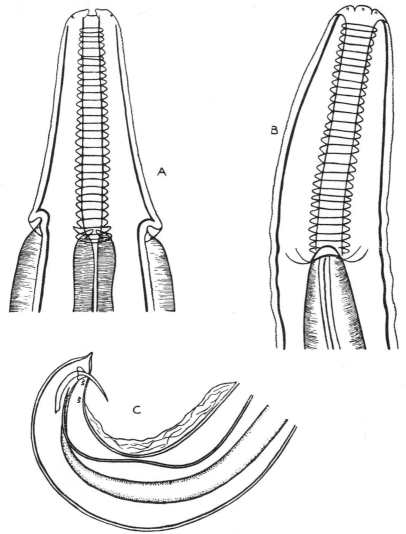

Fig. 212.—*Physocephalus sexalatus.* A. Anterior extremity, ventral view.
× 215.   B. Anterior extremity, lateral view.   × 215.   C. Posterior
extremity of male, lateral view.   × 46.   (Orig.)

P. mediospiralis (Molin, 1860).   In *Dasyprocta agouti.*.
Syn., ? *Spiroptera chrisoptera* Molin, 1858.
Refs. 95, 125, 128, 298, 358, 368, 432, 484, 492.

Genus SIMONDSIA Cobbold, 1864.

Definition.—ARDUENNINÆ : mouth with two lips (stated by
Piana to be dorsal and ventral) ; vestibule cylindrical, with

ringed thickenings ; œsophagus long and cylindrical. Male :
posterior extremity conical and spirally curved ; caudal alæ
present ; four pairs of pedunculated preanal papillæ ; spicules
unequal. Female : body of more or less uniform diameter, but
supporting externally a large rosette-shaped excrescence con-

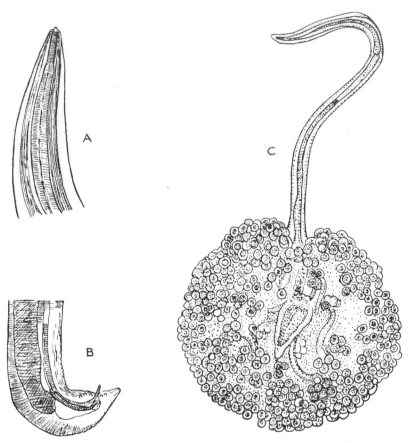

Fig. 213.—*Simondsia paradoxa*. A. Anterior extremity. B. Posterior
extremity of male, lateral view. (After Piana.) C. Female. (After
Cobbold.)

taining the uterus, the walls of which are expanded with branches
terminating in cæca ; vulva in the anterior half of the body.
Males free in stomach of pigs, females encysted within the stomach
wall with their heads projecting into the cavity.

Type species : *S. paradoxa* Cobbold, 1864. ♂ 12 mm., ♀ 15 mm.
In pigs.

Refs. 106, 108, 391, 432.

Genus STREPTOPHARAGUS Blanc, 1912.

Definition.—ARDUENNINÆ : mouth hexagonal, long axis dorso-
ventral, with small trilobed lateral lips each with a large lateral,

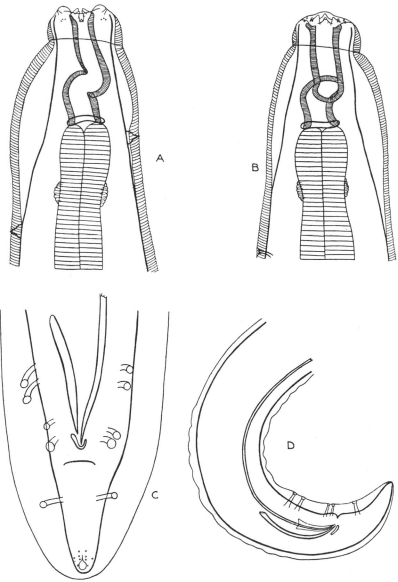

Fig. 214.—*Streptopharagus armatus.* A. Anterior extremity, ventral view.
× 76. B. Anterior extremity, lateral view. × 76. C. Posterior
extremity of male, ventral view. × 64. D. Posterior extremity of
male, lateral view. × 32. (Orig.)

and two groups of three small submedian, papillæ ; cervical cuticle
inflated asymmetrically ; cervical papillæ asymmetrical, one in
front of the nerve ring. Buccal cavity continuous posteriorly with
a thick walled tubular vestibule marked with more or less coarse
transverse ridges, and forming about the middle of its length a
half turn of a spiral ; at the anterior end of the vestibule are a
number of teeth projecting into the buccal cavity—a small, simple
or complex, dorsal and ventral tooth and three larger lateral teeth
on each side ; œsophagus consists of two parts, a short narrow
muscular anterior portion, and a long wider partly glandular
posterior part. Male : tail spiral ; caudal alæ broad ; four pairs
of large pedunculated preanal papillæ, one pair of pedunculated
postanal papillæ, and a group of five pairs of small sessile papillæ
near the tip of the tail ; on the left side of the tail, towards the
mid-ventral line, and extending across it in front of the cloacal
aperture, a series of prominent claw-like cuticular structures,
having their tips hooked and appearing as if chitinized, is sometimes seen (Baylis, 1923) ; spicules very unequal and dissimilar ;
a small asymmetrical gubernaculum present. Female : tail
conical, with a pair of subventral papillæ ; vulva in front of the
middle of the body ; uteri at first parallel, but eventually opposed.
Oviparous, eggs with thick shells, and containing embryos at
deposition. Parasites of stomach of mammals.

Type species : *S. armatus* Blanc, 1912. ♂ 30–32 mm.,
♀ 47–48 mm. In *Macacus* spp.

Other species :

S. numidicus Seurat, 1917. In *Fennecus zerda.*

S. pigmentatus (Linst., 1897). In *Cercopithecus* sp., *Macacus*
sp.

S. sudanensis Baylis, 1923. In *Gerbillus gerbillus.*

Refs. 33, 54, 362, 542, 552, 655.

Subfamily GONGYLONEMINÆ Hall, 1916.

Definition.—SPIRURIDÆ : mouth with four or six small and
indefinite lips ; vestibule short, narrow, and cylindrical ; anterior
end of the body ornamented with cuticular plaques.

KEY TO GENERA.

With numerous cuticular plaques in the
    cephalic and œsophageal regions   .   Gongylonema, p. 313.
With only four cuticular plaques, dorsally
    and ventrally, in the cephalic region .   Squamanema, p. 315.

Genus GONGYLONEMA Molin, 1857.

Syn., *Myzomimus* Stiles, 1892.

Definition.—GONGYLONEMINÆ : mouth with small dorsal and ventral lips, chitinized at their external point and each bearing a

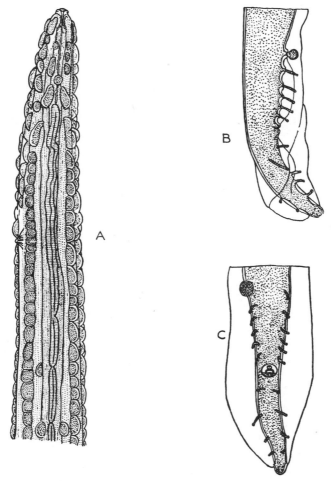

Fig. 215.—*Gongylonema pulchrum.* A. Anterior extremity. × 105. (After Ward.) *Gongylonema scutatum.* B. Posterior extremity, lateral view. C. Posterior extremity, ventral view. (After Seurat.)

tooth on its inner surface, lateral lips narrow and small ; two lateral and four submedian head papillæ ; cuticle thick, with transverse striations ; cervical papillæ at the level of the nerve ring, sometimes in the centre of a cuticular plaque ; cephalic and œsophageal regions ornamented with cuticular plaques irregularly arranged in longitudinal rows on the dorsal and ventral parts of the body; lateral cuticular flanges on the anterior part of the body; two unpaired dorsal cuticular papillæ in the intestinal region—one in the anterior third, and the other in the posterior third of the body; vestibule short, narrow, and cylindrical with thick walls; œsophagus very long and consists of two distinct parts, the anterior being much the shorter. Male : tail twisted slightly on its long axis; caudal alæ generally asymmetrical; papillæ long and pedunculated and of variable number, usually four to five or six preanal, and two to four postanal, with a number of sessile papillæ near the tip of the tail; spicules very unequal; gubernaculum present. Female : posterior extremity bluntly rounded; vulva slightly in front of the anus; ovejector very long, about half the length of the worm; uteri divergent. Oviparous, eggs with a thick shell containing a larva at deposition. Parasites of œsophageal and stomach walls of mammals and birds.

Type species : *G. minimum* Molin, 1857. ♂ 8·8 mm., ♀ 17·5–21·6 mm. In *Mus* spp.

    Syn., *Filaria musculi* Rud., 1819.

Other species :

    G. brevispiculum Seurat, 1914. In *Dipodilla campestris*.

    *G. confusum Sonsino, 1896. In *Equus caballus*.

    *G. hominis Stiles, 1921. In man.

    G. ingluvicola Ransom, 1904. In *Gallus domesticus*.

    *G. labiale (Pane, 1864). In man.

    G. mucronatum Seurat, 1916. In *Erinaceus algirus*.

      Syn., *G. pulchrum* Seurat, 1912 and 1914, not Molin 1857.

    G. neoplasticum (Fibiger and Ditlevsen, 1914). In *Muridæ* *Cavia* sp., *Lepus* sp.

    G. orientale Yokogawa, 1925. In rodents.

    G. problematicum Schulz, 1924. In *Muridæ*.

    G. pulchrum Molin, 1857. In *Sus scrofa*.

    *G. ransomi Chapin, 1922. In pigs.

    *G. scutatum (Leuck., 1873). In horse, ox, goat, and sheep.

      Syn., *Myzomimus scutatus* (Leuckart, 1873) Stiles, 1892.

    *G. spirale Molin, 1857. In *Cervus dama*.

    *G. subtile Alessandrini, 1914. In man.

    G. ursi (Duj., 1845). In *Ursus arctos*.

---

    * According to Baylis (1925) it is probable that these worms are identical with *G. pulchrum*.

G. verrucosum (Giles, 1892). In zebu and sheep.

Syn., *Trichosomum verrucosum* Giles, 1892.

G. crenatum Railliet, 1898.

Refs. 3a, 41b, 41c, 41d, 91, 205, 353, 405, 458, 478a, 481b, 487, 530, 557, 592, 661, 668b.

Genus SQUAMANEMA* Thiel, 1925.

Definition.—GONGYLONEMINÆ : mouth surrounded by six small lips ; cuticle thick with marked transverse striations ; in the

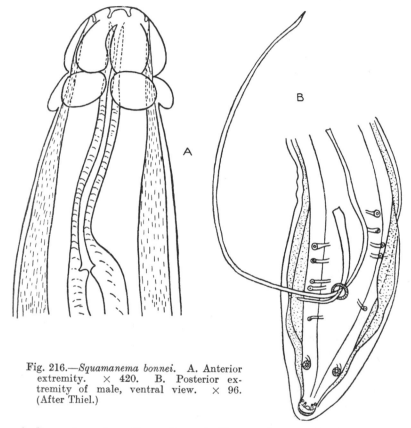

Fig. 216.—*Squamanema bonnei.* A. Anterior extremity. × 420. B. Posterior extremity of male, ventral view. × 96. (After Thiel.)

cephalic region, dorsally and ventrally, are four cuticular thickenings or shields, the rest of the cuticle is free from plaques ; vestibule cylindrical ; cervical papillæ about the level of the nerve ring ; œsophagus of moderate length. Male : posterior extremity twisted spirally ; caudal alæ slightly asymmetrical ; four pairs of long pedunculated preanal papillæ, two pairs of

* Although Thiel considers *Squamanema* to be closely allied to *Gongylonema*, his figure raises in our minds a doubt whether in reality it is not nearer to *Parabronema*.

pedunculated postanal papillæ, and a few sessile papillæ near the tip of the tail ; spicules very unequal. Female : posterior extremity digitiform ; vulva in the posterior third of the body. Parasites of monkeys.

Type species : *S. bonnei* Thiel, 1925. ♂ 13 mm., ♀ 20 mm. In *Mycetes seniculus.*

Ref. 616a.

Family THELAZIIDÆ Railliet, 1916.

Definition.—Spiruroidea : mouth without definite lips, or with two or six small lips ; a short buccal capsule or vestibule usually present ; œsophagus consists of two parts. Male : with or without caudal alæ, preanal papillæ usually simple, sometimes coupled, generally numerous, and arranged in a linear row ; spicules usually very unequal. Female : vulva may be either anterior or posterior. Oviparous or viviparous. Parasites of the orbital, nasal, or oral cavities of mammals and birds, the air-sacs of birds, or of the intestine of fishes.

KEY TO GENERA.

1. Spicules equal . . . . Haplonema, p. 326.
   Spicules unequal 2
2. Males with caudal alæ . . . 3
   Males without caudal alæ . . 4
3. Caudal alæ wide ; preanal papillæ
      simple . . . . . Ceratospira, p. 322.
   Caudal alæ narrow ; preanal papillæ
      coupled . . . . . Cystidicola, p. 322.
4. Walls of vestibule supported by
      longitudinal thickenings ending
      anteriorly as teeth . . . Rhabdochona, p. 324.
   Walls of vestibule without longi-
      tudinal thickenings . . . 5
5. Posterior extremity of both sexes
      finely pointed . . . . Oxyspirura, p. 318.
   Posterior extremity of both sexes
      bluntly rounded . . . 6
6. Vulva near anus . . . . Desmidocerca, p. 321.
   Vulva in œsophageal region or close
      behind it 7
7. Males with numerous preanal papillæ Thelazia, p. 317.
   Males without preanal papillæ . Desmidocercella, p. 321.

Genus THELAZIA Bosc, 1819.

Definition.—THELAZIIDÆ : mouth without lips, followed by a buccal capsule, the anterior border of which is everted and divided into six festoons by indentations, of which four appear to be occupied by a small refractile papilliform organ ; two lateral and four submedian cephalic papillæ ; œsophagus moderately short. Male : tail blunt and recurved, without caudal alæ ; a large

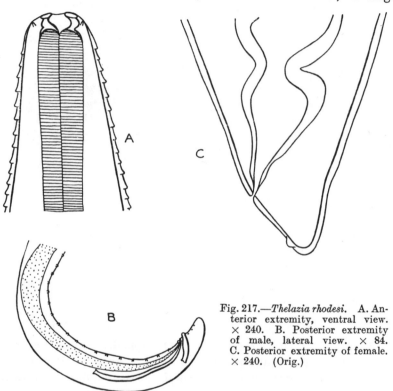

Fig. 217.—*Thelazia rhodesi.* A. Anterior extremity, ventral view. × 240. B. Posterior extremity of male, lateral view. × 84. C. Posterior extremity of female. × 240. (Orig.)

number of preanal papillæ, of which one is unpaired in front of the cloaca, and three or four pairs of postanal papillæ ; spicules unequal. Female : tail bluntly rounded, bearing a pair of lateral papillæ near its extremity ; vulva in œsophageal region ; uterine branches directed backwards and containing embryos. Parasites of the lachrymal ducts and surface of the eye of mammals, or under the nictitating membrane of birds.

Type species : *T. rhodesi* (Desmarest, 1827) Railliet and Henry, 1910. ♂ 8–12 mm., ♀ 12–18 mm. In cattle.

    Syn., *T. rhodesii* (Desmarest, 1827) Blainv., 1828. [Thelazie de Rhodes. Bosc, 1819.]

Syn., *Filaria bovis* Baillet, 1858.

Filaria palpebrarum Baillet, 1858.

Filaria lacrymalis Gurlt of Baillet, 1866, of Railliet, 1893, in part.

Other species :

T. alfortensis Railliet and Henry, 1910.   In cattle.

Syn., *Filaria lacrymalis* Gurlt of Railliet, 1893, in part.

T. anolabiata (Molin, 1860).   In *Crax fasciolata.*

T. callipæda Railliet and Henry, 1910.   In dog.

T. campanulata (Molin, 1858).   In *Rupornis magnirostris.*

? *T. cirrura* (Leidy, 1886).   In *Megaquiscalus major.*

T. dacelonis (Breinl, 1913).   In *Dacelo leachei*.

T. depressa Baylis, 1920.   In *Mungos fasciatus.**

T. digitata Travassos, 1918.   In *Rhamphastus* sp.

T. gulosa Railliet and Henry, 1910.   In cattle.

Syn., *Filaria lacrymalis* Gurlt, 1831, in part.

T. iheringi Travassos, 1918.   In *Dasyprocta* sp.

T. lacrymalis (Gurlt, 1831) Railliet and Henry, 1910.   In horse.

Syn., *Filaria lacrymalis* Gurlt, 1831, in part.

T. leesei Railliet and Henry, 1910.   In camel.

T. lutzi Travassos, 1918.   In *Penelope* sp.

T. papillosa (Molin, 1860).   In *Falco* spp.

? *T. stereura* (Rud., 1819).   In *Aquila nævia.*

Travassos (1918) has divided the genus *Thelazia* into the following subgenera :—

Subgenus THELAZIA (Bosc, 1819) Travassos, 1918.

Definition.—THELAZIA in which the spicules are dissimilar and very unequal. Contains the species : *rhodesi, campanulata, dacelonis, depressa, gulosa, iheringi, leesei, lutzi, papillosa,* and *stereura.*

Subgenus THELAZIELLA Travassos, 1918.

Definition.—THELAZIA in which the spicules are almost the same size. Contains the species : *lachrymalis.*

Refs. 26, 53a, 53b, 74, 121a, 203a, 358, 404, 421, 425, 633a.

Genus OXYSPIRURA Drasche in Stossich, 1897.

Syn., *Cheilospirura* Dies., 1861, in part.

Definition.—THELAZIIDÆ : mouth without lips, followed by a short buccal capsule ; head with two lateral and four submedian

---

* Baylis informs us that this is not the real host and that he has recently obtained *T. depressa* from a bird.

papillæ, rarely with a cuticular dilatation.   Posterior extremity
of both sexes very finely conical.   Male : tail generally incurved
or spiral, caudal alæ absent ; papillæ sessile, the preanal variable

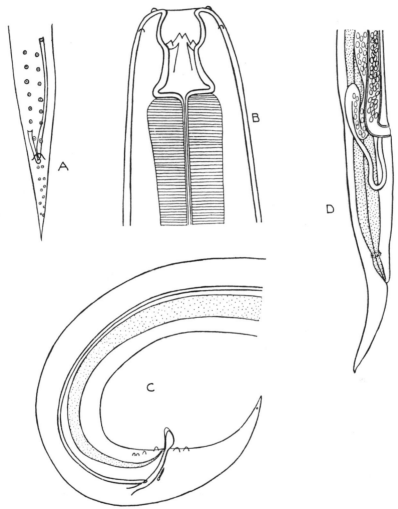

Fig. 218.—*Oxyspirura cephaloptera*. A. Posterior extremity of male, ventral
view.   × 90.   (After Drasche.)   *Oxyspirura mansoni*.   B. Anterior
extremity, ventral view.   × 375.   C. Posterior extremity of male, lateral
view.   × 84.   D. Posterior extremity of female.   × 50.   (Orig.)

in number (two to twenty-eight pairs), the postanal (one to eight
pairs) often asymmetrical ; spicules very unequal.   Female :
posterior extremity straight ; vulva very little in front of the
anus.   Parasites under the nictitating membrane of birds.

Type species : *O. cephaloptera* (Molin, 1860). ♂ 13–15 mm..
♀ 10–13 mm. In *Momotus brasiliensis, Icterus croconotus*.
    Syn., *Spiroptera cephaloptera* Molin, 1860.
        Cheilospirura cephaloptera Diesing, 1861.
Other species :
    O. anacanthura (Molin, 1860).   In *Crotophaga* spp.
    O. anthochæræ (Johnston, 1912).   In *Anthochæra carunculata*.
    O. brevisubulata (Molin, 1860).   In *Otus choliba*.
    O. mansoni (Cobbold, 1879).   In *Gallus* sp., *Meleagris* sp.,
        Pavo sp.
    O. ophthalmica (Linstow, 1903).   In *Turnix* sp.
      Syn., *Cheilospirura ophthalmica* Linstow, 1903.
    O. parvovum Sweet, 1910.   In *Gallus domesticus*.
    O. siamensis (Linstow, 1903).   In *Centropus sinensis*.
    O. tanasijtchuki Skrjabin, 1916.   In *Icteridæ*.
Also possibly :—
    Spiroptera brevipenis Molin, 1860.   In *Cariama* sp.
    Spiroptera heteroclita Molin, 1860.   In *Nothocrax* sp.

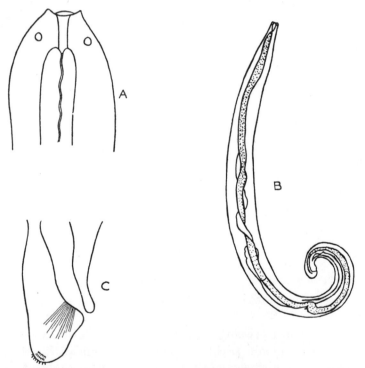

Fig. 219.—*Desmidocerca ærophila*. A. Anterior extremity, ventral view.
B. Male. C. Posterior extremity of female. (After Skrjabin.)

Spiroptera spiralis Molin, 1860. In *Bradypus* sp. and *Cholœpus* sp.

Spiroptera sygmoidea Molin, 1860. In *Corvus frugilegus*.

Refs. 103, 128, 358, 404, 454, 574, 604.

Genus DESMIDOCERCA Skrjabin, 1916.

Definition.—THELAZIIDÆ : very small worms ; mouth with two small conical lateral lips, behind which are four submedian head papillæ ; vestibule short and cylindrical ; œsophagus very long, about two-thirds of the length of the worm. At the caudal extremity of both sexes is a tuft of short filiform processes or spines. Male : posterior extremity bent spirally, tail bluntly rounded ; caudal alæ absent, papillæ absent ; spicules filiform and very unequal. Female : posterior extremity bent spirally, tail bluntly rounded ; vulva in the posterior part of the body. Oviparous, eggs oval. Parasites of the air-sacs of aquatic birds.

Type species : *D. ærophila* Skrjabin, 1916. ♂ 3·9 mm., ♀ 4·4 mm. In herons and cormorants.

Ref. 572.

Genus DESMIDOCERCELLA n.g.

Syn., *Desmidocerca* Skrjabin of Seurat, 1920.

Definition.—THELAZIIDÆ : body short ; mouth with two lateral trilobed lips, each bearing two pairs of large head papillæ, the more lateral inserted near the base of the lips ; lateral areas broad ; lateral flanges present ; cervical papillæ at the level of the nerve ring ; buccal cavity short and infundibuliform ; œsophagus short (one-eighth to one-ninth the length of the worm) and clearly divided into two parts. Male : posterior extremity bent, tail short, bluntly rounded, and bare at its tip ; caudal alæ absent ; a pair of postanal papillæ immediately behind the cloaca ; spicules very unequal. Female : tail short, bluntly rounded, furnished with two small lateral subterminal cuticular swellings ; vulva anterior, situated near the posterior end of the œsophagus ; amphidelphys. Parasites of the air-sacs of aquatic birds.

Type species : *D. numidica* (Seurat, 1920). ♂ 5·3 mm., ♀ 6·8 mm. In herons.

Syn., *Desmidocerca numidica* Seurat, 1920.

Ref. 560.

Genus CERATOSPIRA Schneider, 1866.

Definition.—THELAZIIDÆ : head bare, mouth surrounded by papillæ, and followed by a short buccal capsule. Male : tail very short, blunt, and furnished with large alæ ; preanal papillæ simple and sessile, nine to eleven in number ; spicules very unequal. Female : tail very short and blunt ; vulva very anterior, near the posterior end of the œsophagus. Oviparous or viviparous. Parasites of the orbital, nasal, and oral cavities of birds.

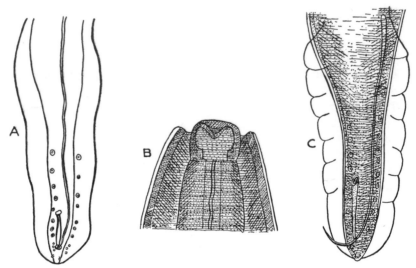

Fig. 220.—*Ceratospira vesiculosa*. A. Posterior extremity of male, ventral view. × 45. (After Schneider.) *Ceratospira ophthalmica*. B. Anterior extremity. C. Posterior extremity of male, ventral view. (After Linstow.)

Type species : *C. vesiculosa* Schneider, 1866. ♂ 20 mm., ♀ ? In *Eclectus pectoralis, Psittacus sinensis*.

Other species :

    C. ophthalmica (Linst., 1898).   In *Zonœnas* sp., *Carpophaga* sp.

    Syn., *Ancyracanthus ophthalmicus* Linstow, 1898.

Refs. 317, 404, 454, 480.

Genus CYSTIDICOLA Fischer, 1798.

    Syn., *Fissula* Lamarck, 1801.

        Ophiostoma Rud., 1801.

        Ancyracanthus Schneider, 1866, in part, not Diesing, 1838.

        Pseudancyracanthus Skrjabin, 1923.

Definition.—THELAZIIDÆ : mouth simple or with small lips ;
followed by a cylindrical vestibule with a thick chitinous wall ;
œsophagus very long.   Male : posterior extremity coiled spirally,

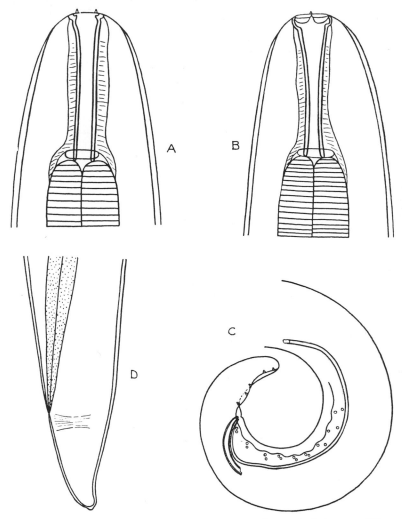

Fig. 221.—*Cystidicola farionis.* A. Anterior extremity, ventral view. × 256.
B. Anterior extremity, lateral view.   × 256. C. Posterior extremity of
male, lateral view.   × 90.   D. Posterior extremity of female, lateral
view.   × 90. (Orig.)

tail rounded at the tip ; caudal alæ narrow ; a long row of
coupled preanal papillæ, and about five simple postanal papillæ ;
spicules unequal and dissimilar.   Female : tail straight and blunt ;
vulva in the middle, or in the anterior region, of the body ; uteri

opposed. Oviparous, eggs numerous, thick-shelled, provided (at least in the type) with polar filaments. Parasites of the swim-bladder, air-vessels, and rarely œsophagus of fresh-water fishes.

Type species : *C. farionis* Fischer, 1798. ♂ 10–20 mm., ♀ 11–36 mm. In trout, etc.

> Syn., *Fissula cystidicola* Lam., 1801.
>> *Fissula farionis* Bosc, 1802.
>> *Spiroptera cystidicola* (Lam., 1801) Rud., 1819.
>> *Ophiostoma cystidicola* (Lam., 1801) Rud., 1809.
>> *Dispharagus cystidicola* (Lam., 1801) Duj., 1845.
>> *Ancyracanthus cystidicola* (Lam., 1801) Schneider, 1866.
>> *Pseudancyracanthus cystidicola* (Lam., 1801) Skrjabin, 1923.

Other species :
> *C. impar* (Schneider, 1866). In *Osmerus* sp., *Trutta* sp., *Coregonus* sp., etc.
> ? *C. serrata* (Wright, 1879). In *Coregonus albus*.
> *C. stigmatura* (Leidy, 1886) Ward and Magath, 1916. In trout, etc.

Refs. 131, 135, 274, 373, 404, 477, 480, 566, 581, 662.

Genus RHABDOCHONA Railliet, 1916.

> Syn., ? *Ichthyospirura* Skrjabin, 1917.
>> *Pseudancyracanthus* Skrjabin, 1923, in part.

Definition.—THELAZIIDÆ : head bare, mouth with two lips bounding an infundibular cavity, supported by longitudinal thickenings terminating anteriorly in pointed teeth ; œsophagus of moderate length, composed of two distinct parts. Male : tail conical, pointed, and recurved ; caudal alæ absent ; numerous simple pre- and post-anal papillæ ; spicules unequal. Female : tail straight and elongate ; vulva near the middle of the body ; uteri opposed. Oviparous, eggs elliptical. Parasites of the intestine of fresh-water fishes.

Type species : *R. denudata* (Duj., 1845). ♂ 6 mm., ♀ 6 mm. In *Cyprinus* sp.

> Syn., *Dispharagus denudatus* Duj., 1845.
>> *Histiocephalus denudatus* (Duj., 1845) Dies., 1851.
>> *Pseudancyracanthus denudatus* (Duj., 1845) Skrjabin, 1923.
>> *Cucullanus pachystomus* Linstow, 1873.
>> ? *Dispharagus filiformis* Zschokke, 1884. In *Alburnus lucidus*.

Other species :

  R. *acuminata* (Molin, 1860). In *Barbus* sp., *Brycon falcatus*.
  R. *cascadilla* Wigdor, 1918. In minnows.

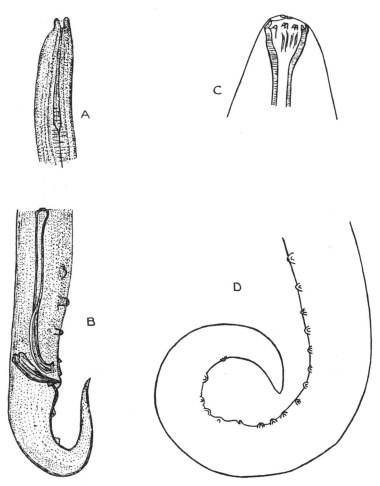

Fig. 222.—*Rhabdochona denudata*. A. Anterior extremity. × 215. B. Posterior extremity of male, lateral view. × 150. (After Dujardin.) *Rhabdochona acuminata*. C. Anterior extremity. D. Posterior extremity of male, lateral view. (After Gendre.)

  R. *gambiana* Gendre, 1922. In a fish.
  R. *macrolaima* Gendre, 1922. In a fish.
? R. *turkestanica* (Skrjabin, 1917). In *Schizothorax intermedius*.
      Syn., *Ichthyospirura turkestanica* Skrjabin, 1917.
Refs. 131, 178, 404, 581, 666, 682a, 682b.

Genus HAPLONEMA Ward and Magath, 1916.

Definition.—THELAZIIDÆ : body rather robust, anterior end bent or coiled, mouth without lips, head papillæ absent ; lateral flanges present ; vestibule absent ; œsophagus entirely muscular, but divided into two portions by a partition near its centre, without a posterior bulb. Male : without caudal alæ ; two pairs of preanal, and three pairs of postanal papillæ ; spicules equal. Female : posterior end of body straight, with two minute papillæ ;

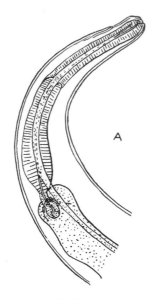

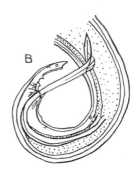

Fig. 223.—*Haplonema immutatum*. A. Anterior extremity, lateral view. × 72. B. Posterior extremity of male, lateral view. × 72. (After Ward and Magath.)

vulva slightly behind the middle of the body ; uteri opposed. Oviparous, eggs with thick smooth shells. Parasites of fresh-water fishes.

Type species : *H. immutatum* Ward and Magath, 1916. ♂ 9·5 mm., ♀ 15 mm. In *Amia calva*.

Ref. 662.

Family ACUARIIDÆ Seurat, 1913.

Definition.—SPIRUROIDEA : usually with two large simple lateral lips : the anterior part of the body is provided with cutaneous cordons (in the form of epaulettes) ; long, cylindrical vestibule present ; œsophagus cylindrical, divided into two parts ; cervical papillæ usually behind the nerve ring ; lateral cuticular flanges usually absent. Male : caudal alæ present, with four pairs of long, pedunculated preanal papillæ ; spicules unequal, and usually quite dissimilar. Female : usually with a short muscular ovejector and a short vagina. Parasites of gizzard and intestine of birds and rarely of mammals.

Subfamily ACUARIINÆ Raillet, Henry, and Sisoff, 1912.

Definition.—ACUARIIDÆ : with the characters of the family.

KEY TO GENERA.

Anterior end without cuticular thickenings or shields 1
Anterior end with cuticular thickenings or shields 4
1. With large bell-shaped collarette in
the region of the cervical papillæ . Chevreuxia, p. 332.
Without large bell-shaped collarette
in the region of the cervical papillæ 2
2. Cordons very short, in the form of a
crescent running from one angle of
the lip to the other   .   .   . Rusguniella, p. 333.
Cordons long, running relatively far
posteriorly 3
3. Cuticle with four longitudinal rows of
spines   .   .   .   .   . Echinuria, p. 331.
Cuticle without spines   .   .   . Acuaria, p. 327.
4. Cordons with posteriorly directed
spines   .   .   .   .   . Seuratia, p. 334.
Cordons without spines .   .   . 5
5. With a dorso-ventral cuticular shield,
and three short crescentic cordons
on each side   .   .   .   . Parabronema, p. 335.
With two cuticular shields on each
side, each bounded by recurved
cordons   .   .   .   .   . Cosmocephalus, p. 337.

Genus ACUARIA Bremser, 1811.

Syn., *Spiroptera* Rud., 1819.
    Anthuris Rud., 1819.
    Dispharagus Duj., 1845.
    Cheilospirura Dies., 1861.

Definition.—ACUARIINÆ : mouth with two simple lateral lips ; cephalic extremity without any cuticular thickenings or shields, but with four cordons in the form of ridges or grooves directed posteriorly, frequently turning forwards again and uniting on the lateral surfaces ; cervical papillæ behind the nerve ring ; lateral flanges absent ; vestibule with thick walls, usually transversely striated ; œsophagus cylindrical, consisting of two parts. Male : posterior extremity rolled spirally ; caudal alæ present ; four pairs of pedunculated preanal papillæ, and a variable number of

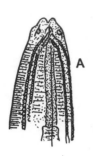
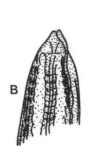
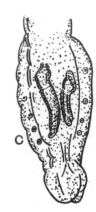

Fig. 224.—*Acuaria (Acuaria) anthuris.* A. Anterior extremity, ventral view. × 66. B. Anterior extremity, lateral view. × 66. C. Posterior extremity of male, ventral view. × 66. (After Dujardin.)

postanal papillæ. Female : posterior extremity blunt ; vulva usually in the posterior third of the body ; ovejector very short ; uteri divergent. Oviparous. Parasites of the œsophagus and gizzard of birds.

Type species : *A. anthuris* (Rudolphi, 1819). ♂ 11 mm., ♀ 22·3 mm. In *Coracias garrula, Oriolus galbula,* and *Corvus* spp.

Syn., *Spiroptera anthuris* Rud., 1819.

Dispharagus anthuris (Rud., 1819) Duj., 1845.

Other species :

A. affinis Seurat, 1916.   In *Strix flammea.*

A. alata (Rud., 1819).   In *Ardea* sp., *Ciconia* sp., and *Buteo* sp.

A. attenuata (Rud., 1819).   In *Hirundo* spp.

A. brevicaudata (Duj., 1845).   In *Botaurus stellaris, Ardetta minuta.*

A. capitata (Molin, 1860).   In *Falco minutus.*

Syn., *Dispharagus capitatus* Molin, 1860.

A. crassissima (Molin, 1860).   In *Rhamphastos* sp.

A. denticulata (Molin, 1860).   In *Falco* sp.

A. depressa (Schneider, 1866).   In *Corvus cornix.*

A. elliptica (Molin, 1858).   In *Falco* sp.

A. gracilis (Gendre, 1912). In *Buchanga* sp. and *Oriolus* sp.

A. gruveli (Gendre, 1913). In *Francolinus* sp.

A. hamata (Linst., 1877). In *Falco nisus*.

A. hamulosa (Dies., 1851). In *Phasianus gallus*.
  Syn., *Cheilospirura hamulosa* Dies., 1851.

A. invaginata (Linst., 1901, of Gendre, 1913). In *Bubulcus lucidus*.

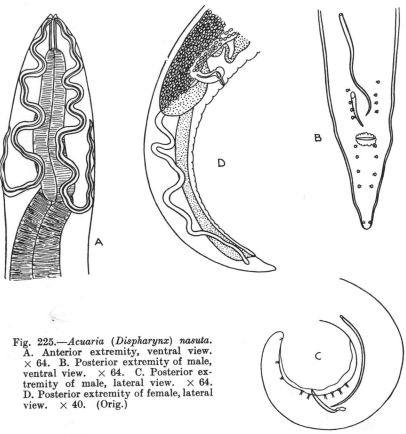

Fig. 225.—*Acuaria (Dispharynx) nasuta.*
A. Anterior extremity, ventral view.
× 64. B. Posterior extremity of male,
ventral view. × 64. C. Posterior extremity of male, lateral view. × 64.
D. Posterior extremity of female, lateral
view. × 40. (Orig.)

A. involuta (Linst., 1879). In *Strix* sp., *Accipiter* sp.

A. laplantei Seurat, 1919. In *Garrulus cervicalis*.

A. laticeps (Rud., 1819). In *Accipiter nisus*.

A. longevaginata (Molin, 1860). In *Ciconia* sp.

A. macrolaima (Linst., 1906). In *Plotus* sp.

A. magnilabiata (Molin, 1860). In *Platalea* sp.

A. mamillaris (Molin, 1860). In *Corvus* sp.

A. muscicapæ (Linst., 1878). In *Muscicapa* sp.

A. nasuta (Rud., 1819). In *Fringilla domestica, Porcellio
  lævis, Gallus* sp.

A. noctuæ Seurat, 1913.   In *Carine noctua glaux*.

A. ornata (Gendre, 1912).   In *Corvus* sp.

A. papillifera (Linst., 1878).   In *Sylvia palustris, Chelidon* sp., *Cotyle* sp., etc.

A. ptilopachydis Gendre, 1920.   In *Ptilopachys fuscus*.

A. quadriloba (Rud., 1819).   In *Picus* sp.

A. recta (Molin, 1860).   In *Falco* spp.

A. rectovaginata (Molin, 1860).   In *Falco* sp.

A. rotundata (Linst., 1907).   In *Lanius* sp.

A. spiralis (Molin, 1858).   In *Caccabis petrosa*, etc.

? *A. squamata* (Linst., 1883).   In *Phalacrocorax carbo*.

A. subrecta Gendre, 1921.   In *Asturinula* sp.

A. subula (Duj., 1845).   In *Sylvia* sp., *Luscinia* sp.

A. sygmoidea (Molin, 1860).   In *Falco tridentatus*.

   Syn., *Dispharagus sygmoideus* Molin, 1860.

A. tarentolæ Seurat, 1916.   In *Tarentola mauritanica*.

A. tenuis (Duj., 1845).   In *Saxicola* sp.

A. vanelli (Rud., 1819).   In *Tringa vanellus*.

Railliet, Henry, and Sisoff (1912) have divided the genus *Acuaria* into the following subgenera :—

Subgenus ACUARIA (Bremser, 1811) Railliet, Henry, and Sisoff, 1912.

Definition.—*Acuaria :* with cordons directed straight backwards, not turning forwards and not anastomosing.   Male : with two short slightly unequal spicules ; six to eight pairs of postanal papillæ.   Contains the species : *anthuris, attenuata, depressa, gracilis, ornata, papillifera, subula, tarentolæ* and *tenuis.*

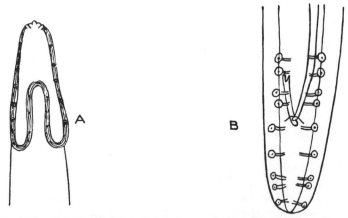

Fig. 226.—*Acuaria (Synhimantus) laticeps.* A. Anterior extremity, lateral view.   × 120.   B. Posterior extremity of male, ventral view.   × 120. (After Drasche.)

Subgenus CHEILOSPIRURA* (Dies., 1861) Railliet, Henry, and Sisoff, 1912.

Definition.—As *Acuaria* (*Acuaria*), but spicules very unequal and dissimilar ; five to seven pairs of postanal papillæ. Contains the species : *hamulosa, elongata, gruveli, magnilabiata, recta,* and *rotundata.*

Subgenus DISPHARYNX Railliet, Henry, and Sisoff, 1912.

Definition.—*Acuaria :* cordons recurrent, but not anastomosing ; cervical papillæ not evident. Male : with unequal dissimilar spicules, as a rule five pairs of postanal papillæ. Contains the species : *nasuta, capitata, crassissima, laplantei, noctuæ, rectovaginata,* and *spiralis.*

Subgenus SYNHIMANTUS Railliet, Henry, and Sisoff, 1912.

Definition.—*Acuaria :* cordons recurrent and anastomosing on each lateral surface ; cervical papillæ tricuspid, when seen. Male : with unequal and dissimilar spicules, ordinarily five pairs of postanal papillæ. Contains the species : *laticeps, affinis, alata, brevicaudata, crassicauda, denticulata, elliptica, hamata, invaginata, involuta, longevaginata,* (?) *squamata, subrecta,* and *sygmoidea.*

Subgenus HAMANNIA Railliet, Henry, and Sisoff, 1912.

This is a synonym of the genus *Echinuria* Solowiow, 1912.

Refs. 75, 131, 167, 168, 169, 170, 172, 174, 358, 452, 477, 533, 572.

Genus ECHINURIA Solowiow, 1912.

Syn., *Hamannia* Railliet, Henry, and Sisoff, 1912.

Definition.—ACUARIINÆ : closely resembling *Acuaria*, cordons not recurrent, but anastomosing posteriorly on the lateral surfaces ; cuticle with four longitudinal rows of spines running practically to the posterior extremity. Male : with unequal and dissimilar spicules ; four or five pairs of postanal papillæ, or papillæ absent. Female : vulva in the posterior portion of the body, sometimes near the anus. Parasites of birds.

Type species : *E. jugadornata* Solowiow, 1912. ♂ 11–12 mm., ♀ 15–16 mm. In *Anas boschas.*

Other species :

E. aculeata (Creplin, 1825). In *Tringa* spp., *Scolopax* sp.

E. calcarata (Molin, 1860). In *Ibis* sp.

E. contorta (Molin, 1858). In *Ibis* sp.

E. hargilæ Baylis and Daubney, 1923. In the adjutant-stork.

E. leptoptili Gedoelst, 1916. In *Leptoptilus* sp.

E. longeornata (Molin, 1860). In *Ciconia* sp.

---

* As Gendre, 1913, has pointed out, the distinction between the subgenera *Acuaria* and *Cheilospirura* is not sharp, intermediate species existing in which the spicules are only moderately unequal, *e.g.*, *A. subula,* where they measure 0·13 and 0·22 mm. respectively.

E. phœnicopteri (Seurat, 1916).   In *Phœnicopterus roseus.*

E. spinifera (Rud., or Schneider) Solowiow, 1912.   In
   Scolopax gallinula.

? *E. squamata* (Linstow, 1883).   In *Phalacrocorax* sp.

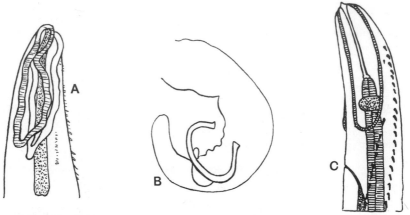

Fig. 227.—*Echinuria jugadornata.* A. Anterior extremity, lateral view. B.
Posterior extremity of male, lateral view. (After Solowiow.) *Echinuria
phœnicopteri.* C. Anterior extremity, lateral view. (After Seurat.)

E. uncinata (Rud., 1819).   In ducks and geese.
   Syn., *Spiroptera uncinata* Rud., 1819.
      Acuaria (*Hamannia*) *uncinata* (Rud., 1819) Railliet,
        Henry, and Sisoff, 1912.
Refs. 44, 151, 171, 452, 528, 532, 572, 584.

Genus CHEVREUXIA Seurat, 1918.

Definition.—ACUARIINÆ : mouth bounded by two lateral lips,
each of which bears a blunt conical process and a pair of papillæ ;
cervical papillæ situated far behind the nerve ring, and lying over
them is a large collarette, attached anteriorly and with a free bell-
shaped posterior margin surrounding this region of the body as a
kind of hyaline ring or sheath.   In addition, the cuticle is ornamented in the anterior region with four longitudinal cordons
arising from the dorsal and ventral lines ; these run posteriorly
along the submedian lines, and unite on the lateral surfaces in a
curve, which lies on the collarette, and fuses with its posterior
border ; the cordons are flanked on their inner border by a strip
of strongly striated cuticle.   Mouth cavity infundibular ; vestibule
long, narrow, and cylindrical ; œsophagus clearly divided into
two parts, the anterior muscular and surrounded by the nerve

ring, and the posterior glandular. Male : posterior extremity spirally rolled ; caudal alæ large ; four pairs of pedunculated preanal papillæ, and five pairs of pedunculated postanal papillæ ; spicules very unequal. Female : tail short and digitiform ; vulva a little behind the middle of the body ; ovejector short, directed posteriorly ; uteri divergent. Oviparous, eggs with a thick shell, containing a larva at deposition. Parasites of the gizzard wall of birds.

Type species : *C. revoluta* (Rudolphi, 1819). ♂ 6·4 mm., ♀ 18·3 mm. In *Himantopus himantopus*.

Syn., *Spiroptera revoluta* Rudolphi, 1819.

Dispharagus revolutus (Rud., 1819) Molin, 1860.

Refs. 477, 547.

Genus RUSGUNIELLA Seurat, 1919.

Definition.—ACUARIINÆ : mouth with two conically projecting lateral lips, each bearing a pair of submedian head papillæ ; on each side there is a short crescentic cordon stretching from one angle of the lip to the other, and only reaching a short distance posteriorly along the body ; lateral flanges present ; cervical papillæ in front of the nerve ring ; vestibule cylindrical, with chitinous walls ; œsophagus clearly divided into two portions. Male : unknown. Female : posterior extremity bent, elongate, and digitiform ; vulva a little in

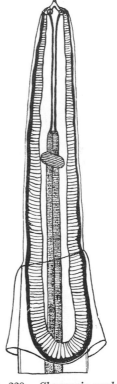

Fig. 228.—*Chevreuxia revoluta.* Anterior extremity, lateral view. × 135. (After Seurat.)

front of the middle of the body ; ovejector cylindrical and directed anteriorly ; uteri opposed. Oviparous, eggs oval, with a thick shell, containing a larva at deposition. Parasites of œsophagus of birds.

Type species : *R. elongata* (Rudolphi, 1819). ♂ 24 mm., ♀ 24–38 mm. In *Sterna nigra*, etc.

Syn., *Spiroptera elongata* Rudolphi, 1819.

Filaria elongata Schneider, 1866.

Refs. 477, 480, 553.

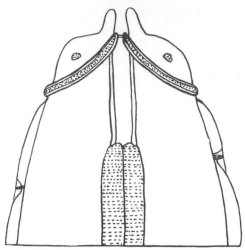

Fig. 229.—*Rusguniella elongata.*   Anterior extremity, ventral view.   (After Seurat.)

Genus **SEURATIA** Skrjabin, 1916.

Syn., *Prionostemma* Gendre, 1921.

Definition.—Acuariinæ : mouth with two lateral lips, each having a small tooth ; vestibule moderately long, narrow, and

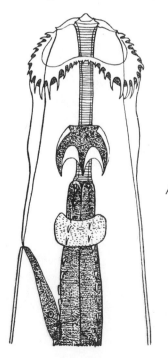

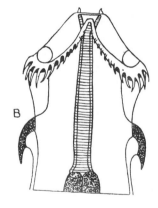

Fig. 230.—*Seuratia shipleyi.*   A. Anterior extremity, lateral view.   B. Anterior extremity, ventral view.   (After Seurat.)

cylindrical, with thick walls, and having a transversely striated appearance ; cephalic region ornamented with four short cordons, slightly recurved and meeting laterally ; these cordons bound areas of raised cuticle, and are provided on their free borders with posteriorly directed spines ; posterior to the cordons on the lateral surface, on each side, is a large trident-shaped chitinous process with the points directed posteriorly ; lateral flanges absent ; the cuticle is, in addition, ornamented along each lateral area with a double row of small posteriorly directed spines gradually disappearing behind the œsophagus and not extending beyond the vulva ; œsophagus cylindrical, divided into two parts, an anterior muscular, and a posterior glandular portion. Male : caudal alæ present, four pairs of preanal and four pairs of postanal papillæ ; spicules unequal. Female : tail short and conical, terminating in a small swelling ; vulva just in front of the middle of the body ; ovejector long ; uteri divergent. Oviparous, eggs oval, small, and contain fully-developed larvæ when deposited. Parasites of birds.

Type species : *S. shipleyi* (Stoss., 1900). ♂ 15 mm., ♀ 32–35 mm. In *Diomedea exulans, Larus* sp., *Puffinus* sp.

    Syn., *Gnathostoma shipleyi* Stossich, 1900.
        Rictularia paradoxa Linstow, 1904.
        Acuaria pelagica Seurat, 1916.

Other species :
    ? *S. decora* (Duj., 1845). In *Alcedo* sp.
    S. procellariæ (Dies., 1851). In *Procellaria anglorum*.
    Syn., *Spiroptera procellariæ-anglorum* Bellingham, 1844.
Refs. 173, 531, 576, 604a.

Genus PARABRONEMA Baylis, 1921.

Definition.—ACUARIINÆ : mouth with two lateral lips, each with three papillæ ; the cephalic extremity is provided with dorsal and ventral cuticular shields and is ornamented with six horseshoe-shaped cordons ; lateral flanges absent ; the cervical papillæ are a short distance behind the nerve ring ; oral aperture is of greatest diameter dorso-ventrally ; vestibule long and cylindrical with thick walls ; œsophagus consists of two portions, both muscular, the anterior part is short and narrow, and the posterior part longer and broad. Male : posterior extremity spirally coiled ventrally with interrupted longitudinal ridges on the ventral surface posteriorly ; small caudal alæ present ; four pairs of preanal, and two pairs of postanal papillæ arranged somewhat

asymmetrically, and in addition an extra double papilla immediately in front of the cloaca ; spicules very dissimilar ; gubernaculum triangular. Female : posterior extremity curved

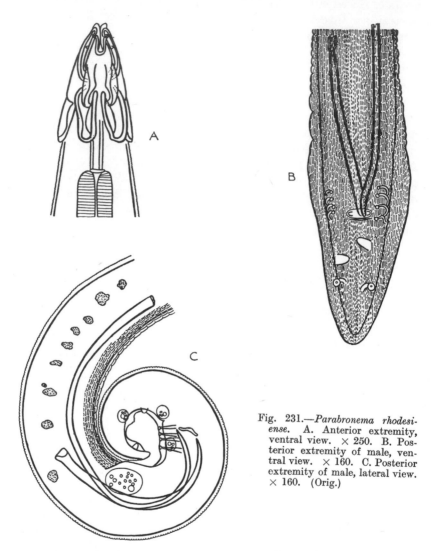

Fig. 231.—*Parabronema rhodesiense.* A. Anterior extremity,
ventral view. × 250. B. Posterior extremity of male, ventral view. × 160. C. Posterior
extremity of male, lateral view.
× 160. (Orig.)

dorsally, tail bluntly conical ; vulva in the anterior part of the
body not far from the termination of the œsophagus. Viviparous.
Parasites of the stomach wall of elephants and camels.

Type species : *P. indicum* Baylis, 1921. ♂ 8 mm., ♀ 13 mm.
In *Elephas indicus.*

Other species :

    P. africanum Baylis, 1921.   In *Elephas africanus.*

      Syn., *Sclerostomum clathratum* (♀) Baird, 1868.

  P. rhodesiense n. sp.   In African elephant.

    P. skrjabini Rasowska, 1924.   In *Camelus dromedarius.*

    P. smithii (Cobbold, 1882).   In *Elephas indicus.*

Refs. 7, 30, 251, 448, 463a.

Genus COSMOCEPHALUS Molin, 1858.

Definition.—ACUARIINÆ : mouth with two lateral lips each with a small external tooth, and a pair of voluminous papillæ at its base ; cephalic region ornamented with four long cordons, greatly recurved and meeting laterally ; the cordons bound shield-like areas of raised cuticle ; in front of these shields, behind the lips, there is often a cuticular swelling, and behind them prominent cervical papillæ in the form of spines in front of the nerve ring ; lateral flanges sometimes present ; vestibule very long, cylindrical, and narrow ; œsophagus consists of two parts. Male : posterior extremity spirally rolled ; caudal alæ present ; four pairs of pedunculated preanal papillæ, and four to six pairs of postanal papillæ ; spicules very unequal. Female : vulva somewhat behind the middle of the body ; uteri opposed. Oviparous, eggs contain larvæ when deposited. Parasites of birds.

    Type species : *C. diesingii* Molin, 1858. ♀ 15 mm. In *Larus oapiolranus.*

    Other species :

      C. aduncus (Creplin, 1846).   In *Colymbus* sp., *Larus* spp.

    †*C. asturis* n. sp.   In *Astur tachino* (from Natal).

---

  * *Parabronema rhodesiense* n. sp. Length of male 7–8 mm., female 9–10 mm. The distance of the posterior end of the cordons from the anterior extremity varies from 115 μ in the male to 130–140 μ in the female ; the cordons are longer than in the other species ; the length of the vestibule varies from 150 μ in the male to 175 μ in the female, and that of the œsophagus from 1,030 μ in the male to 1,230 μ in the female. The spicules are about 612 and 330 μ respectively in length. In the female the distance of the anus from the tip of the tail is about 200 μ, and the vulva is 860–900 μ behind the posterior extremity of the œsophagus.

  † *Cosmocephalus asturis* n. sp. Length of male 9·5 mm., female 12·5–13·5 mm. The distance of the posterior end of the cordons from the anterior extremity is about 460 μ in the male and from 550–650 μ in the female ; the length of the vestibule varies from 220 μ in the male to 360–415 μ in the female. The first part of the œsophagus varies from 664 μ in the male to about 730–800 μ in the female and the second part of the œsophagus from 1,740 μ in the male to 2,700 μ in the female. The cervical papillæ are trifid and are situated about 550 μ in the male and 740 μ in the female from the anterior extremity. The spicules are about 780 and 220 μ respectively in length. In the female the distance of the anus from the tip of the tail is about 170–200 μ ; the vulva is situated about the junction of the middle and posterior thirds of the body.

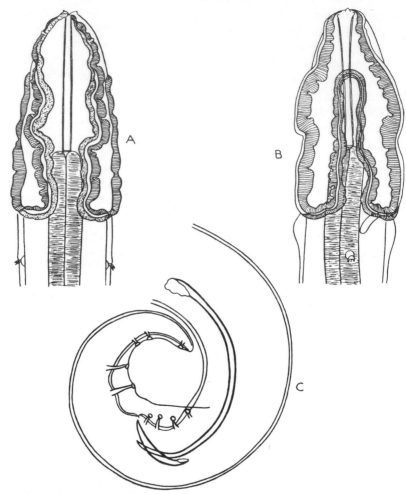

Fig. 232.—*Cosmocephalus asturis*. A. Anterior extremity, ventral view. × 90. B. Anterior extremity, lateral view. × 90. C. Posterior extremity of male, lateral view. × 90. (Orig.)

C. obvelatus (Creplin, 1825).   In *Larus maximus*.
   Syn., *C. alatus* Molin, 1860.
       Histiocephalus spiralis Diesing, 1851.
       C. papillosus Molin, 1859.
Refs. 128, 355, 452, 553.

FAMILY GNATHOSTOMIDÆ RAILLIET, 1895.

Definition.—SPIRUROIDEA : mouth with large distinctly trilobed lateral lips, having the cuticle of their inner surfaces thickened, and usually raised into longitudinal tooth-like ridges, which meet or interlock with those of the opposite lip ; behind the lips is a cuticular head-bulb, provided either with marked transverse striations, or with rows of backwardly directed hooks, and containing four membranous submedian ballonets, the cavity of each of which is in communication with one of four elongated, blind cervical sacs hanging freely in the body cavity. Male : with caudal alæ supported by broad pedunculated papillæ ; spicules equal or unequal. Female : vulva in the posterior half of the body ; vagina directed forwards, and dividing into two or four uterine tubes. Oviparous, eggs with thin shells, ornamented externally with fine granulations. Parasites of the stomach and intestine, rarely of other parts of the body, of fishes, reptiles, and mammals.

Subfamily GNATHOSTOMINÆ Baylis and Lane, 1920.

Definition.—GNATHOSTOMIDÆ : with the characters of the family.

KEY TO GENERA.

1. Head-bulb furnished with transverse cuticular ridges having sharp, backwardly projecting edges, but without hooks . . . . Tanqua, p. 340.
   Head-bulb armed with transverse rows of recurved hooks . . 2.
2. Body unarmed . . . . Echinocephalus, p. 342.
   Body partially or wholly armed with backwardly directed spines . . . . . Gnathostoma, p. 339.

Genus GNATHOSTOMA Owen, 1836.

Syn., *Cheiracanthus* Dies., 1838.

Definition.—GNATHOSTOMINÆ : head-bulb armed with simple hooks ; the ballonets give no external evidence of their presence ; body armed with cuticular spines, anteriorly scale-like with the free edges incised into points varying in number and shape, more posteriorly becoming less subdivided and finally appearing as simple spines, which either continue as such to the posterior end or disappear, leaving the hind part of the body unarmed. Male : spicules unequal ; four pairs of large lateral, and two pairs of small ventral caudal papillæ. Female : vulva behind the middle of the body ; vagina long ; uteri two in number. Oviparous, eggs with a thin colourless shell, a marked thinning at one pole causing a weak spot through which the embryo escapes. Parasites normally of the gastric wall, usually of carnivorous mammals.

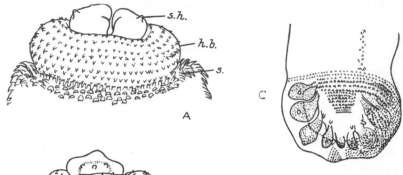

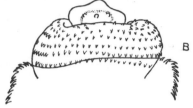

Fig. 233.—*Gnathostoma spinigerum.* A. Anterior extremity, ventral view. *s.h,* submedian head papillæ; *h.b,* head bulb; *s,* spines. × 64. B. Anterior extremity, lateral view. × 64. C. Posterior extremity of male, ventral view. × 64. (After Baylis and Lane.)

Type species : *G. spinigerum* Owen, 1836. ♂ 16–18 mm., ♀ 18–25 mm. In stomach of *Felis tigris, Felis pardus, Canis* sp., *Rattus* sp., and skin of *Homo.*

　　　Syn., *Cheiracanthus robustus* Dies., 1838 [nomen nudum].
　　　　Cheiracanthus siamensis Levinsen, 1889.
　　　　G. sociale (Leidy, 1858).
　　　　Filaria radula Schneider, 1866.
　　　　G. paronai Porta, 1908.

Other species :

　　　G. accipitri Skrjabin, 1916. In *Aquila imperialis.*
　　　G. gracile (Dies., 1839). In *Sudis gigas,* etc.
　　　G. hispidum Fedtsch., 1872. In *Bos taurus,* pig and man.
　　　G. horridum (Leidy, 1856). In *Alligator* sp.
　? *G. pelecani* (Chatin, 1874). In *Pelecanus onocrotalus.*
　　　G. turgidum Stoss., 1902. In *Didelphys azare.*
Refs. 46, 94, 122, 277, 384, 398, 399, 468, 573, 576.

Genus TANQUA Blanchard, 1904.

　　　Syn., *Ctenocephalus* Linstow, 1904, preoccupied.
　　　　Tetradenos Linstow, 1904.

Definition.—GNATHOSTOMINÆ : head-bulb coarsely striated transversely, unarmed, divided externally into two or four swellings containing the ballonets ; each lip with five teeth, interlocking with those of the other lip ; the cuticle behind the head-bulb forms a more or less pronounced collar or invagination ; body unarmed.   Male : caudal alæ well-developed ; eight pairs of papillæ ; spicules equal, tubular, rasp-like, with smooth tips. Female : vulva in the posterior half of the body ; vagina directed forwards ; uterus consists of two opposed branches, or of three anterior, and one posterior, branches. Oviparous, eggs oval, with

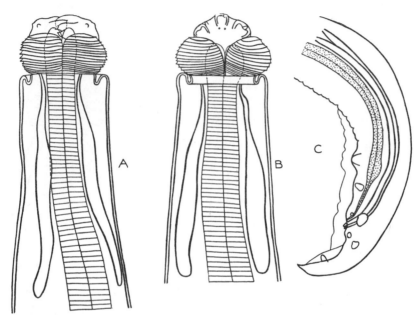

Fig. 234.—*Tanqua tiara*. A. Anterior extremity, ventral view. × 56.
B. Anterior extremity, lateral view.   × 56. C. Posterior extremity of
male, lateral view.   × 56. (Orig.)

a thin shell ornamented with fine granulations, embryos not fully formed at the time of deposition.   Parasites of stomach of semi-aquatic lizards (*Varanidæ*) and semi-aquatic snakes (*Tropidonotus*, etc.).

Type species :   *T. tiara* (Linstow, 1879).   ♂ 20–39 mm., ♀ 26–44 mm. In *Varanidæ*.

Syn., *Ascaris tiara* Linstow, 1879.

Ctenocephalus tiara (Linstow, 1879) Linstow, 1904.

Tetradenos tiara (Linstow, 1879) Linstow, 1904.

Other species :

* *T. anomala* (Linstow, 1904).   In *Tropidonotus piscator*.

Syn., *Heterakis anomala* Linstow, 1904.

* Travassos (1919) erected the subgenus *Anomala*, presumably for those species of *Tanqua* which have only two uterine tubes : it would therefore contain *T. anomala*

T. diadema Baylis, 1916.   In *Helicops angulatus*.

? *T. sphærocephala* (Rud., 1809).   In *Acipenser sturio*.

Refs. 19, 46, 56, 325, 326, 636.

Genus ECHINOCEPHALUS Molin, 1858.

Syn., *Cheiracanthus* Linst, 1904, in part, not Dies., 1838.

Definition.—GNATHOSTOMINÆ: head-bulb armed with transverse rows of hooks, not externally divided into swellings, but con-

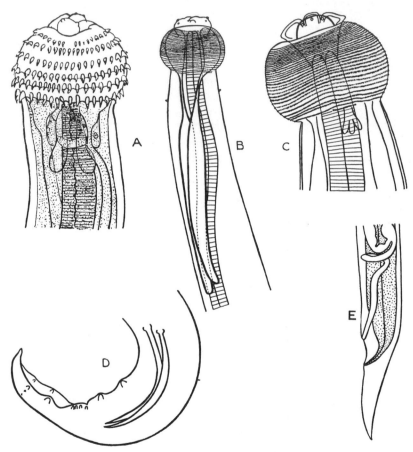

Fig. 235.—*Echinocephalus uncinatus*.   A. Anterior extremity, lateral view of larva.   × 80.   (After Baylis and Lane.)   *Echinocephalus spinosissimus*. B. Anterior extremity, ventral view.   × 35.   C. Anterior extremity, lateral view.   × 72.   D. Posterior extremity of male, lateral view. × 35.   E. Posterior extremity of female, lateral view.   × 18.   (Orig.)

and *T. diadema*.   It should be pointed out, however, that the name is already pre-occupied, *e.g.*, Samouelle, 1819 (*Coleoptera*), Stephens, 1829 (*Coleoptera*), and Möller, 1832 (*Gastropoda*).

taining four ballonets internally ; body unarmed ; no cuticular collar behind the head-bulb. Male : with slight caudal alæ ; eight pairs of papillæ, the most anterior pair always separated by a long interval from the rest ; spicules slightly unequal (left longer than right), tubular, long, slender, and marked with transverse striations. Female : vulva near the posterior end of the body ; vagina long and opening into a wide uterine sac which gives off two branches anteriorly. Oviparous, eggs oval, with thin shells ornamented with fine granulations ; embryos not fully formed at the time of deposition. Parasites of intestine (usually in spiral valve region) of sting rays and other Elasmobranch fishes.

Type species : *E. uncinatus* Molin, 1858, restr. Baylis and Lane, 1920. Larva 12–14 mm. In rays.

> Syn., *Echinocephalus uncinatus* Molin, 1858, in part.
> > *Cheiracanthus uncinatus* (Molin, 1858) Linstow, 1904.
> > *Echinocephalus gracilis* Stossich, 1906.

Other species :

> *E. multidentatus* Baylis and Lane, 1920. In *Urogymnus asperrimus*.
> *E. southwelli* Baylis and Lane, 1920. In *Urogymnus asperrimus*.
> *E. spinosissimus* (Linstow, 1905). In *Myliobatis aquila*, *Trygon* spp., etc.
> > Syn., *Echinocephalus uncinatus* Molin, 1858, in part.
> > *Cheiracanthus spinosissimus* Linstow, 1905.
> *E. striatus* Monticelli, 1889. In *Scyllium* sp.

Refs. 46, 355, 567, 568.

Family RICTULARIIDÆ Railliet, 1916.

Definition.—SPIRUROIDEA : cervical cordons absent ; cuticle armed with chitinous hook-like spines arranged in longitudinal rows, or in circles along the whole, or the anterior portion, of the body.

Subfamily RICTULARIINÆ Hall, 1913.

Definition.—RICTULARIINÆ : with the characters of the family.

KEY TO GENERA.

With two to four longitudinal rows of spines	1
With a series of circles of spines. .	3
1. With two longitudinal rows of spines on each side	Pneumonema, p. 346.

With longitudinal rows of spines on
ventral surface only . . . 2

2. Head with four projecting processes :
with three longitudinal rows of
spines on ventral surface . . Rictularioides, p. 345.
Head without four projecting processes:
with two longitudinal rows of spines
on ventral surface . . . Rictularia, p. 344.

3. Anterior extremity with a hood-like
covering, armed with three circles of
very large spines . . . . Echinonema, p. 347.
Anterior extremity without hood-like
covering . . . . . Spinitectus, p. 348.

Genus RICTULARIA Froelich, 1802.

Syn., *Ophiostoma* Rud., 1801, in part.
Ophiostomum Creplin, 1839, in part.
Laphyctes Duj., 1845 (*Rictularia* renamed).
Pterygodermatites Wedl, 1861.

Definition.—RICTULARIINÆ : buccal capsule well-developed and
narrow, with its aperture more or less distinctly dorsal, surrounded
by a circlet of denticles, and with its base armed with teeth and
spines. Along practically the entire ventral surface of each side

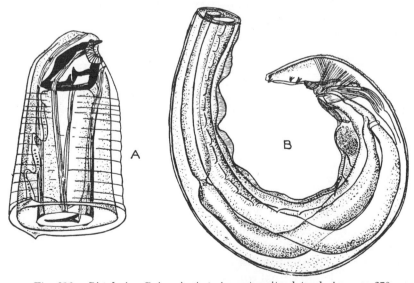

Fig. 236.—*Rictularia affinis.* A. Anterior extremity, lateral view. × 270.
B. Posterior extremity of male, lateral view. × 63. (After Jägerskiöld.)

there are two rows of cuticular combs or spines. Male : tail with or without small alæ ; with pre- and post-anal pedunculated papillæ ; spicules small, and equal or unequal. Female : vulva anterior, near the posterior end of the œsophagus. Oviparous, eggs contain embryos at deposition. Parasites of small intestine of carnivora, rodents, and ? lizards.

Type species : *R. cristata* Froelich, 1802. ♂ unknown, ♀ 22-27 mm. In *Mus sylvaticus.*

Syn., *Ophiostoma cristatum* (Froelich, 1802) Rud., 1819.

Other species :

R. affinis Jaegerskiöld, 1904. In *Vulpes niloticus.*

R. bovieri R. Blanchard, 1886. In *Vespertilio murinus.*

R. cahirensis Jaegerskiöld, 1904. In cat and dog.

R. coloradensis Hall, 1916. In *Eutamias quadrivittatus.*

R. disparalis Irwin-Smith, 1922. In *Hinulia* sp.

R. elviræ Parona, 1889. In *Sciurus* sp., *Dremomys* sp.

R. fallax Jaegerskiöld, 1909. In *Sciurus melanogaster.*

Syn., *R. plagiostoma* Parona, 1889, not Wedl, 1861.

R. macdonaldi (Dobson, 1880). In *Megaderma frons.*

R. plagiostoma (Wedl, 1861). In *Vespertilio mystacinus.*

Syn., *Pterygodermatites plagiostoma* Wedl, 1861.

Ophiostoma spinosum Will.-Suhm, 1869.

R. proni Seurat, 1915. In *Herpestes* sp.

R. splendida Hall, 1913. In *Canis nebracensis.*

Refs. 114, 128, 131, 139, 174, 204, 205, 242, 243, 347b, 521, 664.

Genus RICTULARIOIDES Hall, 1916.

Definition.—RICTULARIINÆ : head with four projecting apices united by chitinous membranes to form two equal lips. Male : unknown. Female : with three series of simple posteriorly directed hooks along the body.

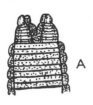
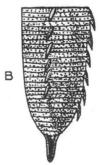

Fig. 237.—*Rictularioides amphiacanthum.* A. Anterior extremity. B. Posterior extremity of female. (After Diesing.)

Type species : *R. amphiacanthum* (Dies., 1851). ♂ ?, ♀ 8–11·5 mm. In *Oxymycterus rufus.*

Syn., *Ophiostomum amphiacanthum* Dies., 1851.

        Rictularia amphiacantha (Dies., 1851) Drasche, 1882.

Refs. 123, 128, 205.

Genus PNEUMONEMA Johnston, 1916.

Definition.—RICTULARIINÆ : anterior extremity bent slightly dorsally ; mouth with two small trilobed lateral lips ; mouth

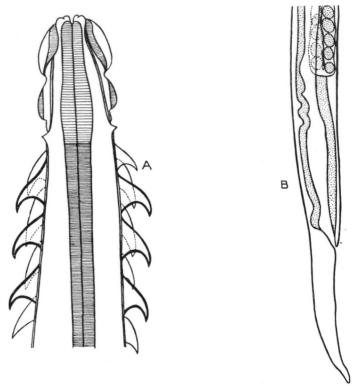

Fig. 238.—*Pneumonema tiliquæ.* A. Anterior extremity, ventral view. × 215. B. Posterior extremity of female, lateral view. × 75. (Orig.)

cavity very small ; vestibule absent, the œsophagus reaching nearly to the anterior extremity ; two cervical alæ on each side, the anterior being more heavily chitinized than the posterior ; behind these alæ are two longitudinal rows of large thorn-like spines on each side, becoming gradually smaller posteriorly, and disappearing about the junction of the anterior and middle thirds of the worm ;

the cervical papillæ lie just behind the more posterior of the cervical alæ ; œsophagus cylindrical and divided into two parts, of which the anterior muscular portion is the shorter. Male : unknown. Female : posterior extremity long and pointed ; vulva near the middle of the body ; uteri opposed. Oviparous, eggs with thin shells, containing a larva when deposited. Parasites of the lung of reptiles.

Type species : *P. tiliquæ* Johnston, 1916. ♂ ?, ♀ 6–9 mm. In *Tiliqua scincoides*.

Refs. 74, 246.

Genus ECHINONEMA Linstow, 1898.

Syn., *Hoplocephalus* Linstow, 1898, preoccupied.

Definition.—RICTULARIINÆ : mouth opens subterminally, with two small lateral lips ; mouth cavity very small, œsophagus

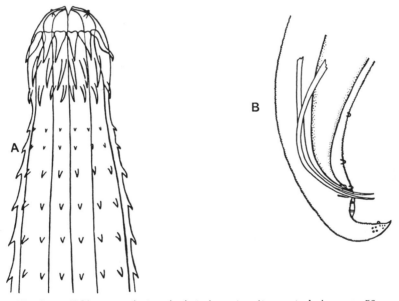

Fig. 239.—*Echinonema cincta*. A. Anterior extremity, ventral view. × 56.
B. Posterior extremity of male, lateral view. × 56. (Orig.)

reaching nearly to the anterior end ; cephalic cuticle somewhat dilated, and ornamented with three circles of very large posteriorly directed spines ; cuticle of anterior portion of worm also provided with circles of spines, which become extremely minute after the first twelve or thirteen circles, each circle consists of about fourteen to sixteen spines arranged in such a manner

that the spines are in longitudinal rows ; œsophagus relatively
short and not clearly divided into two portions.   Male : posterior
extremity short, conical, and ending in a short sharp point ; caudal
alæ absent, with a row of three preanal and three postanal papillæ
subventrally on each side, and more laterally a large papilla about
the level of the cloaca ; there is also a group of very small papillæ
near the tip of the tail ; spicules equal, with simple points ;
gubernaculum present.   Female : posterior extremity sharply
conical ; vulva about the junction of the anterior and middle
thirds of the body.   Oviparous, eggs with a thick shell, containing
an embryo when deposited.

Type species : *E. cincta* Linstow, 1898.   ♂ 14–16 mm.,
♀ 30–32 mm.   In *Perameles obesula.*

Syn., *Hoplocephalus cinctus* Linstow, 1898.
Refs. 316, 316a.

Genus SPINITECTUS Fourment, 1883.

Syn., *Liorhynchus* Rud., 1801, in part.
Goezia Zeder, 1800, in part.

Definition.—RICTULARIINÆ : mouth with indistinct lips ; cuticle
provided with a series of transverse rings to the hinder edge of
which are attached backwardly directed spines, which gradually

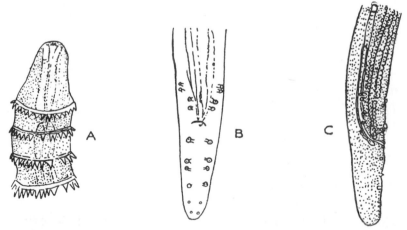

Fig. 240.—*Spinitectus cristatus.*   A. Anterior extremity.   × 300.   B. Posterior
     extremity of male, ventral view.   × 240.   C. Posterior extremity of
     male, semi-lateral view.   × 240.   (After Linton.)

* According to Schneider, Stiles and Hassall, and Railliet, the genus *Liorhynchus*
Rud., 1801, has for its type an undeterminable species *L. truncatus* (Rud., 1873) and
should therefore be abandoned.

diminish in size and number posteriorly ; vestibule cylindrical or funnel-shaped ; œsophagus consists of two parts—muscular and glandular. Male : tail spiral ; caudal alæ narrow ; sometimes with denticulated crests in front of the cloaca ; papillæ apparently present or absent (Linton states, that in *S. cristatus* there are four pairs of preanal and five or six pairs of postanal papillæ, and Ward and Magath state, that in *S. gracilis* papillæ are absent). Female : tail almost straight ; vulva in the posterior part of the body. Oviparous, eggs small, ellipsoidal with a thick shell, and sometimes with polar plugs bearing long filaments. Parasites of stomach and intestine of fishes.

Type species : *S. oviflagellis* Fourment, 1883. ♂ ?, ♀ 12 mm. In *Merlangus vulgaris*.

Other species :

S. cristatus Railliet and Henry, 1915. In *Phycis tenuis*.
  Syn., *Filaria serrata* Linton, 1901, not 1892.

S. echinatus (Linstow, 1878). [Probably larval form of *S. inermis*]. In *Alburnus lucidus*.

S. gracilis Ward and Magath, 1916. In fresh-water fishes— black crappie, white bass, etc.

S. inermis (Zeder, 1800). In eels.
  Syn., *Gœzia inermis* Zeder, 1800.
    Liorhynchus denticulatus Rud., 1809.

Refs. 131, 136, 137, 334, 442, 476, 480, 662.

Family SEURATIDÆ Railliet, 1916.

Definition.—SPIRUROIDEA : mouth bounded by two lateral lips ; without a vestibule ; œsophagus very short, club-shaped, and entirely muscular ; cervical papillæ symmetrical and behind the nerve ring ; cuticle with fine transverse striations and sixty-four longitudinal dark bands.

Subfamily SEURATINÆ Hall, 1916.

Definition.—SEURATIDÆ : with the characters of the family.

Genus SEURATUM* Hall, 1916.

Syn., *Ophiostomum* Creplin, 1839, of Seurat, 1915.

Definition.—SEURATINÆ : mouth elongate dorso-ventrally, bounded by two lateral lips, each with two large papillæ ; buccal cavity very short ; vestibule absent ; lateral cuticular flanges

---

* Baylis (1923) considers that the genus *Seuratum* belongs to the family *Cucullanidæ*.

absent ; cuticle with fine transverse striations and sixty-four longitudinal dark straight bands, presenting in the line of each band
a dentiform thickening of the transverse striations, with the point
directed posteriorly : œsophagus very short, club-shaped, entirely
muscular, and not divided into two parts ; cervical papillæ behind
the nerve ring.   Male : tail short and conical ; caudal alæ narrow ;
with four pairs of large sessile preanal papillæ, and six pairs of

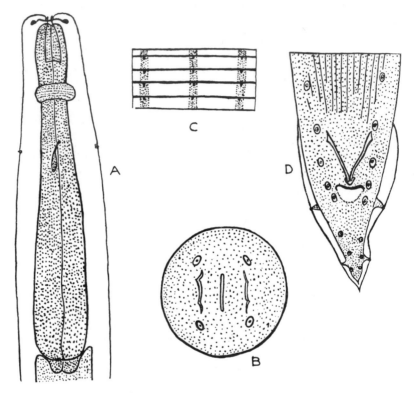

Fig. 241.—*Seuratum tacapense.*   A. Anterior extremity, ventral view.   × 66.
B. Anterior extremity, end-on view.   × 100.   C. Portion of cuticle
showing bands.   D. Posterior extremity of male, ventral view.   × 100.
(After Seurat.)

postanal papillæ, of which the second and fifth are large and
pedunculated ; spicules short and about equal ; gubernaculum
present.   For a short distance in front of the cloaca the ventral
surface is covered with about twenty longitudinal cuticular shields,
which become confluent a little in front of the cloaca.   Female :
vulva slightly in front of the middle of the body ; uteri opposed.
Oviparous, eggs large, subspherical, and containing an embryo
when deposited.   Parasites of rodents.

Type species : *S. tacapense* (Seurat, 1915). ♂ 18·5–22·5 mm.,
♀ 45 mm. In *Ctenodactylus gundi*.

Syn., *Ophistomum tacapense* Seurat, 1915.

Refs. 34, 205, 405, 517, 556.

FAMILY PHYSALOPTERIDÆ LEIPER, 1908.

Definition.—SPIRUROIDEA : mouth with large simple triangular
lateral lips armed with one or more teeth ; cuticle reflected forwards over the lips to form a cephalic collarette ; cutaneous
cordons or epaulettes absent ; usually without a vestibule ;
œsophagus divided into two portions. Male : caudal alæ well-
developed, usually meeting ventrally in front of the cloaca, and
supported by long costiform papillæ.

Subfamily PHYSALOPTERINÆ Railliet, 1893.

Definition.—PHYSALOPTERIDÆ : with the characters of the
family.

KEY TO GENERA.

1. Cervical papillæ modified into large
   crescentic tooth-like structures   .   Streptocara, p. 359.
   Cervical papillæ simple .   .   .   2
2. Without a cephalic collarette ; vestibule present   .   .   .   .   Thubunæa, p. 358.
   With a cephalic collarette ; vestibule
   absent   3
3. Male with caudal alæ not meeting
   ventrally in front of cloaca ; vulva
   near anus   .   .   .   .   .   Proleptus, p. 357.
   Male with caudal alæ meeting ven-
   trally in front of cloaca ; vulva in
   front of middle of body   .   .   4
4. With a prepuce-like sheath over the
   posterior end of body .   .   .   Chlamydonema, p. 356.
   Without a prepuce-like sheath over
   the posterior end of body   .   .   Physaloptera, p. 351.

Genus PHYSALOPTERA Rud., 1819.

Definition.—PHYSALOPTERINÆ : with two large, simple, triangular, lateral lips, each armed with a variable number of teeth
and with two external papillæ ; cuticle generally reflected over
the lips to form a large cephalic collarette ; cervical papillæ

behind the nerve ring ; with a short buccal cavity, but without a definite vestibule ; œsophagus consists of an anterior muscular, and a posterior glandular part. Male : with caudal alæ meeting ventrally in front of the anus, at least four pairs of costiform papillæ, supporting the alæ and surrounding the cloaca, and a variable number of sessile papillæ, of which three are generally preanal and five postanal ; spicules unequal, subequal, or equal. Female : vulva in front of the middle of the body ; uterus with two (didelphys), or four (tetradelphys), or more (polydelphys)

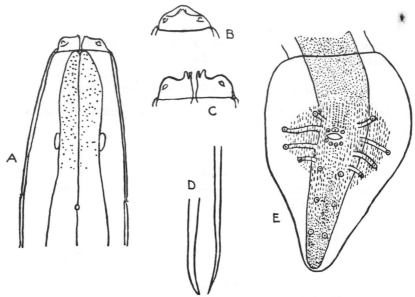

Fig. 242.—*Physaloptera clausa.* A. Anterior extremity, ventral view. × 50. B. Head, lateral view. C. Head, ventral view. D. Spicules. × 50. E. Posterior extremity of male, ventral view. × 32. (After Ortlepp.)

branches. Oviparous, eggs oval, smooth, thick-shelled, and embryonated when deposited. Parasites in the stomach and intestine of mammals, birds, reptiles, and very rarely amphibia.

Type species : *P. clausa* Rudolphi, 1819. ♂ 15–28 mm., ♀ 30–50 mm. In *Erinaceus europæus.*

Other species :

P. abbreviata Rud., 1819. In *Lacerta* spp., etc.

? *P. abjecta* Leidy, 1853. In *Psammophis flagelliformis.*

P. acuticauda Molin, 1860. In *Falco atricapillus*, etc.

P. africana (Monnig, 1924). In *Paraxerus* sp., *Otomys* sp., *Mus* spp.

Syn., *Leptosoma africana* Monnig, 1924.

P. alata Rud., 1819. In *Falco* spp.

Syn., *Spiroptera physalura* Duj., 1845.

P. alata var. *chevreuxi* Seurat, 1914. In hawk.

P. alata var. *nouveli* Seurat, 1915. In *Aquila* sp., *Accipiter* sp.

P. aloisii-sabaudiæ Parona, 1907. In *Agama atricollis*.

P. amphibia v. Linstow, 1899. In *Rana macrodon*.

P. anomala Molin, 1860. In *Felis onça*.

P. antarctica v. Linstow, 1899. In *Acanthophis antarctica, Cyclodus* spp.

Syn., *P. alba* Stoss., 1902.

P. antarctica var. *antarctica* Irwin-Smith, 1922. In *Tiliqua* spp.

P. antarctica var. *lata* Irwin-Smith, 1922. In *Tiliqua* spp.

P. bilabiata Creplin, 1829. In *Lanius minor*.

P. bonnei Ortlepp, 1922. In " Sapakara."

? *P. brevicauda* v. Linstow, 1906. In *Francolinus adspersus*.

P. brevispiculum v. Linstow, 1906. In *Felis rubiginosa*.

P. brevivaginata Seurat, 1917. In *Vespertilio kuehli*.

P. britanica Skrjabin, 1916. In *Agama* sp.

P. capensis Ortlepp, 1922. In *Xerus setosus*.

P. caucasica v. Linstow, 1902. In *Homo sapiens*.

P. cebi Ortlepp, 1923. In *Cebus fatuellus*.

P. cesticillata Sonsino, 1889. In *Canis cerdo, Fennecus* sp.

P. chamæleontis Gedoelst, 1916. In *Chamæleon gracilis*.

Syn., *P. leptosoma* (Gervais) Seurat, 1917.

P. circularis v. Linstow, 1897. In *Mus rattus*.

P. citilli (Rud., 1819) Hall, 1916. In *Citellus citellus*.

Syn., *Spiroptera citilli* Rud., 1819.

P. cœlebs v. Linstow, 1897. In *Centetes ecaudatus*.

P. colubri (Rud., 1819) Dies., 1851. In *Coronella austriaca*.

P. crassa v. Linstow, 1879. In *Alauda arvensis*.

P. crosi Seurat, 1914. In *Accipiter nisus*.

P. dentata v. Linstow, 1883. In *Agama* sp., *Vipera* sp.

P. digitata Schneider, 1866. In *Felis concolor*.

P. dilatata Rud., 1819. In *Lagothrix humboldtii*, etc.

Syn., *Spiroptera dilatata* (Rud., 1819) Duj., 1845.

P. dispar v. Linstow, 1904. In *Erinaceus albiventris*.

P. elegantissima Stossich, 1902. In *Ratelus capensis*.

P. formosana Yokogawa, 1922. In *Sorex* sp.

P. fusiformis v. Linstow, 1902. In *Micropogon* sp.

P. galinieri Seurat, 1914. In eagle.

P. gemina v. Linstow, 1899. In *Felis catus domesticus*.

P. getula Seurat, 1917.   In *Mus rattus.*

P. gracilis Ortlepp, 1922.   In lizards.

P. guiarti Garin, 1913.   In *Leptonychotes weddelli.*

P. incurva v. Linstow, 1908.   In *Erinaceus frontalis.*

P. inermis v. Linstow, 1906.   In *Sciurus prevosti.*

P. inflata (Molin, 1860).   In *Falco unicinctus.*

P. leiperi Skrjabin, 1924.   In *Spermophilopsis leptodactylus.*

P. limbata Leidy, 1856.   In *Scalops canadensis.*

P. longissima Ortlepp, 1922.   In snakes.

P. magnipapilla Molin, 1860.   In *Myrmecophaga bivittata.*

? *P. malleus* v. Linstow, 1883.   In *Corvus cornix.*

P. maxillaris Molin, 1860.   In *Mephitis chinche.*

P. megalostoma Creplin, 1829.   In *Falco nisus.*
  Syn., *P. alata* Rud., 1819, of Stoss., 1889.

P. mephites Solanet, 1909.   In *Mephitis suffocans.*

P. monodens Molin, 1860.   In *Boa constrictor.*

P. mordens Leiper, 1908.   In *Homo sapiens*, monkeys.

P. muris-brasiliensis Diesing, 1861.   In *Mus brasiliensis.*
  Syn., *Spiroptera bilabiata* Molin, 1860 not *Spiroptera
    bilabiata* (Crep., 1829) Duj., 1845.

P. nasilionis Gedoelst, 1916.   In *Nasilio brachyrhynchus.*

P. numidica Seurat, 1917.   In *Dipodillus campestris.*

P. obtusissima Molin, 1860.   In *Bothrops* sp., *Cloelia* spp.,
    Ophis spp., etc.

P. pallaryi Seurat, 1917.   In *Agama bibroni.*

? *P. papilloradiata* v. Linstow, 1899.   In *Canis lupus.*

P. papillotruncata Molin, 1860.   In *Myrmecophaga jubata.*

P. paradoxa v. Linstow, 1908.   In *Varanus albigularis,
    Psammophis sibilans*, etc.
  Syn., *P. affinis* Gedoelst, 1916.

P. phrynosoma Ortlepp, 1922.   In *Phrynosoma cornutum.*

P. physignathi Baylis, 1924.   In *Physignathus* sp.

P. pyramidalis v. Linstow, 1879.   In *Cholœpus didactylus.*

P. quadrovaria Leiper, 1908.   In *Varanus niloticus.*

P. rara Hall and Wigdor, 1918.   In *Canis familiaris.*

P. retusa Rud., 1819.   In *Tupinambis teguixin*, etc.
  Syn., *Spiroptera retusa* (Rud., 1819) Duj., 1845.

P. ruwenzorii Parona, 1907.   In *Arvicanthus* sp., *Mus* sp.

P. sciuri Parona, 1898.   In *Sciurus melanogaster.*

P. semilanceolata Molin, 1860.   In *Nasua narica.*

P. simplicidens Ortlepp, 1922.   In lizard.

P. sonsinoi v. Linstow, 1895.   In *Agama mutabilis.*

P. spiralis Schneider, 1866.   In *Amphisbæna* sp.

? *P. spirula* Hempr. and Ehrenb., 1828.   In *Procavia* spp.

P. subalata Schneider, 1866.   In *Falco* sp.

P. tacapensis Seurat, 1917.   In *Ctenodactylus gundi*.

P. terdentata Molin, 1860.   In *Felis concolor*.

P. torquata Leidy, 1856.   In *Meles labradorica*.

P. torresi (Travassos, 1920).   In *Agouti paca*.

   Syn., *Turgida torresi* Travassos, 1920.

P. truncata Schneider, 1866.   In *Phasianus gallus*.

P. turgida Rudolphi, 1819.   In *Didelphys* spp.

   Syn., *Turgida turgida* (Rud., 1819) Travassos, 1920.

      Spiroptera turgida (Rud., 1819) Duj., 1845.

P. vandenbrandeni Gedoelst, 1924.   In a wild cat.

P. varani Parona, 1889.   In *Varanus* sp.

Travassos (1919 and 1920) has divided the genus *Physaloptera* as follows :—

1. Spicules similar and subequal.
   A. Two uteri.
      a. Four pairs of pedunculated papillæ ; no prepuce-like sheath at posterior end.
                              Physaloptera s.s. Travassos, 1919.
         With a prepuce-like sheath at posterior end.
                              Chlamydonema Hegt, 1910.
      b. Eight pairs of pedunculated papillæ.
                              Thubunæa Seurat, 1914.
   B. Ten uteri .   .   .   .   *Turgida* Travassos, 1919.

2. Spicules dissimilar and very unequal.
   AA. Two uteri.
      aa. Four pairs of pedunculated papillæ.
                              Abbreviata Travassos, 1919.
      bb. Ten pairs of pedunculated papillæ.
      cc. Vulva in anterior half of body, ovejector very long   .   .   .   *Heliconema* Travassos, 1919.
      dd. Vulva near anus, ovejector short.
                              Proleptus Duj., 1845.
   BB. Four uteri   .   .   . *Leptosoma* Travassos, 1919.

The type species are presumably as follows :—

Physaloptera : P. clausa Rud., 1819 ; *Chlamydonema : C. felineum* Hegt, 1910 = *P. præputialis* Linst., 1899 ; *Thubunæa : T. pudica* Seurat, 1914 ; *Turgida : T. turgida* (Rud., 1819) ; *Abbreviata : A. abbreviata* (Rud., 1819) ; *Heliconema :* type not mentioned ; *Proleptus : P. acutus* Duj., 1845 ; *Leptosoma : L. leptosoma* (Gervais, of Seurat, 1917).

A good deal of this classification is, as Ortlepp (1922) has pointed out, very unsatisfactory. *Leptosoma* is preoccupied and *P. leptosoma* has only two uteri, according to Seurat (1917) ; *P. abbreviata* Rud., 1819, has four uteri, according to Seurat (1914) ; and certain of the *Physaloptera* which have a prepuce-like sheath have four uteri.

Refs. 41, 160a, 239, 240, 241, 275, 378, 379, 477, 502, 516, 536, 538, 582a, 635, 638, 668a.

Genus CHLAMYDONEMA Hegt, 1910.

Definition.—PHYSALOPTERINÆ : closely resembles *Physaloptera*, but differs in possessing a prepuce-like sheath over the posterior extremity.   Parasites of carnivora and monkeys.

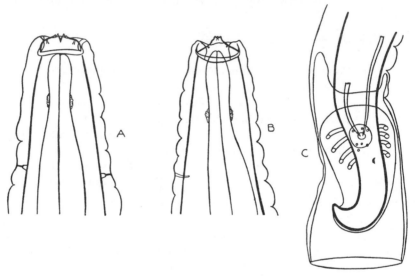

Fig. 243.—*Chlamydonema præputiale.* A. Anterior extremity, ventral view. × 40. B. Anterior extremity, lateral view.   × 40.   C. Posterior extremity of male, ventral view.   × 40. (Orig.)

Type species : *C. præputiale* (Linstow, 1889). ♂ 13–40 mm., ♀ 15–48 mm. In *Felis* spp.

    Syn., *Physaloptera præputialis* Linstow, 1889.
        Chlamydonema felineum Hegt, 1910.

Other species :

    C. malayense (Ortlepp, 1922). In *Felis* spp.
    C. tumefaciens (Henry and Blanc, 1912).   In *Macacus* spp.

Refs. 212, 214, 315a, 378.

Genus PROLEPTUS Duj., 1845.

Syn., *Coronilla* Beneden, 1871.
Spiropterina Beneden, 1858.

Definition.—PHYSALOPTERINÆ : mouth bounded by two simple lateral lips, each bearing a truncated tooth, and two submedian papillæ ; cephalic collarette present ; cervical papillæ sym-

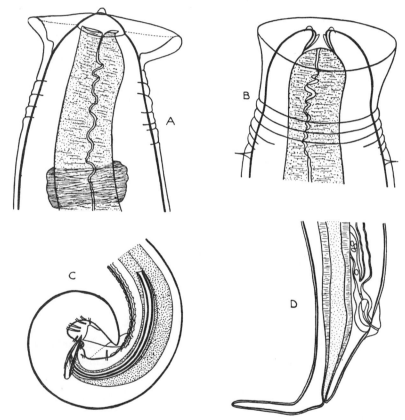

Fig. 244.—*Proleptus obtusus.* A. Anterior extremity, lateral view. × 160.
B. Anterior extremity, ventral view. × 160. C. Posterior extremity of male, lateral view. × 35. D. Posterior extremity of female, lateral view. × 35. (Orig.)

metrical, in front of the nerve ring ; excretory pore some distance posterior to it ; œsophagus clearly divided into two parts, anterior muscular and posterior glandular. Male : posterior extremity spirally coiled ; with large caudal alæ ; with nine pairs of symmetrical pedunculated papillæ, of which three are pre- or ad-anal and six postanal, and, in addition, an unpaired sessile papilla on the anterior lip of the cloaca, and a pair of short pedunculated papillæ immediately behind the cloaca ; spicules very unequal ; gubernaculum absent. Female : vulva projecting, near the anus ; uteri parallel ; ovejector short ; oviducts and ovaries intertwined in the posterior part of the body. Oviparous, eggs small, with a thick shell, containing a larva at deposition. Parasites of stomach and intestines of Selachians, and tortoises.

Type species : *P. acutus* Duj., 1845. ♂ 12 mm., ♀ ? In *Raja clavata*.

Syn., *Spiroptera dacnodes* Creplin, 1851.

Spiropterina dacnodes (Creplin, 1851) Oerley, 1885.

Histiocephalus dacnodes (Creplin, 1851) Molin, 1860.

Other species :

P. coronatus (Beneden, 1858). In *Raja* sp., *Scillium* sp.

Syn., *Spiropterina coronata* Bened., 1858.

P. elegans (Oerley, 1885). In *Hexanchus* sp.

P. gordioides Beneden, 1858. In *Galeus canis*.

P. obtusus Duj., 1845. In *Scyllium catulus*.

Syn., *Coronilla scillicola* Beneden, 1871.

Spiropterina scillicola (Beneden, 1871) Linstow, 1901.

P. rajæ (Dies., 1851). In *Raja clavata*.

P. robustus (Beneden, 1871). In *Raja circularis*.

Syn., *Coronilla robusta* Beneden, 1871.

P. tortus Linstow, 1906. In *Cistudo ornata*.

Refs. 48, 50, 131, 554.

Genus THUBUNÆA Seurat, 1914.

Definition.—PHYSALOPTERINÆ : mouth with two lateral rounded simple lips, the internal surfaces of which are armed with three prominent teeth, and which bear a pair of submedian papillæ ; lateral flanges absent ; cervical papillæ immediately behind the nerve ring ; vestibule short, cylindrical, compressed laterally, and with delicate walls ; œsophagus short with an anterior muscular and a posterior glandular part. Male : posterior extremity rounded terminating in a small conical process ; caudal alæ well-developed exhibiting a verrucose appearance ; four pairs of pedunculated preanal papillæ and four or five pairs of pedunculated postanal papillæ, and, in addition, about a dozen sessile papillæ round the anus ; spicules equal. Female : posterior extremity short, terminating in a small conical point ; vulva in the anterior fifth of the body ; ovejector long ; uteri parallel.

Oviparous, eggs with a thick shell, containing larvæ when deposited.   Parasites of reptiles.

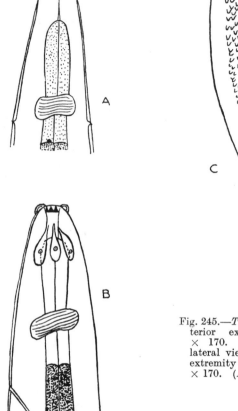

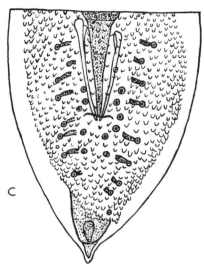

Fig. 245.—*Thubunæa pudica.*   A. Anterior   extremity,   ventral   view.   × 170.   B.   Anterior   extremity, lateral view.   × 170.   C. Posterior extremity   of   male,   ventral   view. × 170.   (After Seurat.)

Type species :   *T. pudica* Seurat, 1914.   ♂ 8 mm., ♀ 9–19 mm. In chameleon.

Refs. 378, 505, 638.

Genus STREPTOCARA Railliet, Henry, and Sisoff, 1912.

Syn., *Yseria* Gedoelst, 1919.

Definition.—PHYSALOPTERINÆ : head with two simple lateral lips, each bearing a dentiform process and two small lateral papillæ ; behind the lips is a collarette, with a dentate anterior margin ; the cervical papillæ are represented by large crescentic structures with five or six small teeth on the posterior concave surface ; behind the buccal cavity is a short vestibule with delicate walls ; œsophagus long and cylindrical. Male : posterior extremity conical, blunt, and spirally coiled ; caudal alæ present ; four pairs of costiform preanal and five or six pairs of costiform postanal papillæ ; spicules very unequal. Female : posterior extremity rounded ; anus subterminal ; vulva a little behind the middle of the body. Oviparous, eggs elliptical with a thin shell, containing an embryo at deposition. Parasites of the gizzard of birds.

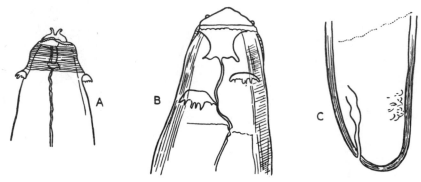

Fig. 246.—*Streptocara crassicauda*. A. Anterior extremity, ventral view. B. Anterior extremity, lateral view. C. Posterior extremity of female. (After Skrjabin.)

Type species : *S. pectinifera* (Neumann, 1900). ♂ 4·5 mm., ♀ 8–9·5 mm. In domestic fowl.

Syn., *Spiroptera pectinifera* Neumann, 1900.

Other species :

S. californica (Gedoelst, 1919). In *Oidemia deglandi*.

S. cirrohamata (Linstow, 1888). In *Phalacrocorax verrucosus*.

S. crassicauda (Creplin, 1829). In *Colymbus rufogularis*, *Mergus merganser*, and *Anas boschas*.

S. crassicauda var. *charadrii* Skrjabin, 1916. In *Vanellus cristatus*.

? *S. decora* (Duj., 1845). In *Alcedo ispida*.

Syn., *Yseria decora* (Duj., 1845) Gedoelst, 1919.

S. recta (Linstow, 1879). In *Podiceps cristatus*.

S. stellæ-polaris (Parona, 1901). In *Fulmarus glacialis*.

S. triænucha (Wright, 1879). In *Botaurus minor*.

S. tridentata (Linstow, 1877). In *Colymbus arcticus* and *Larus* sp.

Refs. 154, 161, 452, 572.

FAMILY TETRAMERIDÆ TRAVASSOS, 1914.

Definition.—SPIRUROIDEA : exhibiting extraordinary sexual dimorphism, the female being greatly distended towards the middle of the body and fusiform in shape ; males filiform. The males are generally free in the crop of birds, and the females are encysted in its wall ; rarely in reptiles.

Subfamily TETRAMERINÆ Railliet, 1915.

Definition.—TETRAMERIDÆ : with the characters of the family.

Genus TETRAMERES Creplin, 1846.

Syn., *Tropisurus* Diesing, 1835.
 Tropidurus* Wiegmann, 1835, preoccupied.
 Tropidocerca Diesing, 1851.
 Astomum Schlotthauber, 1860.
 Acanthophorus Linst., 1876.
Definition.—TETRAMERINÆ : mouth with small lips ; vestibule cylindrical ; œsophagus cylindrical ; intestine a thin-walled, wide tube. Male : thread-like, white, sometimes with spines along the median and lateral lines ; spicules very unequal, the larger sometimes being about two-thirds the length of the body. Female : fusiform, red, with well-marked transverse striations in the middle region, and with longitudinal depressions corresponding to the median and lateral lines ; vulva in the posterior part of the body ; the uterus is enormously developed, occupying the greater part of the body, and containing thin-shelled eggs, with fully-developed embryos. Parasitic in the proventriculus of birds and rarely in reptiles, the females burrow into the glands, and the males lie free in the lumen of the organ.

Type species : *T. paradoxa* Diesing, 1835. ♂ 10–12 mm., ♀ 6–8 mm. In *Catharistes atratus*, etc.
 Syn., *Tropisurus paradoxus* Dies., 1835.
  Tropidurus paradoxus (Dies., 1835) Wiegmann, 1835.
  Tropidocerca paradoxa (Dies., 1835) Diesing, 1852.
Other species :
 T. bispinosa (Molin, 1860). In *Scincus* sp.
 T. certa (Leidy, 1866). In *Diomedea* sp.
 T. coccinea (Seurat, 1914). In *Phœnicopterus* sp.
 T. cochleariæ Travassos, 1917. In *Cancroma cochlearia*.

---

* *Tropidurus* is the emended form for *Tropisurus* and according to Art. 19 of the International Code the emendation was permissible on the ground that *Tropisurus* represents an error of transcription.

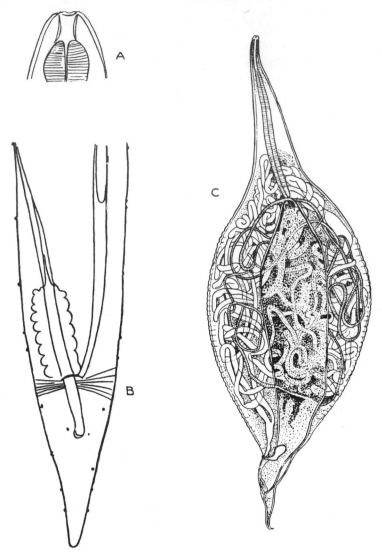

Fig. 247.—*Tetrameres (Tetrameres) paradoxa.* A. Anterior extremity. × 120.
B. Posterior extremity of male, ventral view.   × 53. (After Drasche.)
Tetrameres (Tetrameres) fissispina. C. Female, young. (After Travassos.)

T. confusa Travassos, 1917.   In *Gallus domesticus.*

T. contorta (Weidman, 1913).   In *Dichocerus bicornis.*

T. cruzi Travassos, 1914.   In *Bucco* sp., *Melanerpes* sp.

T. dubia Travassos, 1917.   In *Gallinago* sp.

T. fissispina (Diesing, 1861).   In *Anas* sp., *Gallus* sp., etc.
Syn., *Acanthophorus tenuis* Linstow, 1876.

T. gigas Travassos, 1917.   In *Anas boschas*.

T. globosa (Linstow, 1879).   In *Fulica* sp.

T. gynæcophila (Molin, 1858).   In *Nycticorax* sp.

T. hæmochrous Creplin, 1846.   In *Falco* sp., *Ciconia* sp., etc.

T. inermis (Linstow, 1879).   In *Astur* sp., *Corvus* sp.

T. inflata (Mehlis, 1846).   In *Anas* sp., etc.

T. lhuillieri (Seurat, 1918).   In *Caccabis petrosa*.

T. micropenis Travassos, 1915.   In *Nycticorax* sp., etc.

T. minima Travassos, 1914.   In *Tachyphonus* sp.

T. nouveli (Seurat, 1914).   In *Himantopus* sp.

T. pusilla Travassos, 1915.   In *Turdus* sp.

T. spiralis (Seurat, 1915).   In *Bubulcus* sp.

T. tetrica Travassos, 1917.   In *Aramides* sp.

T. unispina (Diesing, 1861).   In *Corvus cornix*.

Travassos (1915) divided the genus into two subgenera as follows :—

Subgenus TETRAMERES (Creplin, 1846) Travassos, 1915.

Definition.—*Tetrameres* in which the spicules are relatively short, *i.e.*, in proportion to the body length, the larger is three to six times as long

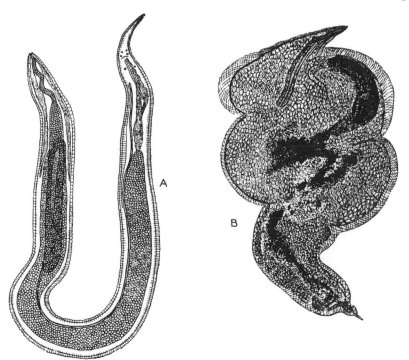

Fig. 248.—*Tetrameres* (*Microtetrameres*) *cruzi*. A. Male. B. Female. (After Travassos.)

as the smaller ; the cuticle is spined in the lateral fields. Contains the species *paradoxa, confusa, dubia, fissispina, gigas, micropenis, nouveli,* and *tetrica.*

Subgenus MICROTETRAMERES Travassos, 1917.

Definition.—*Tetrameres* in which the spicules are relatively very long, the larger being about two-thirds the length of the body, the smaller being slightly chitinized ; the cuticle is not spined in the lateral fields. Females very often with a longitudinal torsion. Contains the species *cruzi, contorta, inermis, inflata. minima, pusilla,* and *spiralis.*

Refs. 115, 123, 128, 131, 310, 503, 506, 507, 548, 622, 625, 634.

Family ANCYRACANTHIDÆ Railliet, 1916.

Definition.—Spiruroidea : head provided with more or less prominent appendages of very diverse appearance.

KEY TO SUBFAMILIES.

Cephalic appendages in form of four long, feathered processes, directed posteriorly . . . . . Ancyracanthinæ, p. 364.

Cephalic appendages not consisting of four long feathered processes . Schistorophinæ, p. 365.

Subfamily ANCYRACANTHINÆ n. sf.

Definition.—Ancyracanthidæ : from each side of the head arise two posteriorly directed feathered processes.

Genus ANCYRACANTHUS Diesing, 1838.

Definition.—Ancyracanthinæ : head composed of two large lateral dome-shaped lips from each of which, and from the adjacent parts of the body, arise two prominent feathered appendages directed backwards and outwards, they are slightly curved with the concavity forwards, and not as figured by Diesing with the convexity forwards ; surrounding the anterior part of the œsophagus are four club-shaped organs (apparently analogous to the blind cervical sacs of the *Gnathostomidæ*). Male : posterior extremity conical and spirally rolled ; small caudal alæ ; spicules long and equal ; two pairs of large preanal, and one pair of small postanal, papillæ. Female : posterior extremity short and slightly bent ; vulva in the posterior third of the body ; vagina long ; uteri divergent. Oviparous, eggs elliptical, with a thin shell.

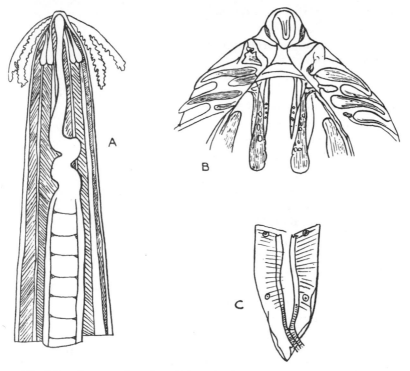

Fig. 249.—*Ancyracanthus pinnatifidus.* A. Anterior extremity, ventral view.
(After Diesing.) B. Anterior extremity. × 85. C. Posterior extremity
of male, ventral view. × 20. (After Drasche.)

Type species : *A. pinnatifidus* Diesing, 1839. ♂ 50 mm.,
♀ 60–62 mm. In *Podocnemis expansa* and *P. tracaxa.*

Syn., *A. pectinatus* Dies., 1838 [renamed].

Refs. 46, 86, 122, 125, 128, 131, 405.

Subfamily SCHISTOROPHINÆ Travassos, 1918.

Definition.—ANCYRACANTHIDÆ : cephalic appendages in the
form of a hood-like covering, or of various cuticular expansions,
appendages, or processes.

KEY TO GENERA.

1. Mouth circular without lips ; head
    provided with a ring-shaped
    cuticular swelling, slightly over-
    lapping the body externally   Viguiera, p. 370.

Mouth oval with two lateral lips ;
head provided with a sort of
double collar (anterior and posterior portions), each subdivided
longitudinally into a number of
prominences . . . . Torquatella, p. 372.
Head with multiple and varied
cuticular expansions . . Serticeps, p. 373.
Head with two or four laterally
placed cuticular wings, directed
postero-externally . . . 2
2. Wings subdivided externally into
finger-like processes . . 3
Wings not subdivided externally
into finger-like processes . . 4
3. With two wings on each side, and
without inflation of cervical
cuticle . . . . . Ancyracanthopsis, p. 369.
With one wing on each side, and
with inflation of cervical cuticle
to form a collar of longitudinal
rib-like thickenings . . Histiocephalus, p. 369.
4. Wings pointed and dorso-ventral
in position. Male with numerous
sessile preanal papillæ . . Schistorophus, p. 366.
Wings hemispherical and lateral in
position. Male with six pairs of
pedunculated preanal papillæ . Sciadiocara, p. 367.

Genus SCHISTOROPHUS Railliet, 1916.

Syn., *Tetracanthus* Hemprich and Ehrenberg, MS. in
Schneider, 1866, preoccupied.
Ancyracanthus Schneider, 1866, in part, not Dies.,
1838.

Definition.—SCHISTOROPHINÆ : mouth with two small lateral
lips ; head furnished with four pointed cuticular wings, two
dorsally and two ventrally, directed outwards and backwards,
merging with the cuticle in front, more or less united at their
origin, especially in the mid-lines, and arranged like a roof ; vestibule long ; œsophagus consists of two parts. Male : tail blunt ;
provided with alæ ; numerous preanal papillæ in a long simple
row ; spicules unequal. Female : tail short and more or less

obtuse or conical ; vulva in the posterior, or middle, region of the body. Sometimes viviparous. Parasites of the coats of the gizzards of birds.

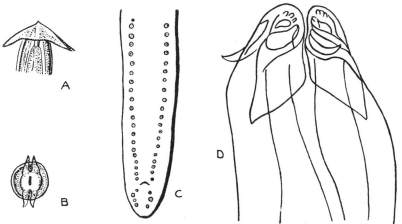

Fig. 250.—*Schistorophus longicornis.* A. Anterior extremity, lateral view. × 90. B. Head, end-on view. × 90. C. Posterior extremity of male, ventral view. × 62. (After Schneider.) *Schistorophus aulieatina.* D. Anterior extremity, ventral view. (After Skrjabin.)

Type species : *S. longicornis* (Hemprich and Ehrenberg, 1866). ♂ 5–10 mm., ♀ 8–20 mm. In *Numenius arquatus, Tringa* sp., *Totanus* sp.

  Syn., *Tetracanthus longicornis* Hemprich and Ehrenberg, 1866.

    Ancyracanthus longicornis (Hemprich and Ehrenberg, 1866) Schneider, 1866.

Other species :

 ? *S. acanthocephalicus* (Molin, 1860). In *Sterna* spp.

 S. aulieatina Skrjabin, 1916. In *Hæmatopus* sp.

 S. bicuspis (Rud., 1819). In *Squatarola helvetica.*

 S. bidens (Rud., 1819). In *Astur* sp., *Merops* sp.

 ? *S. capillaris* (Molin, 1860). In *Sterna hirundo.*

 S. laciniatus (Molin, 1860). In *Rallus cayennensis.*

 ? *S. spinulosus* (Molin, 1860). In *Glareola austriaca.*

Refs. 128, 404, 480, 572, 636.

Genus SCIADIOCARA Skrjabin, 1916.

Definition.—SCHISTOPHORINÆ : mouth with two small lateral conical lips, each bearing two papillæ ; behind each lip is a pair of hemispherical membranous wings, directed posteriorly and forming an acute angle with the body ; vestibule cylindrical, with thick

walls ; œsophagus long and cylindrical, consisting of two parts.
Male : posterior extremity rounded ; caudal alæ present ; six
pairs of pedunculated preanal papillæ, and about five pairs of
postanal papillæ ; spicules very unequal, the smaller being provided with a canal through which the larger moves, thus serving
the function of a gubernaculum.   Female : posterior extremity

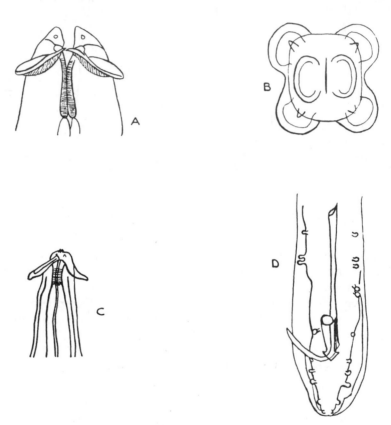

Fig. 251.—*Sciadiocara umbellifera*.   A. Anterior extremity, ventral view.
× 470.   B. Anterior extremity, end-on view.   × 470.   (After Drasche.)
C. Anterior extremity.   D. Posterior extremity of male, ventral view.
(After Skrjabin.)

bent and bluntly rounded ; vulva a little behind the middle of
the body.   Oviparous, eggs oval, with thick shells, containing an
embryo when deposited.   Parasites of the gizzard of birds.

Type species : *S. umbellifera* (Molin, 1860).   ♂ 6·4 mm.,
♀ 9–10 mm.   In gizzard of *Ibis* sp., *Scolopax* sp., *Totanus* sp.

Syn., *Spiroptera umbellifera* Molin, 1860.

Refs. 128, 358, 572.

Genus ANCYRACANTHOPSIS Diesing, 1861.

Definition.—SCHISTOROPHINÆ : body capillary, mouth with two small lips, each furnished with a small inner and a larger outer tooth, from each lip arise two appendages, directed posteriorly. (Molin and Diesing state, that these appendages are feathered, but Drasche (1884), who figures the head of the worm, states that each process subdivides into four equal digitations, and adds, that the head is extremely small. Drasche's figure is quite unlike that of *Ancyracanthus*.) The œsophagus, which is divided into an anterior thin, and a posterior thicker part, is long and measures nearly a third of the length of the worm. Male : posterior extremity bent spirally ; caudal alæ present ; with a number of simple papillæ ; spicule single ! Female : posterior extremity sometimes bent spirally, tail conical ; vulva in the posterior part of body. Parasitic between the coats of the ventriculus of birds.

Fig. 252.—*Ancyracanthopsis bilabiata.* Anterior extremity, lateral view. × 140. (After Drasche.)

Type species : *A. bilabiata* (Molin, 1860). ♂ 7 mm., ♀ 9 mm. In *Eurypyga helias*.

Syn., *Ancyracanthus bilabiatus* Molin, 1860.

Refs. 86, 125, 128, 359.

Genus HISTIOCEPHALUS Diesing, 1851.

Definition.—SCHISTOROPHINÆ : mouth surrounded by four lips, the lateral being much larger and trilobed and each bearing two small papillæ, the dorso-ventral each bear a pair of large papillæ [between the lateral and dorso-ventral lips are four large club-shaped papillæ (Drasche)]. Behind the lips are two lateral membranous appendages directed posteriorly, the free margins of which are split into six or twelve processes, each of which may or may not have a bifid or trifid extremity ; the cervical cuticle is inflated to form a collar, consisting of longitudinal rib-like thickenings ; mouth cavity infundibular ; œsophagus long and cylindrical. Male : with wide caudal alæ ; four pairs of costiform preanal papillæ and two pairs of costiform postanal papillæ ; spicules equal (Drasche states unequal). Female : vulva in front of the middle of the body. Parasites of the gizzard wall of birds and ? fishes.

Type species :   *H. laticaudatus* (Rud., 1819).   ♂ 8–12·5 mm.,
♀ 20–24 mm.   In *Otis tetrax*.
    Syn., *Spiroptera laticaudata* Rud., 1819.
        Dispharagus laticaudatus (Rud., 1819) Duj., 1845.

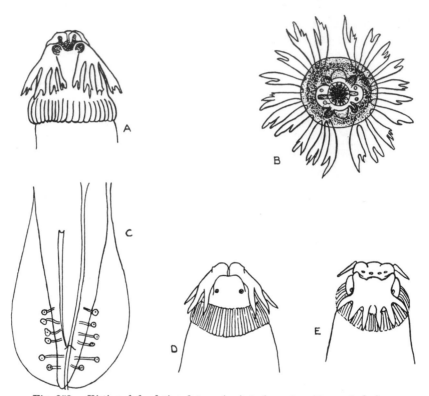

Fig. 253.—*Histiocephalus laticaudatus*. A. Anterior extremity, ventral view.
   × 250.   B. Anterior extremity, end-on view.   × 250.   C. Posterior
   extremity of male, ventral view.   × 250.   (After Drasche.) *Histiocephalus tridens*.   D. Anterior extremity, ventral view.   E. Anterior
   extremity, partial end-on view.   (After Gendre.)

Other species :
  ? *H. coronatus* (Molin, 1860).   In *Alcedo* sp., *Rallus* sp.
  ? *H. minutus* (Rud., 1819).   In *Platessa flesus*.
    H. tridens Gendre, 1921.   In *Trachelotis senegalensis*.
Refs. 123, 128, 154, 175, 477, 572.

Genus VIGUIERA Seurat, 1913.

Definition.—SCHISTOROPHINÆ :   body   sharply   attenuated
anteriorly ; mouth without definite lips, but cephalic extremity

covered by a circular disc or ring-like swelling, which slightly overlaps the subjacent portion externally ; behind this swelling are two large lateral and four small submedian papillæ ; vestibule cylindrical, with thick walls ; lateral flanges absent ; cervical papillæ very far in front of the nerve ring. Male : tail spirally

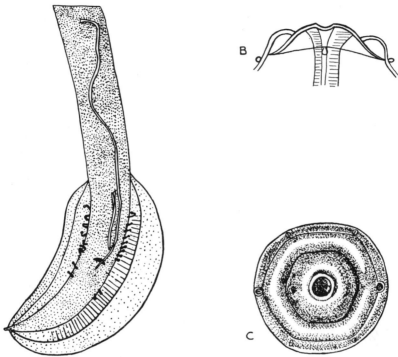

Fig. 254.—*Viguiera euryoptera*. A. Posterior extremity of male, ventral view. × 80. (After Seurat.) *Viguiera turdi*. B. Anterior extremity, lateral view. × 1,000. C. Anterior extremity, end-on view. × 1,000. (After Drasche.)

rolled ; caudal alæ asymmetrical ; with seven to nine pairs of preanal papillæ, and two pairs of postanal papillæ ; spicules very unequal ; gubernaculum absent. Female : tail regularly attenuate to the extremity ; vulva just in front of the anus ; ovejector very long ; uteri divergent. Parasites in wall of stomach of birds.

Type species : *V. euryoptera* (Rud., 1819). ♂ 5 mm., ♀ 9–10 mm. In *Lannius* spp.

Syn., *Spiroptera euryoptera* Rud., 1819.

Acuaria laniorum Molin, 1860.

Other species : *V. turdi* (Molin, 1860). In *Turdus musicus*. Refs. 128, 131, 358, 477, 495, 514.

Genus TORQUATELLA n.g.

Definition.—SCHISTOROPHINÆ : mouth with two lateral lips, limiting a tubular mouth cavity, and bearing posteriorly a number of small teeth ; behind the lips is a complicated cuticular collar consisting of a double circular row (anterior and posterior) of prominences, the continuity of which is interrupted at the level of the submedian lines by four oval depressions, each containing

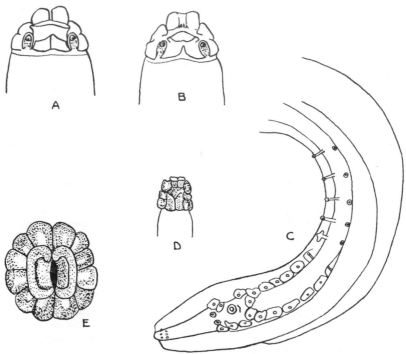

Fig. 255.—*Torquatella torquata*. A. Anterior extremity, ventral view.
B. Anterior extremity, lateral view. C. Posterior extremity of male.
(After Gendre.) *Torquatella conocephala.* D. Anterior extremity, lateral
view. × 280. E. Anterior extremity, end-on view. × 470. (After
Drasche.)

a small papilla ; the number of prominences into which the collar is subdivided varies in the different species, but it is greater in the posterior row than in the anterior ; vestibule cylindrical, with thick walls ; œsophagus cylindrical ; cervical papillæ at the level of the nerve ring. Male : with caudal alæ ; numerous preanal, and about three pairs of postanal, papillæ ; spicules unequal ; gubernaculum lightly chitinized. Female : vulva in the posterior half of the body. Ovejector directed forwards ; uteri divergent. Oviparous. Parasites of birds.

Type species : *T. torquata* (Gendre, 1922). ♂ 7 mm., ♀ 13–19 mm.
In *Centropus monachus.*

Syn., *Spiroptera torquata* Gendre, 1922.

Spiroptera conocephala Molin, 1860, of Gendre, 1921.

Other species :

T. balanocephala (Gendre, 1922).   In *Merops malinbicus.*

Syn., *Spiroptera balanocephala* Gendre, 1922.

T. conocephala (Molin, 1860).   In *Cuculus cayanus.*

Syn., *Spiroptera conocephala* Molin, 1860.

Refs. 128, 176, 177, 358.

Genus SERTICEPS Railliet, 1916.

Definition.—SCHISTOROPHINÆ : mouth surrounded by six small
lips, each bearing a papilla ; the head is provided with the follow-

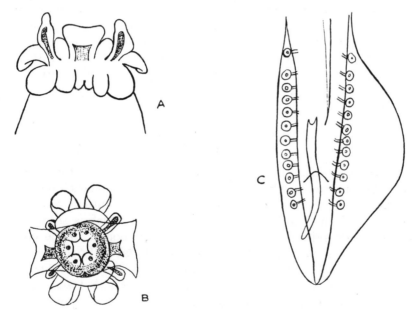

Fig. 256.—*Serticeps vulvoinflatus.* A. Anterior extremity, lateral view.
× 470.   B. Anterior extremity, end-on view.   × 170.   C. Posterior
extremity of male, ventral view.   × 120.   (After Drasche.)

ing complicated arrangement of cuticular appendages : on each
side behind the lips is an outwardly directed bird-tail shaped
delicate appendage, and further backwards, dorsally and ventrally,
is an outwardly directed crescentic appendage, still further backwards are four submedian rectangular outwardly directed lobes
with turned-up edges, and finally there follows a crown of numerous

posteriorly directed appendages of different sizes ; between the dorso-ventral and submedian appendages are four long club-shaped papillæ directed outwards and forwards. Male : posterior extremity obtuse ; caudal alæ asymmetrical supported by twelve pairs of costiform papillæ, of which ten pairs are preanal ; spicules very unequal. Female : tail obtuse ; vulva near anus. Parasites of the gizzard of birds.

Type species : *S. vulvoinflatus* (Molin, 1860). ♂ 10 mm., ♀ 28 mm. In *Trochilus ochropygus*.

Syn., *Spiroptera vulvoinflata* Molin, 1860.

Refs. 128, 358, 404.

Family HEDRURIDÆ Railliet, 1916.

Definition.—SPIRUROIDEA : mouth surrounded by four highly specialized lips ; vestibule narrow and cylindrical. Males always rolled about the females, the posterior end of which is invaginated, forming a sucker-like groove, from which projects a chitinous hook, which serves as a fixation organ. Oviparous, eggs oval, with an operculum at each pole, and containing embryos at deposition.

Genus HEDRURIS Nitzsch, 1821.

Syn., *Heteroura* Sieb., 1836.
Synplecta Leidy, 1851.

Definition.—HEDRURIDÆ : mouth with four lips ; the lateral chitinous, narrower, with the free edges rounded, and each possessing two papillæ ; the two median lips thinner and cuticular, having the form of an isosceles triangle, the apex of which is truncated and the two sides hollowed out, the base is bound to the body only along its middle portion, and projects laterally to such an extent as almost to cover the two lateral lips. Behind the lips are eight cone-shaped cuticular swellings. The mouth leads into a cylindrical vestibule ; œsophagus long and slender, provided at its anterior extremity with a festooned chitinous ring, and apparently undivided. Male : tail spirally twisted, and laterally compressed ; with one preanal papilla, and six postanal papillæ ; spicules equal ; gubernaculum present or absent. Female : thicker posteriorly than anteriorly ; the posterior end can be invaginated forming a sort of sucker from which projects a

* There is apparently an error in the numbering of the figures constituting Plate XII of Drasche's work : the figures representing the head of *Sp. vulvoinflata* should be 15 and 16, and not 14 and 15.

chitinous hook, the worm being attached to the mucous membrane of the stomach by means of this pseudo-sucker ; vulva near anus. Oviparous, eggs elliptical and possess at each pointed end an

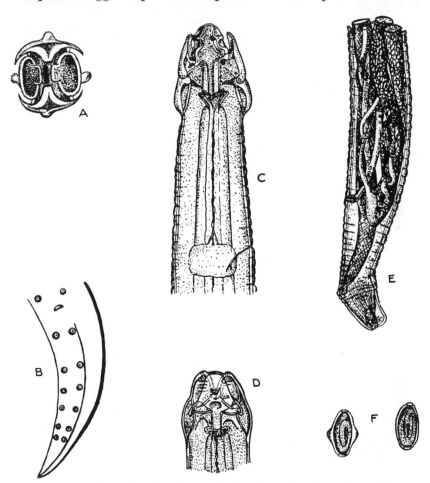

Fig. 257.—*Hedruris androphora.* A. Anterior extremity, end-on view. × 130. B. Posterior extremity of male. (After Schneider.) *Hedruris siredonis.* C. Anterior extremity, lateral view. × 110. D. Anterior extremity, ventral view. × 132. E. Posterior extremity of female. × 28. F. Eggs. × 260. (After Chandler.)

operculum-like structure, they are thickened laterally, and contain embryos at deposition. Parasites of reptiles and amphibia.

Type species : *H. androphora* Nitzsch, 1821. ♂ 8 mm., ♀ 10 mm. In *Triton cristatus.*

Syn., *Heteroura androphora* (Nitzsch, 1821) Sieb., 1836.
   Synplecta pendula Leidy, 1851.

Other species :

H. *armata* Perrier, 1871. In *Clemmys guttata, Chrysemys picta.*

H. *hipsirhinæ* Chatin, 1876. In *Hipsirhina bocourti.*

H. *orestiæ* Moniez, 1889. In *Orestias* sp.

H. *siredonis* Baird, 1858. In *Siredon mexicanus, Notophthalmus torosus.*

H. *squamata* Linst., 1909. In *Clemmys guttata.*

Refs. 87, 131, 272, 374, 405, 480, 569.

Family CAMALLANIDÆ Railliet and Henry, 1915.

Definition.—Spiruroidea : mouth elongate dorso-ventrally ; buccal capsule chitinous, either continuous or consisting of two lateral shell-like valves ; œsophagus composed of an anterior muscular portion, and a long posterior glandular portion. Male : posterior extremity curved ventrally ; caudal alæ present ; papillæ variable in number, mostly pedunculated and projecting into the alæ ; spicules unequal and dissimilar. Female : vulva near the middle of the body ; vagina directed posteriorly ; uteri opposed, the posterior limb ending blindly without an ovary. Viviparous.

KEY TO GENERA.

1. Buccal capsule continuous, not separated into paired lateral valves, the wall may be smooth or with spiral markings internally . . Procamallanus, p. 379.

   Buccal capsule consisting of two lateral valves 2

2. Buccal valves with large external thickenings, and posteriorly directed chitinous structures in the form of simple rods . . . Camallanides, p. 379.

   Buccal valves without large external thickenings, and with posteriorly directed chitinous structures in the form of tridents. . . . 3

3. With a large chitinous buccal cavity or pharynx, behind the chitinous valves . . . . . Paracamallanus, p. 378.

   Without a chitinous buccal cavity behind the valves . . . Camallanus, p. 377.

Genus **CAMALLANUS** Railliet and Henry, 1915.

Syn., *Cucullanus* auctt. not Mueller, 1777.

Definition.—CAMALLANIDÆ : mouth slit-like ; buccal capsule consisting of two lateral chitinous valves, the internal surface of which is furnished with parallel longitudinal ribs, sometimes terminating at the buccal margin as little teeth ; from the point of junction of the valves, dorsally and ventrally, a trident-shaped chitinous process is directed backwards : at its entry into the

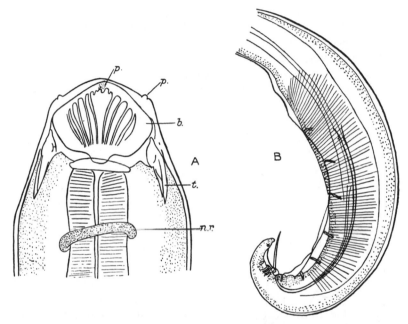

Fig. 258.—*Camallanus kachugæ.* A. Anterior extremity, lateral view. *p,* papilla ; *b,* buccal valve ; *t,* trident ; *n.r,* nerve ring. × 170. B. Posterior extremity of male, lateral view. × 70. (After Baylis and Daubney.)

œsophagus the capsule is surrounded by a circular collar ; œso-phagus in two parts, a short anterior muscular, and a long posterior glandular portion enlarged posteriorly. Male : posterior extremity rolled ventrally ; small caudal alæ present ; about seven pairs of costiform preanal papillæ supporting the alæ, two pairs of small adanal, and a number of postanal papillæ ; spicules usually unequal and dissimilar, one being feebly chitinized ; guber-naculum absent. Female : vulva about the middle of the body ; uteri opposed, the posterior limb ending blindly without an ovary.   Viviparous.   Parasites of stomach and intestine of fishes, batrachians, and reptiles.

Type species : *C. lacustris* Zoega, 1776. ♂ 5 mm., ♀ 9–10 mm. In many species of fishes.

Syn., *Echinorhynchus lacustris* Zoega, 1776.

Cucullanus lacustris (Zoega, 1776) Mueller, 1779.

Cucullanus elegans Zeder, 1800.

Cucullanus coronatus Zeder, 1800.

Cucullanus papillosus Zeder, 1800.

Cucullanus armatus Zeder, 1800.

Cucullanus truncatus Rudolphi, 1814.

Cucullanus viviparus Bloch, 1782, not Linstow, 1906.

Other species :

C. americanus Magath, 1919.   In tortoises.

C. ancylodirus Ward and Magath, 1916.   In carp.

C. kachugæ Baylis and Daubney, 1922.   In *Kachuga smithii.*

C. melanocephalus (Rud., 1819).   In *Pelamys* sp., *Auxis* sp., *Scomber* sp.

C. microcephalus (Duj., 1845).   In *Emys lutaria*, etc.

Syn., ? *C. confusus* Railliet and Henry, 1915.

? *Cucullanus dumerilii* Perrier, 1871.

C. nigrescens (Linstow, 1906).   In *Rana hexadactyla.*

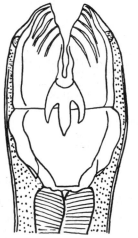

Fig. 259.—*Paracamallanus cyatho-pharynx.*   Anterior extremity, dorsal view.   × 440.   (After Baylis.)

C. oxycephalus Ward and Magath, 1916.   In white bass and black crappie.

C. papilliferus (Molin, 1858).   In *Acipenser sturio.*

C. tridentatus (Drasche, 1884). In *Vastres cuvieri.*

C. trispinosus (Leidy, 1851).   In tortoises.

C. undulatus Railliet and Henry, 1915.   In *Damonia* sp.

Syn., *Cucullanus viviparus* Linstow, 1906, not Bloch, 1782.

Refs. 34, 42, 129, 131, 272, 346a, 443, 522, 662, 681.

Genus PARACAMALLANUS n.g.

Definition.—CAMALLANIDÆ : closely resembling *Camallanus*, but differing in the presence of a large chitinous buccal cavity or pharynx, behind the buccal valves.

Type species : *P. cyathopharynx* (Baylis, 1923). ♂ 5·9 mm.,
♀ 9·2 mm. In *Heterobranchus anguillaris*.
  Syn., *Camallanus cyathopharynx* Baylis, 1923.
  Ref. 34.

Genus CAMALLANIDES Baylis and Daubney, 1922.

Definition.—CAMALLANIDÆ : resembles *Camallanus* except in
the following particulars : each of the lateral chitinous buccal
valves has two large thickenings externally, giving the appearance
of two separate masses of chitin ; the " tridents " are reduced to
a simple rod-like structure on each side ; the right spicule is alate ;
gubernaculum present ; the vulva is borne on a tubular appendage.

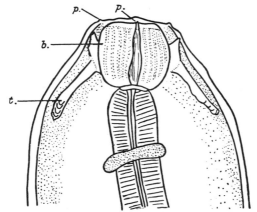

Fig. 260.—*Camallanides prashadi.* Anterior extremity, lateral view.
  p, papilla; *b,* buccal valve; *t,* rod-like structure. × 190. (After Baylis
  and Daubney.)

Type species : *C. prashadi* Baylis and Daubney, 1922. ♂ 5·8–
6·6 mm., ♀ 14·2–17·7 mm. In *Bungarus fasciatus*.
  Ref. 42.

Genus PROCAMALLANUS Baylis, 1923.

Definition.—CAMALLANIDÆ : buccal capsule continuous, and
not separated into paired lateral valves ; the walls of the capsule
may be smooth, or provided with spiral thickenings ; tridents
absent ; œsophagus divided into an anterior muscular, and a
longer posterior glandular part. Male : caudal alæ present ;
with nine pairs of costiform preanal papillæ, a few adanal, and some
postanal papillæ. Female : posterior extremity conical, and
ending in three very short blunt processes ; vulva in front of the
middle of the body ; the posterior limb of the uterus ends blindly.
Viviparous. Parasites of silurid fishes.

Type species : *P. læviconchus* (Wedl, 1862). ♂ 3·65 mm., ♀ up
to 15·5 mm.   In *Synodontis schaal*.
    Syn., *Cucullanus læviconchus* Wedl, 1862.
        Camallanus læviconchus (Wedl, 1862) Railliet and
        Henry, 1915.

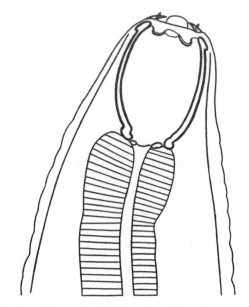

Fig. 261.—*Procamallanus læviconchus*.   Anterior extremity, lateral view.
   × 400.   (Orig.)

Other species : *P. spiralis* Baylis, 1923.   In *Heterobranchus
anguillaris*.
Refs. 34, 35, 443, 664.

Family CUCULLANIDÆ Cobbold, 1864.

Definition.—SPIRUROIDEA : head consisting of two prominent
lateral lips (or lobes) each bearing three papillæ, and bounding a
slit-like mouth ; œsophagus muscular throughout with a club-
shaped swelling posteriorly, and dilating anteriorly into a pseudo-
buccal cavity ; intestine simple or with a cæcum.   Male : preanal
sucker present ; spicules equal or unequal ; gubernaculum usually
present.   Female : caudal extremity terminating conically and
fairly abruptly ; vulva near the middle of the body ; vagina
directed anteriorly, with two ovaries (except in *Dacnitoides*).
Oviparous.

KEY TO SUBFAMILIES.

Without an intestinal cæcum ; with two
    ovaries .   .   .   .   .   . Cucullaninæ, p. 381.
With an intestinal cæcum ; with one ovary Dacnitoidinæ, p. 384.

Subfamily CUCULLANINÆ n.sf.

    Syn., *Cucullanidæ* Barreto, 1916.
        Dacnitidæ Baird, 1853, Lane, 1916.

Definition.—CUCULLANIDÆ : with a simple intestine. Male
with a gubernaculum. Female with two ovaries.

KEY TO GENERA.

1. Dorso-cephalic tubercle present .   . Bulbodacnitis, p. 383.
   Dorso-cephalic tubercle absent .   . 2
2. Cuticular serration in addition to
   cuticular striation   .   .   . Serradacnitis, p. 383.
   Cuticular serration absent   .   . Cucullanus, p. 381.

Genus CUCULLANUS O. F. Mueller, 1777.

    Syn., *Pleurorinchus* Nau, 1787.
        Pleurorhynchus Rud., 1801.
        Ophiostoma Rud., 1801, in part.
        Dacnitis Duj., 1845.
        Stelmius Duj., 1845.
        Dichelyne Jägerskiöld, 1902.

Definition.—CUCULLANINÆ : anterior extremity bent dorsally ;
lips bounding the mouth not chitinized, no chitinous buccal
capsule, but a pseudo-capsule formed by the dilatation of the
anterior end of the œsophagus, which is also enlarged posteriorly ;
intestine simple. Male : preanal sucker without a chitinous rim ;
caudal alæ absent ; spicules equal ; gubernaculum present.
Female : vulva near the middle of the body ; vagina directed
anteriorly ; two ovaries. Oviparous, eggs with a thin shell.
Parasites of intestine of fishes.

    Type species : *C. cirratus* Mueller, 1777. ♂ 16–18 mm.,
♀ 20 mm. In *Gadus morrhua*, etc.
    Syn., *C. muticus* Mueller, 1777.
        C. foveolatus Rud., 1809.
        C. esuriens (Duj., 1845).
        Dacnitis esuriens Duj., 1845.
        Dacnitis⁻gadorum Beneden, 1858.

Other species :
    C. abbreviatus Rud., 1819.   In *Perca* sp.
    C. attenuatus (Molin, 1859).   In *Squalius cavedanus.*

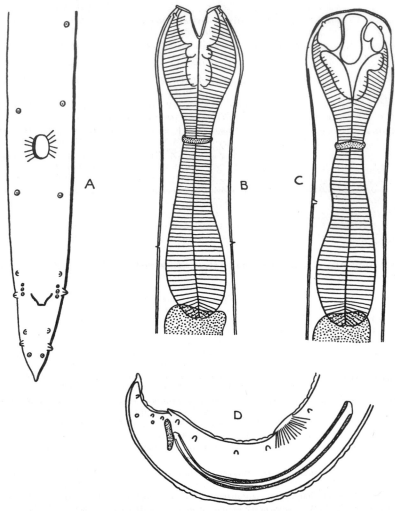

Fig. 262.—*Cucullanus cirratus.* A. Posterior extremity of male, ventral view.
    × 69. (After Schneider.) *Cucullanus carettæ.* B. Anterior extremity,
    ventral view.   × 52. C. Anterior extremity, lateral view.   × 52.
    D. Posterior extremity of male, lateral view. × 52. (Orig.)

    C. barbi Baylis, 1923.   In *Barbus bynni.*
    C. callichroi (Stewart, 1914).   In *Callichrous* sp.
    C. carettæ Baylis, 1923.   In *Thalassochelys caretta.*
    C. clarotis Baylis, 1923.   In *Clarotes* sp., *Synodontis* sp.

C. clitellarius Ward and Magath, 1916. In *Acipenser rubicundus*.

C. dodsworthi Barreto, 1922. In *Spheroides testudineus*.

C. fossor (Jägerskiöld, 1902). In *Lates niloticus*.
Syn., *Dichelyne fossor*. Jägerskiöld, 1902.

C. fusiformis (Molin, 1860). In *Platessa flesus*.

C. hians (Duj., 1845). In *Muræna* sp., *Conger* sp.

? *C. longicollis* (Stossich, 1899). In *Mullus barbatus*.

C. marinus O. F. Mueller, 1779. In *Gadus morrhua*.

C. præcinctus (Duj., 1845). In *Conger vulgaris*.
Syn., *Stelmius præcinctus* Duj., 1845.

C. pulcherrimus Barreto, 1918. In *Caranx lugubris*.

C. rotundatus (Molin, 1860). In *Cantharus vulgaris*.

? *C. sphærocephalus* (Rud., 1809). In *Acipenser* sp.
Syn., *Ascaris sphærocephala* Rud., 1809.
Ophistoma sphærocephalum (Rud., 1809), Rud., 1819.

C. stelmioides (Vessichelli, 1910). In *Petromyzon planeri*.

Refs. 11, 14, 34, 39, 131, 243, 260, 359, 366, 442, 443, 474, 522, 591.

Genus BULBODACNITIS * Lane, 1916.

Definition.—CUCULLANINÆ : differentiated from *Cucullanus* only by the possession of a tubercle on the dorsal aspect of the head. Parasites of intestine of fishes.

Type species : *B. bulbosa* Lane, 1916. ♂ 13·3 mm., ♀ 14 mm. In *Caranx melampygus*.

Other species :
B. globosa (Zeder, 1800) Dujardin, 1845. In *Salmo fario*.
Syn., *Dacnitis globosa* Duj., 1845.
Refs. 16, 34, 260.

Genus SERRADACNITIS * Lane, 1916.

Definition.—CUCULLANINÆ : distinguished from *Cucullanus* only by the presence of cuticular serrations, distinct from and in addition to the cuticular striations. Parasites of intestine of fishes.

Type species : *S. serrata* Lane, 1916. ♂ 15–16 mm., ♀ ? In *Tryonix gangeticus*.

Other species :
S. squali (Dujardin, 1845). In *Squalus galeus*.
Syn., *Dacnitis squali* Duj., 1845.
Refs. 16, 34, 260.

* Barreto, 1922, is unable to find any justification for separating these genera from *Cucullanus*.

Subfamily DACNITOIDINÆ n.sf.

Syn., *Dacnitoididæ* Travassos, 1920.

Definition.—CUCULLANIDÆ : intestine with an anterior cæcum. Male without a gubernaculum. Female with only one ovary.

Genus DACNITOIDES Ward and Magath, 1916.

Definition.—DACNITOIDINÆ : anterior extremity not bent dorsally ; lips bounding mouth not chitinized ; no chitinous

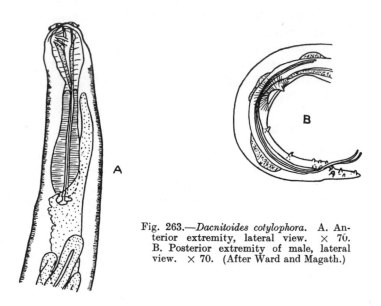

Fig. 263.—*Dacnitoides cotylophora*. A. Anterior extremity, lateral view. × 70. B. Posterior extremity of male, lateral view. × 70. (After Ward and Magath.)

buccal capsule, but a pseudo-capsule, formed by the dilatation of the anterior end of the œsophagus, which is also enlarged posteriorly ; the intestine gives off, just behind the œsophagus, a diverticulum which is directed anteriorly. Male : preanal sucker without a chitinous rim ; caudal alæ absent ; spicules equal ; gubernaculum absent. Female : vulva just behind the middle of the body ; only one ovary, the posterior uterine limb ending blindly. Parasites of intestine of fishes.

Type species : *D. cotylophora* Ward and Magath, 1916. ♂ 4–6 mm., ♀ 4–5·5 mm. In *Perca flavescens* and *Stizostedion vitreum*. Refs. 34, 662.

SPIRUROIDEA insufficiently known.

Genus ASCAROPHIS Beneden, 1871.

Syn., *Ascaropsis* Power and Sedgwick, 1880.

Definition.—SPIRUROIDEA : this genus was made by van Beneden to include a worm *A. morrhuæ* found by him in the

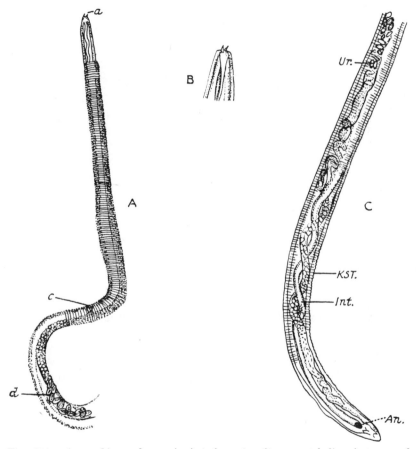

Fig. 264.—*Ascarophis morrhuæ.* A. Anterior extremity. *a,* cephalic spines ; *c,* end of œsophagus ; *d,* ova. B. Head. C. Posterior extremity of female. *Ur.,* uterus ; *Kst.,* ovary ; *Int.,* intestine ; *An.,* anus. (After Nicoll.)

intestine and pyloric cæca of the cod. Very little description of the worm is given. Nicoll (1907) records female specimens from other fishes and gives an incomplete description. Female : body elongate, attenuated anteriorly and posteriorly, with a ventral excavation on the tail. Cuticle annulated by furrows encircling the body, these disappear towards the extremities. Head furnished with two small spines, mouth terminal bordered by two simple lips ; œsophagus long ; posterior extremity tapers to a blunt point a short distance behind the anus.   The ovary (*sic*) is in the posterior part of the body and the uterus (*sic*) occupies the whole of the remainder of the worm, and the middle part of the body is completely filled with eggs ;   vulva in the anterior (?) part of body.   Oviparous, eggs with two filaments at one pole.   Parasites of fishes.

Type species : *A. morrhuæ* Beneden, 1871.   ♂ ?, ♀ 6–8 mm.   In *Gadus morrhua, Gadus æglefinus, Hippoglosus vulgaris*, and *Cottus bubalis*.

Syn., *Ascaropsis morrhuæ* (Beneden, 1871) Power and Sedgwick, 1880.

Refs. 50, 373.

Genus OSLERUS Hall, 1921.

Definition.—SPIRUROIDEA ? : small worms ;   mouth structure unknown, probably without distinct lips.   Male :   posterior extremity rounded ?   Spicules unequal.   Female :   posterior extremity rounded, vulva very close to anus.   Ovoviviparous. Parasites of the respiratory passages of dogs.

Type species : *O. osleri* (Cobbold, 1879).   ♂ 4 mm., ♀ 6·15 mm. In dogs.

Syn., *Strongylus canis bronchialis* Osler, 1877.

Filaria osleri Cobbold, 1879.

Refs. 103, 207, 382, 641.

Generic Names given to Larval Spiruroidea.

Genus ASCAROPS Beneden, 1873.

This generic name was given to a worm *Ascarops minuta* Beneden, 1873, syn., *Spiroptera minuta* (Bened.) Linstow, 1878 and 1909.   This is a larval form of a Spirurid worm encapsuled in the stomach wall of *Vespertilio dasycneme*.

Refs. 51, 311, 332, 535.

Genus CEPHALACANTHUS Diesing, 1853.

This generic name, which is preoccupied by *Cephalacanthus* Lac., 1802, a fish, was created by Diesing for two worms, viz., *C. monacanthus* Dies., 1853, and *C. triacanthus* Dies., 1853, parasitic in insects.   According to Seurat, 1916, the former is the larva of *Protospirura muris* and the latter that of *Physocephalus sexalatus*.

Refs. 125, 535,

Genus DIKENTROCEPHALUS Wedl, 1855.

Syn., *Dicentrocephalus* Dies., 1861.

This generic name was given to a worm *Dikentrocephalus crinalis* Wedl, 1855, found in *Lophius piscatorius*. It is a larval form provided with two lips ; the adult is unknown, but presumably belongs to the *Spiruroidea*.

Refs. 125, 663b.

Genus MASTOPHORUS Diesing, 1853.

Under this generic name Diesing groups two species, viz., *M. echiurus* and *M. globocaudatus*, parasitic in insects. These are probably larval forms, and according to Seurat, 1916, the second is the larva of *Physocephalus sexalatus*.

Refs. 125, 535.

Superfamily FILARIOIDEA Weinland, 1858 ; Stiles, 1907.

Definition.—EUNEMATODA : filiform worms ; mouth usually simple and without lips, occasionally bounded by chitinous structures or by small insignificant lateral lips ; buccal cavity or vestibule absent or very rudimentary, the œsophagus, which is cylindrical and frequently divided into two parts, reaching practically to the anterior extremity ; intestine simple and sometimes atrophied posteriorly. Male : spicules usually very unequal and dissimilar. Female : almost always much longer than the male ; vulva almost always in the œsophageal region. Parasites of the circulatory, lymphatic, muscular, or connective tissues, or of serous cavities, of vertebrates.

KEY TO FAMILIES.

Females enormously longer than males ;
   vulva atrophied in gravid female   .   Dracunculidæ, p. 440.
Females at most three or four times as
   long as males ; vulva not atrophied in
   gravid female .   .   .   .   .   Filariidæ, p. 387.

FAMILY FILARIIDÆ (COBBOLD, 1864) CLAUS, 1885.

Syn., *Filaridæ* Cobbold, 1864.

Definition.—FILARIOIDEA : females not more than three or four times as long as the males ; mouth usually simple rarely bounded by insignificant lateral lips and sometimes by chitinous structures ; cuticle usually smooth or finely striated transversely, but sometimes reinforced by annular thickenings and sometimes furnished with bosses. Male : with or without caudal alæ ; spicules usually quite dissimilar and very unequal, but rarely similar and equal or subequal ; gubernaculum present or absent. Female : vulva almost always in the œsophageal region ; amphidelphys or opisthodelphys. Oviparous or viviparous.

KEY TO SUBFAMILIES.

1. Mouth surrounded by a chitinous ring or by lateral epaulette-like structures or by small spinous teeth . Setariinæ, p. 421.
   Mouth simple not bounded by chitinous structures 2
2. Trident-like chitinous structures on each side of anterior end of œsophagus. . . . . Diplotriæninæ, p. 432.
   Trident-like structures absent . 3
3. Vulva in a constriction just in front of posterior extremity . . Crassicaudinæ, p. 437.
   Vulva near middle of body . . Micropleurinæ, p. 434.
   Vulva in œsophageal region or immediately posterior to it . . . 4
4. Cuticle provided with bosses . . Loainæ, p. 417.
   Cuticle reinforced by annular thickenings . . . . Onchocercinæ, p. 412.
   Cuticle smooth or finely transversely striated 5
5. Spicules dissimilar and unequal · . Filariinæ, p. 388.
   Spicules similar and equal or subequal . . . . . Aproctinæ, p. 404.
   Filariidæ insufficiently known, p. 437.

Subfamily FILARIINÆ Stiles; 1907.

Definition.—FILARIIDÆ : mouth simple or with two insignificant lateral lips, not bounded by a chitinous peribuccal ring or by epaulette-like structures ; cuticle smooth or transversely striated ; without trident-like chitinous structures on each side of the anterior end of the œsophagus ; spicules unequal and dissimilar ; vulva in œsophageal region or just posterior to it.

KEY TO GENERA.

Males without caudal alæ   .   .   1

Males with caudal alæ   .   .   .   5

1. With a definite buccal cavity or vestibule separating the œsophagus from the anterior extremity   2

  Without a buccal cavity or vestibule   4

2. Male with ventral roughened callosity near tip of tail. Parasites of birds   .   .   .   .   Hamulofilaria, p. 398.

  Male without ventral roughened callosity near tip of tail. Parasites of mammals   .   .   3

3. Head papillæ absent ; longer spicule cylindrical proximally, ending in a long lash distally, gubernaculum absent ; vulva at level of posterior end of œsophagus .   .   .   .   Litomosa, p. 398.

  Head papillæ present ; longer spicule gradually tapering distally and shaped like a curved surgical needle, gubernaculum present ; vulva some distance behind end of œsophagus   .   .   .   Breinlia, p. 400.

4. Œsophagus not clearly divided into two parts ; anus not subterminal in either sex   .   .   .   Wuchereria, p. 401.

  Œsophagus clearly divided into two parts ; anus subterminal in both sexes   .   .   .   .   Lemdana, p. 402.

5. Opisthodelphys   .   .   .   6

  Amphidelphys   .   .   .   8

6. Anterior extremity with numerous cuticular papillæ   .   .   .   Parafilaria, p. 391.

  Anterior extremity without numerous cuticular papillæ   .   .   7

7. Mouth with lips ; vulva very near mouth ; caudal papillæ not unusually large .   .   .   Filaria, p. 390.

Mouth without lips ; vulva post-
œsophageal ; caudal papillæ very
large and stout . . . Dirofilaria, p. 393.
8. Mouth simple without lips . . Foleyella, p. 395.
Mouth with small projecting lateral
lips 9
9. With a pair of lateral and four pairs
of submedian head papillæ ;
lateral flanges absent ; spicules
very delicate, the larger being
about ten times as long as the
smaller . . . . Hamatospiculum, p. 395.
With a pair of lateral and two pairs
of submedian head papillæ; lateral
flanges present ; spicules both
relatively short, the larger being
about twice as long as the smaller
and winged about its mid-portion. Politospiculum, p. 396.

Genus FILARIA Mueller, 1787.

Definition.—FILARIINÆ : mouth with four small lips, two
lateral and two median ; with lateral and submedian head papillæ ;
cuticle smooth with lateral flanges along the whole length of the
body ; cervical papillæ present. There is a short narrow vestibule
separating the œsophagus from the mouth opening. Œsophagus
indistinctly divided into a short anterior muscular, and a much
longer posterior glandular part, and surrounded in its anterior
part by the nerve ring. Male : posterior extremity rolled into
loose spiral, tail elongate ; caudal alæ long and broad passing
into the lateral alæ some distance in front of the cloaca and
meeting one another posteriorly behind the tip of the tail ; cloaca
surrounded by a delicate oval ring ; a number of shortly pedunculated pre- and post-anal papillæ present ; spicules very unequal
and dissimilar, the right being small and the left large ; gubernaculum absent. Female : tail robust and digitiform ; anus minute,
terminal portion of intestine atrophied ; vulva large, oval and
subterminal, opening in the median ventral line immediately
behind the mouth ; opisthodelphys. Oviparous, eggs at deposition contain fully-developed larvæ and have remarkably thick
shells with the external surface shagreened. Parasites of subcutaneous tissue of carnivores and rodents.

Type species: *F. martis* Gmelin, 1790. ♂ 80 mm., ♀ 190–217
mm. In *Mustela* spp., *Hystrix* sp., *Ictonyx* sp.

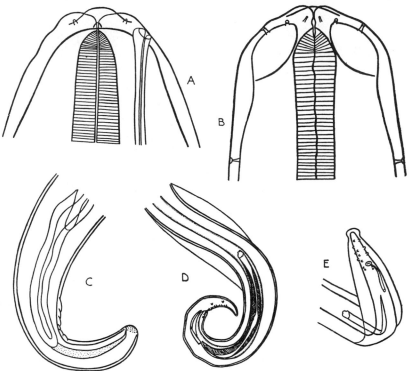

Fig. 265.—*Filaria martis*. A. Anterior extremity of female, lateral view. × 250. B. Anterior extremity of male, ventral view. × 250. C. Posterior extremity of female, lateral view. × 56. D. Posterior extremity of male, lateral view. × 56. E. Posterior extremity of male, ventral view. × 56. (Orig.)

Syn., *Filaria mustelarum* Rud., 1809.
    Filaria quadrispina Dies., 1851.
    Filaria perforans Molin, 1858.
Refs. 123, 185, 205, 354, 362, 367, 480, 559.

Genus PARAFILARIA n. g.

Definition.—FILARIINÆ : mouth with two lateral lips ; cuticle transversely striated except at the anterior extremity where it is covered with numerous elliptical and circular papillæ ; œsophagus very short and not divided into two portions. Male : posterior extremity loosely coiled, tail short and bluntly rounded ; caudal alæ present with large pedunculated pre- and post-anal papillæ ; spicules very unequal ; gubernaculum absent. Female : posterior extremity bluntly rounded ; anus and posterior end of intestine atrophied ; vulva very close to the mouth ; opisthodelphys. Oviparous, eggs containing embryos. Parasites of equines.

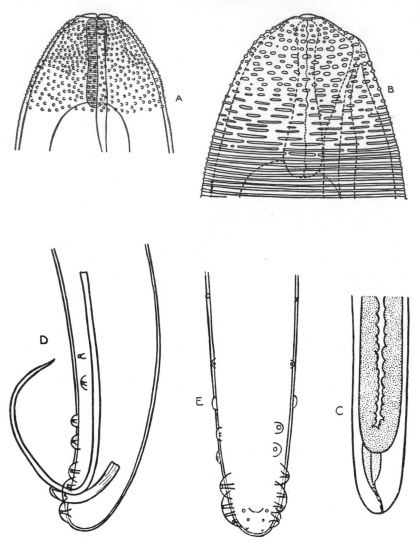

Fig. 266.—*Parafilaria multipapillosa.* A. Anterior extremity of female, ventral view. × 128. B. Anterior extremity of female, lateral view. × 216. C. Posterior extremity of female. × 56. (Orig.) D. Posterior extremity of male, lateral view. × 160. E. Posterior extremity of male, ventral view. × 160. (After Railliet.)

Type species : *P. multipapillosa* (Condamine and Drouilly, 1878). ♂ 28 mm., ♀ 40–70 mm. In equines.

Syn., *Filaria multipapillosa* Condamine and Drouilly, 1878.

Filaria hæmorrhagica Railliet, 1885.

Refs. 110, 396, 398, 453.

Genus DIROFILARIA Railliet and Henry, 1911.

Definition.—FILARIINÆ : mouth without lips, with insignificant head papillæ ; œsophagus relatively short and divided into two parts, but without a sharp line of demarcation. Male : posterior extremity spirally coiled, tail bluntly conical ; caudal alæ present with very large pedunculated preanal papillæ and one or two large, and a number of small, postanal papillæ ; spicules unequal ;

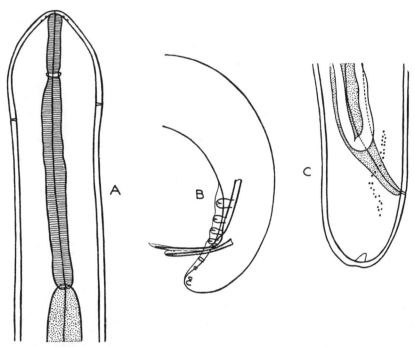

Fig. 267.—*Dirofilaria immitis.* A. Anterior extremity, ventral view. × 52. B. Posterior extremity of male, lateral view. × 100. C. Posterior extremity of female, lateral view. × 52. (Orig.)

gubernaculum absent. Female : posterior extremity rounded ; vulva a little behind the œsophagus ; opisthodelphys. Viviparous, microfilariæ unsheathed and found in the blood. Parasites in heart and connective tissue of primates, carnivora, rodents, and marsupials.

Type species : *D. immitis* (Leidy, 1856). ♂ 120–180 mm., ♀ 250–300 mm. In dogs.

Syn., *Filaria immitis* Leidy, 1856.

Other species :

D. corynodes (Linst., 1899). In monkeys.

D. granulosa (Linst., 1906).   In *Felis pardus.*

D. kuelzi (Rodenwaldt, 1910).   In *Cephalophus maxwelli.*

D. magalhāesi (R. Blanchard, 1895).   In man.

D. repens Railliet and Henry, 1911.   In dogs.

D. scapiceps (Leidy, 1886).   In *Sylvilagus* spp.

D. striata (Molin, 1858).   In *Felis concolor, Felis macroura.*

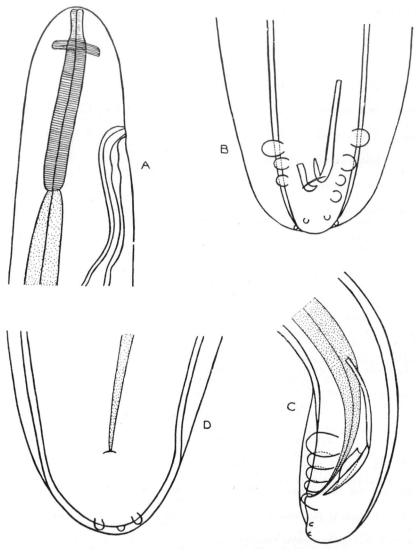

Fig. 268.—*Foleyella agamæ.* A. Anterior extremity of female, lateral view. × 56.
B. Posterior extremity of male, ventral view. × 256. C. Posterior extremity of male, lateral view. × 256. D. Posterior extremity of female, ventral view. × 256. (Orig.)

D. subcutanea (Linstow, 1899). In *Erethizon dorsatus*.

D. sudanensis (Linstow, 1903). In *Felis leo*.

D. websteri (Cobbold, 1879). In *Macropus giganteus*.

Refs. 65, 141, 143, 205, 318, 428, 429, 469.

Genus FOLEYELLA Seurat, 1917.

Definition.—FILARIINÆ : mouth without lips, surrounded by a circle of six small head papillæ and four papillæ more externally ; lateral areas broad and dark-coloured ; cuticle with narrow lateral flanges running the whole length of the body ; œsophagus very short and divided into two parts. Male : with long caudal alæ, pre- and post-anal papillæ shortly pedunculated and very large ; spicules unequal, right short and broad. Female : vulva near the posterior end of the œsophagus ; amphidelphys. Microfilariæ sheathed and found in the blood. Parasites of subcutaneous connective tissue and muscular tissue of saurians and amphibians.

Type species : *F. candezei* (Fraipont, 1882). ♂ 25 mm., ♀ 69 mm. In *Uromastix acanthinurus*.

Syn., *Filaria candezei* Fraipont, 1882.

Other species :

F. agamæ (Rodhain, 1906). In *Agama colonorum*.

F. chlamydosauri (Breinl, 1913). In *Chlamydosaurus kingii*.

F. duboisi (Gedoelst, 1916). In a large toad.

? *F. leiperi* (Railliet, 1916). In *Bufo regularis.*

Syn., *Filaria bufonis* Leiper, 1908.

Refs. 58, 74, 151, 275, 406, 469a, 534, 544, 562.

Genus HAMATOSPICULUM Skrjabin, 1916.

Definition.—FILARIINÆ : mouth with two small projecting lateral lips, anterior extremity rounded, provided with four pairs of submedian head papillæ and a pair of lateral papillæ ; cuticle finely striated transversely ; lateral flanges absent ; œsophagus consists of two parts, an anterior narrow portion, surrounded by the nerve ring, and a posterior broader part. Male : posterior extremity rounded, caudal alæ present with shortly pedunculated pre- and post-anal papillæ ; spicules very unequal, the left being very delicate and barbed at its extremities and about ten times as long as the right, which is thicker. Female : vulva near the anterior extremity, shortly behind the first part of the œsophagus ; amphidelphys. Oviparous. Parasites of the subcutaneous connective tissue of birds.

Type species : *H. brasilianum* (Stoss., 1897). ♂ 27 mm., ♀ 65–120 mm. In *Picus* sp.

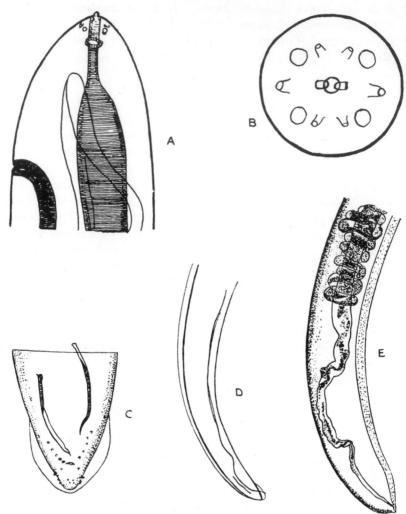

Fig. 269.—*Hamatospiculum brasilianum.* A. Anterior extremity of female, lateral view. B. Head, end-on view (diagram). C. Posterior extremity of male, ventral view. D. Posterior extremity of male, lateral view. E. Posterior extremity of female, lateral view. (After Skrjabin.)

Syn., *Filaria brasiliana* Stoss., 1897.
   Filaria insignis Schneider, 1866, not Leidy, 1858.
Refs. 480, 574, 604.

Genus POLITOSPICULUM Skrjabin, 1916.

Definition.—FILARIINÆ: mouth with two small projecting lateral lips, anterior extremity rounded and provided with two pairs of submedian head papillæ and one pair of lateral papillæ;

cuticle delicately striated transversely, with narrow lateral flanges along the whole length of the body ; œsophagus consists of an anterior thin portion and a posterior thicker portion. Male : posterior extremity rounded, caudal alæ present meeting behind

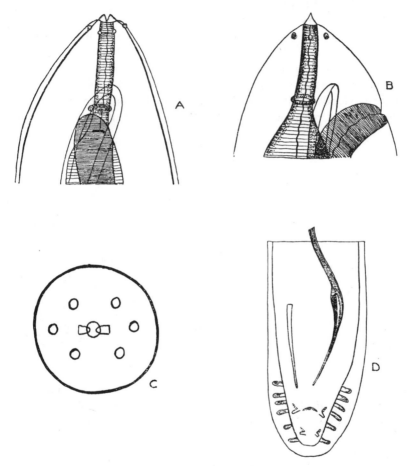

Fig. 270.—*Politospiculum arthricola*. A. Anterior extremity of female, ventral view. B. Anterior extremity of female, lateral view. C. Anterior extremity, end-on view (diagram). D. Posterior extremity of male, ventral view. (After Skrjabin.)

the tail and joining the lateral flanges anteriorly ; with pedunculated pre- and post-anal papillæ ; spicules short and unequal, the larger being bowed and provided with two dissimilar lateral wings in its middle portion. Female : vulva near the end of the first part of the œsophagus ; amphidelphys. Oviparous, parasites of the joint cavities of birds.

Type species : *P. arthricola* Skrjabin, 1916. ♂ 75 mm., ♀ 225–300 mm. In *Alcedo* sp.

Ref. 574.

Genus HAMULOFILARIA Chandler, 1924.

Definition.—FILARIINÆ : mouth without lips, anterior extremity rounded with four head papillæ ; small buccal cavity present, surrounded by a thickened wall resembling lips when seen in optical section. Male : posterior extremity bent ventrally and tapers to a sharp point ; caudal alæ absent ; near the tip of the tail is a roughened callosity ; spicules unequal and dissimilar, the longer is slender and shaped like a surgical needle and is a closed tube up to a point not far from the tip, the shorter is trough-

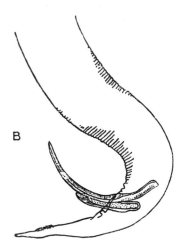

Fig. 271.—*Hamulofilaria indica*. A. Anterior extremity. × 225. B. Posterior extremity of male, lateral view. × 235. (After Chandler.)

shaped and barbed near its tip. Female : unknown. Parasites of mesentery of birds.

Type species : *H. indica* Chandler, 1924. ♂ 7·5 mm., ♀ ?. In *Cissa chinensis*.

Ref. 89.

Genus LITOMOSA n. g.

Syn., *Litosoma* van Beneden, 1873, preoccupied.

Definition.—FILARIINÆ : body attenuated posteriorly, anterior extremity somewhat enlarged ; mouth simple without lips ; head papillæ absent ; small buccal cavity with thickened walls infundibular with apex anteriorly ; cuticle smooth ; œsophagus short and not divided into two parts. Male : posterior extremity coiled spirally, tail digitiform and furnished with a short subterminal point ; caudal alæ absent ; papillæ absent ; spicules very unequal, the longer being cylindrical proximally and ending in a long lash distally, the shorter thicker and of about the same diameter throughout. Female : tail digitiform and provided at its extremity with two small diverging processes between which

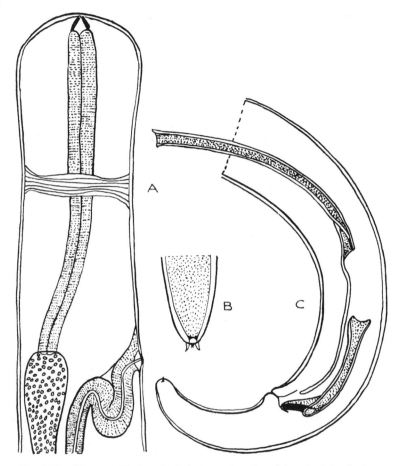

Fig. 272.—*Litomosa filaria*. A. Anterior extremity of female, lateral view. B. Posterior extremity of female, ventral view. C. Posterior extremity of male, lateral view. × 360. (After Seurat.)

are two minute spines ; vulva very small and situated at the level of the posterior end of the œsophagus ; ovejector very long ; uteri parallel ; opisthodelphys. Viviparous, microfilariæ very small. Parasites of abdominal cavity of bats.

Type species : *L. filaria* (Beneden, 1873). ♂ 17 mm., ♀ 26 mm. In *Vespertilio auritus*.

Syn., *Litosoma filaria* Beneden, 1873.
? *Filaria vespertilionis* Rud., 1819.
Refs. 51, 564.

Genus BREINLIA n. g.

Definition.—FILARIINÆ : body attenuated anteriorly ; mouth simple without lips, with four pairs of submedian head papillæ ;

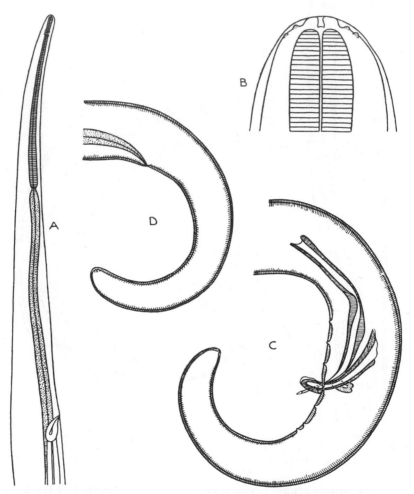

Fig. 273.—*Breinlia trichosuri.* A. Anterior extremity of female, lateral view. × 24. B. Head, ventral view. × 330. C. Posterior extremity of male, lateral view. × 75. D. Posterior extremity of female, lateral view. × 75. (Orig.)

with a short cylindrical buccal cavity ; cuticle transversely striated ; œsophagus divided into two parts, a shorter anterior portion and a longer rather broader posterior portion, but without any very clear line of demarcation between the two parts. Male : posterior extremity coiled spirally, tail digitiform ; caudal alæ absent or extremely narrow ; with about three pairs of preanal and three of postanal papillæ ; spicules unequal, both stout and heavily chitinized, the longer cylindrical proximally, tapering distally and shaped like a curved surgical needle, the shorter cylindrical with a spatulate extremity in which the end of the longer spicule glides ; gubernaculum present. Female : posterior extremity digitiform with a pair of small subterminal papillæ on each side ; vulva some distance behind the termination of the œsophagus ; opisthodelphys. Viviparous ; the microfilariæ are found in the blood. Parasites of marsupials.

Type species : *B. trichosuri* (Breinl, 1913). ♂ 10–14 mm., ♀ 18–36 mm. In *Trichosurus vulpecula*.

Syn., *Filaria trichosuri* Breinl, 1913.

Ref. 74.

Genus WUCHERERIA Silva Araujo, 1877 ; Seurat, 1921.

Definition.—FILARIINÆ : very delicate worms tapering anteriorly ; head definitely enlarged, rounded, and followed by a neck ; mouth circular without lips ; two circles of head papillæ ; cuticle smooth ; œsophagus of moderate length and, although not clearly divided into two portions, really consisting of two parts, the anterior muscular, narrow, short, and surrounded about its middle by the nerve ring, the posterior glandular, thicker, and longer. Male : posterior extremity sharply curved ventrally, tail digitiform ; caudal alæ present ; pre- and post-anal papillæ present ; spicules very unequal, the longer cylindrical, tapering distally to a long lash with delicate alæ, and ending in a spoon-like termination, the shorter spicule thicker and of uniform diameter throughout, gutter-like and coarsely marked near its distal extremity ; gubernaculum crescentic. Female : posterior extremity digitiform, prolonged some distance beyond the anus and bluntly rounded ; vulva slightly posterior to the middle of the œsophagus ; first portion of vagina short, thick, pyriform, and directed posteriorly, the second portion consists of a long cylindrical tube of uniform diameter running straight backwards to end in two parallel uteri ; opisthodelphys. Microfilariæ sheathed and found in the blood. Parasites of mammals.

Type species : *W. bancrofti* (Cobbold, 1877). ♂ 25–40 mm., ♀ 76–100 mm. In man.

Syn., *Filaria bancrofti* Cobbold, 1877.

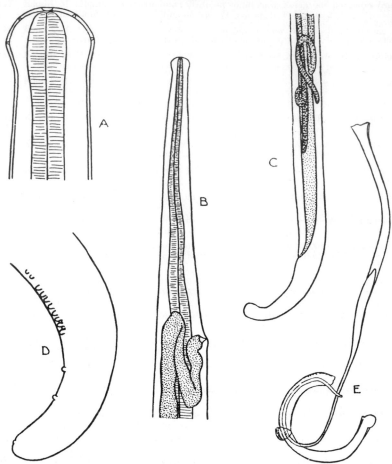

Fig. 274.—*Wuchereria bancrofti.* A. Anterior extremity, ventral view. × 400.
B. Anterior extremity of female, lateral view. × 90. C. Posterior
extremity of female, lateral view. × 90. (Orig.) D. Posterior extremity
of male, lateral view. E. spicules. (After Leiper.)

Other species : ? *W. sagitta* (Linstow, 1907). In *Tragelaphus
scriptus*.

Syn., *Filaria sagitta* Linstow, 1907.

Refs. 102, 291, 329, 562, 571, 652a.

Genus LEMDANA Seurat, 1917.

Definition.—FILARIINÆ : mouth simple without lips, surrounded by very small head papillæ ; body straight, slightly
enlarged opposite the nerve ring, opalescent ; cuticle thick and
smooth, lateral areas narrow, lateral flanges absent ; cervical

papillæ very small, behind the vulva in the female ; œsophagus short, consisting of two parts, the anterior muscular portion being clear and the posterior part darker. Male : posterior extremity

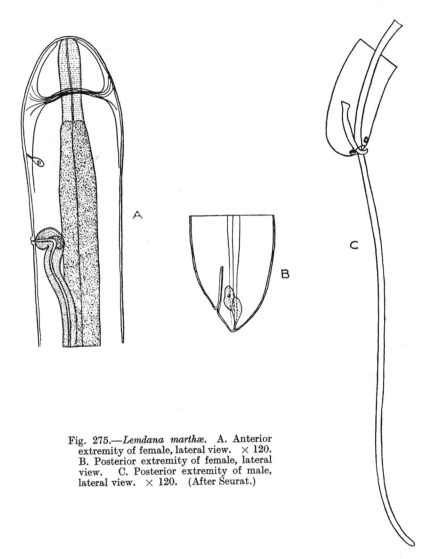

Fig. 275.—*Lemdana marthæ*. A. Anterior extremity of female, lateral view. × 120. B. Posterior extremity of female, lateral view. C. Posterior extremity of male, lateral view. × 120. (After Seurat.)

slightly bowed, tail very short and sharply truncate just behind the anus ; caudal alæ absent ; four large circumanal and two postanal papillæ ; spicules very unequal. Female : tail very short, conical, and bearing three small terminal subventral papillæ ; vulva behind the first part of the œsophagus ; opisthodelphys.

Microfilariæ unsheathed and found in the blood.   Parasites of the external surface of the crop of birds.

Type species : *L. marthæ* Seurat, 1917. ♂ 12·8 mm., ♀ 34 mm. In rock partridge.

Refs. 543, 562.

Subfamily APROCTINÆ n.sf.

Definition.—FILARIIDÆ : mouth simple, not bounded by a peribuccal chitinous ring or epaulette-like structures ; cuticle smooth or transversely striated ; without trident-like structures on each side of the anterior end of the œsophagus ; spicules equal or subequal and similar ; vulva in the œsophageal region or just posterior to it.

KEY TO GENERA.

1. Males with caudal alæ   .   .   . Pelecitus, p. 411.
   Males without caudal alæ .   .   . 2
2. Amphidelphys 3
   Opisthodelphys 4
3. Mouth surrounded by a cuticular collar . Coronofilaria, p. 409.
   Mouth simple without a cuticular collar Chandlerella, p. 411.
4. Œsophagus very narrow and trans-
       parent .   .   .   .   . Eufilaria, p. 406.
   Œsophagus of the ordinary type .   . 5
5. Posterior extremity of both sexes digiti-
       form and prolonged considerably be-
       yond the anus   .   .   . Thamugadia, p. 407.
   Posterior extremity of both sexes termi-
       nates immediately behind the anus . 6
6. Œsophagus clearly divided into two
       parts, the second being much wider
       and longer than the first.   .   . Saurositus, p. 407.
   Œsophagus not clearly divided into two
       parts .   .   .   .   . Aprocta, p. 404.

Genus APROCTA Linstow, 1883.

Syn., *Lissonema* Linstow, 1903.

Definition. — APROCTINÆ : anterior extremity slightly at-tenuated ; extremities of body rounded ; mouth simple, usually not surrounded by lips or papillæ, or rarely with three insignificant flat lips ; without a definite mouth cavity or vestibule ; cuticle with fine longitudinal striations ; œsophagus simple and short ;

posterior end of the gut and anus atrophied or absent.   Male :
without caudal alæ, papillæ usually absent, but occasionally
one or two postanal papillæ ; spicules short and subequal.
Female : vulva in the œsophageal region ; opisthodelphys.
Oviparous, eggs small, thick-shelled and containing embryos at
deposition.   Parasites of orbital and nasal cavities of birds.

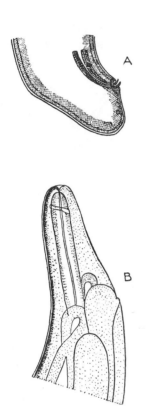

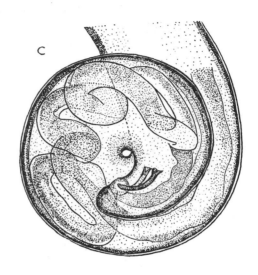

Fig. 276.—*Aprocta cylindrica.*   A. Posterior
extremity of male, lateral view.   (After
Linstow.)   *Aprocta turgida.*   B. Anterior
extremity of female, lateral view.   C. Posterior extremity of male, lateral view. (After
Skrjabin.)

Type species : *A. cylindrica* Linstow, 1883.   ♂ 16 mm., ♀ 27 mm.
In *Petrœca cyanea*.

Other species :

    A. ærophila (Linstow, 1906).   In *Phœnicopterus roseus*.

    A. anthicola (Linstow, 1903).   In *Anthus richardi*.

    A. crassa Railliet and Henry, 1910.   In *Otis tarda*.

    A. matronensis Railliet and Henry, 1910.   In *Corvus cornix*.

? *A. mavis* (Leiper, 1909).   In *Turdus musicus*.

    A. microanalis Skrjabin, 1917.   In *Erithacus* sp.

    A. narium Linstow, 1901.   In *Buteo* sp.

    A. ophthalmophaga Stossich, 1902.   In *Falco* sp.

A. orbitalis Linstow, 1901. In *Falco fuscoater.*

A. rotundata (Linstow, 1903). In *Centropus sinensis.*

Syn., *Lissonema rotundatum* Linstow, 1903.

A. turgida Stossich, 1902. In *Larus argentatus.*

Refs. 278, 313, 324, 424, 577, 578.

Genus EUFILARIA Seurat, 1921.

Definition.—APROCTINÆ : mouth simple without lips or head papillæ ; body turgescent, rounded at the extremities ; cuticle

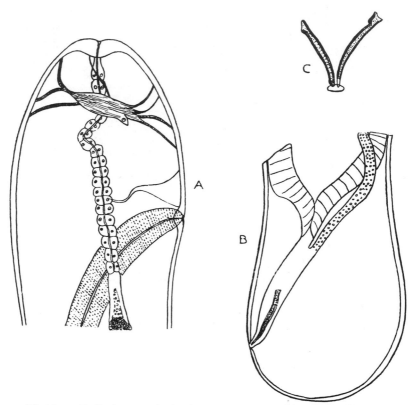

Fig. 277.—*Eufilaria sergenti.* A. Anterior extremity of female, lateral view. B. Posterior extremity of male, lateral view. C. Spicules. (After Seurat.)

smooth, lateral areas very broad ; vestibule narrow and short ; œsophagus short, very narrow, and transparent, and not divided into two parts. Male : straight with very short, rounded tail ; no caudal alæ or papillæ ; cloaca very small ; spicules short, subequal, and acicular. Female : with short, massive, rounded

tail ; vulva in the œsophageal region ; opisthodelphys. Oviparous, eggs with a thin shell, hatching in utero. Microfilariæ
unsheathed. Parasites of subcutaneous tissue of Passeriformes.

Type species : *E. sergenti* Seurat, 1921. ♂ 3·3 mm., ♀ 14 mm.
In *Passer hispaniolensis.*

Other species : *E. capsulata* (Annett, Dutton, and Elliott, 1901).
In *Pycnonotus barbatus, Sitagra*
sp. *Hyphantornis* sp.

    Syn., *Filaria capsulata*
        Annett, Dutton,
        and Elliott, 1901.

Refs. 4, 561, 562.

Genus THAMUGADIA Seurat, 1917.

Definition. — A P R O C T I N Æ :
mouth simple without lips ;
with six small head papillæ ;
cuticle smooth, lateral areas
narrow and not distinguished
from the rest of the skin ; œsophagus short and not divided.
Tails of both sexes relatively
long and digitiform. Male :
caudal alæ and genital papillæ
absent ; spicules short and

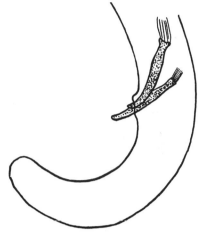

Fig. 278.—*Thamugadia hyalina.* Posterior
extremity of male, lateral view. (After
Seurat.)

equal. Female : vulva slightly posterior to the œsophagus ;
opisthodelphys. Microfilariæ sheathed and found in the blood.
Parasites of the subcutaneous connective tissue of the thoracic
region of geckos.

Type species : *T. hyalina* Seurat, 1917. ♂ 9 mm., ♀ 11 mm.
In *Tarentola mauritanica.*

Refs. 544, 562.

Genus SAUROSITUS Macfie, 1924.

Definition.—APROCTINÆ : mouth simple without lips, with
two lateral and four submedian head papillæ ; cuticle smooth ;
œsophagus short and clearly divided into two portions, a short
narrow anterior part and a much longer and broader posterior
portion ; posterior end of the gut and anus, which is subterminal,
atrophied in both sexes. Male : posterior extremity coiled into
a loose spiral ; caudal alæ absent with a few preanal papillæ ;
spicules subequal ; gubernaculum present. Female : posterior
extremity somewhat attenuated and ending in two more or less

distinct lobes ; vulva just posterior to the end of the œsophagus ; opisthodelphys. Ovoviviparous, embryos sheathed and found in the blood. Parasites of reptiles.

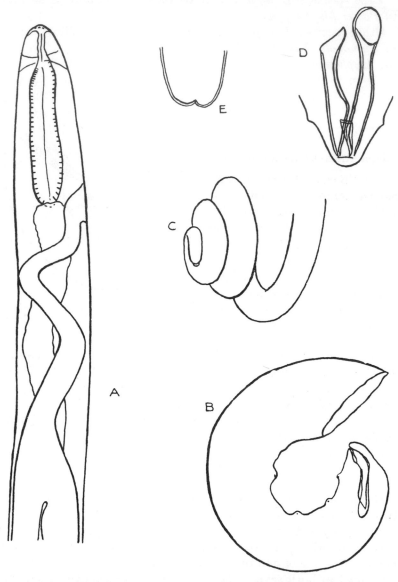

Fig. 279.—*Saurositus agamæ*. A. Anterior extremity of female, lateral view. × 45. B. Posterior extremity of male, lateral view. × 150. C. Posterior extremity of male. × 60. D. Posterior extremity of male, ventral view, showing spicules. × 300. E. Posterior extremity of female, ventral view. × 150. (After Macfie.)

Type species : *S. agamæ* Macfie, 1924. ♂ 42–45 mm., ♀ 80–140 mm. In *Agama colonorum*.

Ref. 345.

Genus CORONOFILARIA n.g.

Syn., ? *Eucamptus* Duj., 1845, preoccupied.

Definition. — APROCTINÆ : tapering slightly towards the extremities ; mouth surrounded by a cuticular collar ; with four

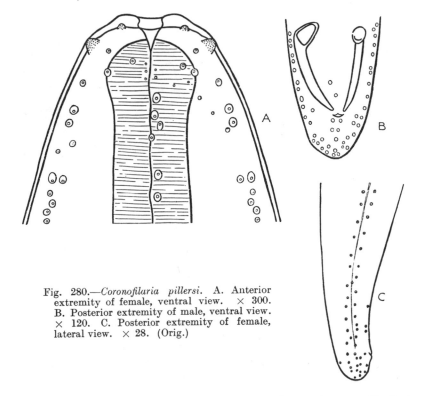

Fig. 280.—*Coronofilaria pillersi*. A. Anterior extremity of female, ventral view. × 300. B. Posterior extremity of male, ventral view. × 120. C. Posterior extremity of female, lateral view. × 28. (Orig.)

pairs of submedian head papillæ ; mouth cavity small, but distinct and infundibular ; cuticle finely transversely striated with small insignificant papillæ scattered irregularly, especially about the middle portion of the worm. In the type species along the lateral areas for the whole length of the worm are two rows of small oval pigmented corpuscles ; the corpuscles are found also on the ventral and dorsal surfaces at the extremities of the worm ; œsophagus relatively narrow and short, cylindrical and not divided into two portions. Male : posterior extremity coiled spirally, tail short and rounded ; caudal alæ absent ; spicules subequal, short, and stout ; about two pairs of preanal papillæ. Female : posterior extremity straight, short, and rounded ; vulva in the œsophageal region ; amphidelphys. Oviparous. Parasites of subcutaneous tissue of birds.

Type species : *C. pillersi* n.sp. ♂ 16 mm., ♀ 32 mm. In blue warbler flycatchers.

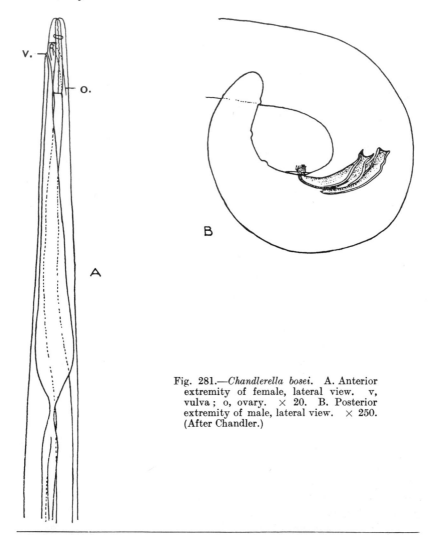

Fig. 281.—*Chandlerella bosei.* A. Anterior extremity of female, lateral view. v, vulva ; o, ovary. × 20. B. Posterior extremity of male, lateral view. × 250. (After Chandler.)

* *Coronofilaria pillersi* n.sp. Length of male about 16 mm., female about 32 mm. Œsophagus in the male about 680–700 μ in length, and in the female about 830–880 μ. Spicules about 180–200 μ in length. Vulva about 630–640 μ from the anterior extremity, and the anus in the female is about 100 μ from the tip of the tail. Cuticle with two rows of oval pigmented corpuscles along the lateral lines and with a few similar corpuscles on the ventral and dorsal surfaces at the extremities.

Other species :

C. *coronata* (Rud., 1809). In *Coracias garrula*.

Syn., *Filaria coronata* Rud., 1809.

? C. *obtusus* (Duj., 1845). In *Caprimulgus europæus*.

Syn., *Eucamptus obtusus* Duj., 1845.

Refs. 131, 313, 321, 476, 479a, 578.

Genus CHANDLERELLA n.g.

Definition.—APROCTINÆ : mouth simple without lips ; without head papillæ ; cuticle smooth ; œsophagus stout, short, and not divided into two parts. Male : posterior extremity extremely coiled, tail digitiform ; caudal alæ absent, with three pairs of inconspicuous postanal papillæ ; spicules equal, stout, and trough-like. Female : tail short and rounded ; vulva in the œsophageal region ; amphidelphys. Microfilariæ found in the blood. Parasites of birds.

Type species : C. *bosei* (Chandler, 1924). ♂ 9–11 mm., ♀ 28 mm. In *Dissemurus paradiseus*.

Syn., *Filaria bosei* Chandler, 1924.

Ref. 89.

Genus PELECITUS Railliet and Henry, 1910.

Definition.—APROCTINÆ : mouth simple without lips ; anterior extremity rounded, provided with a pair of lateral and two to four pairs of submedian head papillæ ; cuticle with fine longitudinal striations and lateral flanges along the whole body ; œsophagus narrow, cylindrical, and not divided into two parts. Male : tail truncate ; caudal alæ large ; preanal papillæ sometimes absent, but there may be two to four pairs ; postanal papillæ variable in number ; spicules equal or subequal † and very short and delicate. Female : tail with one or two pairs of pedunculated papillæ ; vulva near the anterior extremity. Oviparous, eggs oval. Parasites of muscles and tendons of the legs of birds.

Type species : P. *helicinus* (Molin, 1860). ♂ 4 mm., ♀ 5–16 mm. In *Alcedo americana*, *Ampelis* sp., *Anabates* spp., *Corvus* spp., etc.

Syn., *Spiroptera helicina* Molin, 1860.

Other species :

P. *calamiformis* (Schneider, 1866). In *Psittacus æstivus*.

---

* In a paper published whilst this volume was in the press, Schmerling (1925) has erected a new genus *Squamofilaria* for *Filaria coronata* Rudolphi, 1809. Our genus *Coronofilaria* will hence probably fall as a synonym.

† Drasche, 1883, states that P. *helicinus*, P. *circularis*, and P. *serpentulus*, all have very short and almost equal spicules, whereas Skrjabin, 1916, states that in P. *tercostatus* the left spicule is ·136 mm. and the right ·085 mm.

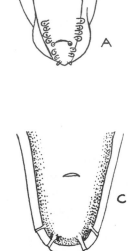

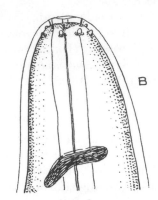

Fig. 282.—*Pelecitus helicinus.* A. Posterior
extremity of male, ventral view. × 120.
(After Drasche.) *Pelecitus tercostatus.* B.
Anterior extremity of female, ventral
view. C. Posterior extremity of female,
ventral view. (After Skrjabin.)

P. circularis (Molin, 1860). In *Corvus* spp. and *Psittacus* spp.
P. quadripapillosus (Molin, 1860). In *Ajaja ajaja.*
P. serpentulus (Dies., 1851). In *Falco* spp.
P. tercostatus (Molin, 1860). In *Psittacus* spp.
Refs. 128, 358, 422, 574.

Subfamily ONCHOCERCINÆ Leiper, 1911.

Definition.—FILARIIDÆ : mouth simple without a chitinous
peribuccal ring or lateral epaulette-like structures ; without
trident-like chitinous structures on each side of the anterior end
of the œsophagus ; cuticle reinforced by external or internal
annular thickenings ; spicules unequal ; vulva in the œsophageal
region.

KEY TO GENERA.

1. Anterior portion of female much
   thinner than remainder, which is
   swollen .   .   .   .   . Elæophora, p. 414.
   Posterior part of female not thickened 2
2. Cuticular thickenings annular .   . Onchocerca, p. 413.
   Cuticular thickenings short and fusi-
   form   .   .   .   .   . Katanga, p. 416.

Genus ONCHOCERCA Diesing, 1841.

Definition.—ONCHOCERCINÆ : both sexes filiform, the female not being swollen posteriorly ; mouth simple and not surrounded

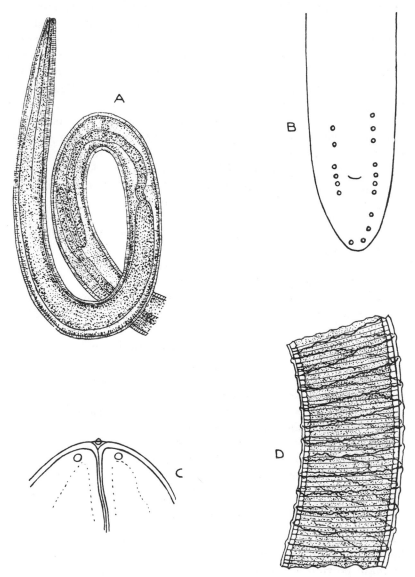

Fig. 283.—*Onchocerca reticulata*. A. Anterior extremity of female. (After Pader.) B. Posterior extremity of male, ventral view (diagram). (Orig.) *Onchocerca gibsoni*. C. Anterior extremity of female. (After Gilruth and Sweet.) *Onchocerca cervicalis*. D. Portion of body showing cuticular striations and thickenings. (After Railliet.)

by lips or papillæ (or if these are present they are extremely minute) ; cuticle, always in the female, especially towards the middle of the body, and sometimes in the male, thick, transversely striated, and reinforced externally by spiral thickenings which are often interrupted in the lateral fields ; œsophagus relatively short and not clearly divided into two portions. Male : posterior extremity spirally coiled ; caudal alæ usually absent (except in. *O. armillata*), four circumanal papillæ, and also one or more papillæ in front of and behind these ; spicules unequal. Female : vulva in the anterior œsophageal region ; opisthodelphys. Microfilariæ unsheathed. Parasites of ligaments, vessels, intramuscular connective tissue, and subcutaneous connective tissue of mammals.

Type species : *O. reticulata* Diesing, 1841. ♂ 270 mm., ♀ 700–800 mm. In horse.

　　Syn., *Filaria reticulata* (Dies., 1841) Creplin, 1846.
　　　　Spiroptera reticulata Dies., 1841, Railliet, 1885, in part.
　　　　Spiroptera cincinnata Ercolani, 1866.

Other species :

　　O. armillata Railliet and Henry, 1909.　In cattle, buffalo.
　　O. bovis Piettre, 1912.　In *Bos taurus*.
　　O. cæcutiens Brumpt, 1919.　In man.
　? *O. capræ* (Linstow, 1883).　In goats.
　　O. cervicalis Railliet and Henry, 1910.　In horse.
　　　Syn., *Spiroptera reticulata* Diesing, 1841, Railliet, 1885, in part.
　　O. fasciata Railliet and Henry, 1910.　In dromedary.
　? *O. flexuosa* (Wedl, 1856).　In Cervidæ.
　　O. gibsoni Cleland and Johnston, 1910.　In cattle.
　　O. gutturosa Neumann, 1910.　In cattle.
　　O. indica Sweet, 1915.　In *Bos bubalis* and *Bos indicus*.
　? *O. lienalis* (Stiles, 1892).　In cattle.
　? *O. spiralis* (Molin, 1860).　In *Bradypus didactylus*.
　　O. volvulus (Leuckart, 1893).　In man.

Refs. 52, 77a, 86a, 109, 140, 183, 184, 285, 289, 305, 385, 422, 434, 608.

Genus ELÆOPHORA Railliet and Henry, 1912.

Definition.—ONCHOCERCINÆ : males and the anterior part of the females, which are embedded in the aortic tissue, are filiform, the main portion of the females, which is free in the lumen of the vessel, is much thicker ; mouth simple without lips ; cuticle in the male and in the anterior portion of the female is transversely striated, in the remaining portion of the female it is much thicker and smooth, but at a deeper level it exhibits marked annulations giving the appearance of an internal striation ; œsophagus cylindrical and very long ; intestine very narrow but not

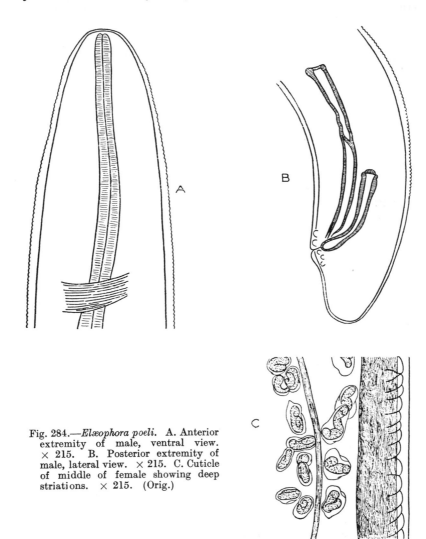

Fig. 284.—*Elæophora poeli*. A. Anterior extremity of male, ventral view. × 215. B. Posterior extremity of male, lateral view. × 215. C. Cuticle of middle of female showing deep striations. × 215. (Orig.)

atrophied. Male : posterior extremity bent ventrally ; caudal alæ absent ; two pairs of preanal, and three of postanal, small sessile papillæ ; spicules unequal. Female : diameter of the posterior portion five or six times that of the anterior part ; vulva in the œsophageal region ; uterus divides into four parallel branches ; four ovaries. Microfilariæ unsheathed. Parasites of the aorta of ruminants.

Type species : *E. poeli* (Vryburg, 1897). ♂ 45–70 mm., ♀ about 200 mm. In the ox.

Syn., *Filaria poeli* Vryburg, 1897.

Refs. 52, 434.

Genus KATANGA n.g.

Syn., *Grammophora* Gedoelst, 1916, preoccupied.

Definition.—ONCHOCERCINÆ : mouth small and round without lips ; head with four very small submedian papillæ ; cuticle in

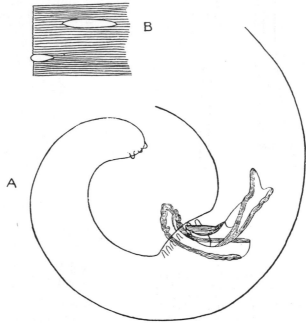

Fig. 285.—*Katanga katangensis*. A. Posterior extremity of male, lateral view. B. Portion of body wall showing fusiform thickenings. (After Gedoelst.)

both sexes with fine transverse superficial striations and with fusiform thickenings distributed irregularly between them ; lateral flanges absent ; œsophagus divided into two parts, the first narrow and short and the second much broader and longer. Male : posterior extremity spirally coiled ; caudal alæ absent, a group of six para-anal papillæ and a pair of subterminal papillæ ; spicules short and subequal. Female : posterior extremity bent ventrally ;

vulva near the anterior extremity. Microfilariæ unsheathed and found in the blood. Parasites of intramuscular connective tissue of mammals.

Type species : *K. katangensis* (Gedoelst, 1916). ♂ 34–39 mm., ♀ 57–65 mm. In *Petrodromus tetradactylus*.

Syn., *Grammophora katagensis* Gedoelst, 1916.

Ref. 151.

Subfamily LOAINÆ n. sf.

Definition.—FILARIIDÆ : mouth simple without a chitinous peribuccal ring or epaulette-like structures ; without trident-like chitinous structures on each side of the anterior end of the œsophagus ; cuticle furnished with bosses ; spicules equal or unequal ; vulva in the œsophageal region or slightly posterior to it.

KEY TO GENERA.

1. Spicules unequal and dissimilar . Loa, p. 417.
   Spicules subequal and similar . . 2
2. With preanal papillæ ; parasites of
   mammals . . . . . Micipsella, p. 418.
   Without preanal papillæ ; parasites of
   birds . . . . . Splendidofilaria, p. 420.

Genus LOA Stiles, 1905.

Definition.—LOAINÆ : mouth simple without lips ; with two lateral and four small submedian head papillæ ; cuticle thick, not striated, but ornamented with small bosses, except at the anterior extremities of both sexes and at the tail of the male, which are smooth ; œsophagus short and divided into two parts. Male : tail bent spirally ; caudal alæ absent ; with five pairs of large pedunculated papillæ and a number of small sessile papillæ ; spicules unequal. Female : posterior extremity rounded with a pair of papillæ near the tip of the tail ; vulva behind the œsophagus ; amphidelphys. Microfilariæ sheathed and found in the blood. Parasites of mammals.

Type species : *L. loa* (Guyot, 1778). ♂ 25–35 mm., ♀ 45–63 mm. In man.

Syn., *Filaria loa* Guyot, 1778.

Refs. 291, 339, 599.

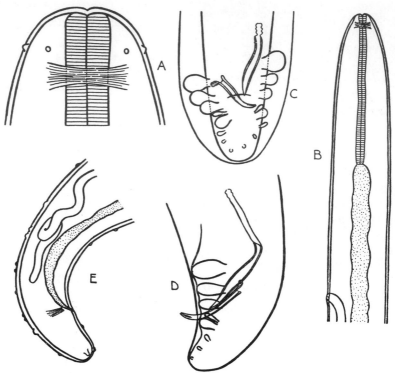

Fig. 286.—*Loa loa*. A. Head, ventral view. × 180. B. Anterior extremity, lateral view. × 32. C. Posterior extremity of male, ventral view. × 180. D. Posterior extremity of male, lateral view. × 180. E. Posterior extremity of female, lateral view. × 64. (Orig.)

Genus **MICIPSELLA** Seurat, 1921.

Syn., *Cercofilaria* Kalantarian, 1924.

Definition.—LOAINÆ: mouth simple without lips and on the summit of a little hemispherical projection which carries a circle of very small papillæ; in addition, there are four submedian papillæ a little further back; body filiform and sharply attenuated at the extremities; cuticle thick and smooth, ornamented with small, slightly projecting bosses arranged in two zig-zag rows along the lateral lines, which are broad and very conspicuous; vestibule with chitinous walls, very short and narrow; œsophagus narrow, of uniform diameter and not divided into two parts; intestine dilated at its origin. Male: tail bent spirally and digitiform, the cloaca being some distance from the tip of the tail; caudal alæ absent; with a variable number (five to seven pairs) of preanal papillæ and two pairs of postanal papillæ; spicules subequal;

the tail of the male is covered on both the ventral and dorsal surfaces with minute papillæ in addition to the above-mentioned rugosities. Female : tail digitiform and long ; vulva near the posterior end of the œsophagus ; opisthodelphys. Viviparous, larvæ unsheathed. Parasites of the abdominal cavity of rodents

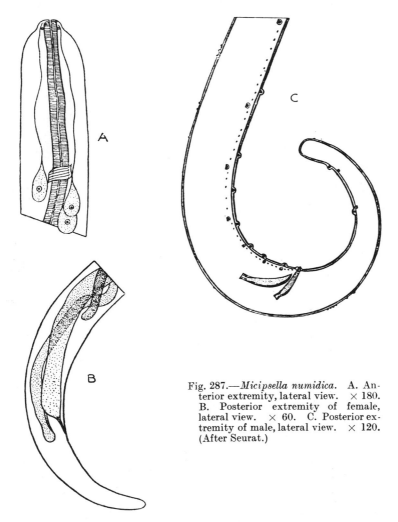

Fig. 287.—*Micipsella numidica*. A. Anterior extremity, lateral view. × 180. B. Posterior extremity of female, lateral view. × 60. C. Posterior extremity of male, lateral view. × 120. (After Seurat.)

Type species : *M. numidica* (Seurat, 1917). ♂ 76 mm., ♀ 130 mm. In *Lepus pallidior* and *Lepus kabylicus*.

Syn., *Filaria numidica* Seurat, 1917.

Cercofilaria numidica (Seurat, 1917) Kalantarian, 1924.

Refs. 246a, 540, 562.

Genus SPLENDIDOFILARIA Skrjabin, 1923.

Definition.—LOAINÆ : mouth simple without lips ; with four submedian and perhaps two lateral head papillæ ; cervical

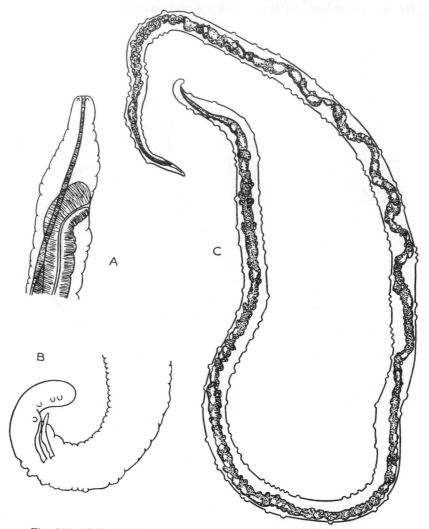

Fig. 288.—*Splendidofilaria pawlowskyi.* A. Anterior extremity of female, lateral view. B. Tail of male, lateral view. C. Female. (After Skrjabin.)

papillæ absent ; cuticle without striations, but furnished with bosses ; œsophagus narrow and not divided into two portions. Male : posterior extremity digitiform, caudal alæ ? absent ; with four pairs of postanal papillæ, preanal papillæ absent ; spicules equal, gubernaculum absent. Female : posterior extremity digitiform ; vulva in the œsophageal region. Parasites of the heart-blood of birds.

Type species : *S. pawlowskyi* Skrjabin, 1923. ♂ 7·4 mm., ♀ 18·9 mm. In *Otomela phœnicuroides*.

Ref. 579a.

Subfamily SETARIINÆ n. sf.

Definition.—FILARIIDÆ : mouth surrounded by a peribuccal chitinous ring, or bounded by lateral epaulette-like structures or by small spinous teeth ; spicules unequal ; vulva in the œsophageal region.

KEY TO GENERA.

Males with caudal alæ . .	1
Males without caudal alæ . .	3
1. Lateral epaulette-like structures not prolonged anteriorly to form lip-like processes . .	Serratospiculum, p. 427.
Lateral epaulette-like structures prolonged anteriorly by the side of the mouth to form two lateral lip-like processes . .	2
2. Large spicule stout and twisted, winged and striated about midpoint. Parasites of birds .	Contortospiculum, p. 428.
Large spicule delicate and of a more or less uniform diameter. Parasites of reptiles . .	Hastospiculum, p. 431.
3. Head with lateral epaulette-like structures	Dipetalonema, p. 425.
Head without lateral epaulette-like structures . . .	4
4. Mouth without peribuccal chitinous ring, but surrounded by four small spinous teeth lying internally to four prominent head papillæ	Icosiella, p. 424.
Mouth surrounded by a peribuccal chitinous ring . .	5
5. Peribuccal chitinous ring prolonged anteriorly into four lips ; cuticle without bosses . .	Setaria, p. 422.

Peribuccal chitinous ring not prolonged anteriorly into four lips ;
cuticle with bosses .   .   .   Papillosetaria, p. 423.

Genus SETARIA Viborg, 1795.

Syn., ? *Hamularia* Treutler, 1793.
    ? *Tentacularia* Zeder, 1800.
    ? *Amularia* Brera, 1810.
    ? *Anchilocephali* Brera, 1810.

Definition.—Setariinæ : mouth surrounded by a chitinous
peribuccal ring which protrudes and is prolonged anteriorly into

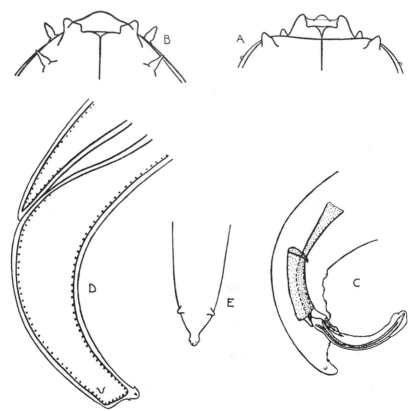

Fig. 289.—*Setaria equina.* A. Head, ventral view. × 180. B. Head, lateral
view. × 180. C. Tail of male, lateral view. × 100. D. Tail of female,
lateral view. × 100. E. Tail of female, dorsal view. × 100. (Orig.)

four lips ; four prominent (sometimes spinous) submedian and
two small lateral head papillæ ; cuticle transversely striated ;
cervical papillæ small ; lateral flanges absent ; œsophagus divided

into two parts, a short, narrow anterior portion and a much thicker posterior portion.   Male : posterior extremity attenuated and spirally rolled with a pair of small lateral cuticular appendages near the tip of the tail ; caudal alæ absent ; about four pairs of preanal papillæ and the same number of postanal ; spicules very unequal, dissimilar, and winged.   Female : posterior extremity attenuated and bent into a loose spiral, the tail ends in a rounded knob and is provided with a pair of small lateral cuticular appendages near the tip ; vulva in the œsophageal region ; opisthodelphys.   Microfilariæ sheathed and found in the blood.   Parasites of the peritoneal cavity and occasionally of other regions—eye, testes, etc.—of mammals.

Type species : *S. equina* (Abildgaard, 1789).   ♂ 54–80 mm., ♀ 90–130 mm.   In equines.

Syn., *Gordius equinus* Abildgaard, 1789.
> ? *Hamularia lymphatica* Treutler, 1793.
> ? *Tentacularia subcompressa* Zeder, 1803.
> ? *Amularia linfatica* Brera, 1810.
> ? *Anchilocephali linfatica* Brera, 1810.

Other species :
S. bernardi Railliet and Henry, 1911.   In pigs, Annam.
S. bicoronata (Linstow, 1901).   In *Adenota* sp.
S. bidentata (Molin, 1858).   In *Cervidæ*, Brazil.
S. cælum (Linstow, 1904).   In *Cephalophus sylvaticultor*.
S. congolensis Raillet and Henry, 1911.   In *Phacochœrus porcus*.
S. cornuta (Linstow, 1899).   In antelope.
S. digitata (Linstow, 1906).   In *Bos indicus*.
S. effilata (Linstow, 1897).   In *Tragulus pygmæus*.
S. hornbyi Boulenger, 1921.   In *Hippotragus niger*.
S. javensis Vevers, 1922.   In *Tragulus stanleyanus*.
S. labiato-papillosa (Aless., 1838).   In cattle.
S. marshalli Boulenger, 1921.   In cattle.
S. nudicauda.   Ortlepp, 1924.   In deer.
S. scalprum (Linstow, 1908).   In *Raphicercus campestris*.
? *S. spelæa* (Leidy, 1875).   In *Macropus* sp.
S. transversata (Linstow, 1907).   In *Cephalophus melanorheus*.
Refs. 2, 66, 381a, 428, 429, 649, 656, 658, 681, 682.

Genus PAPILLOSETARIA Vevers, 1922.

Definition.—SETARIINÆ : body filiform, tapering considerably in both sexes posteriorly ; mouth guarded by two lateral lips which are lined by an oval ring of chitin ; four head papillæ—two lateral and two submedian ; cuticle covered irregularly with bosses except in the head and tail regions ; œsophagus consists of two parts, a short anterior portion and a longer and thicker posterior portion. Male : posterior extremity coiled into a close spiral ; caudal alæ absent ; post- and pre-anal papillæ present ; spicules unequal, dissimilar, and winged. Female : tail curved dorsally

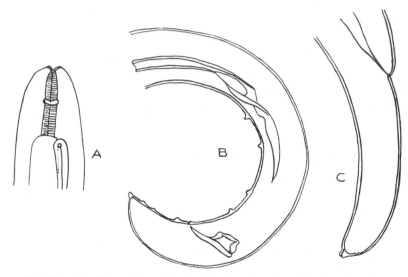

Fig. 290.—*Papillosetaria traguli*. A. Anterior extremity of female, subventral view. × 45. B. Posterior extremity of male, lateral view. × 160. C. Posterior extremity of female, lateral view. × 130. (After Vevers.)

and bearing two lateral appendages close to the tip ; vulva near the anterior end of the body. Ovoviviparous. Parasites of the peritoneal cavity of antelopes.

Type species : *P. traguli* Vevers, 1922. ♂ 57 mm., ♀ 145 mm. In *Tragulus stanleyanus*.

Ref. 656.

Genus ICOSIELLA Seurat, 1917.

Definition.—SETARIINÆ : body thin and straight ; mouth simple and surrounded by four small spinous teeth, external to these are four prominent rounded head papillæ ; cuticle thin and smooth, lateral areas broad ; lateral flanges absent ; œsophagus remarkably long and clearly divided into muscular and glandular portions. Male : tail short and rounded ; caudal alæ and genital papillæ absent ; cloaca bounded by two well-marked lips ; spicules unequal. Female : tail short and rounded ; vulva posterior to the muscular part of the œsophagus ; opisthodelphys.

Microfilariæ sheathed and found in the blood. Parasites of connective, subcutaneous, and intramuscular tissue of frogs.

Type species : *I. neglecta* (Diesing, 1851). ♂ 7·2–11·4 mm., ♀ 21 mm. In *Rana* spp.

   Syn., *Filaria neglecta* Dies., 1851.

Refs. 123, 406, 544.

Genus DIPETALONEMA Diesing, 1861.

   Syn., *Acanthocheilonema* Cobbold, 1870.
      Deraïophoronema Romanovitch, 1916.

Definition.—SETARIINÆ : filiform worms tapering towards each extremity, especially posteriorly ; near the tip of the tail in each sex there is laterally a pair of short conical processes giving the end of the tail a trifid appearance ; in the male the lateral processes are sometimes very small and difficult to see ; mouth simple without lips, but surrounded by a flat cuticular shield which extends further laterally than dorsally and ventrally, so that the anterior extremity appears wider when viewed from the dorsal or ventral aspect than from the lateral ; the cuticular shield bears on each side a large lateral and a pair of smaller submedian papillæ ; cuticle smooth ; œsophagus consists of a short anterior muscular portion and a much longer posterior glandular portion, but sometimes there is no very clear line of demarcation between the two.   Male : posterior extremity spirally rolled, tail long and tapering ; caudal alæ absent or extremely narrow ; three or four pairs of pre- or peri-anal papillæ, and two pairs of postanal papillæ near the tip of the tail ; spicules very unequal and dissimilar, the larger is stout anteriorly and very delicate posteriorly, the smaller is fairly stout and of almost uniform diameter, both end in hooks ; gubernaculum present at least in the type species. Female : posterior extremity long and tapering and extending some distance beyond the anus ; vulva about the middle of the glandular portion of the œsophagus ; opisthodelphys. Viviparous, embryos unsheathed and found in the peripheral blood.   Parasites of serous cavities and connective tissue of mammals.

Type species : *D. gracile* (Rud., 1809). ♂ 100–150 mm., ♀ 300–350 mm.   In Brazilian monkeys.

   Syn., *Filaria gracilis* Rud., 1809.
      Gongylonema filiforme Molin, 1857.
      Filaria caudispina Molin, 1858.
      Dipetalonema caudispina (Molin, 1858) Dies., 1861.

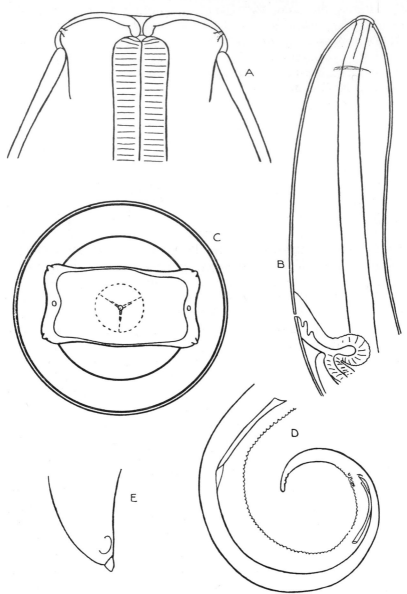

Fig. 291.—*Dipetalonema gracile*. A. Head, ventral view. × 400. B. Anterior extremity of female, lateral view. × 75. C. Head, end-on view. × 400. D. Posterior extremity of male, lateral view. × 80. E. Posterior extremity of female, lateral view. × 400. (Orig.)

Other species :

 D. australe (Linstow, 1897). In *Petrogale penicillata, Trichosurus vulpecula.*

D. diacanthum (Molin, 1858). In *Hystrix prehensilis, Erethizon dorsatum, etc.*

D. dracunculoides (Cobbold, 1870). In hyæna and dogs.

    Syn., *Acanthocheilonema dracunculoides* Cobbold, 1870.

D. evansi (Lewis, 1882). In camels.

    Syn., *Filaria evansi* Lewis, 1882.

        Deraïophoronema cameli Romanovitch, 1916.

D. grassii (G. Noè, 1907). In dogs.

D. perstans (Manson, 1891). In man.

D. reconditum (Grassi, 1890). In dogs.

D. rœmeri (Linstow, 1905). In *Macropus giganteus.*

D. weissi (Seurat, 1914). In *Elephantulus deserti.*

Refs. 41a, 45, 65, 73, 100, 125, 131, 291, 318, 354, 451, 472, 476, 480, 513, 604.

Genus SERRATOSPICULUM Skrjabin, 1916.

Definition.—SETARIINÆ : mouth simple without lips ; on each side a short distance from the buccal orifice are two small epaulette

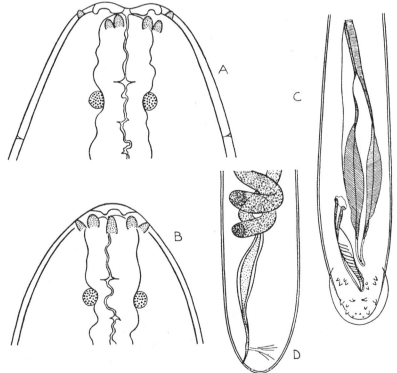

Fig. 292.—*Serratospiculum tendo.* A. Anterior extremity, ventral view. × 160. B. Anterior extremity, lateral view. × 160. C. Posterior extremity of male, ventral view. × 71. D. Posterior extremity of female, lateral view. × 35. (Orig.)

formations, each convex medianly and trilobed laterally, behind these are the lateral and submedian head papillæ ; œsophagus clearly divided into two parts, the first short and narrow and the second long and broad, but gradually tapering posteriorly. Male : posterior extremity rounded with short broad caudal alæ meeting behind the tip of the tail ; about four to six pairs of preanal papillæ and the same number of postanal, some of them are pedunculated ; spicules unequal, of complicated structure, winged, and serrated about the middle of their length ; gubernaculum absent. Female : posterior extremity rounded ; anus terminal ; vulva slightly behind the junction of the two portions of the œsophagus ; amphidelphys. Parasites of serous cavities of carnivorous birds.

Type species : *S. turkestanicum* Skrjabin, 1916. ♂ 100 mm., ♀ 170 mm. In *Falco tinnunculus*.

Other species :

S. guttatum (Schneider, 1866). In *Hieracidea berigora*.

Syn., *F. attenuata* Rud., 1819, in part, not Rud., 1803, not Zeder, 1803.

S. tendo (Nitzsch, 1857). In *Falco peregrinus*.

Syn., *Filaria tendo* Nitzsch, 1857.

Filaria attenuata Rud., 1819, in part, not Rud., 1803, not Zeder, 1803.

Filaria foveolata Molin, 1858.

S. verrucosum (Molin, 1858). In *Falco swainsoni*.

Refs. 41a, 354, 446, 480, 524, 572, 574, 578.

Genus CONTORTOSPICULUM Skrjabin, 1917.

Syn., *Dicheilonema* * Dies., 1861, in part.

? *Monopetalonema* † Dies., 1861.

Definition.—SETARIINÆ : large worms, the female being much longer and stouter than the male ; mouth oval, long axis dorsoventral, surrounded by a chitinous collar which is raised anteriorly beyond the level of the rest of the cuticle and prolonged into two erect lateral processes ; on each side of the mouth is a thick cuticular epaulette-like structure which is attached to the collar internally and ends in three rounded processes externally—a lateral and two submedian : each of these three processes has a large papilla, and there are also two additional papillæ lying in the spaces between them ; cuticle transversely striated ; œsophagus

---

* *Vide* footnote, p. 437.
† *Vide* footnote, p. 438.

clearly divided into two parts, the anterior short and the posterior
broad and very long. Male : posterior extremity bent ventrally ;
large caudal alæ meeting posteriorly behind the tip of the tail
with a number of large pedunculated pre- and post-anal papillæ
on each side ; near the tip of the tail there are a few pairs of

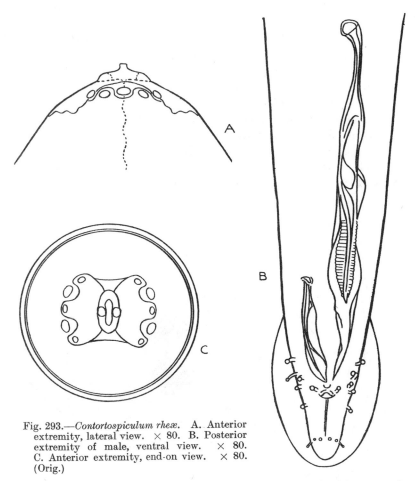

Fig. 293.—*Contortospiculum rheæ*. A. Anterior
extremity, lateral view. × 80. B. Posterior
extremity of male, ventral view.   × 80.
C. Anterior extremity, end-on view.   × 80.
(Orig.)

smaller papillæ of which one at least is pedunculated ; spicules
very unequal, the larger being twisted, strongly striated in its
posterior half, and provided with large wings, the smaller is also
winged in its posterior half. Female : posterior extremity
rounded ; anus atrophied and opening very near the tip of the
tail ; vulva about the junction of the anterior and posterior
portions of the œsophagus ; amphidelphys. Oviparous. Parasites
of birds.

Type species : *C. rheæ* (Owen, 1843).　♂ 175–325 mm., ♀ 665–1,350 mm.　In *Rhea americana, Struthio crux,* and *Otis tarda.*

Syn., *Filaria rheæ* Owen, 1843.

Filaria horrida Dies., 1851.

Dicheilonema horridum (Dies, 1851) Dies., 1861.

Contortospiculum horridum (Dies., 1851) Skrjabin, 1917.

Other species :

C. americanum Railliet, 1918.　In *Asio accipitrinus.*

Syn., *Filaria* sp. Leidy, 1884.

C. ciconiæ (Schrank, 1788).　In *Ciconia nigra.*

Syn., *Filaria ciconiæ* Schrank, 1788.

Filaria labiata Creplin, 1825.

C. nodulosum (Rud., 1820).　In *Lanius* spp.

Syn., *Filaria nodulosa* Rud., 1820.

Filaria obtuso-caudata Rud., 1819.

Monopetalonema obtuse-caudatum Dies., 1861.

Refs. 112, 125, 131, 362, 410, 481, 524, 578.

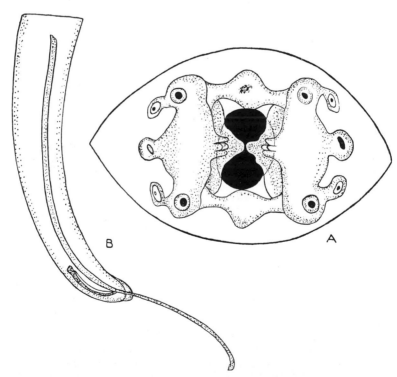

Fig. 294.—*Hastospiculum varani.*　A. Anterior extremity, end-on view.　B. Posterior extremity of male, lateral view.　(After Skrjabin.)

Genus HASTOSPICULUM Skrjabin, 1923.

Definition.—SETARIINÆ : mouth oval, long axis dorso-ventral, bounded on each side by a projecting chitinous process or lip,

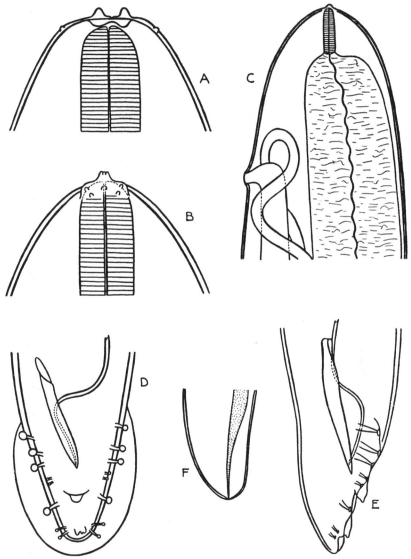

Fig. 295.—*Hastospiculum gouldi.* A. Anterior extremity of male, ventral view. × 180. B. Anterior extremity of male, lateral view. × 180. C. Anterior extremity of female, lateral view. × 40. D. Posterior extremity of male, ventral view. × 180. E. Posterior extremity of male, lateral view. × 180. F. Posterior extremity of female, lateral view. × 20. (Orig.)

externally to which are thick cuticular lateral epaulette-like structures ending in three processes externally and bearing a lateral and two pairs of submedian papillæ ; œsophagus clearly divided into two parts, the anterior short and narrow, and the posterior broad and very long. Male : posterior extremity almost straight ; large caudal alæ meeting posteriorly behind the tip of the tail with a number of large pedunculated preanal papillæ on each side ; on the mid-line ventrally there are (at least in *H. gouldi*) two conical processes, the first in the neighbourhood of the cloaca and the second near the tip of the tail ; spicules very unequal, the longer delicate and the shorter stout and twisted. Female : posterior extremity rounded ; anus atrophied and opening very near the tip of the tail ; vulva slightly behind the termination of the anterior portion of the œsophagus ; amphidelphys. Oviparous. Parasites of reptiles.

Type species : *H. varani* Skrjabin, 1923. ♂ 135–140 mm., ♀ ? In *Varanus griseus*.

Other species : **H. gouldi* n. sp. In *Varanus gouldi*. Ref. 580.

Subfamily DIPLOTRIÆNINÆ Skrjabin, 1916.

Definition.—FILARIIDÆ : mouth simple without peribuccal chitinous ring or epaulette-like structures ; with trident-like chitinous structures on each side of the anterior end of the œsophagus ; spicules unequal ; vulva in œsophageal region.

Genus DIPLOTRIÆNA Railliet and Henry, 1909.

Syn., *Triplotriæna* Connal, 1912.

Definition.—DIPLOTRIÆNINÆ : body slightly attenuated at the two extremities ; mouth simple without lips, surrounded by two lateral and four submedian very small head papillæ ; cuticle smooth ; œsophagus long, consisting of two parts, at its anterior extremity are two lateral chitinous structures, each consisting of a stalk directed forwards and a trident-like process directed backwards. Male : tail rounded, caudal alæ absent, papillæ usually absent ; spicules unequal. Female : vulva shortly behind the muscular part of the œsophagus ; amphidelphys.

---

* *Hastospiculum gouldi* n. sp. Length of male about 45 mm., female about 180 mm. The length of the first part of the œsophagus is about 300 μ in the male and also in the female, and that of the second part of the œsophagus is 9·4 mm. in the male and 16 mm. in the female. Spicules measure about 1·1 mm. and 200 μ respectively in length. In the female the vulva is about 1 mm. from the anterior extremity.

Oviparous, eggs with thick shells and containing fully-developed embryos at deposition. Parasites of cavities of birds.

Type species : *D. ozouxi* Railliet and Henry, 1909.   ♂ 3–4 mm., ♀ 6 mm.   In *Faudias madagascariensis.*

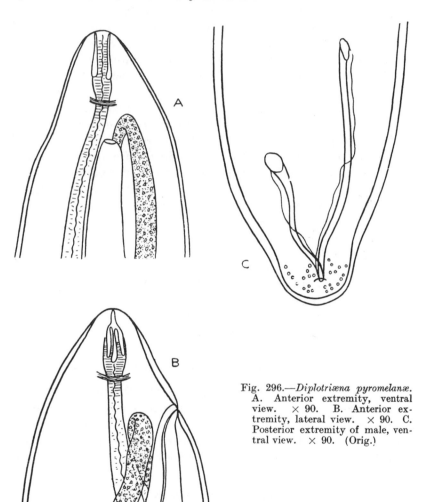

Fig. 296.—*Diplotriæna pyromelanæ.*
A. Anterior extremity, ventral view.   × 90.   B. Anterior extremity, lateral view.   × 90.   C. Posterior extremity of male, ventral view.   × 90.   (Orig.)

Other species :

? *D. abbreviata* (Rud., 1819).   In *Motacilla stapazina.*

D. affinis (Rud., 1819).   In *Fringilla* sp.

D. artemisiana Schmerling, 1925.   In *Coracias garrula.*

D. attenuato-verrucosa (Molin, 1858).   In *Thamnophilus canadensis.*

D. bargusinica Skrjabin, 1917.   In *Turdus* sp.

D. chamoensis (Parona).—Henry and O'Zoux, 1909.

D. diucæ Boulenger, 1920.   In *Diuca grisea.*

D. falconis (Connal, 1912).   In *Falco* sp.

   Syn., *Triplotriæna falconis* Connal, 1912.

D. filiformis (Molin, 1858)   In *Anabates rufifrons.*

D. flabellata (Linstow, 1888).   In *Paradisea apoda.*

D. macrophallos (Parona, 1889).   In *Hydrosaurus salvator.*

D. obtusa (Rud., 1802), not Schnéider, 1866.   In *Hirundo rustica.*

D. paronai (Stossich, 1897).   In *Buceros nasutus.*

D. pungens (Schneider, 1866).   In *Turdus cyaneus.*

**D. pyromelanæ* n. sp.   In *Pyromelana oryx.*

D. quadriverrucosa (Molin, 1858).   In *Dendrocalaptes picus.*

D. sokolowi Skrjabin, 1916.   In *Halcyon senegaloides.*

D. spermospizæ (Linstow, 1879).   In *Spermospiza guttata.*

D. tinamicola Skrjabin, 1916.   In *Tinamus* sp.

D. tricuspis (Fedtsch., 1874).   In *Corvus cornix, Alæmon duponti,* etc.

   Syn., *Filaria tricuspis* Fedtschenko, 1874.

       F. cornicis Gmelin, 1790 [nom. nudum].

       F. attenuata Rud., 1819, in part, not Rud., 1803, not Zeder, 1803.

     ? *F. ecaudata* Oerley, 1882.

     ? *F. ninnii* Stossich, 1891.

     ? *F. sturni* Rud., 1809.

Refs. 65, 111, 215, 446, 479a, 573, 574, 578.

Subfamily MICROPLEURINÆ Baylis and Daubney, 1922.

Definition.—FILARIIDÆ : mouth simple without a chitinous peribuccal ring or epaulette-like structures ; without chitinous tridents on each side of the anterior end of the œsophagus ; cuticle smooth or transversely striated ; spicules equal ; vulva near the middle of the body.

Genus MICROPLEURA Linstow, 1906.

Definition.—MICROPLEURINÆ : mouth simple without lips ; with two lateral and four submedian head papillæ ; cuticle with fine transverse striations and with a few minute papillæ on the

---

* *Diplotriæna pyromelanæ* n. sp.   Length of male 14 mm., female 35–45 mm. Length of œsophagus in the male is about 2·8 mm. and in the female 3–4 mm. Tridents reach back from the anterior extremity in the male about 150 μ and in the female about 160–170 μ.   Spicules measure 690 μ and 415 μ respectively in length ; and the ventral surface of the posterior extremity of the male is furnished with about twelve pairs of sessile papillæ on each side.   In the female the vulva is about 1·2 mm. from the anterior extremity, and the anus is near the tip of the tail.

posterior part of the worm ; œsophagus divided into an anterior narrow muscular portion, and a much longer and wider posterior glandular portion. Male : posterior extremity conical and tapering, with a caudal ala on the right side ; three pairs of preanal

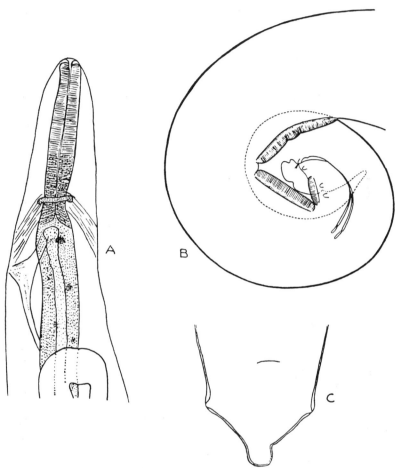

Fig. 297.—*Micropleura vivipara.* A. Anterior extremity, lateral view. × 48. (After Baylis and Daubney.) B. Posterior extremity of male, lateral view. (After Baylis.) C. Posterior extremity of female, ventral view. × 160. (After Baylis and Daubney.)

and four of postanal papillæ ; spicules equal, very slender and tapering to fine points. Female : posterior extremity resembles that of the male, there being a short bluntly rounded tail with a large rounded papillæ on each side of the anus ; vulva slightly in front of the middle of the body ; uteri opposed. Viviparous. Parasites of crocodiles.

Type species: *M. vivipara* Linstow, 1906. ♂ 10 mm. ♀ 43 mm. In *Gavialis gangeticus*.

Refs. 40, 42, 327.

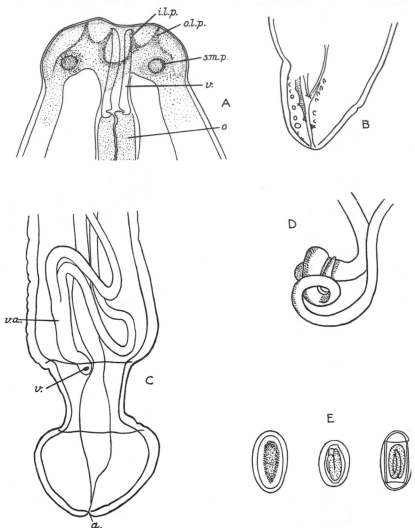

Fig. 298.—*Crassicauda crassicauda*. A. Anterior extremity, ventral view. *i.l.p*, inner lateral papilla ; *o.l.p*, outer lateral papilla ; *s.m.p*, submedian papilla ; *v*, vestibule ; *o*, œsophagus. × 130. B. Posterior extremity of male, subventral view. × 30. C. Posterior extremity of female, subventral view. *va*, vagina ; *v*, vulva ; *a*, anus. × 26. D. Posterior extremities, in copulation. × 5. E. Eggs. × 160. (After Baylis.)

---

* Baylis (1924) suggests that von Linstow's male represents a different worm altogether from *M. vivipara*.

Subfamily CRASSICAUDINÆ n.sf.

Definition.—FILARIIDÆ : mouth simple without lips ; cuticle transversely striated ; posterior extremity bluntly rounded ; anus terminal in both sexes ; vulva near the posterior end of the body in a constriction just in front of the knob-like caudal extremity.

Genus CRASSICAUDA Leiper and Atkinson, 1914.

Definition.—CRASSICAUDINÆ : mouth without lips, but with one small papilla on each side of the head and more externally provided with three larger papillæ on each side ; vestibule cylindrical with thick walls and compressed laterally ; cuticle thick, transversely striated, sometimes raised into a swelling which appears to serve as a fixation organ ; œsophagus divided into a short anterior, and a long posterior, part. Male : posterior extremity laterally compressed and spirally coiled ; with a ventral groove behind the cloaca ; at either side of the groove is a somewhat irregular row of genital papillæ ; spicules small and unequal, or absent. Female : vulva near the posterior end of the body in a constriction just in front of the knob-like caudal extremity ; vagina very short, uteri parallel ; anus terminal. Oviparous, eggs with a thick shell containing an embryo when deposited. Parasites of the urogenital system (or, exceptionally, of other parts of the body) of Cetacea.

Type species : *C. crassicauda* (Creplin, 1829), not Leiper and Atkinson, 1914. ♂ 150–160 mm., ♀ 300–325 mm. In *Balænoptera* spp., etc.

Syn., *Filaria crassicauda* Creplin, 1829.

Other species : *C. boopis* Baylis, 1920. In *Megaptera nodosa.*

Syn., *C. crassicauda* (Creplin, 1829) of Leiper and Atkinson, 1914.

Refs. 18, 25, 32, 113, 295, 296.

FILARIIDÆ insufficiently known.
Genus DICHEILONEMA * Diesing, 1861.

Definition.—FILARIIDÆ : body attenuated at the extremities ; mouth unarmed, elliptical, with two very small rounded unarmed lips ; tip of the tail bifid. Male : caudal extremity spirally coiled ; spicules unequal, the larger being tubular and short. Female :

---

* There is some doubt regarding the type of this genus in which ten species were placed by Diesing. According to Stiles and Hassall (1905), the type should probably be *Filaria labiata* Creplin, 1825, in which case the genus *Dicheilonema* would replace *Contortospiculum* Skrjabin, 1917. Railliet, however, considers that, as Diesing based the genus exclusively on the tubular form of the large spicule, and as this character was known only in *Filaria bifida* Molin, 1858, this species must be considered the type of the genus.

posterior extremity incurved ventrally ; vulva in the anterior part of the body.

Type species : *D. bifidum* (Molin, 1858). ♂ 52 mm., ♀ only fragments found. In *Dactylomys amblyonyx.*

Syn., *Filaria bifida* Molin, 1858.

Refs. 125, 354, 410.

Genus MONOPETALONEMA * Diesing, 1861.

Definition.—FILARIIDÆ : body very long and filiform ; mouth with two lips. Male : posterior extremity bent ventrally ; caudal alæ and papillæ present ; spicule single ! Female : blunt straight tail ; vulva in anterior part of body ? Parasites in connective tissue and abdominal cavity of Brazilian birds and badgers.

Type species : *? M. physalurum* (Bremser, 1851) Dies, 1861. ♂ 37–75 mm., ♀ 150–250 mm.   In *Alcedo amazona.*

Other species : *M. eremita* Leidy, 1886.   In *Meles labradorica.*

Refs. 123, 125, 272, 354, 454, 480, 524.

Genus ELAPHOCEPHALUS Molin, 1860.

Definition.—FILARIIDÆ : mouth with two small conical lips, from each lip two band-like processes are directed posteriorly,

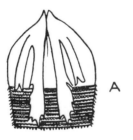
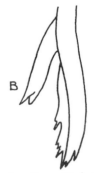

Fig. 299.—*Elaphocephalus octocornutus.* A. Anterior extremity, ventral view. × 140. B. Cephalic process. × 280. (After Drasche.)

each of these processes subdivides into two branches of unequal length, serrated at their terminations ; cuticle furnished with closely set rings of small posteriorly-directed spines. Male : unknown. Female : vulva near mouth. Parasites in the feet of birds.

* The type species of this genus is uncertain. Diesing placed in it two species, viz. *M. physalurum* (Bremser, 1851) and *M. obtuse-caudatum* Diesing, 1861 ; the latter is synonymous with *Filaria nodulosa* Rud., 1820, and belongs to the genus *Contortospiculum.* Very little appears to be known regarding *M. physalurum* (Bremser, 1851), but it seems quite possible that it really belongs to the same genus as *M. obtuse-caudatum,* in which case the genus *Contortospiculum* would fall as a synonym of *Monopetalonema.*

Type species : *E. octocornutus* Molin, 1860. ♂ ?, ♀ 12 mm. In *Psittacus macao*.

Refs. 128, 359.

Genus SOLENONEMA Diesing, 1861.

Definition.—FILARIIDÆ : body very long and filiform ; head continuous with body ; mouth terminal. Male : caudal extremity twisted spirally, papillate ; spicules tubular or subglobular. Female : vulva in anterior part of body. Parasites in subcutaneous and intramuscular connective tissue of American tropical mammals.

Type species ?

Containing the species.

> *S. æquale* (Molin, 1858). ♂ 37 mm., ♀ 60–65 mm. In *Myrmecophaga jubata*.
>
> *S. serpiculum* (Molin, 1858). ♂ 50 mm., ♀ 50–100 mm. In *Phyllostoma brevicaudum*.
>
> *S. striatum* (Molin, 1858). ♂ 110 mm., ♀ 375 mm. In *Felis* spp.

Refs. 125, 354.

Genus TETRACHEILONEMA Diesing, 1861.

Definition.—FILARIIDÆ : body very long and filiform ; four large conical lips. Male : caudal extremity twisted and blunt. Female : vulva in anterior part of body. Viviparous. Parasites of abdominal cavity and subcutaneous tissue of Brazilian birds.

Type species : *T. quadrilabiatum* (Molin, 1858). ♂ 30 mm., ♀ 37–50 mm. In *Tinamus rufescens* and *T. maculosus*.

> Syn., *Filaria quadrilabiata* Molin, 1858.
> *Filaria tinami* Molin, 1858.
> *Filaria labiotruncata* Molin, 1858.

Refs. 125, 354, 454.

Genus FILAROIDES Beneden, 1858.

Definition.—FILARIIDÆ ? : very long filiform worms ; the cuticle is characterised by transverse overriding folds which allow the worm to extend according to the development of its genitalia ; mouth terminal. Male : spicules very short and delicate. Female : vulva near the mouth in the œsophageal region ; two ovaries. Viviparous.

Type species : *F. mustelarum* (Rud., 1819) Beneden, 1858. ♂ ?, ♀ 150–170 mm. Encysted in the lungs of martens, weasels, etc.

> Syn., *Filaria mustelarum pulmonalis* Rud., 1819.

Refs. 48, 125, 131.

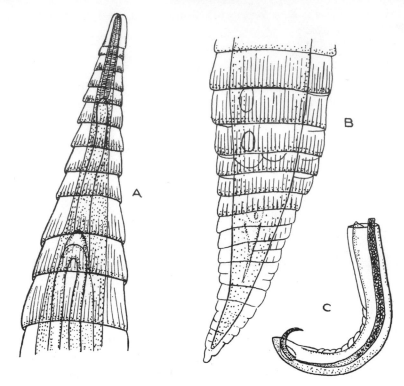

Fig. 300.—*Filaroides mustelarum*. A. Anterior extremity of female, ventral view. B. Posterior extremity of female. C. Posterior extremity of male, lateral view. (After van Beneden.)

Family DRACUNCULIDÆ Leiper, 1912.

Definition.—FILARIOIDEA : females enormously larger than the males ; anus and vulva atrophied in the gravid female.

Subfamily DRACUNCULINÆ (Stiles, 1907).

Syn., *Dracunculiinæ* Stiles, 1907.

Definition.—DRACUNCULIDÆ : with the characters of the family.

KEY TO GENERA.

With a cephalic shield ; vulva near head ; parasites of mammals . . . Dracunculus, p. 442.
Without a cephalic shield ; vulva at junction of middle and posterior thirds of body ; parasites of fishes . . . Philometra, p. 442.

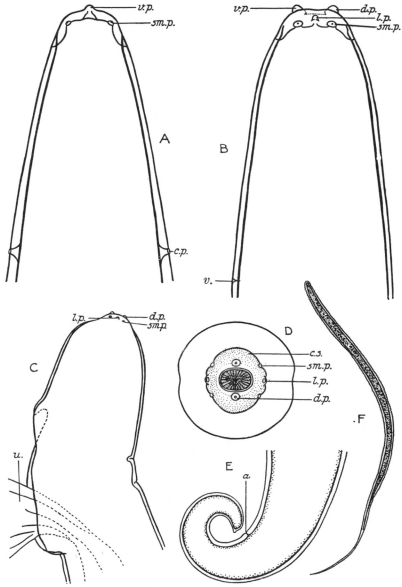

Fig. 301.—*Dracunculus medinensis.* A. Anterior extremity of female, ventral
view. *v.p*, ventral papilla; *sm.p*, submedian papilla; *c.p*, cervical
papilla. × 64. B. Anterior extremity of young female, lateral view.
v.p, ventral papilla; *d.p*, dorsal papilla; *l.p*, lateral papilla; *sm.p*, submedian papilla; *v*, vulva. × 64. C. Anterior extremity of gravid
female, lateral view. *u*, uterus prolapsed through vulva. × 32.
D. Head, end-on view. *c.s*, cephalic shield; *sm.p*, submedian papilla;
l.p, lateral papilla; *d.p*, dorsal papilla. × 64. E. Posterior extremity
of female, lateral view. *a*, anus. × 64. F. Larva. × 160. (Orig.)

Genus DRACUNCULUS Reichard, 1759.

Syn., *Vena* Gallandat, 1773.
Vermiculus Dunglison, 1895.

Definition.—DRACUNCULIDÆ : anterior extremity dome-shaped and provided with a cuticular thickening or shield ; mouth oval and bears on its dorsal and ventral borders a large rounded papilla ; further back on the cuticular shield are two lateral and four submedian papillæ ; cervical papillæ small, about 1 mm. from the anterior extremity ; œsophagus long and cylindrical ; anus and the lower part of the intestine atrophied. Male : practically unknown. Female : vulva and vagina atrophied ; situation of vulva immediately behind the head ; the main bulk of the worm is occupied by a greatly distended uterus filled with embryos ; when ready to discharge its contents, the uterus bursts through the body wall immediately behind the anterior extremity in the neighbourhood of the atrophied vulva ; tail coiled ventrally to a varying extent, tapers rather suddenly near its end, and terminates in a small conical process. Viviparous, the embryos being provided with long pointed tails. Parasites of body tissues of vertebrates.

Type species : *D. medinensis* (Linnæus, 1758). ♂ 22 mm., ♀ 400–900 mm. In man, dog, horse, cattle, jackal, leopard, baboon, cobra, etc.

Syn., *Filaria medinensis* Linnæus, 1758.
Vena medinensis (Linn., 1758). Gallandat, 1773.
Vermiculus capillaris Dunglison, 1895.
? *D. dahomensis* Neum., 1895. In *Python natalensis*.
Refs. 17, 237, 282, 290, 397, 650.

Genus PHILOMETRA Costa, 1845.

Syn., *Ichthyonema* Diesing, 1861.

Definition.—DRACUNCULIDÆ : female enormously larger than male ; body filiform ; anterior and posterior extremities rounded ; mouth with or without lips and head papillæ ; œsophagus cylindrical, very short. Male : posterior extremity rounded, cloaca terminal, bordered by two lips ; spicules equal and needle-like ; gubernaculum present. Female : anus and vulva atrophied ; the situation of the vulva in young worms is at the junction of the middle and posterior thirds of the body ; body occupied almost entirely by the uterus filled with embryos ; there is a small ovary at each end of the body. Parasitic in the body cavities and tissues of fishes (and sea-urchins).

Type species : *P. globiceps* (Rudolphi, 1819). ♂ up to 6–8 mm., ♀ up to 200 mm. or more. In *Blennius phycis, Uranoscopus scaber*.

> Syn., *Filaria globiceps* Rud., 1819.
>
> *Philometra recticaudata* Costa, 1845.

Other species :

P. acipenseris (del Lupo, 1898). In *Acipenser sturio*.

P. congeri-vulgaris (Molin, 1859). In *Conger vulgaris*.

P. cylindracea (Ward and Magath, 1916). In *Perca flavescens*.

P. filiformis (Stoss., 1896). In *Pagellus* sp., *Trachinus* sp.

P. fusca (Rud., 1819). In *Labrax lupus*.

P. grayi (Gemmill and Linstow, 1902). In *Echinus escul*.

P. ovata (Zed., 1803). In *Squalius dobula*.

P. pellucida (Jaegers., 1893). In *Tetrodon stellatus*.

P. rischta Skrjabin, 1923. In *Pseudaspius leptocephalus*.

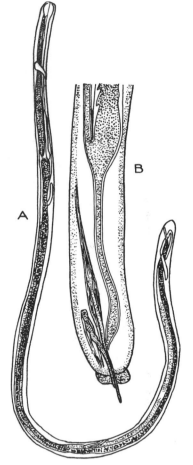

Fig. 302.—*Philometra globiceps*. A. Young female. B. Posterior extremity of male. (After Strassen.)

P. sanguinea (Rud., 1819). In *Abramis vimba*.

Refs. 125, 322, 334, 405, 477, 480, 581, 606, 662.

GENERA INSUFFICIENTLY KNOWN AND OF UNCERTAIN SYSTEMATIC POSITION.

Genus GALEICEPS Railliet, 1916.

Definition.—EUNEMATODA : anterior extremity with a hood-like covering, the circumoral portion of which projects forwards round the mouth as four lip-like projections, the two subdorsal being near together, and the two subventral separated from one another by a space ; the oral border of each of these swellings is provided with a tooth ; cuticle with transverse striations, and also with thick wavy longitudinal lines ; œsophagus long. Male : posterior extremity rounded ; two longitudinal rows of numerous preanal papillæ, and a pair of doubled postanal papillæ ; spicules long and equal. Female : posterior extremity short and pointed. Parasites of insectivorous mammals.

Fig. 303.—*Galeiceps cucullus.* Anterior extremity, ventral view. (After Linstow.)

Type species : *G. cucullus* (Linstow, 1899). ♂ 16 mm., ♀ 24 mm. In *Potamogale velox.*

Syn., *Ancyracanthus cucullus* Linstow, 1899.

Refs. 318, 404.

Genus PTERYGIFER Linstow, 1907.

Definition.—EUNEMATODA : cuticle transversely striated ; head rounded, bearing four movable crescentic wing-like plates ending posteriorly in an inwardly-directed hook ; the plates are attached anteriorly ; cervical papillæ present. Male : unknown. Female : posterior extremity rounded ; vulva just behind the middle of the body. Oviparous. Parasites of eels.

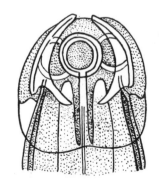

Type species : *P. tetrapteryx* Linstow, 1907. ♂ ?, ♀ 17 mm. In *Synbranchus marmoratus.*

Ref. 329.

Fig. 304.—*Pterygifer tetrapteryx.* Anterior extremity. (After Linstow.)

Genus CYSTOPSIS Wagner, 1867.

Syn., *Cystoopsis* Zykov, 1902.

Definition. — EUNEMATODA : mouth funnel-shaped and surrounded by a small ring, cuticle finely striated ; œsophagus long, cylindrical reaching to near the middle of the worm, followed by a dilated gut-sac which ends blindly at about 70 per cent. of the length of the

worm from the anterior end ; anus absent. Male : sausage-
shaped and extremely small ; spicules absent. Female : anterior
portion cylindrical and thinner than the male ; posterior half
globular ; vulva a little distance from the mouth ; the swollen
posterior part of the body is occupied by the gut-sac, uterus, and
ovary. Oviparous, eggs with a thick shell with a plug at each
end and containing an embryo when born. Parasites of the
subcutaneous tissue of fishes.

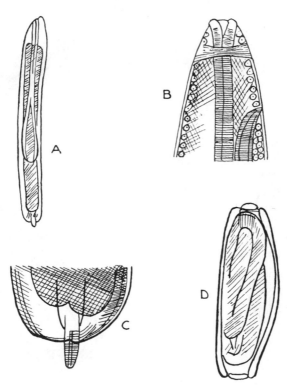

Fig. 305.—*Cystopsis acipenseris.* A. Male. B. Anterior extremity of female,
lateral view. C. Posterior extremity of male. D. Egg. (After Linstow.)

Type species : *C. acipenseris* Wagner, 1867. ♂ 2·1 mm.,
♀ 3·4 mm. In *Acipenser ruthenus.*

Refs. 326, 684.

Genus MUSPICEA Sambon, 1925.

Definition.—The female only is known. Body short and
stout, somewhat attenuated posteriorly and terminating in a
bilobed tail, the lobes being strikingly mammilloid ; cuticle with
marked transverse striations ; mouth simple ; œsophagus appa-

rently terminating in a slight sub-spherical bulb ; anus situated between the tail lobes ; the uterus is apparently a continuous tube in all probability consisting of two opposed branches which appear to end in the ovaries ; vagina probably opens near the middle of the body. Viviparous. Parasites of the subcutaneous connective tissue and in the glands of rodents.

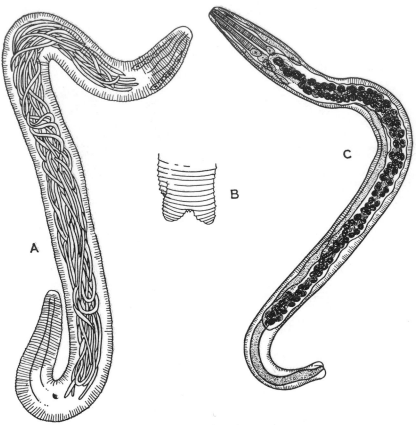

Fig. 306.—*Muspicea borreli*. A. Mature female. B. Tail of female.
C. Young female. (After Sambon.)

Type species : *M. borreli* Sambon, 1925. ♀ 2·9–3·4 mm. In *Mus musculus.*

Ref. 478a.

Genus TRICHEILONEMA Diesing, 1861.

Syn., *Schizocheilonema* Dies., 1861, renamed.

Definition.—Ascaroidea ? : insufficiently described ; body very long and filiform, with three large thick incised lips. Male :

posterior extremity bent and blunt. Female : posterior extremity straight ; vulva in the anterior part of the body. Real habitat unknown.

Type species : *T. megalochilum* (Dies., 1851). ♂ 25–37 mm., ♀ 50–60 mm. In *Zacholus austriacus*. Probably not true host.

> Syn., *Schizocheilonema megalochilum* (Dies., 1851) Dies., 1861, renamed.
> *Filaria megalochila* Dies., 1851.

Refs. 123, 125.

Genus EUSTOMA Beneden, 1870.

The type species is *E. truncata* Beneden, 1870. In *Raja clavata*. No description is given, but two drawings of the anterior extremity from which it is impossible to place the worm.

Ref. 50.

Genus PROTOSTRONGYLUS Leiper, 1908.

A genus belonging to the Subfamily *Metastrongylinæ*. No species is mentioned and no description given.

Ref. 275.

Genus DISCOPHORUS Mehlis in Creplin, 1844, not DISCOPHORA Boisduval, 1836.

The only species mentioned is *Discophorus tenax* Meh'is in Creplin, 1844. In *Raja clavata*. This is apparently a nomen nudum except for the host.

Ref. 115.

Genus DITRACHYCEROS Hermann in Sultzer, 1801.

> Syn., *Ditrachycerosoma* Brera, 1809.
> *Diceras* Rud., 1810, not Lam., 1805.

The only species mentioned is *D. rude* Rud., 1810. In man. This is apparently not a parasite.

Ref. 477.

Genus TIPASELLA ? Seurat, 1921.

The only reference to this genus which we have been able to find is that of Seurat, 1921, who refers to it as belonging to the *Filariidæ*. The only details given are that the œsophagus is divided, that the female is amphidelphys, and that the male is without caudal alæ. No species is mentioned.

Ref. 562.

Genus PIGURIS Schlotthauber, 1860.

The only species mentioned is *Piguris reticulata* Schlotthauber, 1860. In *Equus caballus*. Practically no description is given of the single female specimen found.

Refs. 398, 479.

Genus PHLYCTAINOPHORA Steiner, 1921.

Definition.—This generic name was given to a remarkable ? nematode *Phlyctainophora lamnæ*, found between the hyoman-

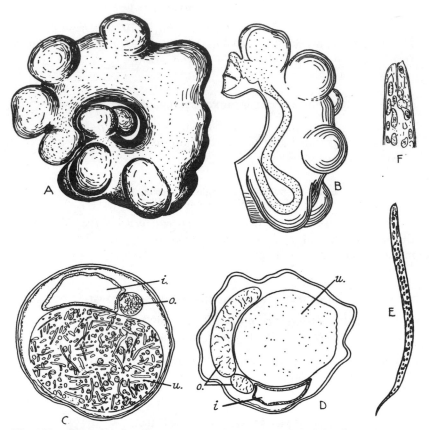

Fig. 307.—*Phlyctainophora lamnæ.* A. Whole worm seen from left side. B. Anterior end seen from left side. C and D. Transverse sections. *i*, intestine; *u*, uterus filled with larvæ; *o*, ovary. E. Larva. F. Larva, anterior extremity. (After Steiner.)

dibula arch and skull of a shark (*Lamna cornubica*). Only a single female was found; it had the appearance of a rolled-up stout cylinder provided on each subdorsal plane with an almost symmetrical series of fifteen large spherical projections recognizable to the naked eye. In addition, at what was apparently the anterior end, was an unpaired spherical swelling, and at the posterior end a pair of spherical swellings. The cuticle covering both the body and swellings was smooth. On the unpaired anterior swelling was what the author took to be a mouth-opening, and at the other end was an anus. Little could be made of the internal structure ; sections showed the body to be full of .sexual tubes loaded with embryos, and a delicate alimentary tube. The length of the adult female was 17 mm. and that of the embryos 330–350 μ.

Ref. 587a.

Collective Group Names for Immature Nematodes.

Agamonema Diesing, 1851.

A collective group for immature nematodes in fishes.

Agamofilaria Stiles, 1907.

A collective group for immature *Filarioidea*.

Microfilaria Cobbold, 1880.

A collective group for young larval *Filarioidea*, especially when found in the blood.

Agamospirura Henry and Sisoff, 1913.

A collective group for immature *Spiruroidea*.

Agamascaris Steiner, 1924.

A collective group for immature *Ascaroidea*.

EXPLANATORY NOTES

In order to avoid misconception, the sense in which a number of the terms found in the preceding pages are used is here defined.

Chitin.—This term is used in a rather broad sense as representing a substance harder than cuticle, and without intimating that it is chemically identical with the chitin of arthropods.

Extremity.—This word is used in a specialized sense ; " anterior extremity " referring to the head-end, and " posterior extremity " to the tail-end.

Middle.—This refers to the equatorial middle and not to the mid-line.

Inner and Internal.—These imply axial ; *e.g.* the inner surface of a lip means the buccal surface.

Œsophagus divided into Two Parts.—This implies tandem-division into anterior and posterior portions.

To prevent confusion which might arise from the different terminology used by various authors for the rays of the strongyl bursa, we have lettered the individual rays of the bursa of *Strongylus equinus* (Fig. 10) and those of a number of others strongyls (Figs. 16, 23, 25, 31, etc.). It should be noted that ventro-ventral + latero-ventral = anterior cleft or doubled, of the French authors; externo-laternal = antero-lateral ; medio-lateral + postero-lateral = median cleft or doubled ; external-dorsal = postero-external ; dorsal = posterior.

Whilst no type species is indicated in the lists of species in the various subgenera, the type species is always placed first in the list.

In the host names we have usually adopted the spelling of the author quoted, as we do not wish to appear to decide points of nomenclature for hosts. In many cases, in order to save printing, we have simply given the generic name of the host and the use of " sp." or " spp." consequently does not necessarily mean that the species is undetermined. The full name of the type hosts of the various species, as stated by the original authors, is given in the alphabetical list of species at the end of the volume.

INDEX OF GENERIC NAMES AND SYNONYMS

PAGE

ABBREVIATA Travassos, 1919 355
ABOMESI Simmonds, 1881. . . . Vide HÆMONCHUS Cobb, 1898 . .
ACANTHOCHEILONEMA Cobbold, 1870 Vide DIPETALONEMA Diesing, 1861.
ACANTHOCHEILUS Molin, 1858. 287
ACANTHOPHORUS Linstow, 1876 . . Vide TETRAMERES Creplin, 1846 .
ACHEILOSTOMA Leiper, 1911 49
ACUARIA Bremser, 1811 . . . . *ANTHURIS* Rudolphi, 1819 . . . 327
                                CHEILOSPIRURA Diesing, 1861 . .
                                DISPHARAGUS Dujardin, 1845 . .
                                SPIROPTERA Rudolphi, 1819 . . .
ACUARIA (Bremser, 1811) Railliet, Subgenus of ACUARIA Bremser, 1811. 330
  Henry, and Sisoff, 1912.
AFRICANA Travassos, 1920. 225
AGAMASCARIS Steiner, 1924 . . . Group name 449
AGAMOFILARIA Stiles, 1907. . . . Group name 449
AGAMONEMA Diesing, 1851. . . . Group name 449
AGAMOSPIRURA Henry and Sisoff, 1913 Group name 449
AGCHYLOSTOMA Dubini, 1843 . . Vide ANCYLOSTOMA (Dubini, 1843)
                                  Creplin, 1845 . . . . . .
AGRIOSTOMUM Railliet, 1902 95
ALÆURIS Thapar, 1925. 203
ALFORTIA Railliet, 1923 . . . . Subgenus of STRONGYLUS Mueller,
                                  1780. 38
ALLODAPA Diesing, 1861 228
AMBLYONEMA Linstow, 1898 210
AMIDOSTOMUM Railliet and Henry,
  1909 153
AMIRA Lane, 1914 . . . . *KHALILIA* Neveu-Lemaire, 1924 . 82
AMPHIBIOPHILUS Skrjabin, 1916 154
AMPLICÆCUM Baylis, 1920. 278
AMULARIA Brera, 1810 . . . . Vide SETARIA Viborg, 1795 . . .
ANANCONUS Railliet and Henry, 1916 Vide COSMOCERCA Diesing, 1861 .
ANCHILOCEPHALI Brera, 1810 . . Vide SETARIA Viborg, 1795 . . .
ANCHYLOSTOMUM Diesing, 1851 . . Vide ANCYLOSTOMA (Dubini, 1843)
                                  Creplin, 1845 . . . . . .
ANCYLOSTOMA (Dubini, 1843) Creplin, *AGCHYLOSTOMA* Dubini, 1843 . . 91
  1845   *ANCHYLOSTOMUM* Diesing, 1851 .
                                  ANKYLOSTOMA Lutz, 1885 . . .
                                  DIPLOODON Molin, 1861 . . . .

Generic names in italics fall as synonyms, or as *nomina nuda*.

PAGE

ANCYLOSTOMA (Creplin, 1845) Lane, 1916   Subgenus of ANCYLOSTOMA (Dubini, 1843) Creplin, 1845 91

ANCYRACANTHOPSIS Diesing, 1861 369

ANCYRACANTHUS Diesing, 1838 364

ANCYRACANTHUS Schneider, 1866, not Diesing, 1838.   Vide SCHISTOPHORUS Railliet, 1916

ANGIOSTOMA Dujardin, 1845, in part   Vide RHABDIAS Stiles and Hassall, 1905. . . . .

ANGUSTICÆCUM Baylis, 1920 279

ANISAKIS Dujardin, 1845 . . . .   *CONOCEPHALUS* Diesing, 1861 . . 272
    PERITRACHELIUS Diesing, 1851 .

ANKYLOSTOMA Lutz, 1885 . . .   Vide ANCYLOSTOMA (Dubini, 1843) Creplin, 1845 . . . . . .

ANOMALA Travassos, 1919, not Samouelle, 1819   Subgenus of TANQUA Blanchard, 1904. 341

ANTHURIS Rudolphi, 1819 . . .   Vide ACUARIA Bremser, 1811 . .

APLECTA Railliet and Henry, 1916 .   Vide APLECTANA Railliet and Henry, 1916. . . . .

APLECTANA Railliet and Henry, 1916.   *APLECTA* Railliet and Henry, 1916. 208
    NEMATOXYS Schneider, 1866, in part

APROCTA Linstow, 1883 . . . .   *LISSONEMA* Linstow, 1903 . . . 404

ARDUENNA Railliet and Henry, 1911. 307

ARTHROCEPHALUS Ortlepp, 1925 107

ASCARIDA Mueller, 1880 . . .   Vide ASCARIDIA . . . . .

ASCARIDIA Dujardin, 1845 . . . .   ? *ASCARIDA* Mueller, 1880 . . . 266

ASCARIS Linnæus, 1758. . . . .   *FUSARIA* Zeder, 1800. 255
    LOMBRICOIDES Mérat, 1821 . .
    STOMACHIDA Pereboom, 1780 . .

ASCAROPHIS Beneden, 1871 . . .   *ASCAROPSIS* Power and Sedgwick, 1880. 385

ASCAROPS Beneden, 1873 386

ASCAROPSIS Power and Sedgwick, 1880.   Vide ASCAROPHIS Beneden, 1871 .

ASIFIA Lane, 1914 . . . . . .   Vide CHONIANGIUM Railliet, Henry, and Bauche, 1914 . . . . .

ASPICULURIS Schulz, 1924 188

ASPIDOCEPHALUS Diesing, 1851 . .   Vide ASPIDODERA Railliet and Henry, 1912 . . . . . .

ASPIDODERA Railliet and Henry, 1912   *ASPIDOCEPHALUS* Diesing, 1851 . 219

ASTOMUM Schlotthauber, 1860 . .   Vide TETRAMERES Creplin, 1846 .

ATRACTIS Dujardin, 1845 244

AUSTROSTRONGYLUS Chandler, 1924 137

BATHMOSTOMUM Railliet and Henry, 1909 104

BELASCARIS Leiper, 1907 . . . .   Vide TOXOCARA Stiles, 1905. . .

BOURGELATIA Railliet, Henry, and Bauche, 1919. 82

BRACHYCLONUS Railliet and Henry. 1910 99

PAGE

BREINLIA n.g. 400
BUISSONIA Neveu-Lemaire, 1924 80
BULBODACNITIS Lane, 1916 383
BUNOSTOMUM Railliet, 1902 . . . *BUSTOMUM* Lane, 1917 107
    MONODONTUS Molin, 1861, in part .
BUSTOMUM Lane, 1917 . . . . Vide BUNOSTOMUM Railliet, 1902 .

CALODIUM Dujardin, 1845 . . . Vide CAPILLARIA Zeder, 1800 . .
CAMALLANIDES Baylis and Daubney,
1922 379
CAMALLANUS Railliet and Henry, 1915 *CUCULLANUS* auctt., not Mueller,
    1777. 377
CAPILLARIA Zeder, 1800 . . . . *CALODIUM* Dujardin, 1845 . . . 23
    LINISCUS Dujardin, 1845 . . .
    THOMINX Dujardin, 1845 . . .
    TRICHOSOMA Rudolphi, 1819 . .
    TRICHOSOMUM Creplin, 1829 . .
CAPILLARIA (Zeder, 1800) Travassos, Subgenus of CAPILLARIA Zeder, 1800
1915 28
CAPSULARIA Zeder, 1800 . . . . Vide PORROCÆCUM Railliet and
    Henry, 1912 . . . . . .
CASTORSTRONGYLUS Chapin, 1925. 46
CEPHALACANTHUS Dies., 1853, not
Lac., 1802 386
CEPHALOSTRONGYLUS Irwin-Smith, Vide ORNITHOSTRONGYLUS Tra-
1920   vassos, 1914 . . . . . .
CERATOSPIRA Schneider, 1866. 322
CERCOFILARIA Kalantarian, 1924 . Vide MICIPSELLA Seurat, 1921 . .
CEYLANCYLOSTOMA Lane, 1916 . . Subgenus of ANCYLOSTOMA (Dubini,
    1843) Creplin, 1845 91
CHABERTIA Railliet and Henry, 1909. 89
CHANDLERELLA n.g 411
CHARACOSTOMUM Railliet, 1902 . . Vide GLOBOCEPHALUS Molin, 1861 .
CHEILOSPIRURA Diesing, 1861 . . Vide ACUARIA Bremser, 1811 . .
    Vide OXYSPIRURA Drasche, 1897 .
CHEILOSPIRURA (Dies., 1861) Railliet, Subgenus of ACUARIA Bremser, 1811
Henry, and Sisoff, 1912 331
CHEIRACANTHUS Diesing, 1838 . . Vide GNATHOSTOMA Owen, 1836 .
CHEVREUXIA Seurat, 1918 332
CHLAMYDONEMA Hegt, 1910 356
CHŒROSTRONGYLUS Gedoelst, 1923 . Subgenus of METASTRONGYLUS
    Molin, 1861. 160
CHONIANGIUM Railliet, Henry, and *ASIFIA* Lane, 1914 . . . . .
Bauche, 1914 40
CISSOPHYLLUS Railliet and Henry,
1912 241
CITELLINEMA Hall, 1916 151
CLOACINA Linstow, 1898 175
CLŒOASCARIS Baylis, 1923. 283
COBBOLDIA Leiper, 1910 . . . . Vide COBBOLDINA Leiper, 1911. .
COBBOLDINA Leiper, 1911 . . . *COBBOLDIA* Leiper, 1910 . . . 250

PAGE

COCHLUS Zeder, 1803 . . . . .   Vide GŒZIA Zeder, 1800 . . .

CODIOSTOMUM Railliet and Henry,
1911 45

CONOCEPHALUS Diesing, 1861, not   Vide ANISAKIS Dujardin, 1845 . .
Thunb., 1812 . . . .

CONOWEBERIA Ihle, 1922 . . . .   Subgenus of ŒSOPHAGOSTOMUM
Molin, 1861. 88

CONTORTOSPICULUM Skrjabin, 1917 .   *DICHEILONEMA* Diesing, 1861, in
part. 428
?*MONOPETALONEMA* Diesing, 1861,
in part . . . .

CONTRACÆCUM Railliet and Henry,   *KATHLEENA* Leiper and Atkinson,
1912   1914. 281

COOPERIA Ransom, 1907 131

CORONILLA Beneden, 1871 . . .   Vide PROLEPTUS Dujardin, 1845 .

CORONOFILARIA n.g. . . . . . .   ?*EUCAMPTUS* Dujardin, 1845 . . 409

COSMOCEPHALUS Molin, 1858 337

COSMOCERCA Diesing, 1861 . . .   *ANANCONUS* Railliet and Henry,
1916. 206
NEMATOXYS Schneider, 1866 . .

COSMOCERCELLA Steiner, 1924. 208

CRASSICAUDA Leiper and Atkinson, 1914 437

CRASSISOMA Alessandrini, 1909 .   Vide GLOBOCEPHALUS Molin, 1861.

CRATEROSTOMUM Boulenger, 1920 45

CRENOSOMA Molin, 1861 165

CROSSOCEPHALUS Railliet, 1909 . .   *PTEROCEPHALUS* Linstow, 1899,
not Schneider, 1887 250

CROSSOPHORUS Hemprich and Ehren-
berg, 1828 286

CRUZIA Travassos, 1917 . . . .   *OXYSOMA* Schneider, 1866, in part 242

CTENOCEPHALUS Linstow, 1904 . .   Vide TANQUA Blanchard, 1904 . .

CUCULLANUS O. F. Mueller, 1777 .   *DACNITIS* Dujardin, 1845 . . . 381
DICHELYNE Jägerskiöld, 1902 . .
OPHIOSTOMA Rudolphi, 1801, in
part . . . .
PLEURORHYNCHUS Rudolphi, 1801
PLEURORINCHUS Nau, 1787 . .
STELMIUS Dujardin 1845 . . .

CUCULLANUS auctt., not Mueller,   Vide CAMALLANUS Railliet and
1777   Henry, 1815 . . . . . .

CYATHOSTOMA E. Blanchard, 1849 .   Vide SYNGAMUS Siebold, 1835 . .

CYATHOSTOMUM Molin, 1861 . . .   Vide TRICHONEMA Cobbold, 1874 .

CYLICHNOSTOMUM Looss, 1901 . .   Vide TRICHONEMA Cobbold, 1874 .

CYLICOBRACHYTUS Cram, 1924 60

CYLICOCERCUS Ihle, 1922 . . . .   Subgenus of TRICHONEMA Cobbold,
1874. 58

CYLICOCYCLUS Ihle, 1922 . . . .   Subgenus of TRICHONEMA Cobbold,
1874. 58

CYLICODONTOPHORUS Ihle, 1922 . .   Subgenus of TRICHONEMA Cobbold,
1874. 59

CYLICOSPIRURA Vevers, 1922 294

PAGE

CYLICOSTEPHANUS Ihle, 1922 . . .   *TRICHONEMA* (Cobbold, 1874) Le
                                    Roux, 1924 . . . . .
                                    Subgenus of TRICHONEMA Cobbold,
                                    1874.   57
CYLICOSTOMIAS Cram, 1925   56
CYLICOSTOMUM Railliet, 1901 . .   Vide TRICHONEMA Cobbold, 1874 .
CYLICOSTOMUM (Railliet, 1901) Ihle,   Vide TRICHONEMA (Cobbold, 1874).
    1922.
CYLICOTETRAPEDON Ihle, 1925 . .   Subgenus of TRICHONEMA Cobbold,
                                    1874   59
CYLICOTOICHUS Cram, 1924   60
CYLINDROPHARYNX Leiper, 1911   64
CYRNEA Seurat, 1914   299
CYRTOSOMUM Gedoelst, 1919   249
CYSTIDICOLA Fischer, 1798 . . .   *ANCYRACANTHUS* Schneider, 1866,
                                    in part, not Diesing, 1838 . .   322
                                    FISSULA Lamarck, 1801 . . . .
                                    OPHIOSTOMA Rudolphi, 1801 . .
                                    PSEUDANCYRACANTHUS Skrjabin,
                                    1923. . . . .
CYSTOCEPHALUS Railliet, 1895 . .   Vide GLOBOCEPHALUS Molin, 1861 .
CYSTOOPSIS Zykov, 1902 . . . .   Vide CYSTOPSIS Wagner, 1867 . .
CYSTOPSIS Wagner, 1867 . . . .   *CYSTOOPSIS* Zykov, 1902 . . .   444

DACNITIS Dujardin, 1845 . . . .   Vide CUCULLANUS Mueller, 1777 .
DACNITOIDES Ward and Magath, 1916   384
DECRUSIA Lane, 1914   38
DECRUSIA (Lane, 1914) Railliet, 1923   Subgenus of STRONGYLUS Mueller,
                                    1780.   38
DELAFONDIA Railliet, 1923 . . .   Subgenus of STRONGYLUS Mueller,
                                    1780.   38
DELETROCEPHALUS Diesing, 1851   172
DERAÏOPHORONEMA Romanovitch,   Vide DIPETALONEMA Diesing, 1861 .
    1916.
DERMATOPALLARYA Skrjabin, 1924   211
DERMATOXYS Schneider, 1866   189
DERMOFILARIA Rivolta, 1884 . .   Vide HABRONEMA Diesing, 1861 .
DESMIDOCERCA Skrjabin, 1916   321
DESMIDOCERCELLA n.g..   321
DIAPHANOCEPHALUS Diesing, 1851   111
DICENTROCEPHALUS Diesing, 1861 .   Vide DIKENTROCEPHALUS Wedl, 1855
DICERAS Rud., 1810 . . . . .   Vide DITRACHYCEROS Hermann in
                                    Sultzer, 1801 . . . . . .
DICHEILONEMA Diesing, 1861   437
DICHEILONEMA Diesing, 1861, in   Vide CONTORTOSPICULUM Skrjabin,
    part.   1917. . . . .
DICHELYNE Jägerskiöld, 1902 . .   Vide CUCULLANUS Mueller, 1777 .
DICTYOCAULUS Railliet and Henry,
    1907   161
DIKENTROCEPHALUS Wedl, 1855 . .   *DICENTROCEPHALUS* Dies., 1861 .   387
DIOCTOPHYME Collet-Meygret, 1802 .   *EUSTRONGYLUS* Diesing, 1851 . .   177

PAGE

DIPETALONEMA Diesing, 1861 . . .   *ACANTHOCHEILONEMA* Cobbold,
                                     1870.   425
                                   DERAÏOPHORONEMA Romanovitch,
                                     1916 . . . .
DIPLOODON Molin, 1861 . . . .   Vide ANCYLOSTOMA (Dubini, 1843)
                                     Creplin, 1845 . . . . . .
DIPLOTRIÆNA Railliet and Henry,   *TRIPLOTRIÆNA* Connal, 1912 . .   432
  1909.
DIROFILARIA Railliet and Henry, 1911   393
DISCOPHORUS Mehlis in Creplin,
  1844   447
DISPHARAGUS Dujardin, 1845 . .   Vide ACUARIA Bremser, 1811 . .
DISPHARYNX Railliet, Henry, and   Subgenus of ACUARIA Bremser, 1811 331
  Sisoff, 1912.
DITRACHYCEROS Hermann in Sultzer, *DICERAS* Rud., 1810   447
  1801.   *DITRACHYCEROSOMA* Brera, 1809 .
DITRACHYCEROSOMA Brera, 1809 .   Vide DITRACHYCEROS Hermann in
                                     Sultzer, 1801 . . . . . .
DOCHMIUS Dujardin, 1845 . . .   Vide UNCINARIA Froelich, 1789. .
DOCHMOIDES Cameron, 1924 . . .   Vide UNCINARIA Froelich, 1789. .
DRACUNCULUS Reichard, 1759 . .   *VENA* Gallandat, 1773   442
                                   VERMICULUS Dunglison, 1895 . .
DUJARDINIA Gedoelst, 1916   275

ECHINOCEPHALUS Molin, 1858 . .   *CHEIRACANTHUS* Linstow, 1904,
                                     in part, not Diesing, 1838 . .   342
ECHINONEMA Linstow, 1898 . . .   *HOPLOCEPHALUS* Linstow, 1898 .   347
ECHINOPHARYNX Thapar, 1925 . .   Vide SAURICOLA Chapin, 1924 . .
ECHINURIA Solowiow, 1912 . . .   *HAMANNIA* Railliet, Henry, and
                                     Sisoff, 1912   331
ELÆOPHORA Railliet and Henry, 1912   414
ELAPHOCEPHALUS Molin, 1860.   438
ENTEROBIUS Leach, 1853 . . . .   *FUSARELLA* Seurat, 1916 . . .   186
                                   LUMBRICULUS Aldrovande ;
                                     Blanchard, 1889 . . . . .
                                   OXYURIAS Stiles, 1905 . . . .
EPOMIDIOSTOMUM Skrjabin, 1916   155
EQUINURBIA Lane, 1914   39
EUCAMPTUS Dujardin, 1845 . . .   Vide CORONOFILARIA n.g. . . .
EUCOLEUS Dujardin, 1845   29
EUCYATHOSTOMUM Molin, 1861   84
EUFILARIA Seurat, 1921   406
EUMONODONTUS Railliet and Henry,   *MONODONTUS* Molin, 1861, not
  1910.   Monodonta Lamarck, 1799 . .   99
                                   Vide NECATOR Stiles, 1903 . . .
EUSTOMA Beneden, 1870   447
EUSTRONGYLIDES Jaegerskiöld, 1909   178
EUSTRONGYLUS Diesing, 1851 . .   Vide DIOCTOPHYME Collet-Meygret,
                                     1802 . . . .
EVANSIA Railliet, Henry, and   Vide QUILONIA Lane, 1914 . . .
  Joyeux, 1913.

PAGE

FALCAUSTRA Lane, 1915 . . . .   Vide SPIRONOURA Leidy, 1856 . .

FILARIA Mueller, 1787   390

FILAROIDES Beneden, 1858   . ′   439

FISSULA Lamarck, 1801 . . . .   Vide CYSTIDICOLA Fischer, 1798 .

FLORENCIOIA Travassos, 1919 . .   Vide SPIRONOURA Leidy, 1856 . .

FOLEYELLA Seurat, 1917   395

FUSARELLA Seurat, 1916 . . . .   Vide ENTEROBIUS Leach, 1853 .

FUSARIA Zeder, 1800 . . . . .   Vide ASCARIS Linnæus, 1758 . .

GAIGERIA Railliet and Henry, 1910   101

GALEICEPS Railliet, 1916   443

GALONCUS Railliet, 1918   94

GANGULETERAKIS Lane, 1914   218

GILSONIA Gedoelst, 1919 . . . .   Vide HADJELIA Seurat, 1916 . .

GIRETERAKIS Lane, 1917   219

GLOBOCEPHALOIDES n.g.   173

GLOBOCEPHALUS Molin, 1861 . . .   *CHARACOSTOMUM* Railliet, 1902 .   48
                                   CRASSISOMA Alessandrini, 1909 .
                                   CYSTOCEPHALUS Railliet, 1895 .
                                   RAILLIETOSTRONGYLUS Lane, 1923 .

GNATHOSTOMA Owen, 1836 . . .   *CHEIRACANTHUS* Diesing, 1838 .   339

GŒZIA Zeder, 1800 . . . . . .   *COCHLUS* Zeder, 1803   284
                                   LECANOCEPHALUS Diesing, 1839 .
                                   PRIONODERMA Rudolphi, 1809,
                                     not Cuvier, 1817 . . . . .
                                   Vide SPINITECTUS Fourment, 1883.

GONGYLONEMA Molin, 1857 . . .   *MYZOMIMUS* Stiles, 1892 . . .   313

GRAMMOCEPHALUS Railliet and Henry,
  1910   102

GRAMMOPHORA Gedoelst, 1916 . .   Vide KATANGA n.g. . . . .

GRAPHIDIOIDES Cameron, 1923   139

GRAPHIDIUM Railliet and Henry, 1909   134

GYALOCEPHALUS Looss, 1900   62

HABRONEMA Diesing, 1861 . . .   *DERMOFILARIA* Rivolta, 1884 . .   296

HADJELIA Seurat, 1916. . . . .   *GILSONIA* Gedoelst, 1919 . . .   301

HÆMONCHUS Cobb, 1898 . . . .   ?*ABOMESI* Simmonds, 1881 . .   122

HÆMOSTRONGYLUS Railliet and Henry,
  1907   164

HALOCERCUS Baylis and Daubney,
  1925   171

HAMANNIA Railliet, Henry, and   Subgenus of ACUARIA Bremser, 1811
  Sisoff, 1912.   Vide ECHINURIA Solowiow, 1912 .

HAMATOSPICULUM Skrjabin, 1916   395

HAMULARIA Treutler, 1793 . . .   Vide SETARIA Viborg, 1795 . . .

HAMULOFILARIA Chandler, 1924   398

HAPLONEMA Ward and Magath, 1916   326

HARTERTIA Seurat, 1914   305

HASTOSPICULUM Skrjabin, 1923   431

HEDRURIS Nitzsch, 1821 . . . .   *HETEROURA* Siebold, 1836 . . .   374
                                   SYNPLECTA Leidy, 1851 . . .

PAGE

HELICONEMA Travassos, 1919 355
HELIGMOSOMOIDES Hall, 1916 146
HELIGMOSOMUM Railliet and Henry,
1909 142
HELIGMOSTRONGYLUS Travassos, 1917 144
HELIGMUS Dujardin, 1845 288
HENRYELLA Neveu-Lemaire, 1924 . Vide MURSHIDIA Lane, 1914 . .
HEPATICOLA Hall, 1916 28
HETERAKIS Dujardin, 1845 215
HETEROCHEILUS Diesing, 1839 . . *LOBOCEPHALUS* Diesing, 1838
                                 [nomen nudum] 269
HETEROURA Siebold, 1836 . . . Vide HEDRURIS Nitzsch, 1821 . .
HETEROXYNEMA Hall, 1916 231
HEXAMETRA Travassos, 1919 266
HEXODONTOSTOMUM Ihle, 1920 . Vide POTERIOSTOMUM Quiel, 1919 .
HISTIOCEPHALUS Diesing, 1851 369
HISTIOSTRONGYLUS Molin, 1861 132
HOPLOCEPHALUS Linstow, 1898 . . Vide ECHINONEMA Linstow, 1898 .
HOPLODONTOPHORUS Turner, 1921 234
HYOSTRONGYLUS Hall, 1921 120
HYPOSTOMUM Stewart, 1898 . . Vide ŒSOPHAGOSTOMUM Molin, 1861
HYSTERACRUM Railliet and Henry,   Subgenus of ŒSOPHAGOSTOMUM
1913. . . . .   Molin, 1861 88
HYSTEROTHYLACIUM Ward and   Vide RAPHIDASCARIS Railliet and
Magath, 1916. . . . . . .   Henry, 1915 . . . . . .
HYSTRICHIS Dujardin, 1845 180

ICHTHYONEMA Diesing, 1861 . . Vide PHILOMETRA Costa, 1845 . .
ICHTHYOSPIRURA Skrjabin, 1917 . Vide RHABDOCHONA Railliet, 1916 .
ICOSIELLA Seurat, 1917 424
IMPALAIA Monnig, 1924 143

KALICEPHALUS Molin, 1861 . . . DIAPHANOCEPHALUS Diesing, 1851,
                                 in part 113
KATANGA n.g. . . . . *GRAMMOPHORA* Gedoelst, 1916 . 416
KATHLANIA Lane, 1914. . . . . *OXYSOMA* Schneider, 1866, in part 235
                                 PSEUDOHETERAKIS Travassos, 1917
KATHLEENA Leiper and Atkinson,   Vide CONTRACÆCUM Railliet and
1914. . . . .   Henry, 1912 . . . . . .
KHALILIA Neveu-Lemaire, 1924 . . Vide AMIRA Lane, 1914 . . . .
KILULUMA Skrjabin, 1916 70

LABIDURIS Schneider, 1866 247
LABIOSTRONGYLUS n.g. 67
LAGOCHILASCARIS Leiper, 1909 260
LAPHYCTES Dujardin, 1845 . . . Vide RICTULARIA Froelich, 1802 .
LECANOCEPHALUS Diesing, 1839 . . Vide GŒZIA Zeder, 1800 . . . .
LEIPERENIA Khalil, 1922 246
LEIURIS Leuckart, 1850 . . . . Vide PHYSOCEPHALUS Diesing, 1861
LEMDANA Seurat, 1917 402

PAGE

LEPTODERA Schneider, 1866, in part, not Dujardin, 1845.   Vide RHABDIAS Stiles and Hassall, 1905 . . . .

LEPTOSOMA Travassos, 1919 355

LEPTURIS Schlotthauber, 1860 . . Vide OXYURIS Rudolphi, 1803 . .

LIBYOSTRONGYLUS Lane, 1923 119

LINISCUS Dujardin, 1845 . . . Vide CAPILLARIA Zeder, 1800 . .

LIORHYNCHUS Rudolphi, 1801 . . Vide SPINITECTUS Fourment, 1883.

LISSONEMA Linstow, 1903 . . . Vide APROCTA Linstow, 1883 . .

LITOMOSA n.g. . . . . *LITOSOMA* Beneden, 1873 . . . 398

LITOSOMA Beneden, 1873 . . . . Vide LITOMOSA n.g. . . . . .

LOA Stiles, 1905 417

LOBOCEPHALUS Diesing, 1838 . . Vide HETEROCHEILUS Diesing, 1839

LOMBRICOIDES Mérat, 1821 . . . Vide ASCARIS Linnæus, 1758 . .

LUMBRICULUS Aldrovande ; Blanchard, 1889.   Vide ENTEROBIUS Leach, 1853 . .

MACRACIS Gedoelst, 1916 191

MACROPOSTRONGYLUS n.g. 75

MASTIGODES Zeder, 1800 . . . . Vide TRICHURIS Roederer, 1761 .

MASTOPHORUS Diesing, 1853 387

MAUPASIELLA Seurat, 1913 . . . Vide MAUPASINA Seurat, 1913 . .

MAUPASINA Seurat, 1913 . . . . *MAUPASIELLA* Seurat, 1913 . . 232

MECISTOCIRRUS (Railliet and Henry, 1912) Neveu-Lemaire, 1914. 138

MEHDIELLA Seurat, 1918 200

MEMPHISIA Khalil, 1922 . . . . Vide MURSHIDIA Lane, 1914 .

METABRONEMA n.g. 299

METASTRONGYLUS Molin, 1861 158

METASTRONGYLUS (Molin, 1861) Gedoelst, 1923.   Subgenus of METASTRONGYLUS Molin, 1861 160

MICIPSELLA Seurat, 1921 . . . . *CERCOFILARIA* Kalantarian, 1924 . 418

MICROCEPHALUS Romanovitch, 1915   Vide NEMATODIRELLA n.g. . . .

MICROFILARIA Cobbold, 1880 . . . Group name 449

MICROPLEURA Linstow, 1906 434

MICROTETRAMERES Travassos, 1915 .   Subgenus of TETRAMERES Creplin, 1846. 364

MOLINEUS Cameron, 1923 125

MONHYSTERIDES Baylis and Daubney, 1922 252

MONODONTELLA n.g. 109

MONODONTUS Molin, 1861 . . . Vide BUNOSTOMUM Railliet, 1902 .

Vide EUMONODONTUS Railliet and Henry, 1910 . . . . . .

Vide NECATOR Stiles, 1903 . . .

MONOPETALONEMA Diesing, 1861 438

MONOPETALONEMA Diesing, 1861, in part.   Vide CONTORTOSPICULUM Skrjabin, 1917. . . . .

MULTICÆCUM Baylis, 1923 283

MURSHIDIA Lane, 1914 . . . . *HENRYELLA* Neveu-Lemaire, 1924 . 78

MEMPHISIA Khalil, 1922 . . . .

PAGE

MURSHIDIA Lane, 1914 . . . . *PTERIDOPHARYNX* Lane, 1921 . .   78
                                   PTERYGOPHARYNX   Witenberg,
                                   1925. . . . .

MUSPICEA Sambon, 1925   445
MYZOMIMUS Stiles, 1892 . . . . Vide GONGYLONEMA Molin, 1857 .

NECATOR Stiles, 1903 . . . . . *?EUMONODONTUS*   Railliet   and
                                   Henry, 1910   97
                                   ?MONODONTUS Molin, 1861, in part
NEMATEVANSIA Ihle, 1919 . . . Vide QUILONIA Lane, 1914 . . . .
NEMATODIRELLA n.g. . . . . . *MICROCEPHALUS*   Romanovitch,
                                   1915.   140
NEMATODIRUS Ransom, 1907   135
NEMATOSPIRA Walton, 1923   147
NEMATOXYS Schneider, 1866 . . . Vide   APLECTANA   Railliet   and
                                   Henry, 1916 . . . . . .
                                   Vide COSMOCERCA Diesing, 1861 .
NIPPOSTRONGYLUS Lane, 1923   147
NUMIDICA Barreto, 1917   229

OBELISCOIDES Graybill, 1924 . . . *OBELISCUS* Graybill, 1923 . . .   129
OBELISCUS Graybill, 1923 . . . Vide OBELISCOIDES Graybill, 1924.
OCCIPITODONTUS Ortlepp, 1923   114
ODONTOGETON Allgén, 1921   212
ŒSOPHAGODONTUS   Railliet   and *PSEUDOSCLEROSTOMUM*   Quiel,
   Henry, 1902.   1919.   42
ŒSOPHAGOSTOMUM Molin, 1861 . . *HYPOSTOMUM* Stewart, 1898 . .   85
ŒSOPHAGOSTOMUM   (Molin,   1861) Subgenus of ŒSOPHAGOSTOMUM
   Railliet and Henry, 1913.   Molin, 1861   87
OLLULANUS Leuckart, 1865   148
ONCHOCERCA Diesing, 1841   413
ONCOPHORA Diesing, 1851   30
OPHIDASCARIS Baylis, 1921   262
OPHIOSTOMA Rudolphi, 1801 . . . Vide CUCULLANUS Mueller, 1777 .
                                   Vide CYSTIDICOLA Fischer, 1798 .
                                   Vide RICTULARIA Froelich, 1802 .
OPHIOSTOMUM Creplin, 1839 . . . Vide *OPHIOSTOMA* Rudolphi, 1801
OPHIOSTOMUM   Creplin,   1839,   of Vide SEURATUM Hall, 1916 . . .
   Seurat, 1915.
ORNEOASCARIS Skrjabin, 1916   264
ORNITHOSTRONGYLUS Travassos, 1914 *CEPHALOSTRONGYLUS*   Irwin-
                                   Smith, 1920   127
OSLERUS Hall, 1921   386
OSTERTAGIA Ransom, 1907   124
OSWALDOCRUZIA Travassos, 1917   126
OXYASCARIS Travassos, 1920   213
OXYNEMA Linstow, 1899   230
OXYSOMA Schneider, 1866 . . . Vide CRUZIA Travassos, 1917 . .
                                   Vide KATHLANIA Lane, 1914 . .
                                   Vide OXYSOMATIUM Railliet and
                                   Henry, 1913 . . . . . .

PAGE

OXYSOMATIUM Railliet and Henry, OXYSOMA Schneider, 1866, in part 203
1913.

OXYSPIRURA Drasche in Stossich, 1897 CHEILOSPIRURA Diesing, 1861, in
part 318

OXYURIAS Stiles, 1905 . . . . Vide ENTEROBIUS Leach, 1853 . .

OXYURIS Rudolphi, 1803 . . . . LEPTURIS Schlotthauber, 1860 . 183

OZOLAIMUS Dujardin, 1845 191

PAPILLOSETARIA Vevers, 1922 423

PARABRONEMA Baylis, 1921 335

PARACAMALLANUS n.g. 378

PARACIS Railliet and Henry, 1916 . Vide TACHYGONETRIA Wedl, 1862 .

PARAFILARIA n.g. 391

PARANISAKIS Baylis, 1923 274

PARAQUILONIA Neveu-Lemaire, 1924. 74

PARASCARIS n.g.. 261

PARASPIDODERA Travassos, 1914 221

PASSALURUS Dujardin, 1845 185

PELECITUS Railliet and Henry, 1910 411

PERITRACHELIUS Diesing, 1851 . . Vide ANISAKIS Dujardin, 1845 . .

PHARURUS Leuckart, 1848 . . . Vide STENURUS Dujardin, 1845 .

PHARYNGODON Diesing, 1861 193

PHARYNGOSTRONGYLUS n.g. 65

PHILOMETRA Costa, 1845 . . . . ICHTHYONEMA Diesing, 1861 . . 442

PHLYCTAINOPHORA Steiner, 1921 448

PHYSALOPTERA Rudolphi, 1819 351

PHYSOCEPHALUS Diesing, 1861 . . LEIURIS Leuckart, 1850 . . . 308

PIGURIS Schlotthauber, 1860 448

PLEURORHYNCHUS Rudolphi, 1801 . Vide CUCULLANUS Mueller, 1777 .

PLEURORINCHUS Nau, 1787 . . . Vide CUCULLANUS Mueller, 1777 .

PNEUMONEMA Johnston, 1916 346

POLITOSPICULUM Skrjabin, 1916 396

POLYDELPHIS Dujardin, 1845 265

PORROCÆCUM Railliet and Henry, 1912 ?CAPSULARIA Zeder, 1800 . . . 279
TERRANOVA Leiper and Atkinson,
1914. . . . .

POTERIOSTOMUM Quiel, 1919 . . . HEXODONTOSTOMUM Ihle, 1920 . 60

PRIONODERMA Rudolphi, 1809, not Vide GŒZIA Zeder, 1800 . . .
Cuvier, 1817.

PRIONOSTEMMA Gendre, 1921 . . Vide SEURATIA Skrjabin, 1916 . .

PROBSTMAYRIA Ransom, 1907 204

PROCAMALLANUS Baylis, 1923 379

PROLEPTUS Dujardin, 1845 . . . CORONILLA Beneden, 1871 . . 357
SPIROPTERINA Beneden, 1858 .

PROSTHECOSACTER Diesing, 1851 . Vide STENURUS Dujardin, 1845 .

PROTERACRUM Railliet and Henry, Subgenus of ŒSOPHAGOSTOMUM
1913. Molin, 1861 88

PROTOSPIRURA Seurat, 1914 304

PROTOSTRONGYLUS Leiper, 1908
[nom. nud.] 447

PROTOZOOPHAGA Travassos, 1923 190

PAGE

PSEUDALIUS Dujardin, 1845 168
PSEUDANCYRACANTHUS Skrjabin, Vide CYSTIDICOLA Fischer, 1798 .
1923. Vide RHABDOCHONA Railliet, 1916 .
PSEUDASPIDODERA Baylis and Daub-
ney, 1922 220
PSEUDOHETERAKIS Travassos, 1917 . Vide KATHLANIA Lane, 1914 . .
PSEUDORHABDITIS Perroncito, 1880 Vide STRONGYLOIDES Grassi, 1879.
PSEUDOSCLEROSTOMUM Quiel, 1919 . Vide ŒSOPHAGODONTUS Railliet and
Henry, 1902 . . . . . .
PTERIDOPHARYNX Lane, 1921 . . Vide MURSHIDIA Lane, 1914 . .
PTEROCEPHALUS Linstow, 1899 . . Vide CROSSOCEPHALUS Railliet, 1909
PTERYGIFER Linstow, 1907 444
PTERYGODERMATITES Wedl, 1861 . Vide RICTULARIA Froelich, 1802 .
PTERYGOPHARYNX Witenberg, 1925 Misprint for PTERIDOPHARYNX
Lane, 1921 . . . .

QUILONIA Lane, 1914 . . . . . EVANSIA Railliet, Henry, and
Joyeux, 1913 71
NEMATEVANSIA Ihle, 1919 . .

RAILLIETOSTRONGYLUS Lane, 1923 . Vide GLOBOCEPHALUS Molin, 1861 .
RANSOMUS Hall, 1916 41
RAPHIDASCARIS Railliet and Henry, HYSTEROTHYLACIUM Ward and
1915. Magath, 1916 274
RHABDIAS Stiles and Hassall, 1905 . ANGIOSTOMA Dujardin, 1845, in
part 17
LEPTODERA Schneider, 1866, in
part, not Dujardin, 1845. . .
RHABDONEMA Leuckart, 1879, pre-
occupied . . . .
RHABDOCHONA Railliet, 1916 . . . ?ICHTHYOSPIRURA Skrjabin, 1917 . 324
PSEUDANCYRACANTHUS Skrjabin,
1923, in part . . . . . .
RHABDONEMA Leuckart, 1879 . . Vide RHABDIAS Stiles and Hassall,
1905. . . . .
RICTULARIA Froelich, 1802 . . . LAPHYCTES Dujardin, 1845 . . 344
OPHIOSTOMA Rudolphi, 1801, in
part . . . .
OPHIOSTOMUM Creplin, 1839, in
part . . . .
PTERYGODERMATITES Wedl, 1861
RICTULARIOIDES Hall, 1916 345
RONDONIA Travassos, 1919 248
RUSGUNIELLA Seurat, 1919 333

SAURICOLA Chapin, 1924 . . . . ECHINOPHARYNX Thapar, 1925 . 61
SAUROSITUS Macfie, 1924 407
SCHISTOROPHUS Railliet, 1916 . . ANCYRACANTHUS Schneider, 1866,
in part, not Diesing, 1838 . . 366
TETRACANTHUS Hemprich and
Ehrenberg, 1866, preoccupied .

PAGE

SCHIZOCHEILONEMA Diesing, 1861 . Vide TRICHEILONEMA Diesing, 1861

SCIADIOCARA Skrjabin, 1916 367

SCLEROSTOMA Rudolphi, 1809 . . Vide STRONGYLUS Mueller, 1780 .

SCLEROTRICHUM Rudolphi, 1819 30

SERRADACNITIS Lane, 1916 383

SERRATOSPICULUM Skrjabin, 1916 427

SERTICEPS Railliet, 1916 373

SETARIA Viborg, 1795 . . . . . . *?HAMULARIA* Brera, 1810 . . . 422

?ANCHILOCEPHALI Brera, 1810 . .

?HAMULARIA Treutler, 1793 . .

?TENTACULARIA Zeder, 1800 . .

SEURATIA Skrjabin, 1916 . . . . *PRIONOSTEMMA* Gendre, 1921 . . 334

SEURATUM Hall, 1916 . . . . . *OPHIOSTOMUM* Creplin, 1839, of

Seurat, 1915 349

SIMONDSIA Cobbold, 1864 309

SOLENONEMA Diesing, 1861 439

SONSINIA Baylis and Daubney, 1922 Vide SPINICAUDA Travassos, 1920 .

SPECTATUS Travassos, 1923 . . . Vide SPIRONOURA Leidy, 1856 . .

SPINICAUDA Travassos, 1920 . . . *SONSINIA* Baylis and Daubney,

1922 223

SPINITECTUS Fourment, 1883 . . . *GŒZIA* Zeder, 1800, in part . . . 348

LIORHYNCHUS Rudolphi, 1801, in

part . . . .

SPIROCERCA Railliet and Henry, 1911 295

SPIRONOURA Leidy, 1856 . . . . *FALCAUSTRA* Lane, 1915 . . . 237

FLORENCIOIA Travassos, 1919 . .

SPECTATUS Travassos, 1923 . .

SPIRURA Diesing, 1861, not Blan-

chard, 1849 . . . . .

SPIROPTERA Rudolphi, 1819 . . . Vide ACUARIA Bremser, 1811 . .

Vide SPIRURA Blanchard, 1849 .

SPIROPTERINA Beneden, 1858 . . Vide PROLEPTUS Dujardin, 1845 .

SPIROSTRONGYLUS n.g. 68

SPIROXYS Schneider, 1866 302

SPIRURA Blanchard, 1849 . . . . *SPIROPTERA* Rud., 1819, in part . 292

SPIRURA Diesing, 1861, not Blan- Vide SPIRONOURA Leidy, 1856 . .

chard, 1849.

SPLENDIDOFILARIA Skrjabin, 1923 420

SQUAMANEMA Thiel, 1925 315

SQUAMOFILARIA Schmerling, 1925 411

STELMIUS Dujardin, 1845 . . . Vide CUCULLANUS Mueller, 1777 .

STENODES Dujardin, 1845 253

STENURUS Dujardin, 1845 . . . . *PHARURUS* Leuckart, 1848 . . . 168

PROSTHECOSACTER Diesing, 1851

STEPHANURUS Diesing, 1839 50

STERCORALIS Tanaka, 1910 . . . Vide STRONGYLOIDES Grassi, 1879 .

STOMACHIDA Pereboom, 1780 . . Vide ASCARIS Linnæus, 1758 . .

STREPTOCARA Railliet, Henry, and *YSERIA* Gedoelst, 1919 . . . . .

Sisoff, 1912 359

STREPTOPHARAGUS Blanc, 1912 311

STRONGYLACANTHA Beneden, 1873 95

PAGE

STRONGYLOIDES Grassi, 1879 . . . *PSEUDORHABDITIS* Perroncito, 1880. 18
STERCORALIS Tanaka, 1910 . .

STRONGYLURIS A. Mueller, 1894 221
STRONGYLUS Mueller, 1780, Gœze, *SCLEROSTOMA* Rud., 1809.
1782. 37
STRONGYLUS (Gœze, 1782) Railliet, Subgenus of STRONGYLUS Mueller,
1923. 1780. 38
SUBULURA Molin, 1860 226
SYNGAMUS Siebold, 1836 . . . . *CYATHOSTOMA* E. Blanchard, 1849. 156

SYNHIMANTUS Railliet, Henry, and Subgenus of ACUARIA Bremser, 1811
Sisoff, 1912 331
SYNPLECTA Leidy, 1851 . . . . Vide HEDRURIS Nitzsch, 1821 . .
SYNTHETOCAULUS Railliet and Henry,
1907 162
SYPHACIA Seurat, 1916 195
SYPHACIELLA Monnig, 1924 209

TACHYGONETRIA Wedl, 1862 . . . *PARACIS* Railliet and Henry, 1916. 198
TANQUA Blanchard, 1904 . . . . *CTENOCEPHALUS* Linstow, 1904 . 340
TETRADENOS Linstow, 1904 . .
TENTACULARIA Zeder, 1800 . . . Vide SETARIA Viborg, 1795 . . .
TERNIDENS Railliet and Henry, 1909. 88
TERRANOVA Leiper and Atkinson, Vide PORROCÆCUM Railliet and
1914. Henry, 1912 . . . . . .
TETRACANTHUS Hemprich and Vide SCHISTOROPHUS Railliet, 1916.
Ehrenberg, 1866.
TETRACHEILONEMA Diesing, 1861 439
TETRADENOS Linstow, 1904 . . . Vide TANQUA Blanchard, 1904 . . .
TETRAGOMPHIUS Baylis and Daubney,
1923 105
TETRAMERES Creplin, 1846 . . . *ACANTHOPHORUS* Linstow, 1876 . 361
ASTOMUM Schlotthauber, 1860
TROPIDOCERCA Diesing, 1851 . .
TROPIDURUS Weigmann, 1835 . .
TROPISURUS Diesing, 1835 . . .
TETRAMERES (Creplin, 1846) Travassos, Subgenus of TETRAMERES Creplin,
1915. 1846. 363
THAMUGADIA Seurat, 1917 407
THEILERIANA Monnig, 1924 76
THELANDROS Wedl, 1862 192
THELAZIA Bosc, 1819 317
THELAZIA (Bosc, 1819) Travassos, 1918 Subgenus of THELAZIA Bosc, 1819 . 318
THELAZIELLA Travassos, 1918 . . Subgenus of THELAZIA Bosc, 1819 . 318
THOMINX Dujardin, 1845 . . . . . Vide CAPILLARIA Zeder, 1800 . .
THOMINX (Duj., 1845) Travassos, 1915. Subgenus of CAPILLARIA Zeder, 1800 28
THUBUNÆA Seurat, 1914 358
TIPASELLA ? Seurat, 1921 447
TONAUDIA Travassos, 1919 236

PAGE

TORQUATELLA n.g. 372
TORYNURUS Baylis and Daubney, 1925 171
TOXASCARIS Leiper, 1907 258
TOXOCARA Stiles, 1905 . . . . .   *BELASCARIS* Leiper, 1907 . . . 257
TRACHYPHARYNX Leiper, 1911 63
TRAVASSOSIUS Khalil, 1922 130
TRICHEILONEMA Diesing, 1861 . .   *SCHIZOCHEILONEMA* Diesing, 1861. 446
TRICHINA Owen, 1835 . . . .   Vide TRICHINELLA Railliet, 1895 .
TRICHINELLA Railliet, 1895 . . .   *TRICHINA* Owen, 1835 32
TRICHOCEPHALUS Schrank, 1788 .   Vide TRICHURIS Roederer, 1761 .
TRICHODES Linstow, 1874 . . .   Vide TRICHOSOMOIDES Railliet, 1895
TRICHOHELIX Ortlepp, 1922 121
TRICHONEMA Cobbold, 1874 . . .   *CYATHOSTOMUM* Molin, 1861, not
                                    Blanchard, 1849 54
                                  CYLICHNOSTOMUM Looss, 1901 .
                                  CYLICOSTOMUM Railliet, 1901 .
TRICHONEMA (Cobbold, 1874); not   *CYLICOSTOMUM* (Railliet, 1901)
   Le Roux, 1924.   Ihle, 1922 56
                                  Subgenus of TRICHONEMA Cobbold,
                                    1874. . . . .
TRICHONEMA (Cobbold, 1874) Le   Vide CYLICOSTEPHANUS Ihle, 1922.
   Roux, 1924.
TRICHOSOMA Rudolphi, 1819 . . .   Vide CAPILLARIA Zeder, 1800 . .
TRICHOSOMOIDES Railliet, 1895 . .   *TRICHODES* Linstow, 1874 . . . 32
TRICHOSOMUM Creplin, 1829 . . .   Vide CAPILLARIA Zeder, 1800 . .
TRICHOSTRONGYLUS Looss, 1905 118
TRICHURIS Roederer, 1761 . . .   *MASTIGODES* Zeder, 1800 . . . 21
                                  TRICHOCEPHALUS Schrank, 1788 .
TRIODONTOPHORUS Looss, 1902 . .   *TRIODONTUS* Looss, 1900 . . . 44
TRIODONTUS Looss, 1900 . . .   Vide TRIODONTOPHORUS Looss, 1902
TRIPLOTRIÆNA Connal, 1912 . .   Vide DIPLOTRIÆNA Railliet and
                                    Henry, 1909 . . . . . .
TRISPICULASCARIS Skrjabin, 1916 263
TROGLOSTRONGYLUS Vevers, 1922 164
TROPIDOCERCA Diesing, 1851 . .   Vide TETRAMERES Creplin, 1846 .
TROPIDURUS Weigmann, 1835 . .   Vide TETRAMERES Creplin, 1846 .
TROPISURUS Diesing, 1835 . . .   Vide TETRAMERES Creplin, 1846 .
TRYPANOXYURIS Vevers, 1923. 198
TURGIDA Travassos, 1919 355
TYPHLOPHORUS Linstow, 1906 271

UNCINARIA Froelich, 1789 . . . .   *DOCHMIUS* Dujardin, 1845 . . 101
                                  DOCHMOIDES Cameron, 1924 . .

VENA Gallandat, 1773 . . . . .   Vide DRACUNCULUS Reichard, 1759
VERMICULUS Dunglison, 1895 . .   Vide DRACUNCULUS Reichard, 1759
VEVERSIA Thapar, 1925 201
VIANNAIA Travassos, 1914 149
VIANNELLA Travassos, 1918 150
VIGUIERA Seurat, 1913 370

PAGE

WARRENIUS Hall, 1916 151

WELLCOMIA Sambon, 1907 198

WUCHERERIA Silvo Araujo, 1877 ;
 Seurat, 1921 401

YSERIA Gedoelst, 1919 . . . . Vide STREPTOCARA Railliet, Henry,
          and Sisoff, 1912 . . . . .

ZANCLOPHORUS Baylis and Daubney,
 1922 210

ZONIOLAIMUS Cobb, 1898 176

INDEX OF SPECIFIC NAMES

abbreviata Rud., 1819, t.h. Lacerta margaritacea. Physaloptera, p. 352.

abbreviata Rud., 1819, t.h. Motacilla stapazina. [Fil.]. Diplotriæna, p. 433.

abbreviatus Rud., 1819, t.h. Perca cirrosa. Cucullanus, p. 382.

abjecta Leidy, 1856, t.h. Psammophis flagelliformis. Physaloptera, p. 352.

abnormalis May, 1920, t.h. sheep and goats. Nematodirus, p. 136.

abstrusus Railliet, 1898, t.h. Felis dom. [Str.]. Synthetocaulus, p. 164.

acanthocephalica Molin, 1860, t.h. Sterna hirundo, S. caspica. [Spiropt.]. Schisto rophus, p. 367.

acanthocephalicus Molin, 1861, t.h. Ibis tubifex. Hystrichis, p. 181.

acanthocirratus Skrjabin, 1916, t.h. Ranidæ. Amphibiophilus, p. 155.

*acanthura Diesing, 1851, t.h. Lacerta muralis. [Asc.]. Pharyngodon, p. 193.

*acanthurus Diesing, 1861, in part. Pharyngodon, p. 193, and p. 194.

accipitri Skrjabin, 1916, t.h. Aquila imperialis. Gnathostoma, p. 340.

acipenseris del Lupo, 1898, t.h. Acipenser sturio. [Ichthyonema]. Philometra, p. 443.

acipenseris Wagner, 1867, t.h. Acipenser ruthenus. Cystopsis, p. 445.

aculeata Creplin, 1825, t.h. Tringa alpina. [Spiropt.]. Echinuria, p. 331.

aculeatum Travassos, 1917, t.h. Muridæ. Heligmosomum, p. 142.

aculeatus Linstow, 1879, t.h. Macacus cynomolgus. [Str.]. Œsophagostomum, p. 87.

acuminata Molin, 1860, t.h. Brycon falcatus. [Spiropt.]. Rhabdochona, p. 325.

acuminata Schrank, 1788, t.h. frogs. [Asc.]. Aplectana, p. 208.

acus Bloch, 1779, t.h. Esox sp. [Asc.]. Raphidascaris, p. 274.

acus Duj., 1845, t.h. an exotic mammal. Stenodes, p. 253.

acuticauda Linstow, 1901, t.h. Numida rikwæ. [Oxysoma]. Subulura, p. 227.

acuticauda Molin, 1860, t.h. Falco cachinans, etc. Physaloptera, p. 352.

acuticaudatum Kotlán, 1919, t.h. Equines. [Cylicost.]. Craterostomum, p. 45.

acuticeps Gedoelst, 1916, t.h. Chamæleon gracilis and C. dilepsis. [Het.]. Africana, p. 225.

acutissima Molin, 1860, t.h. Cuculus melacoryphus, Strix atricapilla. Subulura, p. 227.

acutus Duj., 1845, t.h. Raja clavata. Proleptus, p. 358.

*acutus Lundahl, 1848, t.h. Anas crecca, etc. [Str.]. Amidostomum, p. 153.

additictus Railliet, Henry, and Bauche, 1914, t.h. Elephas indicus. [Str.]. Decrusia, p. 38.

adersi Boulenger, 1920, t.h. donkey. [Cylicost.]. Trichonema, p. 55.

adunca Creplin, 1846, t.h. Colymbus septentrionalis, etc. [Spiropt.]. Cosmocephalus, p. 337.

adunca Rud., 1802, t.h. Clupea alosa. [Asc.]. Contracæcum, p. 282.

ægyptiaca Linstow, 1902, t.h. Ardea garzetta. [Het.]. Ascaridia, p. 266.

*ægyptiacum Railliet, 1923, t.h. Equines. Trichonema, p. 55.

æqualis Molin, 1858, t.h. Myrmecophaga jubata. [Fil.]. Solenonema, p. 439.

ærophila Linstow, 1906, t.h. Phœnicopterus roseus. [Spiropt.]. Aprocta, p. 405.

ærophila Skrjabin, 1916, t.h. Ardea cinerea, Thalacrocorax carbo. Desmidocerca, p. 321.

---

* Species marked thus fall as synonyms, or as *nomina nuda*.

In those cases in which a species has been removed from the genus in which it was first placed, the original genus is given in square brackets.

ærophilum Creplin, 1839, t.h. Canis vulpes. [Trichosomum]. Eucoleus, p. 29.

affine Leidy, 1856, t.h. Cistudo carolina. Spironoura, p. 239.

*affinis Gedoelst, 1916, t.h. Psammophis sibilans. Physaloptera, p. 354.

affinis Graybill, 1924, t.h. rabbit. Trichostrongylus, p. 119.

affinis Jägerskiöld, 1904, t.h. Vulpes niloticus. Rictularia, p. 345.

affinis Mégnin, 1895, t.h. Dolichotis patagonica. [Str.]. Graphidioides, p. 140.

*affinis Rud., 1802, t.h. Ovis aries. [Trichoc.]. Trichuris, p. 23.

affinis Rud., 1819, t.h. Fringilla sp. [Fil.]. Diplotriæna, p. 433.

affinis Seurat, 1916, t.h. Strix flammea. Acuaria, p. 328.

africana Gedoelst, 1916, t.h. Cinixys erosa. Labiduris, p. 247.

africana Gendre, 1909, t.h. Cinixys belliana. [Het.]. Africana, p. 225.

africana Lane, 1921, t.h. African elephant. Quilonia, p. 73.

africana Lane, 1921, t.h. African elephant. [Pteridopharynx]. Murshidia, p. 79.

africana Mönnig, 1924, t.h. Paraxerus cepapi, etc. [Leptosoma]. Physaloptera, p. 352.

africana Neveu-Lemaire, 1924, t.h. African rhinoceros. Buissonia, p. 81.

africana Thapar, 1924, t.h. Rhinoceros africanus. Kiluluma, p. 71.

africanum Baylis, 1921, t.h. Elephas africanus. Parabronema, p. 337.

africanum Taylor, 1924, t.h. Bufo regularis. Amplicæcum, p. 279.

africanus Jägerskiöld, 1909, t.h. Ardea goliath, etc. Eustrongylides, p. 179.

*africanus Looss, 1911, t.h. Anthropopithecus troglodytes. Necator, p. 99.

agamæ Macfie, 1924, t.h. Agama colonorum. Saurositus, p. 409.

agamæ Rodhain, 1906, t.h. Agama colonorum. [Fil.]. Foleyella, p. 395.

agilis Wedl, 1862, t.h. Crocodilus vulg. [Asc.]. Multicæcum, p. 284.

agoutii Neiva, Cunha, and Travassos, 1914, t.h. Dasyprocta agouti. Heligmosomum, p. 142.

alæuris Thapar, 1925, t.h. Testudo ibera. Alæuris, p. 203.

*alata Bellingham, 1839, t.h. Homo. [Asc.]. Toxocara, p. 258.

alata Railliet and Henry, 1909, t.h. Macaques. Cooperia, p. 132.

alata Rud., 1819, t.h. Ardea nigra. [Spiropt.]. Acuaria, p. 328.

alata Rud., 1819, t.h. Falco nisus, etc. Physaloptera, p. 353.

*alata Rud., 1819, of Stoss., 1889, t.h. Nisus communis, etc. Physaloptera, p. 354.

alata Schneider, 1866, t.h. Tinamus sp. Heterakis, p. 216.

alata var. *chevreuxi* Seurat, 1914, t.h. hawk. Physaloptera, p. 353.

alata var. *nouveli* Seurat, 1915, t.h. Accipiter nisus, Aquila chrysaëtos. Physaloptera, p. 353.

alatus Leuckart, 1848, t.h. Monodon monoceros. [Str.]. Stenurus, p. 170.

*alatus Molin, 1860, t.h. Alca torda, etc. Cosmocephalus, p. 338.

alatus Wedl, 1862, t.h. Uromastix spinipes. Thelandros, p. 192.

*alba Stoss., 1902, t.h. Cyclodus boddaërtii. Physaloptera, p. 353.

*albanica Stoss., 1898, t.h. Testudo græca. [Oxyuris]. Mehdiella, p. 201.

alcocki Linstow, 1906, t.h. Cervus eldi. [Trichoc.]. Trichuris, p. 22.

alfortensis Railliet and Henry, 1910, t.h. Bos taurus. Thelazia, p. 318.

allodapa Creplin, 1853, t.h. Dicholophus cristatus. [Oxyuris]. Allodapa, p. 229.

aloisii-sabaudiæ Parona, 1907, t.h. Agama atricollis. Physaloptera, p. 353.

alpha Travassos, 1918, t.h. Muridæ. Heligmosomum, p. 142.

alveatum Looss, 1900, t.h. Equus (donkey). [Cyathost.]. Trichonema, p. 55.

ambigua Rud., 1819, t.h. Lepus cuniculus, L. timidus. [Oxyuris]. Passalurus, p. 185.

amblymoria Drasche, 1883, t.h. Caprimulgus campestris. [Heterakis]. Ascaridia, p. 266.

americana Stiles, 1902, t.h. Homo. [Unc.]. Necator, p. 98.

americanum Railliet, 1918, t.h. Asio accipitrinus. Contortospiculum, p. 430.

americanum Schwartz, 1925, t.h. Scalopus aquaticus. Porrocæcum, p. 280.

americanus Chapin, 1925, t.h. Buteo borealis. Syngamus, p. 157.

americanus Chapin, 1925, t.h. Castor canadensis. Travassosius, p. 131.

americanus Magath, 1919, t.h. tortoises. Camallanus, p. 378.

amphiacanthum Dies., 1851, t.h. Lemmus dasytrichus. [Ophiost.]. Rictularioides, p. 346.

amphibia Linstow, 1899, t.h. Rana macrodon. Physaloptera, p. 353.

anacanthura Molin, 1860, t.h. Crotophaga ani, C. major. [Spiropt.]. Oxyspirura, p. 320.

anatinum Skrjabin, 1916, t.h. Anas boschas. Epomidiostomum, p. 155.

anatis Schrank, 1790, t.h. Anas querquedula. [Trichoc.]. Capillaria, p. 24.

ancylodirus Ward and Magath, 1916, t.h. German carp. Camallanus, p. 378.

andersoni Cobbold, 1876, t.h. Sciurus sp. [Asc.]. Subulura, p. 227.

andersoni Vevers, 1923, t.h. Florida cærulea. Contracæcum, p. 282.

androphora Nitzsch, 1821, t.h. Triton tæniatus. [Asc.]. Hedruris, p. 375.

angusticollis Molin, 1860, t.h. Falco haliaëtus, F. buteo. [Asc.]. Porrocæcum, p. 280.

angustum Duj., 1845, t.h. Fringilla cœlebs. [Trichosomum]. Capillaria, p. 25.

anisa Khalil, 1922, t.h. African elephant. [Pteridopharynx]. Murshidia, p. 79.

annandalei Baylis and Daubney, 1922, t.h. Testudo travancorica. Zanclophorus, p. 241.

annulata Baylis and Daubney, 1922, t.h. Chitra indica. Spiroxys, p. 304.

annulatus Molin, 1860, t.h. Labrax lupus. [Lecanoc.]. Gœzia, p. 285.

annulosum Duj., 1845, t.h. Mus rattus. [Calodium]. Capillaria, p. 25.

anolabiata Molin, 1860, t.h. Crax fasciolata. [Spiropt.]. Thelazia, p. 318.

anomala Linstow, 1904, t.h. Tropidonotus piscator. [Het.]. Tanqua, p. 341.

anomala Molin, 1860, t.h. Felis onça. Physaloptera, p. 353.

anoura Duj., 1845, t.h. Pithon bivittatus. [Asc.]. Polydelphis, p. 265.

anseris Schwartz, 1925, t.h. Anser domesticus. Ascaridia, p. 266.

anseris Zeder, 1800, in part, t.h. Anser. [Str.]. Amidostomum, p. 153.

anseris Zeder, 1800, in part, t.h. Anser. [Str.]. Epomidiostomum, p. 156.

anseris (Zeder, 1800) Railliet and Henry, 1909, in part, t.h. Anser. [Str.] Amidostomum, p. 154.

antarctica Leiper and Atkinson, 1914, t.h. Mustelus antarcticus. [Terranova]. Porrocæcum, p. 280.

antarctica Linstow, 1899, t.h. Acanthophis antarctica, Cyclodus occipitalis. Physaloptera, p. 353.

antarctica var. *antarctica* Irwin-Smith, 1922, t.h. Tiliqua scincoides. Physaloptera, p. 353.

antarctica var. *lata* Irwin-Smith, 1922, t.h. Tiliqua scincoides. Physaloptera, p. 353.

anthicola Linstow, 1903, t.h. Anthus richardi. [Fil.]. Aprocta, p. 405.

anthochæræ Johnston, 1912, t.h. Anthochæra carunculata. [Ceratospira]. Oxyspirura, p. 320.

anthropopetheci Gedoelst, 1916, t.h. chimpanzee. [Oxy.]. Enterobius, p. 188.

anthuris Rudolphi, 1819, t.h. Coracias garrula, Oriolus galbula. [Spiropt.]. Acuaria, p. 328.

anulata Molin, 1860, t.h. Ophis saurocephalus. [Het.]. Subulura, p. 227.

apiensis Gedoelst, 1916, t.h. African elephant. [Evansia]. Quilonia, p. 73.

apiostomum Willach, 1891, t.h. Macacus cynomolgus. [Sclerostomum]. Œsophagostomum, p. 87.

appendiculatus Molin, 1861, t.h. Coluber lichtensteinii. Kalicephalus, p. 114.

apri Gmelin, 1790, t.h. pig. [Trichoc.]. Trichuris, p. 23.

apri Gmelin, 1790, in part, t.h. Sus scrofa. [Asc.]. Metastrongylus, p. 160.

aquillæ Smith, Fox, and White, 1908, t.h. Haliaëtus leucoc. [Asc.]. Contracæcum, p. 282.

ararath Massino, 1924, t.h. Emys orbicularis. Zanclophorus, p. 241.

araxiana Massino, 1924, t.h. Emys orbicularis. [Falcaustra]. Spironoura, p. 239.

arcticus Cobb, 1888, t.h. Beluga leucas. [Str.]. Stenurus, p. 170.

arcuata Gedoelst, 1916, t.h. heron. [Kathleena]. Contracæcum, p. 282.

ardeæ Smith, Fox, and White, 1908, t.h. Ardea herodias. [Asc.]. Porrocæcum, p. 281.

armata Perrier, 1871, t.h. Emys picta. Hedruris, p. 376.

armatus Blanc, 1912, t.h. Macacus cynomolgus. Streptopharagus, p. 312.

armatus Rud., 1802, t.h. Equus cab. Strongylus, p. 37.

armatus Zeder, 1800, t.h. Perca vulg. [Cucullanus]. Camallanus, p. 378.

armatus Zeder, 1803, t.h. Silurus glanis. [Cochlus.]. Gœzia, p. 285.

armenica Massino, 1924, t.h. Emys orbicularis. [Falcaustra]. Spironoura, p. 239.

armillata Railliet and Henry, 1909, t.h. Bos. Onchocerca, p. 414.

arnfieldi Cobbold, 1884, t.h. Equus asinus. [Str.]. Dictyocaulus, p. 162.

arquata Schneider, 1866, t.h. Crypturus cupreus. Heterakis, p. 216.

artemisiana Schmerling, 1925, t.h. Coracias garrula. Diplotriæna, p. 433.

arthricola Skrjabin, 1916, t.h. Alcedo sp. Politospiculum, p. 398.

ascaroidea Hall, 1916, t.h. Geomys breviceps. Protospirura, p. 305.

ascaroides Gœze, 1782, t.h. Silurus glanis. [Cucullanus]. Gœzia, p. 285.

ashworthi Le Roux, 1924, t.h. Equines. Trichonema, p. 56.

asini Boulenger, 1920, t.h. Equines. Strongylus, p. 37.

asmilium Railliet, Henry, and Joyeux, 1913, t.h. Cercopithecus callitrichus, C. patas. [Characost.]. Globocephalus, p. 49.

asperum Railliet and Henry, 1913, t.h. goat. Œsophagostomum, p. 87.

asturis n.sp., t.h. Astur tachino. Cosmocephalus, p. 337.

asymmetrica Ware, 1925, t.h. Cervus dama. Ostertagia, p. 125.

asymmetricum Theiler, 1923, t.h. Equines. [Cylicostomum]. Trichonema, p. 55.

attenuata Molin, 1858, t.h. Pithon tigris. [Asc.]. Polydelphis, p. 266.

attenuata Molin, 1858, of Linstow, 1899, t.h. Coluber cobella, Python spp. [Asc.]. Polydelphis, p. 265.

attenuata Molin, 1858, of Stoss., 1896, t.h. Boa constrictor. [Asc.]. Polydelphis, p. 265.

attenuata Molin, 1859, t.h. Leuciscus cavedanus. [Dacnitis]. Cucullanus, p. 382.

attenuata Rud., 1819, t.h. Hirundo urbica, etc. [Spiropt.]. Acuaria, p. 328.

attenuata Rud., 1819, in part, not Rud., 1803, not Zeder, 1803, t.h. Corvus cornix. [Fil.]. Diplotriæna, p. 434.

attenuata Rud., 1819, in part, not Rud., 1803, not Zeder, 1803, t.h. Falco peregrinus. [Fil.]. Serratospiculum, p. 428.

attenuato-verrucosa Molin, 1858, t.h. Thamnophilus canadensis. [Fil.]. Diplotriæna, p. 433.

attenuatus Leidy, 1856, t.h. Cynocephalus porcarius. [Str.]. Œsophagostomum, p. 87.

attenuatus Molin, 1860, not Leidy, 1856, t.h. Dicotyles albirostris. [Str.]. Hyostrongylus, p. 121.

aucta Rud., 1802, t.h. Blennius viviparus. [Asc.]. Contracæcum, p. 282.

aulieatina Skrjabin, 1916, t.h. Hæmatopus ostralegus. Schistorophus, p. 367.

auricularis Leidy, 1856, not Zeder, 1800, t.h. Bufo americanus, Cistudo carolina. [Str.]. Oswaldocruzia, p. 127.

auricularis Zeder, 1800, t.h. Rana temp. [Str.]. Oswaldocruzia, p. 127.

auriculatum Looss, 1900, t.h. Equus (donkey). [Cyathost.]. Trichonema, p. 55.

auritæ Travassos, 1914, t.h. Didelphys aurita. Capillaria, p. 25.

australis Linstow, 1897, t.h. Petrogale penicillata. [Fil.]. Dipetalonema, p. 426.

australis Linstow, 1898, t.h. Macropygia nigrirostris. [Het.]. Ascaridia, p. 267.

australis n.sp. t.h. Macropus sp. Macropostrongylus, p. 75.

auziensis Seurat, 1917, t.h. Scincus officinalis. Pharyngodon, p. 194.

axei Cobbold, 1879, t.h. Equus asinus. [Str.]. Trichostrongylus, p. 119.

aziza Khalil, 1922, t.h. African elephant. [Memphisia]. Murshidia, p. 79.

bacillatum Eberth, 1863, t.h. Mus musculus. [Trichosoma]. Capillaria, p. 25.

balanocephala Gendre, 1922, t.h. Merops malinbicus. [Spiropt.]. Torquatella, p. 373.

bancrofti Cobbold, 1877, t.h. Homo. [Fil.]. Wuchereria, p. 401.

bancrofti Johnston, 1912, t.h. Catheturus lathami. Heterakis, p. 216.

barbatum Smit and Notosœdiro, 1923, t.h. Equines. [Cylicost.]. Trichonema, p. 55.

barbi Baylis, 1923, t.h. Barbus bynni. Cucullanus, p. 382.

barbi Baylis and Daubney, 1922, t.h. Barbus tor. [Falcaustra]. Spironoura, p. 239.

bargusinica Skrjabin, 1917, t.h. Turdus sp. Diplotriæna, p. 434.

baylisi Skrjabin, 1924, t.h. Spermophilopsis leptodactylus. Dermatopallarya, p. 212.

bentocruzi Barreto, 1919, t.h. Trogon spp. Subulura, p. 227.

beramporia Lane, 1914, t.h. dom. fowl. Heterakis, p. 216.

bernardi Railliet and Henry, 1911, t.h. pig. Setaria, p. 423.

beta Travassos, 1918, t.h. Muridæ. Heligmosomum, p. 142.

bialatus Molin, 1861, t.h. Pelophylax escul. [Str.]. Oswaldocruzia, p. 127.

*bicolor Baird, 1868, t.h. Trichechus rosmarus. [Asc.]. Anisakis, p. 273.

bicoronata Linstow, 1901, t.h. Adenota sp. [Fil.]. Setaria, p. 423.

bicoronatum Looss, 1900, t.h. Equus (donkey). [Cyathost.]. Trichonema, p. 55.

*bicostatus Linstow, 1906, t.h. Phocæna communis. [Pseudalius]. Torynurus, p. 171.

bicuspis Rud., 1819, t.h. Tringa helvetica. [Spiropt.]. Schistorophus, p. 367.

bicuspis Wedl, 1855, t.h. Scyllium catulus. [Asc.]. Acanthocheilus, p. 288.

bidens Rud., 1819, t.h. Merops apiaster. [Spiropt.]. Schistorophus, p. 367.

bidentata Linstow, 1899, t.h. Acipenser ruthenus. [Asc.]. Contracæcum, p. 282.

bidentata Molin, 1858, t.h. Cervus nambi, etc. [Fil.]. Setaria, p. 423.

bidentatum Ihle, 1925, t.h. Equines. [Cylicost.]. Trichonema, p. 55.

bifida Molin, 1858, t.h. Dactylomys amblyonyx. [Fil.]. Dicheilonema, p. 438.

bifurcatum Hall, 1916, t.h. Citellus elegans. Citellinema, p. 152.

bifurcatus Sleggs, 1925, t.h. Citellus richardsonii. Warrenius, p. 151.

*bifurcatus Theobald, 1896, t.h. poultry. Syngamus, p. 157.

bifurcus Creplin, 1849, t.h. Cercopithecus ruber. [Str.]. Œsophagostomum, p. 87.

bilabiata Creplin, 1829, t.h. Lanius minor. Physaloptera, p. 353.

*bilabiata Molin, 1860, t.h. Mus braziliensis. [Spiropt.]. Physaloptera, p. 354.

bilabiatus Molin, 1860, t.h. Eurypyga helias. [Ancyracanthus]. Ancyracanthopsis, p. 369.

binansata Railliet and Henry, 1913, t.h. Dasypus villosus. Aspidodera, p. 220.

bipapillata Gedoelst, 1916, t.h. monkey. [Oxy.]. Enterobius, p. 188.

*biramosum Cuillé, Marotel, and Panisset, 1911, t.h. cattle. Œsophagostomum, p. 87.

bisonis Chapin, 1925, t.h. Bison bison. Ostertagia, p. 125.

bisonis Cram, 1925, t.h. Bison bison. Cooperia, p. 132.

bispinosa Molin, 1860, t.h. Scincus officialis. [Tropidocerca]. Tetrameres, p. 361.

bispinosus Molin, 1860, t.h. Cervus nambi. [Str.]. Hæmonchus, p. 123.

blanchardi Railliet and Henry, 1912, t.h. Orang outan. Œsophagostomum, p. 87.

*blasii Linstow, 1887, t.h. Lepus cuniculus ferox. [Str.]. Graphidium, p. 135.

*blomei Travassos, 1914, t.h. Tetrao urogallus. Capillaria, p. 27.

boæ R. Blanchard, 1886, t.h. Boa constrictor. [Ankylostoma]. Kalicephalus, p. 114.

boddaërtii Baird, 1860, t.h. Herpetodryas boddaërtii. [Asc.]. Polydelphis, p. 266.

bombinatoris Linst., 1892, t.h. Bombinator igneus. [Trichosoma]. Capillaria, p. 25.

bonnei Ortlepp, 1922, t.h. " Sapakara." Physaloptera, p. 353.

bonnei Ortlepp, 1924, t.h. rat. Protospirura, p. 305.

bonnei Thiel, 1925, t.h. Mycetes seniculus. Syphacia, p. 196.

bonnei Thiel, 1925, t.h. Mycetes seniculus. Squamanema, p. 316.

boopis Baylis, 1920, t.h. Megaptera nodosa. Crassicauda, p. 437.

borealis Linst., 1884, t.h. Lagopus mutus. [Het.]. Ascaridia, p. 267.

borreli Sambon, 1925, t.h. Mus musculus. Muspicea, p. 446.

bosei Chandler, 1924, t.h. Dissemurus paradiseus. [Fil.]. Chandlerella, p. 411

bosia Lane, 1914, t.h. Ceriornis satyra. Heterakis, p. 216.

bothropis Molin, 1861, t.h. Bothrops jararaca. Kalicephalus, p. 114.

boueti Gendre, 1911, t.h. Xerus erythropus. [Het.]. Oxynema, p. 231.

boularti Mégnin, 1844, t.h. Casuarius galeatus. [Sclerost.]. Syngamus, p. 157.

bovieri R. Blanchard, 1866, t.h. Vespertilio murinus. Rictularia, p. 345.

*bovis Baillet, 1858, t.h. Bos taurus. [Fil.]. Thelazia, p. 318.

bovis Piettre, 1912, t.h. Bos taurus. Onchocerca, p. 414.

bovis Schnyder, 1906, t.h. Bos taurus. [Trichosoma]. Capillaria, p. 25.

*bovis Schnyder, 1906, t.h. Bos taurus. Œsophagostomum, p. 87.

bozasi Neveu-Lemaire, 1924, t.h. Afr. rhinoceros. [Henryella]. Murshidia, p. 79.

brachylaimus Linstow, 1901, t.h. Heterohyrax mossambica. [Deletrocephalus]. Theileriana, p. 77.

brachyurum Ward and Magath, 1916, t.h. black bass. [Hysterothylacium]. Raphidascaris, p. 275.

brasiliana Linstow, 1899, t.h. Perdix sp. [Het.]. Ascaridia, p. 267.

brasiliana Stossich, 1897, t.h. Picus sp. [Fil.]. Hamatospiculum, p. 395.

brasiliensis Magalhães, 1892, t.h. Gallus dom. [Het.]. Ascaridia, p. 268.

braziliense de Faria, 1910, t.h. Felis dom. [Ancylostomum]. Ancylostoma, p. 92.

braziliense Travassos, 1914, t.h. Mus decumanus. Heligmosomum, p. 142.

breve Linstow, 1877, t.h. Totanus fuscus. [Trichosoma]. Capillaria, p. 25.

brevicapsulatum Ihle, 1920, t.h. Equines. [Cylicost.]. Trichonema, p. 55.

brevicauda Boulenger, 1916, t.h. Equus cab. Triodontophorus, p. 45.

brevicauda Khalil, 1922, t.h. African elephant. Quilonia, p. 73.

brevicauda Leiper, 1911, t.h. zebra. Cylindropharynx, p. 64.

brevicauda Linstow, 1906, t.h. Francolinus adspersus. Physaloptera, p. 353.

brevicauda Rátz, 1897, t.h. Lucioperca sandra. [Het.]. Ascaridia, p. 268.

brevicauda Thapar, 1925, t.h. Rhinoceros africanus. Kiluluma, p. 71.

brevicaudata Müller, 1894, t.h. Agama colonum. Strongyluris, p. 222.

brevicaudata Zeder, 1800, t.h. Rana bufa. [Fus.]. Aplectana, p. 208.

*brevicaudatum Schneider, 1866, t.h. Rana temp. [Oxysoma]. Oxysomatium, p. 204.

brevicaudatus Baylis and Daubney, 1923, t.h. Rhinoceros indicus. Crossocephalus, p. 250.

brevicaudatus Cobb, 1898, t.h. Macropus sp. Zoniolaimus, p. 176.

brevicaudatus Duj., 1845, t.h. Ardea stellaris. [Disph.]. Acuaria, p. 328.

*brevicolle Rud., 1819, t.h. Anser, Anas querquedula. [Trichos.]. Capillaria, p. 25.

brevipenis Molin, 1860, t.h. Dicholophus margravi. [Spiropt.]. Oxyspirura, p. 320.

brevipenis Molin, 1861, t.h. Dryophis fulgidus, etc. Kalicephalus, p. 114.

brevipes Ransom, 1911, t.h. Ovis aries. Capillaria, p. 25.

brevispiculum Chapin, 1924, t.h. Testudo denticulata. Angusticæcum, p. 279.

brevispiculum Gendre, 1911, t.h. Gallus gallinaceus, etc. Heterakis, p. 216.

brevispiculum Linstow, 1873, t.h. Blicca bjœrkna. [Trichosoma]. Capillaria, p. 25.

brevispiculum Linstow, 1906, t.h. Felis rubiginosa. Physaloptera, p. 353.

brevispiculum Seurat, 1914, t.h. Dipodilla campestris. Gongylonema, p. 314.

brevisubulata Molin, 1860, t.h. Strix atricapilla. [Spiropt.]. Oxyspirura, p. 320.

brevivaginata Seurat, 1917, t.h. Vespertilio kuehli. Physaloptera, p. 353.

brevivaginata Thapar, 1925, t.h. Rhinoceros africanus. Kiluluma, p. 71.

*brevivaginatus Railliet and Henry, 1907, t.h. Sus scrofa dom. Metastrongylus, p. 160.

brigantiaca Blanchard, 1909, t.h. Rupicapra rupicapra. Ostertagia, p. 125.

britanica Skrjabin, 1916, t.h. Agama sp. Physaloptera, p. 353.

brodeni Gedoelst, 1916, t.h. Chamæleon gracilis. [Het.]. Africana, p. 225.

bronchialis Muehlig, 1884, t.h. Anser sp. Syngamus, p. 157.

brumpti Neveu-Lemaire, 1924, t.h. Rhinoceros bicornis. Paraquilonia, p. 75.

brumpti Railliet and Henry, 1905, t.h. Homo. Œsophagostomum, p. 87.

*bufonis Gedoelst, 1916, t.h. large toad. [Asc.]. Amplicæcum, p. 279.

*bufonis Leiper, 1908, t.h. Bufo regularis. [Fil.]. Foleyella, p. 395.

bufonis Schrank, 1788, t.h. Rana sp., Bufo sp. [Asc.]. Rhabdias, p. 18.

bulbosa Lane, 1916, t.h. Caranx melampygus. Bulbodacnitis, p. 383.

bulbosa Linstow, 1899, t.h. Scincus ocellatus. [Oxyuris]. Thelandros, p. 193.

bulbosa Linstow, 1906, t.h. Pavo spicifer. [Physaloptera]. Cyrnea, p. 300.

bullosa Ransom and Hall, 1912, t.h. Ovis aries. Ostertagia, p. 125.

cæcutiens Brumpt, 1919, t.h. Homo. Onchocerca, p. 414.

cælum Linstow, 1904, t.h. Cephalobus sylvaticultor. [Fil.]. Setaria, p. 423.

cahirensis Jaegerskiöld, 1904, t.h. cat. Rictularia, p. 345.

calamiformis Schneider, 1866, t.h. Psittacus æstivus. [Fil.]. Pelecitus, p. 411.

calcarata Gendre, 1909, t.h. Numida meleagris. [Het.]. Ascaridia, p. 268.

calcaratus Molin, 1860, t.h. Ibis guarauna. [Disph.]. Echinuria, p. 331.

calcaratus Ransom, 1911, t.h. Lepus sylvaticus. Trichostrongylus, p. 119.

*calicatiforme Kotlán, 1919, t.h. Equines. [Cylicost.]. Trichonema, p. 56.

calicatum Looss, 1900, t.h. Equus cab. [Cyathost.]. Trichonema, p. 55.

*calicatum var. minor Kotlán, 1920, t.h. Equines. [Cylicost.]. Trichonema, p. 56.

californica Gedoelst, 1919, t.h. Oidemia deglandi. [Yseria]. Streptocara, p. 360.

callichroi Stewart, 1914, t.h. Callichrous macrophth. [Dacnitis]. Cucullanus, p. 382.

callipæda Railliet and Henry, 1910, t.h. Canis fam. Thelazia, p. 318.

callis Travassos, 1914, t.h. Didelphys aurita. [Trichostr.]. Ostertagia, p. 125.

calotis Baylis and Daubney, 1923, t.h. Calotes nigrilabris. Strongyluris, p. 222.

*cameli Romanovitch, 1916, t.h. Camelus bactrianus. [Deraïophoronema]. Dipetalonema, p. 427.

cameli Rud., 1819, t.h. Camelus bactrianus, C. dromedarius. [Trichoc.]. Trichuris,
  p. 22.

campanula Linstow, 1889, t.h. Felis catus dom. [Trichoc.]. Trichuris, p. 23.

campanula Linstow, 1899, t.h. Lacerta campestris. [Het.]. Spinicauda, p. 225.

campanulata Molin, 1858, t.h. Falco magnirostris. [Fil.]. Thelazia, p. 318.

candezei Fraipont, 1882, t.h. Uromastix acanthinurus. [Fil.]. Foleyella, p. 395.

caninum Ercolani, 1859, t.h. Canis fam. [Sclerost.]. Ancylostoma, p. 92.

canis Brumpt, 1922, t.h. dog. Strongyloides, p. 20.

canis Werner, 1782, t.h. Canis fam. [Lumbricus]. Toxocara, p. 258.

*canis bronchialis Osler, 1877, t.h. Canis fam. [Str.]. Oslerus, p. 386.

capensis Monnig, 1924, t.h. Pteroclurus namaqua, Pterocles bicinctus. Syphaciella,
  p. 210.

capensis Ortlepp, 1922, t.h. Xerus setosus. Physaloptera, p. 353.

*capillaris Dunglison, 1895, t.h. Homo. [Vermiculus]. Dracunculus, p. 442.

capillaris Molin, 1860, t.h. Sterna hirundo. [Spiropt.]. Schistorophus, p. 367.

capillaris Mueller, 1889, t.h. Ovis aries. [Pseudalius]. Synthetocaulus, p. 164.

*capillaris Rud., 1809, t.h. Anser, Anas querquedula. [Trichoc.]. Capillaria, p. 25.

capitatus Looss, 1900, t.h. Equus mulus. Gyalocephalus, p. 62.

capitatus Molin, 1860, t.h. Falco minutus. [Disph.]. Acuaria, p. 328.

capræ Linstow, 1883, t.h. Capra hircus. [Fil.]. Onchocerca, p. 414.

capricola Ransom, 1907, t.h. goats, sheep. Trichostrongylus, p. 119.

caprimulgi Rud., 1819, t.h. Caprimulgus europæus. [Trichosoma]. Capillaria, p. 25.

*capsularia Rud., 1802, t.h. Salmo salar. [Asc.]. Porrocæcum, p. 280.

capsulata Annett, Dutton, and Elliott, 1901, t.h. Pycnonotus barbatus, etc. [Fil.].
  Eufilaria, p. 407.

carbonis Rud., 1819, t.h. Pelecanus carbo. [Trichosoma]. Capillaria, p. 25.

carettæ Baylis, 1923, t.h. Thalassochelys caretta. Cucullanus, p. 382.

carlieri Gedoelst, 1916, t.h. Cricetomys gambianus. Trichuris, p. 23.

carlosi Barreto, 1919, t.h. Piaya cayanna. Subulura, p. 227.

cascadilla Wigdor, 1918, t.h. minnows. Rhabdochona, p. 325.

castoris Chapin, 1925, t.h. Castor canadensis. Castorstrongylus, p. 47.

catheturinus Johnston, 1912, t.h. Catheturus lathami. [Het.]. Ascaridia, p. 268.

*cati Schrank, 1788, in part, t.h. Felis dom. [Asc.]. Toxocara, p. 258, and Toxascaris,
  p. 260.

catinatum Looss, 1900, t.h. Equus. [Cyathost.]. Trichonema, p. 55

catinatum var. *litoraurea* Yorke and Macfie, 1920, t.h. Equines. [Cylicost.]. Trichonema, p. 55.

catinatum var. *pseudocatinata* Yorke and Macfie, 1919, t.h. Equines. [Cylicost.]. Trichonema, p. 55.

caucasica Linstow, 1902, t.h. Homo sapiens. Physaloptera, p. 353.

caudata Linstow, 1906, t.h. Lampronessa sponsa. Heterakis, p. 216.

caudispina Molin, 1858, t.h. Ateles variegatus, etc. [Fil.]. Dipetalonema, p. 425.

cayugensis Wigdor, 1918, t.h. Esox americanus. [Hysterothylacium]. Raphidascaris, p. 275.

cebi Ortlepp, 1923, t.h. Cebus fatuellus. Physaloptera, p. 353.

cebus Darling, 1911, t.h. Cebus hypoleucus. Strongyloides, p. 20.

cephaloptera Molin, 1860, t.h. Momotus braziliensis. [Spiropt.]. Oxyspirura, p. 320.

cernuus Creplin, 1829, t.h. Ovis aries. [Str.]. Bunostomum, p. 109.

certa Leidy, 1866, t.h. Diomedea exulans. [Tropidocerca]. Tetrameres, p. 361.

cervicalis Railliet and Henry, 1910, t.h. Equus cab. Onchocerca, p. 414.

cervicornis McFadyean, 1897, t.h. Ovis aries. [Str.]. Ostertagia, p. 125.

cervinus Baylis and Daubney, 1922, t.h. Cervus axis. Hæmonchus, p. 123.

cesticillata Sonsino, 1889, t.h. Megalotis cerdo. Physaloptera, p. 353.

ceylanicum Looss, 1911, t.h. Viverricula malaccensis. [Agchylostoma]. Ancylostoma, p. 92.

chamæleonis Baylis and Daubney, 1922, t.h. Chamæleon vulgaris. Strongyluris, p. 222.

chamæleonis Skrjabin, 1916, t.h. Chamæleontidæ. [Angiost.]. Rhabdias, p. 18.

chamæleontis Gedoelst, 1916, t.h. Chamæleon gracilis. Physaloptera, p. 353.

chamoensis (Parona) Henry and O'Zoux, 1909, t.h. ? [Fil.]. Diplotriæna, p. 434.

chapini Boulenger, 1923, t.h. Cistudo carolina. [Falcaustra]. Spironoura, p. 239.

charadrii Rud., 1819, t.h. Charadrius minor, C. himantopus. [Trichosoma]. Capillaria, p. 25.

chenonettæ Johnston, 1912, t.h. Chenonetta jubata. Heterakis, p. 216.

chevreuxi Seurat, 1913, t.h. Felis ocreata. Habronema, p. 297.

chevreuxi Seurat, 1918, t.h. Himantopus himantopus. Amidostomum, p. 154.

chlamydosauri Breinl, 1913, t.h. Chlamydosaurus kingii. [Fil.]. Foleyella, p. 395.

chrisoptera Molin, 1858, t.h. Tapirus americanus. [Spiropt.]. Physocephalus, p. 309.

chrysanthemoides Skrjabin, 1916, t.h. Bufo sp. Orneoascaris, p. 264.

chrysotidis Walter, 1866, t.h. Chrysotis amazonicus. [Trichosoma]. Capillaria, p. 25.

ciconiæ Schrank, 1788, t.h. Ciconia nigra. [Fil.]. Contortospiculum, p. 430.

cincinnata Ercolani, 1866, t.h. Equus cab., E. asinus. [Spiropt.]. Onchocerca, p. 414.

cincta Linstow, 1897, t.h. Stellio vulg. [Oxyuris]. Thelandros, p. 193.

cinctus Linstow, 1898, t.h. Perameles obesula. [Hoploc.]. Echinonema, p. 348.

circularis Linstow, 1897, t.h. Mus rattus. Physaloptera, p. 353.

circularis Linstow, 1903, t.h. Centropus sinensis. [Het.]. Ascaridia, p. 268.

circularis Molin, 1860, t.h. Corvus cyanomelas, etc. [Spiropt.]. Pelecitus, p. 412.

circumcinctus Stadelmann, 1894, t.h. Ovis aries. [Str.]. Ostertagia, p. 125.

circumvallata Linstow, 1906, t.h. Cygnus atratus. Heterakis, p. 216.

cirrata Linstow, 1906, t.h. Iguana tuberculata. [Oxyuris]. Ozolaimus, p. 191.

cirratus Mueller, 1777, t.h. Gadus morrhua, etc. Cucullanus, p. 381.

cirrohamata Linstow, 1888, t.h. Phalacrocorax verrucosus. [Fil.]. Streptocara, p. 360.

cirrura Leidy, 1886, t.h. Quiscalus major. [Fil.]. Thelazia, p. 318.

citilli Rud., 1819, t.h. Arctomys citillus. [Spiropt.]. Physaloptera, p. 353.

clarotis Baylis, 1923, t.h. Clarotes laticeps, Synodontis schaal. Cucullanus, p. 382.

clathratum Baird, 1868, t.h. Loxodonta africana. [Sclerost.]. Grammocephalus, p. 104.

*clathratum ♀ Baird, 1868, t.h. Loxodonta africana. [Sclerost.]. Parabronema, p. 337.

*clathratus (Baird, 1868) of Railliet and Henry, 1910, t.h. Elephas indicus. Grammocephalus, p. 104.

clausa Rudolphi, 1819, t.h. Erinaceus europæus. Physaloptera, p. 352.

clavata Rud., 1809, t.h. Gadus barbatus. [Asc.]. Contracæcum, p. 282.

clitellarius Ward and Magath, 1916, t.h. Acipenser rubicundus. Cucullanus, p. 383.

coccinea Seurat, 1914, t.h. Phœnicopterus roseus. [Tropidocerca]. Tetrameres, p. 361.

cochleariæ Travassos, 1917, t.h. Cancroma cochlearia. Tetrameres, p. 361.

cœlebs Linstow, 1897, t.h. Centetes ecaudatus. Physaloptera, p. 353.

cœlebs Schlotthauber, 1860, t.h. Falco lagopus. Syngamus, p. 157.

colaptes Walton, 1923, t.h. Colaptes auratus luteus. Habronema, p. 297.

collare Linstow, 1873, t.h. Gallus dom. [Trichosoma]. Capillaria, p. 25.

collaris Hemprich and Ehrenberg, 1828, t.h. Hyrax capensis. Crossophorus, p. 287.

coloradensis Hall, 1916, t.h. Eutamias quadrivittatus. Rictularia, p. 345.

colubri Ortlepp, 1923, t.h. colubrine snake. Kalicephalus, p. 114.

colubri Rud., 1819, t.h. Coluber austriacus. [Str.]. Physaloptera, p. 353.

colubriformis Giles, 1892, t.h. Ovis aries. Trichostrongylus, p. 119.

columbæ Gmelin, 1790, t.h. Columba dom. [Asc.]. Ascaridia, p. 268.

columbæ Rud., 1819, t.h. Columba dom. [Trichosoma]. Capillaria, p. 25.

columbianum Curtice, 1890, t.h. Ovis aries. Œsophagostomum, p. 87.

columnaris Leidy, 1856, t.h. Mephitis chinga. Ascaris, p. 257.

colura Baylis, 1919, t.h. Lophoaëtus occipitalis. [Asc.]. Amplicæcum, p. 278.

commutata Diesing, 1851, t.h. Bufo viridis. [Asc.]. Cosmocerca, p. 207.

commutatus Diesing, 1851, t.h. Lepus timidus. [Str.]. Synthetocaulus, p. 163.

*commutatus Schneider, 1866, t.h. Rana temporaria, R. esculenta. [Nematoxys]. Aplectana, p. 208.

compar Schrank, 1790, t.h. Tetrao lagopus. [Asc.]. Ascaridia, p. 268.

compressa Schneider, 1866, t.h. Gallus dom. [Het.]. Ascaridia, p. 268.

conepati Solanet, 1911, t.h. Conepatus suffocans. [Agchylostoma]. Ancylostoma, p. 93.

confusa Travassos, 1917, t.h. Gallus domesticus. Tetrameres, p. 362.

confusum Sonsino, 1896, t.h. Equus cab. Gongylonema, p. 314.

*confusus Railliet and Henry, 1915, t.h. Emys sp. Camallanus, p. 378.

congeri-vulgaris Molin, 1859, t.h. Conger vulgaris. [Fil.]. Philometra, p. 443.

congolense Taylor, 1925, t.h. Congo fish. Spironoura, p. 239.

congolensis Gedoelst, 1916, t.h. chimpanzee. Necator, p. 99.

congolensis Railliet and Henry, 1911, t.h. Phacochœrus porcus. Setaria, p. 423.

conica Drasche, 1884, t.h. Testudo græca. [Oxy.]. Tachygonetria, p. 199.

*connorfilii Lane, 1922, t.h. domestic pig. Globocephalus, p. 49.

conocephala Molin, 1860, t.h. Cuculus cayanus. [Spiropt.]. Torquatella, p. 373.

*conocephala Molin, 1860, of Gendre, 1921, t.h. Centropus monachus. [Spiropt.]. Torquatella, p. 373.

conspicua Travassos, 1914, t.h. Didelphis opossum. Viannaia, p. 149.

constricta Leidy, 1856, t.h. Tropidonotus sipedon. [Physalopt.]. Spiroxys, p. 304.

contorta Rud., 1819, t.h. Testudo orbicularis. [Spiropt.]. Spiroxys, p. 303.

contorta Weidman, 1913, t.h. Dichocerus bicornis. [Tropidocerca]. Tetrameres, p. 362.

contortum Creplin, 1839, t.h. Charadrius hiaticula, etc. [Trichosoma]. Capillaria, p. 25.

contortum Linstow, 1906, t.h. Bufo vulg. [Oxysoma]. Aplectana, p. 209.

contortus Molin, 1858, t.h. Ibis falcinellus. [Disph.]. Echinuria, p. 331.

contortus Rud., 1803, t.h. Ovis aries. [Str.]. Hæmonchus, p. 122.

contortus Rud., 1819, t.h. Mus capensis. [Trichoc.]. Trichuris, p. 23.

*convoluta Zeder, 1803, t.h. Talpa. [Fus.]. Spirura, p. 294.

convolutum Fourm., 1885, t.h. Ossifraga gigantea. [Calodium]. Capillaria, p. 25.

convolutus Kuhn, 1829, t.h. Delphinus phocæna. [Str.]. Torynurus, p. 171.

*convolutus Ostertag, 1890, t.h. Bos taurus. [Str.]. Ostertagia, p. 125.

cordata Linstow, 1906, t.h. Callipepla squamata. [Het.]. Ascaridia, p. 268.

*cornicis Gmelin, 1790, t.h. Corvus cornix. [Fil.]. Diplotriæna, p. 434.

cornuta Linstow, 1899, t.h. antelope. [Fil.]. Setaria, p. 423.

cornuta Stossich, 1904, t.h. Thynnus vulg. [Asc.]. Contracæcum, p. 282.

coronata Beneden, 1858, t.h. Raja radians, Scillium canicula. [Spiropterina]. Proleptus, p. 358.

coronata Molin, 1860, t.h. Alcedo americana, Rallus cayennensis. [Spiropt.]. Histio-cephalus, p. 370.

coronata Rud., 1809, t.h. Coracias garrula. [Fil.]. Coronofilaria, p. 411.

coronatum Looss, 1900, t.h. Equus cab., etc. [Cyathost.]. Trichonema, p. 55.

coronatus Molin, 1861, t.h. Mergus merganser. Hystrichis, p. 181.

coronatus Molin, 1861, t.h. Phyllostoma discolor. Histiostrongylus, p. 133.

*coronatus Zeder, 1800, t.h. Muræna anguilla. [Cucullanus]. Camallanus, p. 378.

coronellæ Ortlepp, 1923, t.h. Coronella triangulum. Kalicephalus, p. 114.

corvorum Rud., 1819, t.h. Corvus caryocatactes, etc. [Trichosoma]. Capillaria, p. 25.

corynodes Linstow, 1899, t.h. Cercocebus fuliginosus, etc. [Fil.]. Dirofilaria, p. 393.

coscorobæ Chapin, 1925, t.h. Coscoroba coscoroba. [Cyathost.]. Syngamus, p. 157.

costatus Rud., 1819, t.h. Coluber sp. [Str.]. Kalicephalus, p. 114.

costellatus Duj., 1845, t.h. Arvicola arvalis. [Str.]. Heligmosomum, p. 142.

cotylophora Ward and Magath, 1916, t.h. Perca flavescens, Stizostedion vitreum. Dacnitoides, p. 384.

crassa Deslongchamps, 1824, t.h. Anas bosches dom. [Asc.]. Porrocæcum, p. 279.

crassa Linstow, 1879, t.h. Alauda arvensis. Physaloptera, p. 353.

crassa Railliet and Henry, 1910, t.h. Otis tarda. Aprocta, p. 405.

crassicauda Bellingham, 1840, t.h. Norway rat. [Trichosoma]. Trichosomoides, p. 32.

crassicauda Creplin, 1829, t.h. Balæna rostrata. [Fil.]. Crassicauda, p. 437.

crassicauda Creplin, 1829, t.h. Colymbus rufogularis, Anas glacialis. [Spiropt.]. Streptocara, p. 360.

*crassicauda (Creplin, 1829) of Leiper and Atkinson, 1914, t.h. Megaptera. Crassicauda, p. 437.

crassicauda var. charadrii Skrjabin, 1916, t.h. Vanellus cristatus. Streptocara, p. 360.

crassispiculum Sonsino, 1889, t.h. Megalotis cerdo. [Het.]. Oxynema, p. 230.

crassissimus Molin, 1860, t.h. Rhamphastos vitellinus. [Disph.]. Acuaria, p. 328.

*crenatum Railliet, 1898, t.h. sheep. Gongylonema, p. 315.

*crenatus Rud., 1809, t.h. Sus scrofa dom. et fera. [Trichoc.]. Trichuris, p. 23.

crenulata Bremser, 1824, t.h. Felis onça. [Asc.]. Toxocara, p. 258.

crinalis Wedl, 1855, t.h. Lophius piscatorius. Dikentrocephalus, p. 387.

criniformis Gœze, 1782, t.h. Ursus meles. [Asc.]. Uncinaria, p. 102.

cristata Froelich, 1802, t.h. Mus sylvaticus. Rictularia, p. 345.

cristata Linstow, 1901, t.h. Balearica regulorum. [Het.]. Ascaridia, p. 268.

cristatum Gedoelst, 1917, t.h. Sciurus prevosti. Heligmosomum, p. 142.

cristatus Railliet and Henry, 1915, t.h. Phycis tenuis. Spinitectus, p. 349.

cristatus (Seurat, 1912) Railliet, 1915, t.h. dromedary. [Spiropt.]. Physocephalus, p. 308.

crocodili Taylor, 1924, t.h. crocodile. Porrocæcum, p. 280.

crosi Seurat, 1914, t.h. Accipiter nisus. Physaloptera, p. 353.

crotali Rud., 1819, t.h. Crotalus durissus. [Trichosoma]. Capillaria, p. 25.

cruzi Travassos, 1914, t.h. Bucco swainsoni, Melanerpes flavifrons. Tetrameres, p. 362.

crypturi Rud., 1819, t.h. Crypturus. [Trichosoma]. Capillaria, p. 25.

cucullatum Hall, 1916, t.h. Eutamias amœnus operarius. Heteroxynema, p. 232.

cucullus Linstow, 1899, t.h. Potamogale velox. [Ancyracanthus]. Galeiceps, p. 444.

cuniculi Graybill, 1923, t.h. rabbit. [Obeliscus]. Obeliscoides, p. 130.

curticei Railliet, 1893, for *curticii* Giles, 1892. [Str.]. Cooperia, p. 132.

curticii Giles, 1892, t.h. Ovis aries. [Str.]. Cooperia, p. 132.

curvata Linstow, 1883, t.h. Perdix græca. [Het.]. Subulura, p. 227.

curvicauda Duj., 1845, t.h. Hirundo rustica. [Trichosoma]. Capillaria, p. 25.

curvula Rud., 1803, t.h. Equus cab. Oxyuris, p. 185.

cyathopharynx Baylis, 1923, t.h. Heterobranchus anguillaris. [Camallanus]. Paracamallanus, p. 379.

cylindracea Ward and Magath, 1916, t.h. Perca flavescens. [Ichthyonema]. Philometra, p. 443.

cylindrica Blome, 1909, t.h. Tetrao urogallus. [Het.]. Ascaridia, p. 268.

cylindrica Linstow, 1883, t.h. Petrœca cyanea. Aprocta, p. 405.

cylindrica Thapar, 1925, t.h. Rhinoceros africanus. Kiluluma, p. 71.

cylindricum Eberth, 1863, t.h. Falco buteo. [Trichosoma]. Capillaria, p. 25.

cymatostomum Kotlán, 1919, t.h. Equines. [Cylicost.]. Trichonema, p. 56.

cystidicola Lamarck, 1801, t.h. Salmo fario. [Fissula]. Cystidicola, p. 324.

dacelonis Breinl, 1913, t.h. Dacelo leachii. [Fil.]. Thelazia, p. 318.

dacnodes Creplin, 1851, t.h. Raja clavata. [Spiropt.]. Proleptus, p. 358.

dactyluris Rud., 1819, t.h. Testudo græca. [Asc.]. Atractis, p. 244.

dahli Linstow, 1898, t.h. Macropus browni. Cloacina, p. 176.

dahomensis Gendre, 1911, t.h. Cricetomys gambianus. Heterakis, p. 216.

dahomensis Neumann, 1895, t.h. Python natalensis. [Fil.]. Dracunculus, p. 442.

dasypodina Baylis, 1922, t.h. Dasypus gymnurus. Ascaris, p. 257.

decipiens Krabbe, 1878, t.h. Cystophora cristata, etc. [Asc.]. Porrocæcum, p. 280.

decorata Travassos, 1923, t.h. Cœndu brandti. Wellcomia, p. 197.

decoratus Creplin, 1847, t.h. Canis vulpes. [Str.]. Crenosoma, p. 166.

decorus Duj., 1845, t.h. Alcedo ispida. [Disph.]. Seuratia, p. 335, or Streptocara, p. 360.

decrusi Lane, 1914, t.h. Elephas indicus. Decrusia, p. 38.

delicatus Hall, 1916, t.h. Sciurus aberti mimus. Trichostrongylus, p. 119.

delphini Baylis and Daubney, 1925, t.h. Delphinus delphis. Halocercus, p. 171.

delta Travassos, 1918, t.h. Muridæ. Heligmosomum, p. 142.

deminutus Railliet and Henry, 1905, t.h. Homo. [Triodontophorus]. Ternidens, p. 89.

dentata Drasche, 1884, t.h. Testudo græca. [Oxy.]. Tachygonetria, p. 199.

dentata Linstow, 1883, t.h. Agama sanguinolenta, etc. Physaloptera, p. 353.

dentata Linstow, 1904, t.h. Sus cristatus. [Spiropt.]. Arduenna, p. 308.

dentatus Diesing, 1839, t.h. Sus scrofa dom. Stephanurus, p. 52.

dentatus Rud., 1803, t.h. Sus scrofa. [Str.]. Œsophagostomum, p. 87.

denticulata Molin, 1860, t.h. Falco palumbarius, Merops apiaster. [Spiropt.]. Acuaria, p. 328.

denticulatus Rud., 1819, t.h. Muræna anguilla. [Lior.]. Spinitectus, p. 349.

dentigerum Railliet and Henry, 1906, t.h. Anthropopithecus troglodytes. Œsophagostomum, p. 87.

denudatus Duj., 1845, t.h. Cyprinus erythrophthalmus. [Disph.]. Rhabdochona, p. 324.

denudatus Rud., 1819, t.h. Coluber tesselatus. [Str.]. Oswaldocruzia, p. 127.

depressa Baylis, 1920, t.h. Mungos fasciatus (true host birds). Thelazia, p. 318.

depressa Schneider, 1866, t.h. Corvus cornix. [Fil.]. Acuaria, p. 328.

depressa Zeder, 1800, t.h. Falco albicillæ. [Fus.]. Porrocæcum, p. 281.

depressiusculus Rud., 1809, t.h. Vulpes. [Trichoc.]. Trichuris, p. 23.

depressus Duj., 1845, t.h. Sorex tetragonurus. [Str.]. Viannaia, p. 149.

diacantha Molin, 1858, t.h. Hystrix prehensilis, etc. [Fil.]. Dipetalonema, p. 427.

diadema Baylis, 1916, t.h. Helicops angulatus. Tanqua, p. 342.

didelphis Travassos, 1914, t.h. Didelphys aurita. [Nematodirus]. Heligmosomum, p. 142.

didieri Neveu-Lemaire, 1924, t.h. African rhinoceros. [Henryella]. Murshidia, p. 79.

diducta Railliet, Henry, and Bauche, 1919, t.h. pig. Bourgelatia, p. 82.

diesingii Molin, 1858, t.h. Larus capistranus. Cosmocephalus, p. 337.

differens Sonsino, 1890, t.h. Gallus dom. [Het.]. Subulura, p. 227.

digitata Linstow, 1906, t.h. Bos indicus. [Fil.]. Setaria, p. 423.

digitata Schneider, 1866, t.h. Felis concolor. Physaloptera, p. 353.

digitata Travassos, 1918, t.h. Rhamphastus sp. Thelazia, p. 318.

digitatus Linstow, 1906, t.h. Bos indicus. [Str.]. Mecistocirrus, p. 139.

dilatata Rud., 1819, t.h. Simia rosalia. Physaloptera, p. 353.

dilatatus Railliet, 1884, t.h. cattle. [Str.]. Œsophagostomum, p. 87.

dimidiatus Diesing, 1851, t.h. Rhea americana. Deletrocephalus, p. 173.

diomedeæ Linstow, 1888, t.h. Diomedea brachyura. [Asc.]. Anisakis, p. 272.

discolor Linstow, 1906, t.h. Bos indicus. [Trichoc.]. Trichuris, p. 23.

dispar Diesing, 1851, t.h. Felis concolor. [Sclerost.]. Syngamus, p. 157.

dispar Duj., 1845, t.h. Anguis fragilis. [Str.]. Oswaldocruzia, p. 127.

dispar Duj., 1845, t.h. Falco subbuteo. [Trichosoma]. Capillaria, p. 25.

dispar Linstow, 1904, t.h. Erinaceus albiventris. Physaloptera, p. 353.

dispar Rud., 1802, t.h. Homo. [Trichoc.]. Trichuris, p. 22.

dispar Schrank, 1790, t.h. Anser dom. [Asc.]. Heterakis, p. 216.

disparalis Irwin-Smith, 1922, t.h. Hinulia sp. Rictularia, p. 345.

distans Rud., 1809, t.h. Simia sabæa. [Asc.]. Subulura, p. 227.

diucæ Boulenger, 1920, t.h. Diuca grisea. Diplotriæna, p. 434.

dodsworthi Barreto, 1922, t.h. Spheroides testudineus. Cucullanus, p. 383.

dogieli Skrjabin, 1916, in Bufonidæ. [Oxysomatium]. Aplectana, p. 209.

dolichocerca Stoss., 1902, t.h. Circus spilothorax. [Het.]. Ascaridia, p. 268.

douglasi Gedoelst, 1911, for *douglassii* Cobbold, 1882. [Str.]. Libyostrongylus, p. 120.

douglassii Cobbold, 1882, t.h. Struthio camelus. [Str.]. Libyostrongylus, p. 120.

dracunculoides Cobbold, 1870, t.h. Proteles cristatus. [Acanthocheilonema]. Dipetalonema, p. 427.

draschei Stossich, 1898, t.h. Testudo græca. [Oxy.]. Mehdiella, p. 201.

dromedarii May, 1920, t.h. dromedary. Nematodirus, p. 136.

droummondi Travassos, 1915, t.h. Cygnus melanocoryphus. Capillaria, p. 25.

dubia Travassos, 1917, t.h. Atilla cinerea. Capillaria, p. 25.

dubia Travassos, 1917, t.h. Gallinago paraguayæ. Tetrameres, p. 362.

duboisi Gedoelst, 1916, t.h. toad. [Fil.]. Foleyella, p. 395.

dujardini Maupas, in Seurat, 1916, t.h. Anguis fragilis. [Angiost.]. Rhabdias, p. 18.

dujardini Travassos, 1914, t.h. Columba livia dom., etc. Capillaria, p. 25.

dujardini Travassos, 1920, t.h. Crocodilus spp. Dujardinia, p. 277.

duodenale Dubini, 1843, t.h. Homo. [Agchylostoma]. Ancylostoma, p. 92.

dumerilii Perrier, 1871, t.h. Emys picta. [Cucullanus]. Camallanus, p. 378.

dussumierii Beneden, 1870, t.h. Delphinus sp. [Asc.]. Anisakis, p. 272.

ecaudata Oerley, 1882, t.h. Lamprotornis æneus. [Fil.]. Diplotriæna, p. 434.

echinata Linstow, 1878, t.h. Alburnus lucidus. [Fil.]. Spinitectus, p. 349.

echinata Rud., 1819, t.h. Lacerta (Gecko) stellio. [Asc.]. Thelandros, p. 193.

echinatus Rud., 1809, t.h. Lacerta apus. [Trichoc.]. Sclerotrichum, p. 30.

echinophallus Nitzsch, 1849, t.h. Camelus dromedarius. [Trichoc.]. Trichuris, p. 23.

echinopharynx Thapar, 1925, t.h. Testudo tabulata. [Echinopharynx]. Sauricola, p. 62.

echiurus Diesing, 1853, t.h. Tenebrio molitor. Mastophorus, p. 387.

edentatum Looss, 1900, t.h. Equus cab. [Sclerost.]. Strongylus, p. 37.

effilata Linstow, 1897, t.h. Tragulus pygmæus. [Fil.]. Setaria, p. 423.

elegans Gendre, 1909, t.h. Chamæleon gracilis. [Het.]. Strongyluris, p. 223.

elegans Oerley, 1885, t.h. Hexanchus griseus. [Spiropterina]. Proleptus, p. 358.

elegans Olfers, 1816, t.h. Merganser merganser. [Str.]. Eustrongylides, p. 179.

*elegans Olfers of Railliet, 1895, in part. [Str.]. Eustrongylides, p. 179.

elegans Travassos, 1921, t.h. Cœndu villosus. Heligmosomum, p. 142.

*elegans Zeder, 1800, t.h. Lucioperca. [Cucullanus]. Camallanus, p. 378.

elegantissima Stossich, 1902, t.h. Ratelus capensis. Physaloptera, p. 353.

ellipticus Molin, 1858, t.h. Falco nisus. [Disph.]. Acuaria, p. 328.

elongata Rud., 1819, t.h. Sterna nigra. [Spiropt.]. Rusguniella, p. 333.

elongata Seurat, 1914, t.h. Dipodilla campestris. Allodapa, p. 229.

elongatum Looss, 1900, t.h. Equus. [Cyathost.]. Trichonema, p. 56.

elongatum var. *kotláni* Ihle, 1920, t.h. Equus. [Cylicost.]. Trichonema, p. 56.

*elongatum var. *macrobursata* Kotlán, 1920, t.h. Equus. [Cylicost.]. Trichonema, p. 56.

elongatus Duj., 1845, t.h. Sus scrofa. [Str.]. Metastrongylus, p. 160.

elviræ Parona, 1889, t.h. Sciurus rufigenis. Rictularia, p. 345.

encapsulatum Schwartz, 1925, t.h. Blarina brevicauda. Porrocæcum, p. 281.

engonium Baylis and Daubney, 1922, t.h. Ciconia nigra. Contracæcum, p. 282.

ensicaudata Zeder, 1800, t.h. Turdus merula. [Fus.]. Porrocæcum, p. 281.

entomelas Duj., 1845, t.h. Anguis fragilis. [Angiost.]. Rhabdias, p. 18.

entomelas Duj., 1845, t.h. Mustela foina. [Trichosoma]. Capillaria, p. 25.

epistomum Piana and Stazzi, 1900, t.h. Elephas. [Sclerost.]. Choniangium, p. 41.

equi Schrank, 1788, t.h. Equus cab. [Trichoc.]. Oxyuris, p. 185.

*equi Schrank, 1788, t.h. Equus cab. [Asc.]. Parascaris, p. 262.

equi Yorke and Macfie, 1918, t.h. Equines. Gyalocephalus, p. 62.

equinus Abildgaard, 1789, t.h. Equus cab. [Gordius]. Setaria, p. 423.

equinus Mueller, 1780, t.h. Equus cab. Strongylus, p. 37.

equorum Gœze, 1782, t.h. Equus cab. [Asc.]. Parascaris, p. 262.

eremita Leidy, 1886, t.h. Meles labradorica. Monopetalonema, p. 438.

erinacei Rud., 1819, t.h. Erinaceus europæus. [Trichosoma]. Capillaria, p. 25.

ersiliæ Stossich, 1896, t.h. Python molurus. [Str.]. Kalicephalus, p. 114.

*esuriens Duj., 1845, t.h. Pleuronectes latus, P. soleæ. [Dacnitis]. Cucullanus, p. 381.

ethiopica Khalil, 1922, t.h. African elephant. Quilonia, p. 73.

euproctum Boulenger, 1917, t.h. Equus cab. [Cylichnost.]. Trichonema, p. 56.

eurycephalum Goodey, 1924, t.h. roan antelope. Œsophagostomum, p. 87.

eurycerca Seurat, 1914, t.h. Perdix rouge. Cyrnea, p. 300.

euryoptera Rud., 1819, t.h. Lanius collurio, etc. [Spiropt.]. Viguiera, p. 371.

evansi Lewis, 1882, t.h. camel. [Fil.]. Dipetalonema, p. 427.

evoluta Linstow, 1899, t.h. Hystrix brachyura. [Oxy.]. Wellcomia, p. 197.

excisa Molin, 1860, t.h. Ciconia maguari. [Spiropt.]. Cyrnea, p. 300.

excisus Jaegerskiöld, 1909, t.h. Phalacrocorax carbo, P. pygmæus. Eustrongylides, p. 180.

exiguum Duj., 1845, t.h. Erinacæus europæus. [Trichosoma]. Capillaria, p. 25.

exile Duj., 1845, t.h. Turdus merula. [Trichosoma]. Capillaria, p. 25.

exilidens Looss, 1912, t.h. Anthropopithecus troglodytes. Necator, p. 99.

*exilis Duj., 1845, t.h. Sorex tetragonurus. [Liniscus]. Capillaria, p. 26.

extenuata Rud., 1819, t.h. Lacerta margaritacea. [Asc.]. Pharyngodon, p. 194.

extenuatus Railliet, 1898, t.h. Ovis aries. [Str.]. Trichostrongylus, p. 119.

fabri Rud., 1819, t.h. Zeus faber. [Asc.]. Contracæcum, p. 282.

falcatum Linstow, 1906, t.h. Nicoria trijuga. [Oxysoma]. Spironoura, p. 239.

falcifer Cobbold, 1882, t.h. Elephas indicus. [Str.]. Murshidia, p. 79.

falcigera Railliet and Henry, 1907, t.h. Leptonychotes weddelli, Omnatophoca rossi. [Asc.]. Contracæcum, p. 282.

falconis Connal, 1912, t.h. Falco sp. [Triplotriæna]. Diplotriæna, p. 434.

falconum Rud., 1819, t.h. Falco buteo, F. milvus. [Trichosoma]. Capillaria, p. 26.

falculatus Ransom, 1911, t.h. Capra hircus. Trichostrongylus, p. 119.

fallax Jaegerskiöld, 1909, t.h. Sciurus melanogaster. Rictularia, p. 345.

fariai Travassos, 1913, t.h. Odontophorus capueira. Heterakis, p. 216.

fariai Travassos, 1914, t.h. Leptoptila rufaxila. Ornithostrongylus, p. 128.

fariai Travassos, 1915, t.h. Lepus brasiliensis. [Viannaia]. Viannella, p. 150.

farionis Fischer, 1798, t.h. trout. Cystidicola, p. 324.

fasciata Baylis, 1920, t.h. Vinago delalandii. Ascaridia, p. 268.

fasciata Railliet and Henry, 1910, t.h. dromedary. Onchocerca, p. 414.

fasciata Schneider, 1866, t.h. Dasypus novemcinctus. [Het.]. Aspidodera, p. 220.

fasciolata Gendre, 1909, t.h. Cinixys belliana. Atractis, p. 244.

*felineum Hegt, 1910. t.h. Felis dom. Chlamydonema, p. 356.

felineus Cameron, 1923, t.h. Felis yaguarundi. Molineus, p. 126.

feliscati Bellingham, 1844, t.h. Felis catus ferus. [Trichosomum]. Capillaria, p. 26.

*ferox Hemprich and Ehrenberg, 1828, t.h. Hyrax syriacus. [Asc.]. Crossophorus, p. 287.

fiberius Barker and Noyes, 1915, t.h. Fiber zibethicus. Trichostrongylus, p. 119.

ficheuri Seurat, 1916, t.h. Bubulcus lucidus. Habronema, p. 297.

filaria Beneden, 1873, t.h. Vespertilio auritus. [Litosoma]. Litomosa, p. 399.

filaria Duj., 1845, t.h. a snake, probably python. [Asc.]. Ophidascaris, p. 263.

filaria Rud., 1809, t.h. Ovis aries. [Str.]. Dictyocaulus, p. 162.

filicollis Rud., 1802, t.h. Ovis aries. [Asc.]. Nematodirus, p. 135.

filiforme Linstow, 1885, t.h. Triton alpestris, T. cristatus. [Trichosoma]. Capillaria. p. 26.

*filiforme Molin, 1857, t.h. Simia inuus. [Gongylonema]. Dipetalonema, p. 425.

filiformis (Gœze, 1782) Travassos, 1917, t.h. Rana temporia, etc. [Asc.]. Oswaldo-cruzia, p. 127.

filiformis Molin, 1858, t.h. Anabates rufifrons. [Fil.]. Diplotriæna, p. 434.

filiformis Stossich, 1896, t.h. Pagellus erythrinus, Trachinus draco. [Ichthyonema]. Philometra, p. 443.

filiformis Stossich, 1904, t.h. Uranoscopus scaber. [Asc.]. Contracæcum, p. 282.

*filiformis Zschokke, 1884, t.h. Alburnus lucidus. [Dispharagus]. Rhabdochona, p. 324.

*filum Duj., 1845, t.h. Delphinus phocæna. Pseudalius, p. 168.

fimbriatus Ortlepp, 1923, t.h. Bungarus fasciatus. Occipitodontus, p. 115.

fissispina Diesing, 1861, t.h. Anas boschas dom., etc. [Tropidocerca]. Tetrameres, p. 362.

flabellata Linstow, 1888, t.h. Paradisea apoda. [Fil.]. Diplotriæna, p. 434.

flagellum Hemprich and Ehrenberg, 1828, t.h. Hyrax capensis. [Oxy.]. Hoplodon-tophorus, p. 234.

flexuosa Schneider, 1866, t.h. Crotalus. [Het.]. Ascaridia, p. 268.

flexuosa Wedl, 1856, t.h. Cervus elaphus. [Fil.]. Onchocerca, p. 414.

fœcunda Rud., 1819, t.h. Rana cornuta, Hyla sp. [Asc.]. Aplectana, p. 209.

foliatus Cobbold, 1882, t.h. Elephas indicus. [Str.]. Bunostomum, p. 109.

forcipata Rud., 1819, t.h. Cuculus nævius. [Asc.]. Subulura, p. 228.

*fordi (Daniels) Neveu-Lemaire, 1914, for *fordii* Daniels, 1908. Mecistocirrus, p. 139.

*fordii Daniels, 1908, t.h. Indian buffalo. [Str.]. Mecistocirrus, p. 139.

formosana Yokogawa, 1922, t.h. Sorex sp. Physaloptera, p. 353.

fossor Hall, 1916, t.h. Thomomys fossor. Trichuris, p. 23.

fossor Jaegerskiöld, 1902, t.h. Lates niloticus. [Dichelyne]. Cucullanus, p. 383.

*foveolata Molin, 1858, t.h. Corvus frugilegus, etc. [Fil.]. Serratospiculum, p. 428.

*foveolatus Rud., 1809, t.h. Gadus. Cucullanus, p. 381.

francolina Linstow, 1899, t.h. Francolinus bicalcaratus. [Het.]. Ascaridia, p. 268.
fringillæ Rud., 1819, t.h. Fringilla cælebs. [Trichosoma]. Capillaria, p. 26.
fritschi Travassos, 1914, t.h. Malapterurus electricus. Capillaria, p. 26.
fulicæ Rud., 1819, t.h. Fulica atra. [Spiropt.]. Amidostomum, p. 154.
fülleborni Linstow, 1905, t.h. Anthropopithecus troglodytes. Strongyloides, p. 20.
furcatus May, 1920, t.h. sheep. Nematodirus, p. 136.
fusca Rud., 1819, t.h. Pleuronectes mancus. [Fil.]. Philometra, p. 443.
fuscovenosum Railliet, 1899, t.h. Tropidonotus natrix. [Angiost.]. Rhabdias, p. 18.
fusiformis Linstow, 1902, t.h. Micropogon sp. Physaloptera, p. 353.
fusiformis Molin, 1860, t.h. Platessa flesus. [Dacnitis]. Cucullanus, p. 383.

gadorum Beneden, 1858, t.h. Gadus morrhua. [Dacnitis]. Cucullanus, p. 381.
galeatus Rud., 1819, t.h. Lacerta teguixin. [Str.]. Diaphanocephalus, p. 113.
galebi Khalil, 1922, t.h. Indian elephant. Leiperenia, p. 247.
galinieri Seurat, 1914, t.h. eagle. Physaloptera, p. 353.
galloperdicis Baylis and Daubney, 1922, t.h. Galloperdix spadicea. Subulura, p. 228.
gambiana Gendre, 1922, t.h. a fish. Rhabdochona, p. 325.
gambiensis Ortlepp, 1925, t.h. African mongoose. Arthrocephalus, p. 107.
gamma Travassos, 1918, t.h. Mesomys guira. Heligmosomum, p. 142.
gangetica Baylis and Lane, 1920, t.h. Trionyx gangeticus. Spiroxys, p. 304.
gangula Lane, 1914, t.h. Mus decumanus. [Ganguleterakis]. Heterakis, p. 216, or Ganguleterakis, p. 218.
gastrophila Mueller, 1894, t.h. Felis dom. [Fil.]. Spirura, p. 294.
gastrophila Seurat, 1913, not Mueller, 1894, t.h. Elephantulus deserti. Spirura, p. 294.
gedoelsti nom. nov., t.h. large toad. Amplicæcum, p. 279.
gemina Linstow, 1899, t.h. Felis catus dom. Physaloptera, p. 353.
gestri Parona, 1890, t.h. Tropidonotus quincunciatus. [Asc.]. Ophidascaris, p. 263.
getula Seurat, 1915, t.h. Xerus getulus. Dermatoxys, p. 190.
getula Seurat, 1917, t.h. Mus rattus. Physaloptera, p. 354.
gibbosus Rud., 1819, t.h. Scomber thynnus. [Trichoc.]. Oncophora, p. 31.
gibsoni Cleland and Johnston, 1910, t.h. Bos taurus. Onchocerca, p. 414.
gibsoni Stephens, 1909, t.h. Homo. [Str.]. Mecistocirrus, p. 139.
gigas Rud., 1802, t.h. Phoca vitulina. [Str.]. Dioctophyme, p. 178.
gigas Spaul, 1923, t.h. Agama distanti. Strongyluris, p. 223.
gigas Travassos, 1917, t.h. Anas boschas. Tetrameres, p. 363.
gilsoni Gedoelst, 1917, t.h. Sciurus prevosti. Ancylostoma, p. 93.
giraffæ Diesing, 1851, t.h. Camelopardalis giraffa. [Trichoc.]. Trichuris, p. 23.
giraffæ n. sp., t.h. giraffe. Monodontella, p. 111.
girardi Lane, 1917, t.h. Hystrix bengalensis. [Gireterakis]. Heterakis, p. 216, or Gireterakis, p. 219.
globicephalæ Baylis and Daubney, 1925, t.h. Globicephala melæna. Stenurus, p. 170.
globiceps Rud., 1819, t.h. Blennius phycis, Uranoscopus scaber. [Fil.]. Philometra, p. 443.
globocaudatus Diesing, 1853, t.h. Geotrupes stercorarius. Mastophorus, p. 387.
globosa Linstow, 1879, t.h. Fulica atra. [Tropidocerca]. Tetrameres, p. 363.
globosa Zeder, 1800, t.h. Salmo trutta. [Cucullanus]. Bulbodacnitis, p. 383.
globulosus Linstow, 1901, t.h. Camelus dromedarius. [Trichoc.]. Trichuris, p. 23.
glycirrhiza Beneden, 1873, t.h. Rhinolophus ferrum-equinum. Strongylacantha, p. 96.
goldi Boulenger, 1917, t.h. Equus cab. [Cylichnost.]. Trichonema, p. 56.
goodeyi Thapar, 1925, t.h. Rhinoceros africanus. Kiluluma, p. 71.
gordioides Beneden, 1858, t.h. Galeus canis. Proleptus, p. 358.
gouldi n. sp., t.h. Varanus gouldi. Hastospiculum, p. 432.
gracile Leidy, 1856, t.h. Emys serrata. Spironoura, p. 239.
gracile Linstow, 1899, t.h. Francolinus sp. [Oxysoma]. Subulura, p. 228.

gracilis Bellingham, 1840, t.h. Gadus merluccius. [Trichosoma]. Capillaria, p. 26.

gracilis Chapin, 1925, t.h. Corvus brachyrhynchos. Syngamus, p. 157.

gracilis Cram, 1924, t.h. cat. Protospirura, p. 305.

gracilis Diesing, 1839, t.h. Sudis gigas. [Cheiracanthus]. Gnathostoma, p. 340.

gracilis Gendre, 1912, t.h. Buchanga atra asimilis, Oriolus auratus. [Disph.]. Acuaria, p. 329.

gracilis Leuckart, 1842, t.h. Myoxus glis. [Str.]. Heligmosomum, p. 142.

*gracilis McFadyean, 1896, not Leuck., 1842, t.h. Bos taurus. [Str.]. Trichostrongylus, p. 119.

gracilis Ortlepp, 1922, t.h. lizard. Physaloptera, p. 354.

gracilis Rud., 1809, t.h. Simia capucina. [Fil.]. Dipetalonema, p. 425.

gracilis Rud., 1819, t.h. Cavia aguti. [Trichoc.]. Trichuris, p. 23.

gracilis Rud., 1819, t.h. Bradypus tridactylus. [Spiropt.]. Physocephalus, p. 308.

*gracilis Stossich, 1906, t.h. larva in Margaritifera vulg. Echinocephalus, p. 343.

gracilis Ward and Magath, 1916, t.h. black crappie, etc. Spinitectus, p. 349.

granulosa Linstow, 1906, t.h. Felis pardus. [Fil.]. Dirofilaria, p. 394.

granulosa Linstow, 1906, t.h. Gallus gallinaceus. [Het.]. Ascaridia, p. 268.

grassii G. Noè, 1907, t.h. Canis fam. [Fil.]. Dipetalonema, p. 427.

grayi Gemmill and Linstow, 1902, t.h. Echinus escul. [Ichthyonema]. Philometra, p. 443.

grimaldiæ Seurat, 1915, t.h. Vulpes atlantica. Habronema, p. 297.

gruveli Gendre, 1913, t.h. Francolinus bicalcaratus. [Disph.]. Acuaria, p. 329.

guianensis Ortlepp, 1924, t.h. "Monki-monki." Protospirura, p. 305.

guiarti Garin, 1913, t.h. Leptonychotes weddelli. Physaloptera, p. 354.

gulosa Railliet and Henry, 1910, t.h. cattle. Thelazia, p. 318.

gulosa Rud., 1819, t.h. Testudo tabulata. [Asc.]. Labiduris, p. 247.

guttata Schneider, 1866, t.h. Falco borigera. [Fil.]. Serratospiculum, p. 428.

gutturosa Neumann, 1910, t.h. Bos taurus. Onchocerca, p. 414.

gymnurus Railliet, 1899, t.h. Phoca vitulina. [Pseudalius]. Halocercus, p. 171.

gynæcophila Molin, 1858, t.h. Ardea nycticorax. [Tropidocerca]. Tetrameres, p. 363.

haberi Steiner, 1924, t.h. Hyla carolinensis. Cosmocercella, p. 208.

hadia Khalil, 1922, t.h. African elephant. Murshidia, p. 79.

hadweni Chapin, 1925, t.h. Bison bison. Dictyocaulus, p. 162.

hæmochrous Creplin, 1846, t.h. Falco peregrinus. Tetrameres, p. 363.

*hæmorrhagica Railliet, 1885, t.h. Equus cab. [Fil.]. Parafilaria, p. 392.

haliaëti Baylis and Daubney, 1923, t.h. Haliaëtus leucogaster. Contracæcum, p. 282.

halicoris Owen, 1833, t.h. Halicore dugong. [Asc.]. Dujardinia, p. 277.

halli Barreto, 1917, t.h. Tetrax tetrax. Subulura, p. 228.

hamata Daubney, 1923, t.h. Phacochœrus æthiopicus. Murshidia, p. 79.

hamata Linstow, 1877, t.h. Falco nisus. [Fil.]. Acuaria, p. 329.

hamata Travassos, 1914, t.h. Didelphis aurita. Viannaia, p. 150.

*hamia Lane, 1914, t.h. domestic fowl. Ascaridia, p. 268.

hamulosa Diesing, 1851, t.h. Phasianus gallus. [Spiropt.]. Acuria, p. 329.

hamulus Linstow, 1906, t.h. Pavo spicifer. Heterakis, p. 216.

hargilæ Baylis and Daubney, 1923, t.h. adjutant-stork. Echinuria, p. 331.

*harkeri Stödter, 1901, in part, t.h. Bos taurus. [Str.]. Ostertagia, p. 125.

hastatus Linstow, 1905, t.h. Tetrao tetrix. [Str.]. Ornithostrongylus, p. 128.

hebrenicutus Lane, 1923, t.h. gorilla. Libyostrongylus, p. 120.

helicina Molin, 1860, t.h. Alcedo americana, etc. [Spiropt.]. Pelecitus, p. 411.

helicina Molin, 1860, t.h. Crocodilus acutus. [Asc.]. Dujardinia, p. 276.

*helicina (Molin, 1860) of Skrjabin, 1916, t.h. Crocodilus acutus. Trispiculascaris, p. 264.

helvetianus May, 1920, t.h. cattle. Nematodirus, p. 136.

henryi Skrjabin, 1915, t.h. Vanellus cristatus. Amidostomum, p. 154.

hepaticus Bancroft, 1893, t.h. common rat. [Trichoc.]. Hepaticola, p. 28.

hermaphrodita Frölich, 1789, t.h. Psittacus æstivus. [Asc.]. Ascaridia, p. 266.

heteroclita Molin, 1860, t.h. Crax uru-mutum. [Spiropt.]. Oxyspirura, p. 320.

*heterolobus Diesing, 1838, t.h. Manatus australis. [Loboc.]. Heterocheilus, p. 270.

heteroura Creplin, 1829, t.h. Charadrius pluvialis. [Asc.]. Porrocæcum, p. 281.

hexametra Gedoelst, 1916, t.h. Chamæleon dilepis. [Asc.]. Polydelphis, p. 266.

hexauterina Skrjabin, 1916, t.h. Bothrops sp. Polydelphis, p. 266.

hians Duj., 1845, t.h. Muræna conger. [Dacnitis]. Cucullanus, p. 383.

hilgerti Seurat, 1914, t.h. Ctenodactylus gundi. [Oxy.]. Wellcomia, p. 197.

hindlei Thapar, 1925, t.h. Tiligua senicordis. Pharyngodon, p. 194.

hippopotami Gedoelst, 1924, t.h. hippopotamus. Syngamus, p. 157.

hipsirhinæ Chatin, 1876, t.h. Hipsirhina bocourti. Hedruris, p. 376.

hirundinis Rud., 1819, t.h. Hirundo rustica. [Trichosoma]. Capillaria, p. 26.

hispidum Fedtsch., 1872, t.h. Bos taurus. Gnathostoma, p. 340.

holoptera Rud., 1819, t.h. Testudo mydas. [Asc.]. Angusticæcum, p. 279.

*hominis Schrank, 1788, t.h. Homo. [Trichoc.]. Trichuris, p. 22.

hominis Stiles, 1921, t.h. Homo. Gongylonema, p. 314.

hopkeni Leiper, 1910, t.h. hippopotamus. Nematodirus, p. 136.

hornbyi Boulenger, 1921, t.h. Hippotragus niger. Setaria, p. 423.

*horrida Diesing, 1851, t.h. Rhea americana. [Fil.]. Contortospiculum, p. 430.

horridus Leidy, 1856, t.h. Alligator mississippiensis. [Cheiracanthus]. Gnatho-stoma, p. 340.

hyalina Seurat, 1917, t.h. Tarentola mauritanica. Thamugadia, p. 407.

hybridum Kotlán, 1920, t.h. Equines. [Cylicost.]. Trichonema, p. 56.

hydrochœri Travassos, 1914, t.h. Hydrochœrus capibara. [Viannaia]. Viannella, p. 150.

hydrochœri Travassos, 1916, t.h. Hydrochœrus capibara. Capillaria, p. 26.

*hypostomum (Rud., 1819) Duj., 1845, t.h. Antilope rupicapra, Cervus capreolus, Ovis aries. [Sclerost.]. Bunostomum, p. 109.

*hypostomus Rud., 1819, t.h. Antilope rupicapra. [Str.]. Chabertia, p. 89.

hystrix Diesing, 1851, t.h. Podocnemis erythroc. [Asc.]. Atractis, p. 245.

icosiensis Seurat, 1917, t.h. Gingylus ocellatus. [Strongyluris]. Spinicauda, p. 225.

ignotus Jaegerskiöld, 1909, t.h. Ardea cocoi, etc. Eustrongylides, p. 180.

iguanæ Thapar, 1925, t.h. Iguana tuberculata. Alæuris, p. 203.

iheringi Travassos, 1918, t.h. Dasyprocta sp. Thelazia, p. 318.

*ihlei Kotlán, 1921, t.h. Equines. [Cylicost.]. Trichonema, p. 56.

immitis Leidy, 1856, t.h. Canis fam. [Fil.]. Dirofilaria, p. 393.

immutatum Ward and Magath, 1916, t.h. Amia calva. Haplonema, p. 326.

impar Schneider, 1866, t.h. Osmerus eperlanus. [Ancyracanthus]. Cystidicola, p. 324.

imparidentatum Quiel, 1919, t.h. Equines. Poteriostomum, p. 61.

incerta Smith, 1908, t.h. parrakeets. [Spiropt.]. Habronema, p. 297.

incrassatum Diesing, 1851, t.h. Sorex tetragonurus. [Trichosoma]. Capillaria, p. 26.

incurva Linstow, 1908, t.h. Erinaceus frontalis. Physaloptera, p. 354.

incurva Rud., 1819, t.h. Xiphias gladius. [Asc.]. Contracæcum, p. 282.

indica Chandler, 1924, t.h. Cissa chinensis. Hamulofilaria, p. 398.

indica Sweet, 1915, t.h. Bos bubalis, B. indicus. Onchocerca, p. 414.

indica Ware, 1924, t.h. Indian elephant. [Pteridopharynx]. Murshidia, p. 79.

indicum Baylis, 1921, t.h. Elephas indicus. Parabronema, p. 336.

indicus Ortlepp, 1923, t.h. Zamenis mucosus, Tropidonotus piscator. Kalicephalus, p. 114.

indicus Railliet and Henry, 1910, t.h. Tapirus indicus. Brachyclonus, p. 101.

inermicauda Baylis, 1923, t.h. Tarentola annularis. Pharyngodon, p. 194.

inermis Gedoelst, 1919, t.h. Cranorrhinus corrugatus. [Gilsonia]. Hadjelia, p. 302.

inermis Linstow, 1879, t.h. Astur nisus. [Tropidocerca]. Tetrameres, p. 363.

inermis Linstow, 1906, t.h. Sciurus prevosti. Physaloptera, p. 354.

inermis Molin, 1861, t.h. Bothrops jararaca, etc. Kalicephalus, p. 114.

inermis Zeder, 1800, t.h. Muræna anguilla. [Gœzia]. Spinitectus, p. 349.

*inflata Drasche, 1884, not Linstow, 1883, t.h. Testudo græca. [Oxy.]. Mehdiella, p. 201.

inflata Mehlis, 1846, t.h. Charadrius pluvialis, Ciconia nigra. [Spiropt.]. Tetramere:, p. 363.

inflata Molin, 1860, t.h. Falco unicinctus. [Spiropt.]. Physaloptera, p. 354.

*inflatus Schneider, 1866, t.h. Bos taurus. [Str.]. Œsophagostomum, p. 87.

*inflexa Zeder, 1800, of Rud., 1819, t.h. Anas boschas dom., etc. [Fus.]. Ascaridia, p. 268.

inflexocaudata von Siebold, 1842, t.h. common dolphin. [Fil.]. Halocercus, p. 171.

inflexum Rud., 1819, t.h. Turdus cyaneus. [Trichosoma]. Capillaria, p. 26.

*inflexus Duj., 1845, not Rud., 1809, t.h. Delphinus phocæna. Stenurus, p. 170.

inflexus Rud., 1809, t.h. Delphinus phocæna. [Str.]. Pseudalius, p. 168.

*infundibulicola Linstow, 1903, t.h. Python reticulatus. [Asc.]. Ophidascaris, p. 263.

infundibulum Linstow, 1906, t.h. Hystrix cristata. [Trichoc.]. Trichuris, p. 23.

ingluvicola Ransom, 1904, t.h. Gallus domesticus. Gongylonema, p. 314.

insigne Boulenger, 1917, t.h. Equus cab. [Cylichnost.]. Trichonema, p. 56.

insignis Diesing, 1851, t.h. Delphinus amazonicus. [Peritrachelius]. Anisakis, p. 273.

*insignis Schneider, 1866, t.h. Picus. [Fil.]. Hamatospiculum, p. 396.

instabilis Railliet, 1893, t.h. Ovis aries, etc. [Str.]. Trichostrongylus, p. 119.

interlabiata Ortlepp, 1923, t.h. Rhizothera longirostris. Heterakis, p. 216.

intermedia Theiler, 1923, t.h. zebra. Cylindropharynx, p. 64.

intermedius Monning, 1924, t.h. Varanus sp. Strongylus, p. 37.

intermedius Neveu-Lemaire, 1924, t.h. Rhinoceros bicornis. Grammocephalus, p. 104.

intermedius Oerley, 1885, t.h. Mustelus lævis. Acanthocheilus, p. 288.

*intermedius Sweet, 1909, t.h. Equus cab. Triodontophorus, p. 45.

*intestinalis Bavay, 1877, t.h. Homo. [Anguillula]. Strongyloides, p. 20.

intorta Gedoelst, 1916, t.h. Bitis spp. [Asc.]. Ophidascaris, p. 263.

invaginata Linstow, 1901, t.h. according to Gendre, 1913, Bubulcus lucidus. [Disph.]. Acuaria, p. 329.

involuta Gedoelst, 1916, t.h. Chamæleon dilepis. [Asc.]. Amplicæcum, p. 279.

involuta Linstow, 1879, t.h. Strix flammea. [Fil.]. Acuaria, p. 329.

*irritans Rivolta, 1884, t.h. Equus cab. [Dermofil.]. Habronema, p. 298.

isolonche Linstow, 1906, t.h. Thaumalea amherstiæ. Heterakis, p. 216.

jacchi Marcel, 1857, t.h. Jacchus sp. [Asc.]. Subulura, p. 228.

javensis Vevers, 1922, t.h. Tragulus stanleyanus. Setaria, p. 423.

jugadornata Solowiow, 1912, t.h. Anas boschas. Echinuria, p. 331.

jugurthæ Seurat, 1918, t.h. tortoises. Tachygonetria, p. 199.

kachugæ Baylis and Daubney, 1922, t.h. Kachuga smithii. Camallanus, p. 378.

kachugæ Stewart, 1914, t.h. Kachuga lineata. [Oxysoma]. Spironoura, p. 239.

kachugæ Stewart, 1914, t.h. Kachuga lineata. Atractis, p. 245.

*kashinathi Lane, 1917, t.h. Capra hircus. Bunostomum, p. 109.

katangensis Gedoelst, 1916, t.h. Petrodromus tetradactylus. [Grammophora]. Katanga, p. 417.

*kathlena Lane, 1914, t.h. Chelone midas. Kathlania, p. 236.

kempi Baylis and Daubney, 1922, t.h. Testudo elongata. Zanclophorus, p. 241.

kingi Leiper, 1913, t.h. Homo. Syngamus, p. 157.

kirghisensis Skrjabin, 1916, t.h. Aguila imperialis. [Asc. Porrocæcum, p. 281.

kollari Molin, 1858, t.h. Chrysophrys aurata. [Lecanoc.]. Gœzia, p. 285.
kuelzi Rodenwaldt, 1910, t.h. Cephalophus maxwelli. [Fil.]. Dirofilaria, p. 394.
kükenthallii Cobb, 1888, t.h. Beluga leucas. [Asc.]. Anisakis, p. 273.

labialis Pane, 1864, t.h. Homo. [Fil.]. Gongylonema, p. 314.
*labiata Creplin, 1825, t.h. Ciconia nigra. [Fil.]. Contortospiculum, p. 430.
labiato-papillosa Aless., 1838, t.h. Bos taurus. [Fil.]. Setaria, p. 423.
labiatum Looss, 1901, t.h. Equus. [Cylichnost.]. Trichonema, p. 56.
*labiatum var. *digitata* Ihle, 1921, t.h. Equines. [Cylicost.]. Trichonema, p. 56.
labiodentata Linstow, 1899, t.h. Mus navalis. [Spiropt.]. Protospirura, p. 305.
labiostrongylus n. sp., t.h. Macropus sp. Labiostrongylus, p. 67.
*labiotruncata Molin, 1858, t.h. Tinamus adspersus. [Fil.]. Tetracheilonema, p. 439.
labratum Looss, 1900, t.h. Equus. [Cyathost.]. Trichonema, p. 56.
*lacertæ Schrank, 1788, t.h. lizards. [Trichoc.]. Sclerotrichum, p. 30.
laciniatus Molin, 1860, t.h. Rallus cayennensis. [Histioc.]. Schistorophus, p. 367.
*lacrymalis Gurlt, 1831, in part, t.h. Equus cab., Bos taurus. [Fil.]. Thelazia, p. 318.
*lacrymalis Gurlt of Baillet, 1866, of Railliet, 1893, t.h. Equus cab., Bos taurus. [Fil.]. Thelazia, p. 318.
lacrymalis (Gurlt, 1831) Railliet and Henry, 1910, t.h. Equus cab. Thelazia, p. 318.
lacustris Zoega, 1776, t.h. many species of fishes. [Echinor.]. Camallanus, p. 378.
lævicauda Seurat, 1914, t.h. Acanthodactylus blanci, Scincus officinalis. [Oxy.]. Pharyngodon, p. 194.
læviconchus Wedl, 1862, t.h. Synodontis schaal. [Cucullanus]. Procamallanus. p. 380.
lævis Duj., 1845, t.h. Arvicola subterraneus, etc. [Str.]. Heligmosomum, p. 142.
lagenorhynchi Baylis and Daubney, 1925, t.h. Lagenorhynchus albirostris. Halo-cercus, p. 172.
lambdiensis Seurat, 1918, t.h. Clemmys leprosa. [Falcaustra]. Spironoura, p. 239.
lambdiensis Seurat, 1918, t.h. tortoises. Tachygonetria, p. 199.
lamellaris Linstow, 1906, t.h. Gavialis gangeticus. Typhlophorus, p. 271.
lamnæ Steiner, 1921, t.h. Lamna cornubica. Phlyctainophora, p. 448.
*lanceolata Molin, 1860, t.h. Crotophaga major. [Spiropt.]. Cyrnea, p. 300.
lanei Witenberg, 1925, t.h. elephant. Murshidia, p. 79.
*laniorum Molin, 1860, t.h. Lanius collurio. [Acuaria]. Viguiera, p. 371.
laplantei Seurat, 1919, t.h. Garrulus glandarius cervicalis. Acuaria, p. 329.
lari E. Blanchard, 1849, t.h. Larus ridibundus. [Cyathost.]. Syngamus, p. 157.
laryngeus Railliet, 1899, t.h. cattle. Syngamus, p. 157.
laticaudata Rud., 1819, t.h. Otis tetrax. [Spiropt.]. Histiocephalus, p. 370.
laticeps Rud., 1819, t.h. Falco lagopus. [Spiropt.]. Acuaria, p. 329.
laverani Railliet and Henry, 1912, t.h. Testudo emys. Cissophyllus, p. 242.
leesei Railliet and Henry, 1910, t.h. camel. Thelazia, p. 318.
leidyella Travassos, 1915, t.h. Colaptes maximus. Capillaria, p. 26.
leidyi Travassos, 1914, t.h. Mus norwegicus. Capillaria, p. 26.
leidyi Travassos, 1917, t.h. Bufo americanus, Cistudo carolina. Oswaldocruzia, p. 127.
leiperi Khalil, 1922, t.h. African elephant. Leiperenia, p. 247.
leiperi Railliet, 1916, t.h. Bufo regularis. [Fil.]. Foleyella, p. 395.
leiperi Skrjabin, 1924, t.h. Spermophilopsis leptodactylus. Physaloptera, p. 354.
lemmi Retzius, 1841, t.h. Lemmus amphibius. [Trichosoma]. Capillaria, p. 26.
leonina Linstow, 1902, t.h. Felis leo. [Asc.]. Toxascaris, p. 259.
leporis Chandler, 1924, t.h. rabbit. Nematodirus, p. 136.
leporis Diesing, 1851, t.h. Lepus timidus. [Trichosoma]. Capillaria, p. 26.
leporis Froelich, 1789; Rud., 1809, t.h. Lepus. [Trichoc.]. Trichuris, p. 23.
*leporis pulmonalis Froelich, 1802; Rud., 1819, t.h. Lepus timidus. [Fil.]. Synthe-tocaulus, p. 163.
*leporum Moniez, 1880, t.h. Lepus cuniculus, etc. [Spiropt.]. Graphidium, p. 135.

leprincei Gendre, 1909, t.h. Macrodipteryx macrodipterus. [Het.]. Allodapa, p. 229.

leptocephala Baylis and Daubney, 1922, t.h. Barbus tor. [Falcaustra]. Spironoura, p. 239.

leptocephalus Rud., 1819, t.h. Bradypus tridactylus. [Leiuris]. Physocephalus, p. 308.

*leptoptera Rud., 1809, t.h. Felis leo. [Asc.]. Toxocara, p. 258, or Toxascaris, p. 260.

leptoptera Rud., 1819, t.h. Falco buteo. [Spiropt.]. Habronema, p. 297.

leptoptili Gedoelst, 1916, t.h. Leptoptilus crumenifer. Echinuria, p. 331.

*leptosomus (Gervais) Seurat, 1917, t.h. Uromastix acanthinurus. [Str.]. Physaloptera, p. 353.

leptostomum Kotlán, 1920, t.h. Equines. [Cylicost.]. Trichonema, p. 56.

leptura Rud., 1819, t.h. Testudo mydas. [Asc.]. Kathlania, p. 236.

leucisci Hesse, 1923, t.h. Leuciscus phoxinus. Capillaria, p. 26.

lhuillieri Seurat, 1916, t.h. Caccabis petrosa. Hadjelia, p. 302.

lhuillieri Seurat, 1918, t.h. Caccabis petrosa. [Tropidocerca]. Tetrameres, p. 363.

lienalis Stiles, 1892, t.h. Bos taurus. [Fil.]. Onchocerca, p. 414.

limbata Leidy, 1856, t.h. Scalops canadensis. Physaloptera, p. 354.

*limbata Railliet and Henry, 1911, t.h. Canis spp., Homo. Toxascaris, p. 260.

lineare Leidy, 1856, t.h. Felis catus. [Trichosoma]. Capillaria, p. 26.

linearis Marotel, 1913, t.h. Ovis aries. Synthetocaulus, p. 164.

lineata Schneider, 1866, t.h. Gallus sp. [Het.]. Ascaridia, p. 268.

*linfatica Brera, 1810, for *lymphatica* Treutler, 1793. [Amularia]. Setaria, p. 423.

*linstowi Hall, 1916, t.h. Microtus arvalis. Heligmosomoides, p. 146.

linstowi Khalil, 1922, t.h. African elephant. Murshidia, p. 79.

linstowi Travassos, 1914. t.h. Crocidura russulus, Talpa europæa. Capilaria, p. 26.

linstowi Travassos, 1918, t.h. Talpa europæa. Viannaia, p. 150.

linstowi nom. nov., t.h. Bufo viridis. Aplectana, p. 209.

loa Guyot, 1778, t.h. Homo. [Fil.]. Loa, p. 417.

lobulata Schneider, 1866, t.h. Delphinus gangeticus. [Asc.]. Contracæcum, p. 282.

lonchoptera Diesing, 1851, t.h. Elephas indicus. [Asc.]. Toxocara, p. 258.

longecaudata Linstow, 1879, t.h. Megacephalon maleo. Heterakis, p. 216.

longecirrata Linstow, 1789, t.h. Geopelia sp. ? [Het.]. Ascaridia, p. 268.

longecirratus Linstow, 1879, t.h. Bos grunniens. [Str.]. Bunostomum, p. 109.

longemucronatus Molin, 1861, t.h. Sus scrofa dom. Globocephalus, p. 48.

longeornatus Molin, 1860, t.h. Ciconia maguari. [Disph.]. Echinuria, p. 331.

longespiculum Railliet and Henry, 1916, t.h. Rana temp. Oxysomatium, p. 203.

longesubulatum Molin, 1861, t.h. Cervus campestris, C. rufus. Eucyathostomum, p. 85.

longevaginatum Linstow, 1879, t.h. Alauda arvensis. [Trichosoma]. Capillaria, p. 26.

*longevaginatus Diesing, 1851, t.h. Homo. [Str.]. Metastrongylus, p. 160.

longevaginatus Molin, 1860, t.h. Ciconia maguari. [Disph.]. Acuaria, p. 329.

longibursa Neveu-Lemaire, 1924, t.h. African rhinoceros. Buissonia, p. 81.

longibursatum Yorke and Macfie, 1918, t.h. Equines. [Cylicost.]. Trichonema, p. 56.

longicauda Leiper, 1911, t.h. zebra. Cylindropharynx, p. 64.

longicaudatus Baylis, 1919, t.h. Rhinoceros sumatrensis. Crossocephalus, p. 250.

longicirrus Dujardin, 1845, t.h. Pleuronectes platessa. Heligmus, p. 288.

longicolle Rud., 1819, t.h. Phasianus gallus, etc. [Trichosoma]. Capillaria, p. 26.

*longicollis Drasche, 1885, not Schneider, 1866, t.h. Testudo græca. [Oxy.]. Tachygonetria, p. 200.

longicollis Schneider, 1866, t.h. Testudo græca. [Oxy.]. Tachygonetria, p. 199.

longicollis Stossich, 1899, t.h. Mullus barbatus. [Dacnitis]. Cucullanus, p. 383.

longicornis Hemprich and Ehrenberg, 1866, t.h. Numenius arquatus, etc. [Ancyracanthus]. Schistorophus, p. 367.

longifilum Duj., 1845, t.h. Accentor modularis. [Calodium]. Capillaria, p. 26.

longipes Ransom, 1911, t.h. Antilocapra americana, Ovis aries. Capillaria, p. 26.

longispiculata nom. nov., t.h. Tarandus rangifer. Nematodirella, p. 140.

longispiculum Sonsino, 1889, t.h. Python molurus. [Trichosoma]. Capillaria, p. 2ʒ.

longissima Ortlepp, 1922, t.h. snakes.   Physaloptera, p. 354.

*longissime spiculatus Romanovitch, 1915, t.h. Tarandus rangifer.   [Microc.].   Nema todirella, p. 140.

longistipes Railliet and Henry, 1909, t.h. dromedary.   Hæmonchus, p. 123.

longistriata Walton, 1923, t.h. Colaptes auratus luteus.   Capillaria, p. 26.

*longus Grassi and Segré, 1885, t.h. Lepus cuniculus.   [Rhabdonema].   Strongyloides, p. 20.

*loveridgei Baylis, 1920, t.h. Mungos fasciatus.   Subulura, p. 228.

lumbricoides Linnæus, 1758, t.h. Homo.   Ascaris, p. 256.

lunatus Travassos, 1914, t.h. Bos taurus.   Hæmonchus, p. 123.

lutzi Barreto, 1918, t.h. Strix sp.   Subulura, p. 228.

lutzi Travassos, 1918, t.h. Penelope sp.   Thelazia, p. 318.

*lymphatica Treutler, 1793, t.h. Homo.   [Hamularia].   Setaria, p. 423.

*macaci Smith, Fox, and White, 1908, t.h. Macacus nemestrinus.   [Globoc.].   Ternidens, p. 89.

macdonaldi Bell, 1881, for *macdonaldii* Dobson, 1880.   Rictularia, p. 345.

macdonaldi Thapar, 1924, t.h. Rhinoceros africanus.   Kiluluma, p. 71.

macdonaldii Dobson, 1880, t.h. Megaderma frons.   [Pterygodermatites].   Rictularia, p. 345.

macieli Travassos, 1915, t.h. Tatus novemcinctus.   [Trichostr.].   Cooperia, p. 132.

macrolaima Gendre, 1922, t.h. a fish.   Rhabdochona, p. 325.

macrolaimus Linstow, 1899, t.h. Testudo pardalis.   [Oxy.].   Tachygonetria, p. 199.

macrolaimus Linstow, 1906, t.h. Plotus melanogaster.   [Disph.].   Acuaria, p. 329.

macronis Stewart, 1914, t.h. Macrones aor.   [Het.].   Subulura, p. 228.

macrophallos Parona, 1889, t.h. Hydrosaurus salvator.   [Fil.].   Diplotriæna, p. 434.

macropodis Chandler, 1924, t.h. Macropus bennetti.   Austrostrongylus, p. 138.

macropodis n.sp., t.h. Macropus sp.   Pharyngostrongylus, p. 67.

macropodis n.sp., t.h. Macropus sp.   Globocephaloides, p. 174.

macropostrongylus n.sp., t.h. Macropus sp.   Macropostrongylus, p. 75.

*macrostoma Linstow, 1875, t.h. Angius fragilis.   [Angiost.].   Rhabdias, p. 18.

macroura Linstow, 1883, t.h. Megaloperdix nigelii.   Heterakis, p. 216.

maculosa Rud., 1802, t.h. Columba dom. gutturosa.   [Asc.].   Ascaridia, p. 268.

magalhãesi R. Blanchard, 1895, t.h. Homo.   [Fil.].   Dirofilaria, p. 394.

magalhãesi Travassos, 1913, t.h. Geotrygon montana.   Ascaridia, p. 268.

magna Taylor, 1925, t.h. Trochurus declivus, Sparus sp.   [Habronema].   Metabronema, p. 299.

magna Thapar, 1924, t.h. Rhinoceros africanus.   Kiluluma, p. 71.

magnilabiatus Molin, 1860, t.h. Platalea ajaja.   [Disph.].   Acuaria, p. 329.

magnipapilla Linstow, 1906, t.h. Lyrurus tetrix.   Ascaridia, p. 268.

magnipapilla Molin, 1860, t.h. Myrmecophaga bivittata.   Physaloptera, p. 354.

major Leiper, 1910, t.h. Felis leo sabakiensis.   Lagochilascaris, p. 261.

*major Raspail, 1829, t.h. Delphinus phocæna.   [Str.].   Pseudalius, p. 168.

malapteruri Baylis, 1923, t.h. Malapterurus electricus.   Dujardinia, p. 277.

malayana Aless., 1905, t.h. Helarctos (Ursus) malayanus.   [Unc.].   Ancylostoma, p. 93.

malayense Ortlepp, 1922, t.h. Felis chaus, Felis tigris, etc.   [Physaloptera].   Chlamydonema, p. 356.

malleus Linstow, 1883, t.h. Corvus cornix.   Physaloptera, p. 354.

mamillaris Molin, 1860, t.h. Corvus cajanus.   [Disph.].   Acuaria, p. 329.

mamillata Linstow, 1897, t.h. Plestiodon aldrovandi.   [Oxy.]   Pharyngodon, p. 194.

manica Duj., 1845, t.h. Fringilla cœlebs.   [Thominx].   Capillaria, p. 26.

mansioni Seurat, 1914, t.h. Buteo vulgaris.   Habronema, p. 297.

mansoni Cobbold, 1879, t.h. Gallus gallus.   [Fil.].   Oxyspirura, p. 320.

*marginata Rud., 1802, t.h. Canis dom.   [Asc.].   Toxocara, p. 258.

*marginata Rüd., 1802, of Leiper, 1907, t.h. Canis dom. Toxascaris, p. 260.

marinus O. F. Mueller, 1779, t.h. Gadus morrhua. Cucullanus, p. 383.

*markusi Ihle, 1920, t.h. Equines. [Hexodontostomum]. Poteriostomum, p. 61.

marshalli Boulenger, 1921, t.h. cattle. Setaria, p. 423.

marshalli Ransom, 1907, t.h. Ovis aries. Ostertagia, p. 125.

marthæ Seurat, 1917, t.h. rock partridge. Lemdana, p. 404.

martis Gmelin, 1790, t.h. Mustela foina, etc. Filaria, p. 390.

mascula Rud., 1819, t.h. Coluber sp. [Asc.]. Spironoura, p. 239.

masculior Railliet and Henry, 1911, t.h. Fennecus zerda. [Belasc.]. Toxocara, p. 258.

massinissæ Seurat, 1918, t.h. tortoise. Tachygonetria, p. 199.

*mastigodes Nitzsch, 1857, t.h. Equus cab. Oxyuris, p. 185.

matronensis Railliet and Henry, 1910, t.h. Corvus cornix. Aprocta, p. 405.

mauritanicus Maupas and Seurat, 1912, t.h. dromedary. Nematodirus, p. 137.

mavis Leiper, 1909, t.h. Turdus musicus. [Fil.]. Aprocta, p. 405.

maxillaris Molin, 1860, t.h. Mephitis chinche. Physaloptera, p. 354.

medinensis Linnæus, 1758, t.h. Homo. [Fil.]. Dracunculus, p. 442.

mediospiralis Molin, 1860, t.h. Dasyprocta agouti, Tapirus americanus. [Spiropt.]. Physocephalus, p. 309.

*megalocephala Cloquet, 1824, t.h. Equus cab. [Asc.]. Parascaris, p. 262.

megalocerca Skrjabin, 1916, t.h. Geckonidæ. Pharyngodon, p. 194.

megalochila Diesing, 1851, t.h. Zacholus austriacus. [Fil.]. Tricheilonema, p. 447.

megaloon Gedoelst, 1917, t.h. Sciurus prevosti. Trichuris, p. 23.

megalostoma Creplin, 1829, th. Falco nisus. Physaloptera, p. 354.

megastoma Rud., 1819, t.h. Equus. [Spiropt.]. Habronema, p. 298.

megatyphlon Rud., 1819, t.h. Lacerta iguana. [Asc.]. Ozolaimus, p. 191.

melanocephalus Rud., 1819, t.h. Scomber colias, etc. [Cucullanus]. Camallanus, p. 378.

meleagris-gallopavo Barile, 1912, t.h. Meleagris gallopavo dom. [Trichosomum]. Capillaria, p. 26.

melis Gedoelst, 1920, t.h. badger. [Belascaris]. Toxocara, p. 258.

membranosa Schneider, 1866, t.h. Rana sp. [Leptodera]. Aplectana, p. 209.

memphisia Khalil, 1922, t.h. African elephant. [Memphisia]. Murshidia, p. 80.

mentulata Railliet and Henry, 1909, t.h. dromedary. Ostertagia, p. 125.·

mephites Solanet, 1909, t.h. Mephites suffocans. Physaloptera, p. 354.

mettami Leiper, 1913, t.h. Equus cab. [Cylicost.]. Trichonema, p. 56.

micipsæ Seurat, 1917, t.h. Chalcides micipsæ. Thelandros, p. 193.

microanalis Skrjabin, 1917, t.h. Erithacus sp. Aprocta, p. 405.

microcephala Rud., 1809, t.h. Ardea comata. [Asc.]. Contracæcum, p. 282.

microcephalus Duj., 1845, t.h. Emys orbicularis. [Cucullanus]. Camallanus, p. 378.

microlaimus Linstow, 1899, t.h. Testudo pardalis. [Oxy.]. Tachygonetria, p. 199.

micropapillata Stossich, 1890, t.h. Pelecanus sp. [Asc.]. Contracæcum, p. 282.

micropenis Travassos, 1915, t.h. Nicticorax violacens, Cancroma cochlearia. Tetrameres, p. 363.

*microptera Rud., 1819, t.h. Canis lupus. [Asc.]. Toxascaris, p. 260.

microspiculum Skrjabin, 1915, t.h. Phalacrocorax carbo. Syngamus, p. 157.

microstoma Drasche, 1884, t.h. Testudo græca. [Oxy.]. Mehdiella, p. 201.

microstoma Schneider, 1866, t.h. Equus cab. [Fil.]. Habronema, p. 298.

micrurus Daubney, 1923, t.h. Macrelaps microlepidotus. [Diaphanocephalus]. Kalicephalus, p. 114.

*micrurus Mehlis, 1831, t.h. Bos taurus. [Str.]. Dictyocaulus, p. 162.

mingazzinii Rizzo, 1902, t.h. Tropidonotus natrix. [Trichosoma]. Capillaria, p. 26.

minima Travassos, 1914, t.h. Tachyphonus cristatus bruneus. Tetrameres, p. 363.

minimum Linstow, 1906, t.h. Felis rubiginosa. [Ankylostomum]. Ancylostoma, p. 93.

minimum Molin, 1857, t.h. Mus musculus. Gongylonema, p. 314.

minor Kuhn, 1829, t.h. Delphinus phocæna. [Str.]. Stenurus, p. 169.

minor Leiper, 1909, t.h. Homo. Lagochilascaris, p. 260.

minor Looss, 1900, t.h. Equus. [Triodontus]. Triodontophorus, p. 45.

minuscula Travassos, 1915, t.h. Tamandua tetradactyla. Viannaia, p. 150.

minuta Beneden, 1873, t.h. Vespertilio dasycneme. Ascarops, p. 386.

minuta Schneider, 1866, t.h. Ateles paniscus, Mycetes seniculus. [Oxy.]. Enterobius, p. 188.

minutum Yorke and Macfie, 1918, t.h. Equines. [Cylicost.]. Trichonema, p. 56.

minutus Baylis and Daubney, 1922, t.h. Naja tripudians. [Diaphanocephalus]. Kalicephalus, p. 114.

minutus Duj., 1845, t.h. Mus sylvaticus, etc. [Str.]. Heligmosomum, p. 142.

minutus Rud., 1819, t.h. Pleuronectes passer. [Cucullanus]. Histiocephalus, p. 370.

mitchelli Sambon, 1907, t.h. Pedetes caffer. Wellcomia, p. 197.

modiglianii Parona, 1897, t.h. Trimeresurus formosus. [Trichosoma]. Capillaria, p. 26.

molini Railliet, 1898, t.h. Dicotyles albirostris. [Str.]. Nematodirus, p. 137.

mombasica Baylis, 1921, t.h. Psammophis subtæniatus. Ophidascaris, p. 263.

monacanthus Diesing, 1853, t.h. Tenebrio molitor. Cephalacanthus, p. 386.

monhystera Linstow, 1902, t.h. Metopoceros (Iguana) cornutus. [Oxy.]. Macracis, p. 191.

monodens Molin, 1860, t.h. Boa constrictor. Physaloptera, p. 354.

monodon Linstow, 1882, t.h. Oidemia nigra. [Str.]. Amidostomum, p. 153.

monopterum Gendre, 1923, t.h. nocturnal birds of prey. Habronema, p. 298.

montgomeryi Boulenger, 1920, t.h. Equines. [Cylicost.]. Trichonema, p. 56.

monticelliana Stossich, 1892, t.h. Otis tarda. Heterakis, p. 216.

mordens Leiper, 1908, t.h. Homo. Physaloptera, p. 354.

morrhuæ Beneden, 1871, t.h. Gadus morrhua. Ascarophis, p. 386.

moucheti Railliet, 1918, t.h. Thryonomys swinderianus. Acheilostoma, p. 49.

mucronata Froelich, 1791, not Schrank, 1780, t.h. Anas. [Asc.]. Amidostomum, p. 153.

mucronatum Ihle, 1920, t.h. Equines. [Cylicost.]. Craterostomum, p. 45.

mucronatum Molin, 1858, t.h. Mustela foina. [Calodium]. Capillaria, p. 26.

mucronatum Molin, 1861, t.h. Dasypus gilvipes. [Diploodon]. Ancylostoma, p. 93.

mucronatum Seurat, 1916, t.h. Erinaceus algirus. Gongylonema, p. 314.

mucronatus Molin, 1861, t.h. Crotalus horridus. Kalicephalus, p. 114.

mucronatus Schlotthauber, 1860, t.h. Picus canis, P. major. Syngamus, p. 157.

multidentatus Baylis and Lane, 1920, t.h. Urogymnus asperrimus. Echinocephalus, p. 343.

multipapillata Drasche, 1882, t.h. Tantalus loculator. [Asc.]. Contracæcum, p. 282.

multipapillosa Condamine and Drouilly, 1878, t.h. Equus cab. [Fil.]. Parafilaria, p. 392.

muricola Gedoelst, 1916, t.h. rat. Protospirura, p. 305.

murinæ Travassos, 1914, t.h. Eunectes murina. Capillaria, p. 26.

muris Gmelin, 1790, t.h. Mus decumanus. [Asc.]. Protospirura, p. 305.

muris Schrank, 1788, t.h. Mus musculus. [Trichoc.]. Trichuris, p. 23.

muris Yokogawa, 1920, t.h. rat. [Heligmosomum]. Nippostrongylus, p. 148.

muris-brasiliensis Diesing, 1861, t.h. Mus brasiliensis. Physaloptera, p. 354.

muris-musculi Diesing, 1861, t.h. Mus musculus. [Trichosoma]. Capillaria, p. 26.

muris-sylvatici Diesing, 1851, t.h. Mus sylvaticus. [Trichosoma]. Capillaria, p. 26.

murshida Lane, 1914, t.h. Elephas indicus. Murshidia, p. 79.

muscæ Carter, 1861, t.h. larval stage in Musca dom., adult in Equines. [Fil.]. Habronema, p. 297.

muscicapæ Linstow, 1878, t.h. Muscicapa atricapilla. [Fil.]. Acuaria, p. 329.

musculi Rud., 1819, t.h. Mus musculus. [Fil.]. Gongylonema, p. 314.

mustelarum Rud., 1809, t.h. Mustela foina, etc. Filaria, p. 391.

mustelarum (Rud., 1819) Beneden, 1858, t.h. Mustela foina, etc. Filaroides, p. 439.

mustelarum pulmonalis Rud., 1819, t.h. Mustela foina, etc. [Fil.]. Filaroides, p. 439.

muticus Mueller, 1777, t.h. Gadus morrhua. Cucullanus, p. 381.

mwanzæ Daubney, 1924, t.h. warthog, roan antelope. Œsophagostomum, p. 87.

mycetis nom. nov., t.h. Micetes coraya. Ancylostoma, p. 93.

myoxi-nitelæ Diesing, 1851, t.h. Myoxus nitela. [Trichosoma]. Capillaria, p. 26.

mystax Zeder, 1800, t.h. Felis dom. [Fus.]. Toxocara, p. 258.

naiæ Gedoelst, 1916, t.h. Naja nigricollis. [Asc.]. Ophidascaris, p. 263.

nanum Ihle, 1919, t.h. Equines. [Cylicost.]. Trichonema, p. 56.

narium Linstow, 1901, t.h. Buteo sp. Aprocta, p. 405.

nasicola Linstow, 1899, t.h. Capra hircus, Cervus rufus. Syngamus, p. 157.

nasilionis Gedoelst, 1916, t.h. Nasilio brachyrhynchus. Physaloptera, p. 354.

nassatum Looss, 1900, t.h. Equus. [Cyathost.]. Trichonema, p. 56.

nassatum var. *parva* Yorke and Macfie, 1918, t.h. Equines. [Cylicost.]. Trichonema, p. 56.

nasua Darling, 1911, t.h. Nasua nasica panamensis. Strongyloides, p. 20.

nasuta Rud., 1819, t.h. Fringilla dom. [Spiropt.]. Acuaria, p. 329.

nasuta Schneider, 1866, t.h. Pelecanus onocrotalus. [Asc.]. Contracæcum, p. 282.

nattereri Cobbold, 1879, t.h. Sus scrofa dom. Stephanurus, p. 52.

nattereri Travassos, 1923, t.h. Crax blumenbachi. Heterakis, p. 216.

neglecta Diesing, 1851, t.h. Pelophylax escul. [Fil.]. Icosiella, p. 425.

neglecta Diesing, 1851, t.h. Thynnus vulg. Oncophora, p. 31.

neglectus Jægerskiöld, 1909, t.h. Numenius arquatus, etc. Hystrichis, p. 181.

nematodiriformis Travassos, 1918, t.h. Muridæ. Heligmosomum, p. 143.

neoplastica Fibiger and Ditlevsen, 1914, t.h. Mus decumanus, etc. [Spiropt.]. Gongylonema, p. 314.

neotoma Hall, 1916, t.h. Neotoma cinerea rupicola, etc. Nematodirus, p. 137.

neveu-lemairei Witenberg, 1925, t.h. elephant. [Pterygopharynx, misprint for Pteridopharynx]. Murshidia, p. 80.

nicollei Seurat, 1918, t.h. tortoise. Tachygonetria, p. 199.

nidifer Linton, 1900, t.h. Galeocerdo tigrinus. Acanthocheilus, p. 288.

nigeriæ Leiper, 1911, t.h. large rodent. Trachypharynx, p. 64.

nigeriensis Ortlepp, 1923, t.h. Nigerian snake. Kalicephalus, p. 114.

nigra Gedoelst, 1916, t.h. Crocodilus niloticus. [Asc.]. Dujardinia, p. 277.

nigrescens Linstow, 1906, t.h. Rana hexadactyla. [Cucullanus]. Camallanus, p. 378.

nigrovenosa Gœze, 1800, t.h. frogs, toads. [Asc.]. Rhabdias, p. 18.

ninnii Stossich, 1891, t.h. Corvus cornix. [Fil.]. Diplotriæna, p. 434.

nitida Travassos, 1919, t.h. Cobra sp. [Florencioia]. Spironoura, p. 239.

noctuæ Seurat, 1913, t.h. Carine noctua glaux. Acuaria, p. 330.

noctuæ Seurat, 1914, t.h. Carine noctua glaux. Allodapa, p. 229.

nodosus Rud., 1809, t.h. Mus musculus. [Trichoc.]. Trichuris, p. 23.

nodularis Rud., 1809, t.h. Anser. [Str.]. Amidostomum, p. 153.

nodulosa Rud., 1820, t.h. Lanius collurio. [Fil.]. Contortospiculum, p. 430.

nodulosus Rud., 1803, t.h. Anser. [Str.]. Amidostomum, p. 153.

nœrneri Railliet and Henry, 1907, t.h. deer. Dictyocaulus, p. 162.

nouveli Seurat, 1914, t.h. Himantopus himant. [Tropidocerca]. Tetrameres, p. 363.

nouveli Seurat, 1915, t.h. Genetta afra bonapartei. Habronema, p. 298.

nudicauda Ortlepp, 1924, t.h. deer. Setaria, p. 423.

numidæ Leiper, 1908, t.h. Numida ptilorhyncha. Heterakis, p. 216.

numidica Seurat, 1914, t.h. Felis ocreata. Protospirura, p. 305.

numidica Seurat, 1915, t.h. Vulpes vulpes atlantica. [Allodapa]. Numidica, p. 230.

numidica Seurat, 1917, t.h. Dipodillus campestris. Physaloptera, p. 354.

numidica Seurat, 1917, t.h. Lepus pallidior, L. kabylicus. [Fil.]. Micipsella, p. 419.

numidica Seurat, 1918, t.h. tortoise. Tachygonetria, p. 200.

numidica Seurat, 1920, t.h. heron. [Desmidocerca]. Desmidocercella, p. 321.

numidicum Seurat, 1917, t.h. Rana ridibunda. [Porrocæcum]. Angusticæcum, p. 279.

numidicus Seurat, 1917, t.h. Fennecus zerda. Streptopharagus, p. 312.

numidicus Seurat, 1918, t.h. tortoise. Thelandros, p. 193.

obconica Baird, 1860, t.h. Uranops angulatus. [Asc.]. Ophidascaris, p. 263.

obesa Diesing, 1851, t.h. Hydrochœrus capybara. [Oxy.]. Protozoophaga, p. 191.

obesa Seurat, 1915, t.h. Caccabis petrosa spatzi. Hartertia, p. 305.

obliquus Daubney, 1923, t.h. Bitis arietans, B. gabonica, etc. [Diaphanocephalus]. Kalicephalus, p. 114.

*obtusa Rud., 1819, t.h. Mus musculus. [Spiropt.]. Protospirura, p. 305.

obtusa Rud., 1802, not Schneider, 1866, t.h. Hirundo rustica. [Fil.]. Diplotriæna, p. 434.

*obtuse-caudatum Diesing, 1861, t.h. Brazilian birds. [Monopetalonema]. Contortospiculum, p. 430.

obtusissima Molin, 1860, t.h. Bothrops jararacca, etc. Physaloptera, p. 354.

obtusiusculum Rud., 1819, t.h. Ardea grus. [Trichosoma]. Capillaria, p. 26.

*obtuso-caudata Rud., 1819, t.h. Picus lineatus. [Fil.]. Contortospiculum, p. 430.

obtusus Duj., 1845, t.h. Caprimulgus europæus. [Eucamptus]. Coronofilaria, p. 411.

obtusus Duj., 1845, t.h. Scyllium catulus. Proleptus, p. 358.

obvelata Creplin, 1825, t.h. Larus maximus, etc. [Spiropt.]. Cosmocephalus, p. 338.

obvelata Rud., 1802, t.h. Mus musculus. [Asc.]. Syphacia, p. 195.

occidentalis Ransom, 1907, t.h. Ovis aries. Ostertagia, p. 125.

ocreatus Railliet and Henry, 1907, t.h. sheep. Synthetocaulus, p. 164.

octocornutus Molin, 1860, t.h. Psittacus macao. Elaphocephalus, p. 439.

oculata Linstow, 1899, t.h. Python reticulatus. [Asc.]. Polydelphis, p. 266.

oldi Goodey, 1924, t.h. warthog, roan antelope. Œsophagostomum, p. 87.

olympioi Barreto, 1918, t.h. Crypturus parvirostris, etc. Subulura, p. 228.

omœnsis Neveu-Lemaire, 1924, t.h. African rhinoceros. [Pteridopharynx]. Murshidia, p. 80.

*omra Lane, 1914, t.h. Elephas indicus. Amira, p. 83.

oncophorus Railliet, 1898, t.h. cattle. [Str.]. Cooperia, p. 132.

opaca Barker and Noyes, 1915, t.h. Fiber zibethicus. Trichuris, p. 23.

opeatura Leidy, 1891, t.h. Cyclura bæolopha. Atractis, p. 245.

ophidia Goodey, 1924, t.h. Coluber leopardinus. Rhabdias, p. 18.

*ophisauris Froriep MS. in Rud., 1809, t.h. Lacerta apus. [Trichoc.]. Sclerotrichum, p. 30.

ophthalmica Linstow, 1903, t.h. Turnix taigor. [Cheilospirura]. Oxyspirura, p. 320.

ophthalmicus Linstow, 1898, t.h. Carpophaga brenchleyi. [Ancyracanthus]. Ceratospira, p. 322.

ophthalmophaga Stossich, 1902, t.h. Falco sp. Aprocta, p. 405.

orbitalis Linstow, 1901, t.h. Falco fuscoater. Aprocta, p. 406.

orestiæ Moniez, 1889, t.h. Orestias mülleri. Hedruris, p. 376.

orientale Yokogawa, 1925, t.h. rodents. Gongylonema, p. 314.

orientalis Jimbo, 1914, t.h. Homo. Trichostrongylus, p. 119.

orispinus Molin, 1858, t.h. Ibis falcinellus. Hystrichis, p. 181.

orispinus Molin, 1861, t.h. Anas anser dom, etc. [Str.]. Epomidiostomum, p. 156.

ornata Cram, 1924, t.h. zebra. Cylindropharynx, p. 65.

ornata Duj., 1845, t.h. Rana esculata, R. temporaria. [Oxy.]. Cosmocerca, p. 207.

ornata Linstow, 1897, t.h. Stellio vulg. [Het.]. Strongyluris, p. 223.

*ornata Walter, 1856, not Duj., 1845, t.h. Triton alpestris. [Oxy.]. Cosmocerca, p. 207.

ornatum Duj., 1843, t.h. Anthus pratensis. [Trichosoma]. Capillaria, p. 26.

ornatum Kotlán, 1919, t.h. Equines. [Cylicost.]. Trichonema, p. 56.

*ornatus Dujardin of Schneider, 1866, t.h. Rana temporaria, R. esculenta, etc. [Nematoxys]. Cosmocerca, p. 207.

ornatus Gendre, 1912, t.h. Corvus scapulatus. [Disph.]. Acuaria, p. 330.

orthocerca Stoss., 1902, t.h. Rhea americana. [Het.]. Ascaridia, p. 268.

ortleppi Thapar, 1925, t.h. Podocnemis unifilis. Atractis, p. 245.

oscari Travassos, 1923, t.h. Tropidurus sp. Strongyluris, p. 223.

osculata Rud., 1802, t.h. Phoca vitulina. [Asc.]. Contracæcum, p. 282.

osleri Cobbold, 1879, t.h. Canis fam. [Fil.]. Oslerus, p. 386.

*os-papillatum Piana and Stazzi, 1900, t.h. Elephas indicus. [Unc.]. Bathmostomum, p. 105.

ostertagi Stiles, 1892, t.h. Bos taurus. [Str.]. Ostertagia, p. 125

otolicni Beneden, 1890, t.h. Otolicnus peli. [Str.]. Subulura, p. 228.

ovalis Linstow, 1907, t.h. Podiceps cristatus. [Asc.]. Contracæcum, p. 282.

ovata Linstow, 1907, t.h. Astur melanoleucus. [Physalopt.]. Cyrnea, p. 300.

ovata Zeder, 1803, t.h. Cyprinus gobio. [Fil.]. Philometra, p. 443.

ovatus Linstow, 1906, t.h. Hylobates syndactylus, H. agilis. [Str.]. Œsophagostomum, p. 87.

ovatus Linstow, 1910, t.h. Delphinus tursio. [Pseudalius]. Stenurus, p. 170.

oviflagellis Fourment, 1883, t.h. Merlangus vulgaris. Spinitectus, p. 349.

ovinus Fabricius, 1788 or 1794, t.h. Ovis aries. [Str.]. Chabertia, p. 89.

*ovinus Gmelin, 1790, t.h. Ovis aries. [Str.]. Chabertia, p. 89.

ovis Abildgaard, 1795, t.h. Ovis aries, Bos taurus. [Trichoc.]. Trichuris, p. 23.

ovis Rud., 1819, t.h. Ovis dom. Ascaris, p. 257.

ovocinctus Ransom, 1911, t.h. Antilocapra americana. Strongyloides, p. 20.

ovopunctatum Linstow, 1873, t.h. Sturnus vulg. [Trichosoma]. Capillaria, p. 26.

oxyascaris Travassos, 1920, t.h. Drymobius bifossatus. Oxyascaris, p. 214.

oxycephalus Ward and Magath, 1916, t.h. white bass, black crappie. Camallanus, p. 378.

ozouxi Railliet and Henry, 1909, t.h. Faudias madagascariensis. Diplotriæna, p. 433.

pachicephalus Molin, 1861, t.h. Cygnus olor. Hystrichis, p. 181.

pachycephalum Molin, 1861, t.h. Cercopithecus nictitans, C. sabæus. Œsophagostomum, p. 87.

pachyderma Linstow, 1877, t.h. Podiceps minor. [Trichosoma]. Capillaria, p. 26.

pachyderma Thapar, 1924, t.h. Rhinoceros africanus. Kiluluma, p. 71.

pachykeramotum Wedl, 1856, t.h. Felis guttata. [Trichosoma]. Capillaria, p. 27.

pachyscelis Railliet and Henry, 1910, t.h. sheep, cattle. Gaigeria, p. 101.

*pachystomus Linstow, 1873, t.h. Bliccopsis rutiloides. [Cucullanus]. Rhabdochona, p. 324.

pallaryi Seurat, 1915, t.h. Xerus getulus. [Oxy.]. Syphacia, p. 196.

pallaryi Seurat, 1917, t.h. Agama bibroni. Physaloptera, p. 354.

*pallasii Beneden, 1870, t.h. Beluga leucus. [Str.]. Stenurus, p. 170.

*palpebrarum Baillet, 1858, t.h. Bos taurus. [Fil.]. Thelazia, p. 318.

papillatus Linstow, 1882, t.h. Otis tarda. [Str.]. Ornithostrongylus, p. 128.

papillifer Linstow, 1877, t.h. Hirundo urbica. [Trichosoma]. Capillaria, p. 27.

papillifera Linstow, 1878, t.h. Sylvia palustris. [Fil.]. Acuaria, p. 330.

papillifera Linstow, 1898, t.h. a snake. [Asc.]. Ophidascaris, p. 263.

papilliferus Molin, 1858, t.h. Accipenser sturio. [Cucullanus]. Camallanus, p. 378.

papilligerum Railliet and Henry, 1911, t.h. Tetrao urogallus. [Trichosoma]. Capillaria, p. 27.

papilloradiata Linstow, 1899, t.h. Canis lupus. Physaloptera, p. 354.

*papillosa Bloch, 1782, in part, t.h. bustard. [Asc.]. Heterakis, p. 216.

papillosa Molin, 1860, t.h. Corvus cajanus. [Asc.]. Subulura, p. 228.

papillosa Molin, 1860, t.h. Falco destructor, F. gracilis. [Spiropt.]. Thelazia, p. 318.

*papillosum Blome, 1909, t.h. Tetrao urogallus. [Trichosoma]. Capillaria, p. 27.

papillosum Polonio, 1860, t.h. Mus rattus. [Calodium]. Capillaria, p. 27.
papillosum Wedl, 1856, t.h. sheep. [Trichosoma]. Strongyloides, p. 20.
*papillosus Molin, 1859, t.h. Larus ridibundus. Cosmocephalus, p. 338.
papillosus Rud., 1802, t.h. Corvus caryocatactes. [Str.]. Eustrongylides, p. 180.
*papillosus Zeder, 1800, t.h. Esox lucius. [Cucullanus]. Camallanus, p. 378.
papillotruncata Molin, 1860, t.h. Myrmecophaga jubata. Physaloptera, p. 354.
paradoxa Cobbold, 1864, t.h. Sus scrofa dom. Simondsia, p. 310.
*paradoxa Linstow, 1904, host unknown. [Rictularia]. Seuratia, p. 335.
paradoxa Linstow, 1906, t.h. Didelphys dorsigera. Heterakis, p. 216.
paradoxa Linstow, 1908, t.h. Varanus albigularis. Physaloptera, p. 354.
paradoxus Diesing, 1835, t.h. Cathartes urubu. [Tropisurus]. Tetrameres, p. 361.
*paradoxus Mehlis, 1831, in part, t.h. Sus scrofa dom. [Str.]. Metastrongylus, p. 160.
paradoxus Travassos, 1918, t.h. Mollossidæ. Histiostrongylus, p. 133.
paranecator Travassos and Horta, 1915, t.h. Equus asinus. Acheilostoma, p. 49.
parile Kowalewsky, 1903, t.h. Bubo maximus. [Trichosoma]. Capillaria, p. 27.
paronai Linstow, 1893, t.h. Macroscincus coctei. [Oxy.]. Tachygonetria, p. 200.
*paronai Porta, 1908, t.h. Mus rajah. Gnathostoma, p. 340.
paronai Stossich, 1897, t.h. Buceros nasutus. [Fil.]. Diplotriæna, p. 434.
paronai Stossich, 1902, t.h. Amphibolurus muricatus. [Str.]. Strongyluris, p. 223.
parroti Seurat, 1917, t.h. rock partridge. Cyrnea, p. 300.
parva Gendre, 1923, t.h. Trachelotis senegalensis. Hadjelia, p. 302.
parva Neveu-Lemaire, 1925, t.h. African rhinoceros. Quilonia, p. 73.
parvovum Sweet, 1910, t.h. Gallus domesticus. Oxyspirura, p. 320.
parvumspinosa Railliet and Henry, 1911, t.h. Rhea americana, Capillaria, p. 27.
parvus Chapin, 1925, t.h. Nucifraga caryocatactes. Syngamus, p. 157.
parvus Ortlepp, 1923, t.h. Coronella getula. Kalicephalus, p. 114.
patagonica Linstow, 1880, t.h. Phoca jubata. [Asc.]. Anisakis, p. 273.
pateratum Yorke and Macfie, 1919, t.h. Equines. [Cylicost.]. Trichonema, p. 56.
pavonis Baylis and Daubney, 1922, t.h. Pavo muticus, P. cristatus. Pseudaspidodera. p. 221.
pawlowskyi Skrjabin, 1923, t.h. Otomela phœnicuroides. Splendidofilaria, p. 421.
pectinata Ransom, 1907, t.h. Bos taurus. Cooperia, p. 132.
*pectinatus Diesing, 1838, t.h. Podocnemis expansa. Ancyracanthus, p. 365.
pectinifera Neumann, 1900, t.h. Gallus dom. [Spiropt.]. Streptocara, p. 360.
*pelagica Seurat, 1916, t.h. Larus canus, Puffinus kuhli. [Acuaria]. Seuratia, p. 335.
pelecani Chatin, 1874, t.h. Pelecanus onocrotalus. [Sclerost.]. Gnathostoma, p. 340.
pellucidum Jaegerskiöld, 1893, t.h. Tetrodon stellatus. [Ichthyonema]. Philometra, p. 443.
*pendula Leidy, 1851, t.h. Emys guttata. [Synplecta]. Hedruris, p. 375.
penita Leidy, 1886, t.h. Trachemys scabra. [Asc.]. Cissophyllus, p. 242.
perarmata Linstow, 1910, t.h. Cinixys belliana. Atractis, p. 245.
perarmata Ratzel, 1868, t.h. Tarsius spectrum. [Het.]. Subulura, p. 228.
*pereboomii Gœze, 1782, t.h. man. [Stomachida]. Ascaris, p. 256.
perezi Gendre, 1911, t.h. Chamæleon gracilis. [Oxysoma] Aplectana, p. 209.
*perforans Molin, 1858, t.h. Mustela martes, etc. Filaria, p. 391.
pergracilis Cobbold, 1873, t.h. grouse. [Str.]. Trichostrongylus, p. 119.
perniciosum Linstow, 1885, t.h. Felis tigris. [Ankylostomum]. Galoncus, p. 95.
perpapillatus Jaegerskiöld, 1909, t.h. Ardea leuce, Herodias egretta. Eustrongylides, p. 180.
perspicillum Rud., 1803, t.h. Meleagris gallopavo. [Asc.]. Ascaridia, p. 268.
perstans Manson, 1891, t.h. Homo. [Fil.]. Dipetalonema, p. 427.
phacochœri Allgén, 1921, t.h. Phacochœrus æthiopicus. Odontogeton, p. 213.
phacochœri Gedoelst, 1916, t.h. Phacochœrus africanus. Ascaris, p. 257.
philodryadus Ortlepp, 1923, t.h. Philodryas serra. Kalicephalus, p. 114.
phlebotomus Railliet, 1900, t.h. ruminants. [Monodontus]. Bunostomum, p. 109

phœnicopteri Seurat, 1916, t.h. Phœnicopterus roseus. [Acuaria]. Echinuria, p. 332.

phoxini Linstow, 1887, t.h. Phoxinus lævis. [Asc.]. Contracæcum, p. 282.

phrynosoma Ortlepp, 1922, t.h. Phyrnosoma cornutum. Physaloptera, p. 354.

physalura Bremser, 1851, t.h. Alcedo amazona, etc. [Fil.]. Monopetalonema, p. 438.

*physalura Duj., 1845, t.h. Falco com., etc. [Spiropt.]. Physaloptera, p. 353.

physeteris Baylis, 1923, t.h. Physeter catodon. Anisakis, p. 273.

physignathi Baylis, 1924, t.h. Physignathus lesueurii. Physaloptera, p. 354.

*picorum Leidy, 1856, not Rud., 1819, t.h. Picus colaris. [Trichosoma]. Capillaria, p. 26.

picorum Rud., 1819, t.h. Picus canus, etc. [Trichosoma]. Capillaria, p. 27.

*pictus Creplin, 1849, *trachealis* re-named. [Str.]. Syngamus, p. 157.

pigmentata Gedoelst, 1917, t.h. Sciurus prevosti. Subulura, p. 228.

pigmentata Linstow, 1897, t.h. Cercopithecus albigularis. [Spiropt.]. Streptopharagus, p. 312.

pigmentatus Linstow, 1904, t.h. Lepus nigricollis. [Str.]. Trichostrongylus, p. 119.

pileatum Railliet, Henry, and Bauche, 1914, t.h. elephant. [Cylicost.]. Amira, p. 83.

pillersi n.sp., t.h. blue warbler flycatcher. Coronofilaria, p. 410.

*pinguicola Verrill, 1870, t.h. Sus scrofa dom. [Sclerost.]. Stephanurus, p. 52.

pinnatifidus Diesing, 1839, t.h. Podocnemis expansa. Ancyracanthus, p. 365.

piscicola Baylis and Daubney, 1922, t.h. Barbus tor. Monhysterides, p. 253.

*plagiostoma Parona, 1889, not Wedl, 1861, t.h. Sciurus melanogaster. Rictularia, p. 345.

plagiostoma Wedl, 1861, t.h. Erinaceus auritus. [Pterygodermatites]. Rictularia, p. 345.

plica Rud., 1819, t.h. Canis lupus. [Trichosoma]. Capillaria, p. 27.

plotina Baylis, 1919, t.h. Plotus rufus. Subulura, p. 228.

pluridentatum Alessandrini, 1905, t.h. Oncoides (Felis) mitis. [Unc.]. Ancylostoma, p. 93.

*pluridentatum Quiel, 1919, t.h. Equines. Poteriostomum, p. 61.

poculatum Looss, 1900, t.h. Equus cab. [Cyathost.]. Trichonema, p. 56.

poculum Linstow, 1904, t.h. Equus cab. Oxyuris, p. 185.

poculum Linstow, 1909, t.h. Francolinus adspersus. [Het.]. Subulura, p. 228.

poeli Vryburg, 1897, t.h. ox. [Fil.]. Elæophora, p. 416.

*polaris Looss, 1911, t.h. Vulpes lagopus. Uncinaria, p. 102.

polygyrus Duj., 1845, t.h. Arvicola arvalis, Mus sylvaticus. [Str.]. Heligmosomoides, p. 146.

polyoon Linstow, 1909, t.h. Xerus setosus. [Oxy.]. Dermatoxys, p. 190.

præcinctus Duj., 1845, t.h. Muræna conger. [Stelmius]. Cucullanus, p. 383.

prælonga Duj., 1845, t.h. Colymbus auritus. [Asc.]. Porrocæcum, p. 281.

præputialis Linstow, 1889, t.h. Felis catus. [Physalopt.]. Chlamydonema, p. 356.

prashadi Baylis and Daubney, 1922, t.h. Bungarus fasciatus. Camallanides, p. 379.

*primitivus Molin, 1861, t.h. Phasianus gallus, etc. Syngamus, p. 157.

prionodes Kotlán, 1921, t.h. Equines. [Cylicost.]. Trichonema, p. 56.

pristis Baylis and Daubney, 1922, t.h. Pristis perotteti. Porrocæcum, p. 281.

problematicum Schulz, 1924, t.h Muridæ. Gongylonema, p. 314.

probolurus Railliet, 1896, t.h Camelus dromedarius. [Str.]. Trichostrongylus, p. 119.

procellariæ Diesing, 1851, t.h. Procellaria anglorum. [Spiropt.]. Seuratia, p. 335.

procyonis Baylis and Daubney, 1923, t.h. Procyon sp. Tetragomphius, p. 107.

proni Seurat, 1915, t.h. Herpestes ichneumon. Rictularia, p. 345.

protractum Duj., 1845, t.h. Vanellus cristatus. [Trichosoma]. Capillaria, p. 27.

psophiæ Travassos, 1913, t.h. Psophia viridis. Heterakis, p. 216.

pterophora Creplin, 1854, t.h. Dicholophorus cristatus. [Asc.]. Ascaridia, p. 268.

ptilopachydis Gendre, 1020, t.h. Ptilopachys fuscus. Acuaria, p. 330.

pudendotectus Wostokow, 1905, t.h. pig. Metastrongylus, p. 160.

pudica Seurat, 1914, t.h. Cerastes vipera, etc. Thubunæa, p. 359.

pudica Travassos, 1921, t.h. Dasyprocta agouti.   Viannaia, p. 150.

pugionatus Schlotthauber, 1860, t.h. Corvus pica, Sturnus vulg.   Syngamus, p. 157.

pugnicaudatum Leiper, 1909, t.h. Phacochœrus æliani massaicus. [Cylichnost.].
   Murshidia, p. 80.

pulcherrimus Barreto, 1918, t.h. Caranx lugubris.   Cucullanus, p. 383.

pulchrum Molin, 1857, t.h. Sus scrofa fera.   Gongylonema, p. 314.

**pulchrum* Seurat, 1912 and 1914, not Molin, 1857, t.h. Erinaceus algirus.   Gongy-
   lonema, p. 314.

**pulmonalis* Froelich, 1802, in part, t.h. Lepus sp. [Fil.].   Capillaria, p. 26, and
   Synthetocaulus, p. 163.

punctata Gedoelst, 1916, t.h. Pseudotantulus ibis. [Kathleena].   Contracæcum,
   p. 282.

punctatus Linstow, in Schnyder, 1907, t.h. Bos taurus. [Str.].   Cooperia, p. 132.

pungens Schneider, 1866, t.h. Turdus cyaneus. [Fil.].   Diplotriæna, p. 434.

pusilla Miranda, 1924, t.h. Amphisbæna sp.   Aplectana, p. 209.

pusilla Seurat, 1918, t.h. tortoises.   Tachygonetria, p. 200.

pusilla Travassos, 1914, t.h. Didelphis aurita.   Viannaia, p. 150.

pusilla Travassos, 1914, t.h. Sturnira lilium.   Capillaria, p. 27.

pusilla Travassos, 1915, t.h. Turdus rufiventris, Platycichla flavipes.   Tetrameres,
   p. 363.

putaustralis Lane, 1914, t.h. domestic fowl.   Heterakis, p. 216.

putorii Rud., 1819, t.h. Mustela putorius. [Trichosoma].   Capillaria, p. 27.

pyramidalis Linstow, 1879, t.h. Cholœpus didactylus.   Physaloptera, p. 354.

pyromelanæ n.sp., t.h. Pyromelana oryx.   Diplotriæna, p. 434.

**pythonis* Retzius, 1830, of Railliet and Henry, 1910, in part, t.h.   Python bivittatus.
   [Asc.].   Polydelphis, p. 266.

quadricornis Wedl, 1862, t.h. Uræus haje. [Asc.].   Polydelphis, p. 266.

quadricuspe Walton, 1923, t.h. Buforides virescens virescens.   Contracæcum, p. 282.

**quadridentatum* Molin, 1861, t.h. Mycetes coraya. [Diploodon].   Ancylostoma, p. 93.

quadridentatus Molin, 1858, t.h. Mustelus plebejus.   Acanthocheilus, p. 288.

**quadridentatus* Siebold, 1851, *duodenale* re-named. [Str.].   Ancylostoma, p. 92.

quadrilabiata Molin, 1858 , t.h. Tinamus rufescens, T. maculosus. [Fil.].   Tetracheilonema, p. 439.

quadriloba Rud., 1819, t.h. Picus viridis. [Spiropt.].   Acuaria, p. 330.

quadripapillosa Molin, 1860, t.h. Platalea ajaja. [Spiropt.].   Pelecitus, p. 412.

quadriradiatus Stevenson, 1904, t.h. Columba livia dom. [Str.].   Ornithostrongylus,
   p. 128.

**quadrispina* Diesing, 1851, t.h. Mustela foina, etc.   Filaria, p. 391.

quadriverrucosa Molin, 1858, t.h. Dendrocalaptes picus. [Fil.].   Diplotriæna, p. 434.

quadrivittati Hall, 1916, t.h. Eutamias quadrivittatus.   Warrenius, p. 151.

quadrovaria Leiper, 1908, t.h. Varanus niloticus.   Physaloptera, p. 354.

**quilona* Lane, 1914, t.h. Elephas indicus.   Quilonia, p. 73.

radiata Linstow, 1906, t.h. Leptonychotes weddelli. [Asc.]   Contracæcum, p. 282.

radiatum Looss, 1900, t.h. Equus. [Cyathost.].   Trichonema, p. 56.

radiatus Rud., 1803, t.h. Bos taurus. [Str.].   Œsophagostomum, p. 87.

**radiatus* Rud. of Schneider, 1866, t.h. Bos taurus. [Str.].   Bunostomum, p. 109.

radiosa Schneider, 1866, t.h. Echidna rhinocerotis. [Asc.].   Ophidascaris, p. 263.

**radula* Schneider, 1866, t.h. Paradoxurus philippinensis. [Fil.].   Gnathostoma, p. 340.

raillieti Neveu-Lemaire, 1924, t.h. African rhinoceros. [Henryella].   Murshidia,
   p. 80.

raillieti Skrjabin, 1915, t.h. Fulica atra.   Amidostomum, p. 154.

raillieti Travassos, 1913, t.h. Didelphis aurita.   Aspidodera, p. 220.

rajæ Diesing, 1851, t.h. Raja batis, R. clavata. [Spiropt.].   Proleptus, p. 358.

ransomi Chapin, 1922, t.h. pig. Gongylonema, p. 314.

ransomia Barker and Noyes, 1915, t.h. Fiber zibethicus. Capillaria, p. 27.

rara Hall and Wigdor, 1918, t.h. Canis familiaris. Physaloptera, p. 354.

rátzii Kotlán, 1919, t.h. Equines. [Cylicost.]. Poteriostomum, p. 61.

rátzii var. *nana* Theiler, 1923, t.h. Equines. Poteriostomum, p. 61.

reclinata Rud., 1819, t.h. Crotophaga major, C. minor. [Asc.]. Subulura, p. 228.

recondita Grassi, 1890, t.h. Canis fam. [Fil.]. Dipetalonema, p. 427.

recta Linstow, 1879, t.h. Podiceps cristatus. [Fil.]. Streptocara, p. 360.

rectangula Linstow, 1906, t.h. Leptonychotes weddelli. [Asc.]. Contracæcum, p. 282.

*recticaudata Costa, 1845, *globiceps* re-named. Philometra, p. 443.

rectovaginatus Molin, 1860, t.h. Falco ater. [Disph.]. Acuaria, p. 330.

*rectum Linstow, 1907, t.h. Elephas africanus. [Sclerost.]. Murshidia, p. 80.

*rectum Linstow, 1899, t.h. Canis megalotis, C. vulpecula. Oxynema, p. 230.

*rectus Linstow, 1906, t.h. Dolichotis patagonica. [Str.]. Graphidioides, p. 140.

rectus Molin, 1860, t.h. Falco femoralis, F. unicinctus. [Disph.]. Acuaria, p. 330.

recurvata Linstow, 1901, t.h. Eurystomus afer. [Het.]. Subulura, p. 228.

recurvum Solger, 1877, t.h. Crocodilus acutus. [Trichosoma]. Capillaria, p. 27.

renalis Gœze, 1782, t.h. Canis familiaris. [Asc.]. Dioctophyme, p. 178.

*renium Drabble, 1922, t.h. pig. [Sclerost.]. Stephanurus, p. 52.

renniei Railliet, Henry, and Joyeux, 1913, t.h. elephant. [Evansia]. Quilonia, p. 73.

repens Railliet and Henry, 1911, t.h. Canis fam. Dirofilaria, p. 394.

resectum Duj., 1843, t.h. Corvus monedula. [Trichosoma]. Capillaria, p. 27.

reticulata Diesing, 1841, t.h. Equus cab. Onchocerca, p. 414.

reticulata Linstow, 1899, t.h. Ardea cocoi. [Asc.]. Porrocæcum, p. 281.

reticulata Schlotthauber, 1860, t.h. Equus cab. Piguris, p. 448.

*retortæformis Bremser, 1811, not Zeder, 1800, t.h. Lepus cuniculus fer. [Str.]. Graphidium, p. 135.

retortæformis Zeder, 1800, t.h. Lepus. [Str.]. Trichostrongylus, p. 119.

retusa Rud., 1819, t.h. Lacerta teguixin. Physaloptera, p. 354.

retusum Railliet, 1893, t.h. Gallus gallus. [Trichosoma]. Capillaria, p. 27.

revoluta Rud., 1819, t.h. Charadrius himantopus. [Spiropt.]. Chevreuxia, p. 333.

rheæ Owen, 1843, t.h. Rhea americana, etc. [Fil]. Contortospiculum, p. 430.

rhinocerotis Neveu-Lemaire, 1924, t.h. African rhinoceros. Buissonia, p. 80.

rhinocerotis Neveu-Lemaire, 1924, t.h. African rhinoceros. [Memphisia]. Murshidia, p. 80.

rhinocerotis Neveu-Lemaire, 1924, t.h. rhinoceros. [Khalilia]. Amira, p. 84.

rhinocerotis Neveu-Lemaire, 1924, t.h. rhinoceros. Quilonia, p. 73.

rhinocerotis Thapar, 1924, t.h. African rhinoceros. Kiluluma, p. 71.

rhodesi (Desmarest, 1827) Railliet and Henry, 1910, for *rhodesii* (Desmarest, 1827) Blainville, 1828. Thelazia, p. 317.

rhodesiense n. sp., t.h. African elephant. Parabronema, p. 337.

rhodesiensis Yorke and Macfie, 1920, t.h. zebra. Cylindropharynx, p. 65.

rhodesii (Desmarest, 1827) Blainville, 1828, t.h. Bos taurus. Thelazia, p. 317.

rigida Rud., 1909, t.h. Lophius piscatorius. [Asc.]. Contracæcum, p. 282.

rigidulum Duj., 1845, t.h. Accentor modularis. [Trichosoma]. Capillaria, p. 27.

rima Linstow, 1906, t.h. Otis haubara. [Het.]. Subulura, p. 228.

rimula Linstow, 1903, t.h. Centropus sinensis. [Het.]. Subulura, p. 228.

rischta Skrjabin, 1923, t.h. Pseudaspius leptocephalus. Philometra, p. 443.

robusta Beneden, 1871, t.h. Raja circularis. [Coronilla]. Proleptus, p. 358.

*robusta Drasche, 1884, t.h. Testudo græca. [Oxy.]. Mehdiella, p. 201.

robustum Giles, 1892, t.h. Equus mulus. [Sclerost.]. Œsophagodontus, p. 43.

*robustus Diesing, 1838, t.h. Felis concolor. [Cheiracanthus]. Gnathostoma, p. 340.

rodentorum Hall, 1916, t.h. Thomomys fossor. Ransomus, p. 42.

rodhaini Gedoelst, 1916, t.h. Plotus rufus. [Kathleena]. Contracæcum, p. 282.

ræmeri Linstow, 1905, t.h. Macropus antilopinus. [Fil.]. Dipetalonema, p. 427.

rondoni Travassos, 1919, t.h. Piaractus brachypomus. Rondonia, p. 249.

rosarius Connal, 1912, t.h. Nycticorax griseus. [Asc.]. Contracæcum, p. 282.

roscidus Railliet, 1911, t.h. Cervus sp. Nematodirus, p. 137.

roseus Leidy, 1851, t.h. Testudo sp. [Cucullanus]. Cissophyllus, p. 242.

rosmari Baylis, 1916, *bicolor* Baird, 1868, re-named. [Asc.]. Anisakis, p. 273.

rothschildi Seurat, 1915, t.h. Elephantulus deserti. Spirura, p. 294.

rotundata Linstow, 1883, t.h. Otis macquini. [Fil.]. Hartertia, p. 306.

rotundata Molin, 1860, t.h. Cantharus vulg. [Dacnitis]. Cucullanus, p. 383.

rotundatum Linstow, 1903, t.h. Centropus sinensis. [Lissonema]. Aprocta, p. 406.

rotundatum Linstow, 1906, t.h. Bufo viridis. [Angiost.]. Rhabdias, p. 18.

rotundatus Linstow, 1907, t.h. Lanius minor. [Disph.]. Acuaria, p. 330.

*rubicunda Schneider, 1866, t.h. Python molurus. [Asc.]. Ophidascaris, p. 263.

rubidus Hassall and Stiles, 1892, t.h. Sus scrofa dom. [Str.]. Hyostrongylus, p. 121.

rubrovenosa Schneider, 1866, t.h. Bufo cinereus. [Leptodera]. Rhabdias, p. 18.

rubrum Linton, 1892, t.h. Spizella socialis. [Trichosoma]. Capillaria, p. 27.

rude Rud., 1810, t.h. Homo. (not a parasite). [Diceras]. Ditrachyceros, p. 447.

rudicaudatum Railliet and Henry, 1909, t.h. Lagost. trichodactylus. [Graphidium]. Graphidioides, p. 140.

rufescens Leuckart, 1865, t.h. Ovis aries. [Str.]. Synthetocaulus, p. 164.

rufus Khalil, 1922, t.h. beaver. Travassosius, p. 131.

rugatus Monnig, 1925, t.h. sheep. Trichostrongylus, p. 119.

ruwenzorii Parona, 1907, t.h. Arvicanthus abyssinicus, Mus ugandæ. Physaloptera, p. 354.

rytipleurites Deslongchamps, 1824, t.h. Blatta orientalis. [Fil.]. Spirura, p. 294.

sagitta Linstow, 1907, t.h. Tragelaphus scriptus. [Fil.]. Wuchereria, p. 402.

sagittatum Kotlán, 1920, t.h. Equines. [Cylicost.]. Trichonema, p. 56.

sagittatus Mueller, 1890, t.h. Cervus elephas. [Str.]. Synthetocaulus, p. 164.

saimiris Cameron, 1923, t.h. Saimiris sciurea. Viannaia, p. 150.

*salaris (Gmelin, 1790) Zeder, 1800, t.h. Salmo salar. [Capsularia]. Porrocæcum, p. 280.

salmi Gedoelst, 1923, t.h. pig. Metastrongylus, p. 160.

samboni Baylis, 1922, t.h. Cœndou (Sphingurus) villosus. Wellcomia, p. 197.

sameera Khalil, 1922, t.h. African elephant. Amira, p. 84.

samoense Lane, 1922, t.h. pig. [Crassisoma]. Globocephalus, p. 49.

*sangeri Alessandrini, 1905, not Railliet, 1897, t.h. Elephas indicus. [Uncinaria]. Bunostomum, p. 109.

sangeri Cobbold, 1879, t.h. Elephas indicus. [Doch.]. Bathmostomum, p. 105.

sanguinea Rud., 1819, t.h. Cyprinus gibelio. [Fil.]. Philometra, p. 443.

sanguinolenta Rud., 1819, t.h. Canis lupus. [Spiropt.]. Spirocerca, p. 296.

sarasinorum Meyer, 1896, t.h. Stenops gracilis. [Fil.]. Subulura, p. 228.

sauricola Chapin, 1924, t.h. Testudo denticulata. Sauricola, p. 62.

scalprum Linstow, 1908, t.h. Raphicercus campestris. [Fil.]. Setaria, p. 423.

scapiceps Leidy, 1866, t.h. Lepus sylvaticus. [Fil.]. Dirofilaria, p. 394.

scelopori Gedoelst, 1919, t.h. Sceloporus undulatus. Crytosomum, p. 249.

schebeni Linstow, 1909, t.h. Cynictis penicillata. [Het.]. Subulura, p. 228.

schizothoracis Baylis and Daubney, 1922, t.h. Schizothorax zarudnyi. Contracæcum, p. 282.

schmidtii Linstow, 1874, t.h. Mus decumanus. [Trichosoma]. Capillaria, p. 27.

*scillicola Beneden, 1871, t.h. Mustelus vulg. [Coronilla]. Proleptus, p. 358.

sciuri Parona, 1898, t.h. Sciurus melanogaster. Physaloptera, p. 354.

scleratus Travassos, 1923, t.h. Tropidurus sp. Thelandros, p. 193.

*sclerostomum Molin, 1861, t.h. Ciconia nigra. Syngamus, p. 157.

scoleciformis Diesing, 1851, t.h. Dasypus uncinatus, etc. [Aspidoc.]. Aspidodera, p. 220.

scotti Leiper and Atkinson, 1914, t.h. Diomedea melanophrys. [Kathleena]. Contracæcum, p. 282.

scutata Leuckart, 1873, t.h. Bos taurus. [Fil.]. Gongylonema, p. 314.

*securiferum Quiel, 1919, t.h. Equines. [Pseudosclerostomum]. Œsophagodontus, p. 44.

sedecimradiatus Linstow, 1899, t.h. Cavia paca. [Str.]. Heligmostrongylus, p. 145.

*semiarmatum Molin, 1861, t.h. Canis vulpes. Crenosoma, p. 166.

semicircularis Molin, 1861, t.h. Dicotyles torquatus. [Monodontus]. Eumonodontus, p. 99.

semilanceolata Molin, 1860, t.h. Nasua narica. Physaloptera, p. 354.

semilunaris Molin, 1860, t.h. Trogon, etc. T. melanurus. [Spiropt.]. Cyrnea, p. 300.

semiteres Zeder, 1800, t.h. Tringa vanellus. [Fusaria]. Porrocæcum, p. 281.

sergenti Seurat, 1921, t.h. Passer hispaniolensis. Eufilaria, p. 407.

serpentulus Diesing, 1851, t.h. Falco rufipes, etc. [Spiropt.]. Pelecitus, p. 412.

serpentulus Rud., 1809, t.h. Ardea cinerea. [Asc.]. Porrocæcum, p. 281.

serpicula Molin, 1858, t.h. Phyllostoma brevicaudum, etc. [Fil.]. Solenonema, p. 439.

serrata Lane, 1916, t.h. Tryonix gangeticus. Serradacnitis, p. 383.

*serrata Linton, 1901, t.h. Phycis tenuis. [Fil.]. Spinitectus, p. 349.

serrata Schneider, 1866, t.h. Penelope humeralis. [Het.]. Ascaridia, p. 268.

serratus Linstow, 1879, t.h. Felis dom. [Trichoc.]. Trichuris, p. 23.

serratus Looss, 1900, t.h. Equus. [Triodontus]. Triodontophorus, p. 45.

serratus Wright, 1879, t.h. Coregonus albus. [Ancyracanthus]. Cystidicola, p. 324.

setifera Cobb, 1898, t.h. Macropus sp. Zoniolaimus, p. 176.

setosa Seurat, 1918, t.h. tortoise. Tachygonetria, p. 200.

seurati Barreto, 1917, t.h. Caccabis rufa, C. petrosa. Subulura, p. 228.

seurati Skrjabin, 1917, t.h. Falco cenchris. Habronema, p. 298.

sewelli Baylis and Daubney, 1922, t.h. Cœlopeltis monspessulana. Polydelphis, p. 266.

sexalata Molin, 1860, t.h. Dicotyles albirostris, Sus scrofa fera. [Spiropt.]. Physocephalus, p. 308.

*sexalata var. *cristata* Seurat, 1912, t.h. dromedary. [Spiropt.]. Physocephalus, p. 308.

shipleyi Stossich, 1900, t.h. Diomedea exulans. [Gnathost.]. Seuratia, p. 335.

siamensis Baylis, 1920, t.h. Hieremys (Cyclemys) annandalei. [Falcaustra]. Spironoura, p. 239.

*siamensis Levinsen, 1889, t.h. Homo. [Cheiracanthus]. Gnathostoma, p. 340.

siamensis Linstow, 1903, t.h. Centropus sinensis. [Cheilospirura]. Oxyspirura, p. 320.

simiæ Hung See Lu and Höppli, 1923, t.h., macaques. Strongyloides, p. 20.

simile Kowalewsky, 1903, t.h. Turdus pilaris. [Trichosoma]. Capillaria, p. 27.

similis Baird, 1853, t.h. seal. [Asc.]. Anisakis, p. 273.

similis Gendre, 1909, t.h. Coracias abyssinicus, etc. [Het.]. Subulura, p. 228.

similis Travassos, 1914, t.h. Bos taurus. Hæmonchus, p. 123.

similis Travassos, 1920, t.h. Leptodactylus ocellatus. Oxyascaris, p. 214.

*simplex Duj., 1845, Delphinus phocæna. Anisakis, p. 272.

simplex Rud., 1809, t.h. delphin. [Asc.]. Anisakis, p. 273.

simplicidens Ortlepp. 1922, t.h. sleeping lizard. Physaloptera, p. 354.

simpsoni Goodey, 1924, t.h. warthog, roan antelope. Œsophagostomum, p. 87.

simpsoni Leiper, 1911, t.h. a large rodent. Acheilostoma, p. 49.

simus Daubney, 1923, t.h. Naja nigricollis. [Diaphanocephalus]. Kalicephalus, p. 114.

sipunculiforme Baird, 1859, t.h. elephant. [Sclerost.]. Equinurbia, p. 39.

siredonis Baird, 1858, t.h. Siredon mexicanus. Hedruris, p. 376.

skrjabini Baskakow, 1924, t.h. Camellus bactrianus, C. dromedarius. Trichuris, p. 23.

skrjabini Rasowska, 1924, t.h. Camelus dromedarius. Parabronema, p. 337.

smithii Cobbold, 1882, t.h. Elephas indicus. [Fil.]. Parabronema, p. 337.

*socialis Leidy, 1858, t.h. Mustela vison. [Cheiracanthus]. Gnathostoma, p. 340.

sokolowi Skrjabin, 1916, t.h. Halcyon senegaloides. Diplotriæna, p. 434.

solitaria Linstow, 1903, t.h. Dipsadomorphus dendrophilus. [Asc.]. Ophidascari:, p. 263.

solitaria Thapar, 1924, t.h. Rhinoceros africanus. Kiluluma, p. 71.

sonsinoi Linstow, 1894, t.h. Chamæleo vulg. [Het.]. Spinicauda, p. 225.

sonsinoi Linstow, 1895, t.h. Agama mutabilis. Physaloptera, p. 354.

sonsinoi Parona, 1897, t.h. Zamenis viridiflavus. [Trichosoma]. Capillaria, p. 27.

soricicola Nishigori, 1924, t.h. Sorex sp. Hepaticola, p. 28.

southwelli Baylis and Lane, 1920, t.h. Urogymnus asperrimus. Echinocephalus, p. 343.

spathiger Railliet, 1896, t.h. Camelus dromedarius. [Str.]. Nematodirus, p. 137.

speciosum Beneden, 1873, t.h. Vespertilio daubentonii, etc. [Trichosoma]. Capillaria, p. 27.

spectatus Travassos, 1923, t.h. Piaractus brachypomus. [Spectatus]. Spironoura, p. 239.

spelæa Leidy, 1875, t.h. Macropus sp. [Fil.]. Setaria, p. 423.

spermospizæ Linstow, 1879, t.h. Spermospiza guttata. [Fil.]. Diplotriæna, p. 434.

sphærocephala Goodey, 1924, t.h. Bufo vulgaris. Rhabdias, p. 18.

sphærocephala Rud., 1809, t.h. Acipenser sturio. [Asc.]. Tanqua, p. 342, or Cucullanus, p. 383.

spiculigera Rud., 1809, t.h. Pelecanus onocrotalus. [Asc.]. Contracæcum, p. 282.

spinicauda Duj., 1845, t.h. Lacerta muralis. [Oxy.]. Pharyngodon, p. 193.

spinicauda Olfers, 1819, t.h. Lacerta teguixin. [Asc.]. Spinicauda, p. 224.

spinicollis Baylis, 1923, t.h. Lutra sp., Atilax paludinosus. Clœoascaris, p. 283.

spinifera (Rud. or Schneider) Solowiow, 1912, t.h. Scolopax gallinula. Echinuria, p. 332.

spinigerum Owen, 1836, t.h. Felis tigris. Gnathostoma, p. 340.

spinosa Gendre, 1923, t.h. Falco tinnunculus. Habronema, p. 298.

spinosissimus Linstow, in Shipley and Hornell, 1905, t.h. Myliobatis aquila. [Cheiracanthus]. Echinocephalus, p. 343.

*spinosum Willemose-Suhm, 1869, t.h. Brachyotus mystacinus. [Ophiost.]. Rictularia, p. 345.

spinulosum Linstow, 1890, t.h. Fuligula ferina. [Trichosoma]. Capillaria, p. 27.

spinulosus Diesing, 1839, t.h. Sudis gigas. [Lecanoc.]. Gœzia, p. 286.

spinulosus Linstow, 1879, t.h. Capra ibex. [Str.]. Eucyathostomum, p. 85.

spinulosus Molin, 1860, t.h. Glareola austriaca. [Fil.]. Schistorophus, p. 367.

spirale Molin, 1857, t.h. Cervus dama. Gongylonema, p. 314.

spirale Molin, 1858, t.h. Ibis falcinellus. [Trichosoma]. Capillaria, p. 27.

spiralis Baylis, 1923, t.h. Heterobranchus anguillaris. Procamallanus, p. 380.

*spiralis Diesing, 1851, t.h. Alca torda, Larus maximus, etc. [Histioc.]. Cosmocephalus, p. 338.

spiralis Molin, 1858, t.h. Phasianus gallus. [Disph.]. Acuaria, p. 330.

spiralis Molin, 1860, t.h. Bradypus didactylus. [Spiropt.]. Oxyspirura, p. 321, or Onchocerca, p. 414.

spiralis Owen, 1835, t.h. Homo. [Trichina]. Trichinella, p. 33.

spiralis Rud., 1795, t.h. Strix aluco. [Asc.]. Porrocæcum, p. 281.

spiralis Schneider, 1866, t.h. Amphisbæna sp. Physaloptera, p. 354.

spiralis Seurat, 1915, t.h. Bubulcus lucidus. [Tropidocerca]. Tetrameres, p. 363.

*spirillum Pallas, 1781, t.h. Lacerta apoda. [Tænia]. Sclerotrichum, p. 30.

spirostrongylus n. sp., t.h. Macropus sp. Spirostrongylus, p. 70.

spirula Hempr. and Ehrenb., 1828, t.h. Hyrax capensis. Physaloptera, p. 355.

splenæcum Duj., 1843, t.h. Sorex araneus. [Trichosoma]. Capillaria, p. 27.

splendida Hall, 1913, t.h. Canis nebracensis. Rictularia, p. 345.

spumosa Schneider, 1866, t.h. Mus decumanus. [Het.]. Ganguleterakis, p. 218.

squali Duj., 1845, t.h. Squalus galeus. [Dacnitis]. Serradacnitis, p. 383.

squamata Linstow, 1883, t.h. Phalacrocorax carbo. [Fil.]. ? Acuaria, p. 330, and ? Echinuria, p. 332.

squamata Linstow, 1909, t.h. Clemmys guttata. Hedruris, p. 376.

squatinæ Baylis, 1923, t.h. Squatina squatina. Paranisakis, p. 274.

stellæ-polaris Parona, 1901, t.h. Fulmarus glacialis. [Histioc.]. Streptocara, p. 360.

stelmoides Vessichelli, 1910, t.h. Petromyzon planeri. [Dacnitis]. Cucullanus, p. 383.

stenocephala Railliet and Henry, 1907, t.h. Leptonychotes weddelli, Stenorhynchus leptonyx. [Asc.]. Contracæcum, p. 282.

stenocephalus Railliet, 1884, t.h. Canis familiaris. [Dochmius]. Uncinaria, p. 102.

stephanostomum Stossich, 1904, t.h. gorilla. Œsophagostomum, p. 87.

stephanostomum var. *thomasi* Railliet and Henry, 1909, t.h. Homo. Œsophagostomum, p. 87.

stercoralis Bavay, 1876, t.h. Homo. [Anguillula]. Strongyloides, p. 19.

stereura Rud., 1819, t.h. Falco nævius. [Spiropt.]. Thelazia, p. 318.

stewarti Baylis and Daubney, 1922, t.h. Kachuga smithii, Hardella thurgi. [Falcaustra]. Spironoura, p. 239.

stigmatura Leidy, 1866, t.h. Salvelinus namaycush. [Fil.]. Cystidicola, p. 324.

stossichi Setti, 1897, t.h. Hystrix cristata. [Oxy.]. Syphacia, p. 196.

strelnikowi Skrjabin, 1916, t.h. Tinamus sp. Ascaridia, p. 268.

streptœsophageus Connal, 1912, t.h. Agama colonorum. Strongyluris, p. 223.

striata Linstow, 1883, t.h. Tropidonotus hydrus, Ciconia alba. [Physalopt.]. Cyrnea, p. 300.

striata Molin, 1858, t.h. Felis concolor, F. macroura. [Fil.]. Dirofilaria, p. 394.

striata Molin, 1858, t.h. Felis concolor, F. macroura. [Fil.]. Solenonema, p. 439.

striatum Linstow, 1879, t.h. Astur nisus. [Trichosoma]. Capillaria, p. 27.

striatus Monticelli, 1889, t.h. Scyllium sp. Echinocephalus, p. 343.

striatus Zeder, 1800, t.h. Erinaceus europæus. [Str.]. Crenosoma, p. 165.

strigosus Duj., 1845, t.h. Lepus cuniculus fer. [Str.]. Graphidium, p. 135.

stroma Linstow, 1884, t.h. Mus sylvaticus. [Oxy.]. Syphacia, p. 196.

stroma Linstow, 1899, t.h. Grus paradisea. [Het.]. Ascaridia, p. 268.

strongylina Rud., 1819, t.h. Crypturus sp., Tetrao uru. [Asc.]. Subulura, p. 228.

strongylina Rud., 1819, t.h. Sus fera. [Spiropt.]. Arduenna, p. 308.

strongyloides Dies., 1851, t.h. Podinema teguixin. Diaphanocephalus, p. 113.

strongyloides Leuckart, 1883, t.h. man. [Rhabdonema]. Strongyloides, p. 20.

strumosa Frœlich, 1791, t.h. Talpa. [Asc.]. Spirura, p. 294.

strumosum Reibisch, 1893, t.h. Phasianus colchicus. [Trichosomum]. Capillaria, p. 27.

strumosus Molin, 1861, t.h. Coluber lichtensteinii. Kalicephalus, p. 114.

struthionis Horst, 1885, t.h. Struthio molybdophanes. [Sclerost.]. Codiostomum, p. 46.

sturni Rud., 1809, t.h. Sturnus. [Fil.]. Diplotriæna, p. 434.

stylosa Linstow, 1907, t.h. Otis tarda. Heterakis, p. 216.

stylosa Thapar, 1925, t.h. Testudo ibera. Tachygonetria, p. 200.

stylosus Linstow, 1907, t.h. Rhinoceros africanus. [Deletroc.]. Kiluluma, p. 71.

styphlocerca Stossich, 1904, t.h. ducks. [Het.]. Ascaridia, p. 268.

subæqualis Molin, 1860, t.h. Felis concolor, F. mellivora. [Spiropt.]. Cylicospirura, p. 295.

subalata Schneider, 1866, t.h. Falco sp. Physaloptera, p. 355.

subauricularis Rud., 1819, t.h. Rana musica. [Str.]. Oswaldocruzia, p. 127.
subcompressa Zeder, 1803, t.h. Homo. [Tentacularia]. Setaria, p. 423.
subcrenatus Railliet and Henry, 1913, t.h. Felis pardus. Hæmostrongylus, p. 164.
subcutanea Linstow, 1899, t.h. Erethizon dorsatus. [Fil.]. Dirofilaria, p. 395.
subrecta Gendre, 1921, t.h. Asturinula monogrammica. Acuaria, p. 330.
subtile Alessandrini, 1914, t.h. man. Gongylonema, p. 314.
subtilis Looss, 1895, t.h. Homo. [Str.]. Trichostrongylus, p. 119.
subula Duj., 1845, t.h. Sylvia rubecula. [Disph.]. Acuaria, p. 330.
subulata Rud., 1819, t.h. Caprimulgus ruficollis. [Asc.]. Subulura, p. 228.
subulatum Molin, 1861, t.h. Sus scrofa dom., etc. Œsophagostomum, p. 87.
subulatus Molin, 1860, t.h. Didelphys myosurus. [Histioc.]. Aspidodera, p. 220.
subulatus Molin, 1861, t.h. Lachesis rhombeata, etc. Kalicephalus, p. 114.
subventricosus Schneider, 1866, t.h. Rana cornuta. [Str.]. Oswaldocruzia, p. 127.
suctoria Molin, 1860, in part, Drasche, 1883, t.h. Caprimulgus campestris. [Het.].
    Allodapa, p. 229.
sudanensis Baylis, 1923, t.h. Gerbillus gerbillus. Streptopharagus, p. 312.
sudanensis Linstow, 1903, t.h. Felis leo. [Fil.]. Dirofilaria, p. 395.
suilla Duj., 1845, t.h. Sus scrofa dom. Ascaris, p. 256.
suillus Ackert and Payne, 1922, t.h. pig. Necator, p. 98.
suis (Lutz, 1894) Linstow, 1905, t.h. pig. [Rhabdonema]. Strongyloides, p. 20.
suis Rud., 1809, in part, t.h. Aper. [Str.]. Metastrongylus, p. 160.
suis Schrank, 1788, t.h. Sus scrofa fera. [Trichoc.]. Trichuris, p. 23.
sulcata Rud., 1819, t.h. Testudo mydas. [Asc.]. Porrocæcum, p. 281.
suum Gœze, 1782, t.h. Sus scrofa dom. Ascaris, p. 256.
sygmoidea Molin, 1860, t.h. Corvus frugilegus. [Spiropt.]. Oxyspirura, p. 321.
sygmoideus Molin, 1860, t.h. Falco tridentatus. [Disph.]. Acuaria, p. 330.

tacapense Seurat, 1915, t.h. Ctenodactylus gundi. [Ophiost.]. Seuratum, p. 351.
tacapensis Seurat, 1917, t.h. Ctenodactylus gundi. Physaloptera, p. 355.
tadornæ Chatin, 1874, t.h. Anas tadorna, Tadorna beloni. [Cyathost.]. Syngamus,
    p. 157.
tagumai Morishita, 1922, t.h. Bos taurus. Mecistocirrus, p. 139.
talpæ Gmelin, 1790, t.h. Talpa europæa. [Asc.]. Spirura, p. 294.
talpæ Siebold, 1850, t.h. Talpa europæa. [Nematoideum]. Capillaria, p. 27.
tanasijtchuki Skrjabin, 1916, t.h. Icteridæ. Oxyspirura, p. 320.
tarentolæ Seurat, 1916, t.h. Tarentola mauritanica. Acuaria, p. 330.
tectipenis Gedoelst, 1919, t.h. grey lizard. Pharyngodon, p. 194.
tenax Mehlis in Creplin, 1844, t.h. Raja clavata. Discophorus, p. 447.
tendo Nitzsch, 1857, t.h. Falco tendo. [Fil.]. Serratospiculum, p. 428.
tentaculata Rud., 1819, t.h. Didelphys cayopollin, D. quoaiquiqua. [Asc.]. Cruzia,
    p. 242.
tentaculatus Hemprich and Ehrenberg, 1828, t.h. Hyrax capensis. Crossophorus,
    p. 287.
tenue Duj., 1845, t.h. Columba dom. [Calodium]. Capillaria, p. 25.
tenuicauda Boulenger, 1920, t.h. Equines. Craterostomum, p. 45.
tenuicauda Linstow, 1883, t.h. Perdix græca. Heterakis, p. 216.
tenuicauda Linstow, 1901, t.h. Equus crawshayi. Oxyuris, p. 185.
tenuicollis Boulenger, 1916, t.h. Equus. Triodontophorus, p. 45.
tenuis Duj., 1845, t.h. Saxicola rubetra. [Disph.]. Acuaria, p. 330.
tenuis Duj., 1845, t.h. Erinacæus europæus. Eucoleus, p. 29.
tenuis Linstow, 1876, t.h. Mergus merganser. [Acanthophorus]. Tetrameres, p. 362.
tenuis Mehlis, 1846, t.h. Phasianus colchicus. [Str.]. Trichostrongylus, p. 119.
tenuissimum Diesing, 1851, t.h. Columba dom., C. livia. [Trichosomum]. Capillaria,
    p. 25.
tenuissimum Leidy, 1891, t.h. Mus decumanus. [Trichosomum]. Capillaria, p. 26.

tenuissimus Rud., 1803, t.h. Strix bubo. [Trichoc.]. Capillaria, p. 27.

tercostata Molin, 1860, t.h. Psittacus æstivus, P. maximiliani. [Spiropt.]. Pelecitus, p. 412.

terdentata Molin, 1860, t.h. Felis concolor, F. tigrina. Physaloptera, p. 355.

terdentatum Linstow, 1898, t.h. Ceratodus forsteri. Amblyonema, p. 211.

testudinis Baylis and Daubney, 1922, t.h. Testudo elongata. [Falcaustra]. Spironoura, p. 239.

tetracanthum Mehlis, 1831, of Looss, 1900, t.h. Equus cab. [Cylichnost.] Trichonema, p. 55.

tetraptera Nitzsch, 1821, t.h. Mus musculus. [Asc.]. Aspiculuris, p. 189.

tetrapteryx Linstow, 1907, t.h. Synbranchus marmoratus. Pterygifer, p. 444.

tetrica Travassos, 1917, t.h. Aramides cajanea. Tetrameres, p. 363.

*texana Smith and Goeth, 1904, t.h. Homo. Ascaris, p. 256.

tiara Linstow, 1879, t.h. Varanus ornatus. [Asc.]. Tanqua, p. 341.

tiliquæ Johnston, 1916, t.h. Tiliqua scincoides. Pneumonema, p. 347.

*tinami Molin, 1858, t.h. Tinamus. [Fil.]. Tetracheilonema, p. 439.

tinamicola Skrjabin, 1916, t.h. Tinamus sp. Diplotriæna, p. 434.

tipula Beneden, 1873, t.h. Vespertilio daubentonii, etc. [Str.]. Histiostrongylus, p. 133.

tomentosum Duj., 1843, t.h. Cyprinus idus, etc. [Trichosoma]. Capillaria, p. 27.

tonaudia Lane, 1914, t.h. Chelone midas. [Kathlania]. Tonaudia, p. 237.

torquata Gendre, 1922, t.h. Centropus monachus. [Spiropt.]. Torquatella, p. 373.

torquata Leidy, 1856, t.h. Meles labradorica. Physaloptera, p. 355.

torresi Travassos, 1920, t.h. Agouti paca. [Turgida]. Physaloptera, p. 355.

tortus Linstow, 1906, t.h. Cistudo ornata. Proleptus, p. 358.

torulosus Molin, 1861, t.h. Cebus capucinus. [Str.]. Molineus, p. 126.

totani Linstow, 1875, t.h. Totanus hypoleucos. [Trichosoma]. Capillaria, p. 27.

trachea Montagu, 1811, t.h. Gallus, etc. [Fasciola]. Syngamus, p. 157.

*trachealis Siebold, 1836, *trachea* Montague, 1811, re-named. Syngamus, p. 157.

traguli Vevers, 1922, t.h. Tragulus stanleyanus. Papillosetaria, p. 424.

transfuga Rud., 1819, t.h. Ursus arctos, U. maritimus. [Asc.]. Toxascaris, p. 260.

transversata Linstow, 1907, t.h. Cephalophus melanorheus, Troglodytes niger. [Fil.]. Setaria, p. 423.

travancra Lane, 1914, t.h. Elephas indicus. Quilonia, p. 73.

travassosi Barreto, 1919, t.h. Bucco swainsoni, B. chacuru. Subulura, p. 228.

triacanthus Diesing, 1853, t.h. Scarabæus stercorarius. Cephalacanthus, p. 386.

triænucha Wright, 1879, t.h. Botaurus minor. [Fil.]. Streptocara, p. 360.

trichiura Linnæus, 1771, t.h. Homo. [Asc.]. Trichuris, p. 22.

trichosuri Breinl, 1913, t.h. Trichosurus vulpecula. [Fil.]. Breinlia, p. 401.

tricolor Duj., 1845, t.h. Anas boschas dom., A. b. fera. Hystrichis, p. 180.

tricuspis Fedtschenko, 1874, t.h. Corvus cornix. [Fil.]. Diplotriæna, p. 434.

tricuspis Gedoelst, 1916, t.h. heron. [Kathleena]. Contracæcum, p. 283.

tricuspis Leuckart, 1865, t.h. Felis dom. Ollulanus, p. 149.

tricuspis Marotel, 1912, t.h. Ovis aries. Ostertagia, p. 125.

tridens Duj., 1845, t.h. Sylvia luscinia. [Thominx]. Capillaria, p. 27.

tridens Gendre, 1921, t.h. Trachelotis senegalensis. Histiocephalus, p. 370.

tridentata Linstow, 1877, t.h. Colymbus arcticus. [Fil.]. Streptocara, p. 360.

*tridentatum Yorke and Macfie, 1920, t.h. Equines. [Cylicost.]. Trichonema, p. 56.

tridentatus Drasche, 1884, t.h. Vastres cuvieri. [Cucullanus]. Camallanus, p. 378.

tridentatus Khalil, 1922, t.h. leopard. Galoncus, p. 95.

trifida Cuillé, Marotel, and Panisset, 1911, t.h. Ovis aries. Ostertagia, p. 125.

trifurcata Ransom, 1907, t.h. Capra hircus, Ovis aries. Ostertagia, p. 125.

trigonocephalus Rud., 1808, t.h. Ovis aries. [Str.]. Bunostomum, p. 108.

trilabium Linstow, 1904, t.h. Centropus sinesis. [Het.]. Ascaridia, p. 268.

trilobum Linstow, 1875, t.h. Vanellus cristatus. [Trichosoma]. Capillaria, p. 27.

*triquetra Schrank, 1790, t.h. Vulpes. [Asc.]. Toxocara, p. 258.

triradiata Hall, 1916, t.h. Ammospermophilus leucurus cinnamomeus, Callospermophilus lateralis. Oxyuris, p. 185.

triramosum Yorke and Macfie, 1920, t.h. Equines. [Cylicost.]. Trichonema, p. 56.

trispiculascaris Travassos, 1920, t.h. crocodile. Trispiculascaris, p. 264.

trispinosa Railliet and Henry, 1916, ornata Walter re-named. Cosmoceroa, p. 207.

trispinosus Leidy, 1851, t.h. Emys guttata. [Cucullanus]. Camallanus, p. 378.

tritonis-cristati Diesing, 1861, t.h. Triton cristatus. [Trichosoma]. Capillaria, p. 27.

tritonis-punctati Diesing, 1851, t.h. Lissotriton punctatus. [Trichosomum]. Capillaria, p. 27.

troglostrongylus Vevers, 1922, t.h. Felis bengalensis. Troglostrongylus, p. 165.

trogoni Barreto, 1919, t.h. Trogon viridis. Subulura, p. 228.

truncata Beneden, 1870, t.h. Raja clavata. Eustoma, p. 447.

truncata Creplin, 1825, t.h. Upupa epops. [Spiropt.]. Hadjelia, p. 302.

truncata Schneider, 1866, t.h. Phasianus gallus. Physaloptera, p. 355.

*truncata Zeder, 1803, t.h. Psittacus æstivus. [Fus.]. Ascaridia, p. 266.

*truncatus Rud., 1814, t.h. Silurus glanis. [Cucullanus]. Camallanus, p. 378.

trypanuris Vevers, 1923, t.h. Pithecia monachus. Trypanoxyuris, p. 198.

tuberculata Linstow, 1904, t.h. Trachysaurus rugosus. [Oxy.]. Veversia, p. 202.

tuberculata Monnig, 1924, t.h. Æpyceros melampus. Impalaia, p. 144.

tuberculatum Linstow, 1914, t.h. Acipenser ruthenus. [Trichosoma]. Capillaria, p. 27.

tuberculatum Parona and Stossich, 1901, t.h. Dasypus sp., D. villosus. [Œsophagostomum]. Trichohelix, p. 122.

tubifex Nitzsch, 1819, t.h. Mergus merganser. [Str.]. Eustrongylides, p. 179.

*tubifex Nitzsch of Diesing, 1851, in part. [Eustrongylus]. Hystrichis, p. 181.

tulostoma Hemprich and Ehrenberg, in Schneider, 1866, t.h. Vultur percnopterus. [Spiropt.]. Habronema, p. 299.

tumefaciens Henry and Blanc, 1912, t.h. Macacus cynomolgus. [Physalopt.]. Chlamydonema, p. 356.

*tumida Zeder, 1803, t.h. Anas querquedula. Capillaria, p. 25.

tunicatus Diesing, 1839, t.h. Manatus exunguis. Heterocheilus, p. 270.

turdi Molin, 1860, t.h. Turdus musicus. [Spiropt.]. Viguiera, p. 371.

turdi Rud., 1819, t.h. Turdus viscivorus. [Trichosoma]. Capillaria, p. 27.

turgida Rud., 1819, t.h. Didelphys cayopollin. Physaloptera, p. 355.

turgida Stossich, 1902, t.h. Didelphys crassicaudata. [Asc.]. Lagochilascaris, p. 261.

turgida Stossich, 1902, t.h. Larus argentatus. Aprocta, p. 406.

turgida Walton, 1923, t.h. Microtus arvalis. Nematospira, p. 147.

turgidum Stossich, 1902, t.h. Didelphys azare. Gnathostoma, p. 340.

turkestanica Skrjabin, 1917, t.h. Schizothorax intermedius. [Ichthospirura]. Rhabdochona, p. 325.

turkestanicum Skrjabin, 1916, t.h. Falco tinnunculus. Serratospiculum, p. 428.

turkestanicum Skrjabin, 1923, t.h. Mergus merganser. Contracæcum, p. 283.

*typica Diesing, 1861, t.h. Dicholophus marcgravi. Allodapa, p. 229.

typicus Diesing, 1861, t.h. Delphinus. [Conoc.]. Anisakis, p. 273.

uganda Khalil, 1922, t.h. Elephas africanus. Quilonia, p. 73.

ultrajectinum Ihle, 1920, t.h. Equines. [Cylicost.]. Trichonema, p. 56.

umbellifera Molin, 1860, t.h. Ibis rubra, Totanus melanoleucus. [Spiropt.]. Sciadiocara, p. 368.

uncinata Drasche, 1884, t.h. Testudo græca. [Oxy.]. Mehdiella, p. 201.

uncinata Rud., 1819, t.h. Anser dom. [Spiropt.]. Echinuria, p. 332.

uncinata Rud., 1819, t.h. Cavia aperea, C. paca. [Asc.]. Oxynema, p. 231.

uncinata (Rud., 1819) of Hall, 1916, t.h. Cavia aperea. Subulura, p. 228.

uncinata (Rud., 1819) of Travassos, 1914, t.h. Cavia spp. Paraspidodera, p. 221.
uncinatus Lundhal, 1848, t.h. Anser albifrons. [Str.]. Epomidiostomum, p. 155.
uncinatus Molin, 1858, t.h. Trygon brucho. Echinocephalus, p. 343.
unciphorus Railliet and Henry, 1907, t.h. goat, sheep. Synthetocaulus, p. 164.
undulatus Railliet and Henry, 1915, t.h. Damonia revesii. Camallanus, p. 378.
unguiculata Rud., 1819, t.h. Amphisbæna sp. [Asc.]. Aplectana, p. 209.
unguiculatus Linstow, 1906, t.h. Bufo viridis. [Nematoxys]. Aplectana, p. 209.
unguiculatus Rud., 1809, t.h. Lepus. [Trichoc.]. Trichuris, p. 23.
unilateralis Molin, 1860, t.h. Cephalopterus ornatus. [Spiropt.]. Habronema, p. 299.
unispina Diesing, 1861, t.h. Corvus cornix. [Tropidocerca]. Tetrameres, p. 363.
uromasticola Galeb, 1899, t.h. Uromastix. [Oxy.]. Thelandros, p. 192.
urosubulatum Alessandrini, 1909, t.h. Sus scrofa dom. [Crassisoma]. Globocephalus, p. 49.
ursi Duj., 1845, t.h. Ursus arctos. [Spiropt.]. Gongylonema, p. 314.

vallei Stossich, 1895, t.h. Vipera ammodytes. [Doch.]. Kalicephalus, p. 114.
valvata Schneider, 1866, t.h. Crypturus cupreus. Heterakis, p. 216.
vandenbrandeni Gedoelst, 1924, t.h. wild cat. Physaloptera, p. 355.
vanelli Rud., 1819, t.h. Tringa vanellus. [Spiropt.]. Acuaria, p. 330.
vanelli Rud., 1819, t.h. Tringa vanellus. [Trichosoma]. Capillaria, p. 27.
varani Baylis and Daubney, 1924, t.h. Varanus salvator. Amplicæcum, p. 279.
varani Parona, 1889, t.h. Varanus bengalensis. Physaloptera, p. 355.
varani Skrjabin, 1923, t.h. Varanus griseus. Hastospiculum, p. 432.
varedatus Lane, 1921, t.h. Indian elephant. Grammocephalus, p. 104.
variabilis Chapin, 1924, t.h. Testudo denticulata. [Deletrocephalus]. Theileriana, p. 78.
variegatus Creplin, 1849, t.h. Ciconia nigra. Syngamus, p. 157.
varispinosus Jægerskiöld, 1909, t.h. Mergus serrator. Hystrichis, p. 181.
vasifa Lane, 1914, t.h. Elephas indicus. [Asifia]. Choniangium, p. 41.
vasorum Baillet, 1866, t.h. Canis fam. [Str.]. Hæmostrongylus, p. 164.
veligera Rud., 1819, t.h. Lepus brasiliensis. [Asc.]. Dermatoxys, p. 190.
ventri Thornton, 1924, t.h. Brazilian wild cat. Œsophagostomum, p. 87.
ventricosus Rud., 1809, in part, t.h. Cervus elaphus. [Str.]. Cooperia, p. 132.
ventricosus Rud., 1809, of Curtice, 1890, t.h. Ovis aries. Cooperia, p. 132.
venulosus Rud., 1809, t.h. Capra hircus. [Str.]. Œsophagostomum, p. 87.
vermicularis Linnæus, 1758, t.h. Homo. [Asc.]. Enterobius, p. 187.
verrucosa Molin, 1858, t.h. Falco swainsonii. [Fil.]. Serratospiculum, p. 428.
verrucosum Giles, 1892, t.h. sheep. [Trichosomum]. Gongylonema, p. 315.
vesicularis Frœlich, 1791, t.h. Phasianus colchicus. [Asc.]. Heterakis, p. 216, and p. 218.
vesiculosa Schneider, 1866, t.h. Psittacus sinensis. Ceratospira, p. 322.
vesiculosum Rátz, 1898, t.h. cattle. Œsophagostomum, p. 87.
vespertilionis Rud., 1819, t.h. Vespertilio lasiopterus. [Trichosoma]. Capillaria, p. 27.
vespertilionis Rud., 1819, t.h. Vespertilio discolor. [Fil.]. Litomosa, p. 400.
vexillatum Hall, 1916, t.h. Thomomys fossor. Heligmosomum, p. 143.
viannai Travassos, 1914, t.h. Didelphis aurita. Viannaia, p. 149.
vicarius Stadelmann, 1894, t.h. Ovis aries. [Str.]. Ostertagia, p. 125.
viperæ Rud., 1819, t.h. Vipera redii. [Str.]. Kalicephalus, p. 114.
viscaciæ Goodey, 1925, t.h. Viscacia viscacia. Viannella, p. 150.
visceralis Gmelin, 1790, t.h. Canis fam. [Asc.]. Dicotophyme, p. 178.
vitrinus Looss, 1905, t.h. Camelus dromedarius, etc. Trichostrongylus, p. 119.
vituli Brumpt, 1921, t.h. cattle. Strongyloides, p. 20.
vitulorum Gœze, 1782, t.h. Bos taurus. Ascaris, p. 257.

vivipara Leiper, 1910, t.h. hippopotamus. [Cobboldia]. Cobboldina, p. 252.

vivipara Linstow, 1906, t.h. Gavialis gangeticus. Micropleura, p. 436.

vivipara Probstmayr, 1865, t.h. Equus cab. [Oxy.]. Probstmayria, p. 204.

vivipara Wedl, 1862, t.h. Uromastix spinipes. Tachygonetria, p. 199.

viviparus Bloch, 1782, t.h. Bos taurus. [Gord.]. Dictyocaulus, p. 162.

*viviparus Bloch, 1782, t.h. Perca fluv. [Cucullanus]. Camallanus, p. 378.

viviparus Linstow, 1899, t.h. Equus böhmi. [Pteroc.]. Crossocephalus, p. 250.

*viviparus Linstow, 1906, t.h. Damonia revesii. [Cucullanus]. Camallanus, p. 378.

volvulus Leuckart, 1893, t.h. Homo. [Fil.]. Onchocerca, p. 414.

vryburgi Railliet, 1902, t.h. Bibos indicus. Agriostomum, p. 95.

vulgare Looss, 1900, t.h. Equus. [Sclerost.]. Strongylus, p. 37.

*vulgaris Mérat, 1821, t.h. Homo. [Lombricoides]. Ascaris, p. 256.

vulpis Frœlich, 1789, t.h. Canis vulpes. [Trichoc.]. Trichuris, p. 23.

vulpis Frœlich, 1789, t.h. fox. [Asc.]. Toxocara, p. 258.

vulvoinflata Molin, 1860, t.h. Trochilus ochropygus. [Spiropt.]. Serticeps, p. 374.

waterstoni Baylis, 1921, t.h. Zamenis gemonensis var. caspia. Polydelphis, p. 266.

websteri Cobbold, 1879, t.h. Macropus giganteus. [Fil.]. Dirofilaria, p. 395.

wedlii Linstow, 1879, t.h. Fulica atra. Hystrichis, p. 181.

*wedlii Molin, 1861, t.h. Antilope rupicapra, Capra aries, etc. [Monodontus]. Buno-stomum, p. 109.

weinbergi Railliet and Henry, 1909, t.h. chimpanzee. Nematodirus, p. 137.

weissi Seurat, 1913, t.h. Macroscelides rozeti. [Maupasiella]. Maupasina, p. 233.

weissi Seurat, 1914, t.h. Elephantulus deserti. [Acanthocheilonema]. Dipeta-lonema, p. 427.

weissi Seurat, 1918, t.h. tortoise. Tachygonetria, p. 200.

*werneri Rud., 1793, t.h. Canis fam. [Asc.]. Toxocara, p. 258.

westeri Ihle, 1917, t.h. Equus cab. Strongyloides, p. 20.

willeyi Linstow, 1904, not 1908, t.h. Coluber helena. Kalicephalus, p. 114.

*willeyi Linstow, 1908, not 1904, t.h. Bungarus fasciatus. [Kalicephalus]. Occipi-todontus, p. 115.

*wisei Philpot, 1922, t.h. " Saki " monkey. [Oswaldocruzia]. Molineus, p. 126.

woodlandi Baylis, 1923, t.h. Gavialis gangeticus. Dujardinia, p. 277.

xeri Ortlepp, 1922, t.h. Xerus setosus. Œsophagostomum, p. 87.

yorkei Thornton, 1924, t.h. Phacocœrus æthiopicus. Œsophagostomum, p. 87.

zchokkei Linstow, 1899, t.h. Testudo tabulata. Labiduris, p. 247.

*zebræ Boulenger, 1920, t.h. Equines. [Cylicost.]. Trichonema, p. 56.

zebræ Skrjabin, 1916, t.h. zebra. [Asc.]. Parascaris, p. 262.

zebræ Theiler, 1923, t.h. zebra. Habronema, p. 299.

*zebræ Turner, 1920, t.h. zebra. [Cylichnost.]. Poteriostomum,·p. 61.

*zebræ Yorke and Southwell, 1920, t.h. zebra. Crossocephalus, p. 250.

zeltneri Neveu-Lemaire, 1924, t.h. Rhinoceros africanus. [Henryella]. Murshidia, p. 80.

REFERENCES

1 Ackert, J. E., and Payne, F. K. (1923). Investigations on the Control of Hook-worm Disease. XII. Studies on the Occurrence, Distribution and Morphology of *Necator suillus*, including Descriptions of the other Species of *Necator*. *Am. Jl. of Hygiene*, vol. 3, p. 1.

2 Alessandrini, A. (1838). Osservazioni anatomiche intorno a diverse specie di entozoarii del genere *Filaria*. *N. Ann. d. sc. nat.*, Bologna, vol. 1, p. 1.

3 Alessandrini, G. (1909). Su di un raro parassita dell' intestino del maiale. *Archives de Parasitologie*, vol. 13, p. 458.

3a Alessandrini, G. (1914). Nuovo caso di parassitismo nell' uomo da *Gongylonema*. *Boll. R. Accad. Med. Roma*, vol. 40, No. 4.

3b Allgén, C. (1921). Über die Natur und die Bedeutung der Fasersysteme im Œsophagus einiger Nematoden. *Zool. Anz.*, vol. 53, p. 76.

4 Annett, H. E., Dutton, J. E., Elliott, J. H. (1901). Report of the Malaria Expedition to Nigeria. Part 2. *Liverpool Sch. Trop. Med.*, Memoir 4.

4a Baillet, C. C. (1866). Histoire naturelle des helminthes des principaux mammi-fères domestiques. Paris. 172 pp.

5 Baird, W. (1853). Catalogue of the Species of Entozoa, or Intestinal Worms, contained in the Collection of the British Museum, London. 132 pp.

6 Baird, W. (1853). Descriptions of some New Species of Entozoa from the Collection of the British Museum. *Proc. Zool. Soc.*, London, p. 18.

7 Baird, W. (1868). Description of a New Species of *Sclerostoma* from the Stomach of the African Elephant (*Loxodonta africana*). *Ibid.*, p. 262.

8 Balbiani, E. G. (1870). Recherches sur le développement et le mode de propa-gation du strongyle géant (*Eustrongylus gigas* Dies.). *Jl. Anat. et Physiol.*, Paris, vol. 7, p. 180.

9 Bancroft, T. L. (1893). On the Whip Worm of the Rat's Liver. *Jl. and Proc. Roy. Soc. N. S. Wales*. Sydney, vol. 27, p. 86.

10 Barker, F. D. (1915). Parasites of the American Muskrat (*Fiber zibethicus*). *Jl. of Parasitology*, vol. 1, p. 184. Urbana.

11 Barreto, A. L. de Barros (1916). Nota sobre *Cucullanidæ* nov. fam. *Brazil Med.*, vol. 30, p. 388. Rio de Janeiro.

12 Barreto, A. L. de Barros (1917). Notas helminthologicas. I. Sobre o genero *Allodapa* Diesing, 1860. *Ibid.*, vol. 31, p. 243.

13 Barreto, A. L. de Barros (1917). Notas helminthologicas. II. Sobre o genero *Oxynema* Linstow, 1899. *Ibid.*, vol. 31, p. 305.

14 Barreto, A. L. de Barros (1918). Notas helminthologicas. III. *Cucullanus pulcherrimus*. *Ibid.*, vol. 32, p. 137.

15 Barreto, A. L. de Barros (1919). On the Brazilian Species of the Sub-family *Subulurinæ* Travassos, 1914. *Mem. Inst. Oswaldo Cruz*, vol. 11, p. 6. Rio de Janeiro.

16 Barreto, A. L. de Barros (1922). Revision of the Family *Cucullanidæ* Barreto, 1916. *Ibid.*, vol. 14, p. 61.

16a Baskakow, V. P. (1924). Parasitic Worms in Turkestan Dromedaries. *Reports of the State Experimental Institute*, Moscow, vol. 2, No. 1. [In Russian].

17 Bastian, H. C. (1863). On the Structure and Nature of the *Dracunculus*, or Guinea-worm. *Trans. Linn. Soc.*, vol. 24, p. 101. London.

18 Baylis, H. A. (1916). On *Crassicauda crassicauda* (Crepl.) [Nematoda] and its Hosts. *Ann. and Mag. Nat. Hist.*, ser. 8, vol. 17, p. 144. London.

19 Baylis, H. A. (1916). The Nematode genus *Tanqua*, R. Blanchard. *Ibid.*, vol. 17, p. 223.

20 Baylis, H. A. (1916). Some Ascarids in the British Museum (Natural History). *Parasitology*, vol. 8, p. 360. Cambridge.

21 Baylis, H. A. (1916). The Types of the Species of *Ascaris* described by Baird. *Ibid.*, vol. 8, p. 411.

22 Baylis, H. A. (1919). Some New Entozoa from Birds in Uganda. *Ann. and Mag. Nat. Hist.*, ser. 9, vol. 3, p. 457.

23 Baylis, H. A. (1919). A New Species of the Nematode genus *Crossocephalus* from the Rhinoceros. *Ibid.*, ser. 9, vol. 4, p. 94.

24 Baylis, H. A. (1919). *Crossophorus collaris*, Hemprich and Ehrenberg, a little known Nematode Parasite of the Hyrax. *Ibid.*, ser. 9, vol. 4, p. 343.

25 Baylis, H. A. (1920). Observations on the genus *Crassicauda*. *Ibid.*, ser. 9, vol. 5, p. 410.

26 Baylis, H. A. (1920). Notes on some Parasitic Worms from East Africa. *Ibid.*, vol. 6, p. 283.

27 Baylis, H. A. (1920). A New Siamese Nematode of the genus *Falcaustra*. *Ibid.*, vol. 6, p. 408.

28 Baylis, H. A. (1920). On the Classification of the *Ascaridæ*. (i.) Systematic Value of Certain Characters of the Alimentary Canal. *Parasitology*, vol. 12, p. 253.

29 Baylis, H. A. (1921). On the Classification of the *Ascaridæ*. (ii.) The Poly-delphis group ; with some account of other Ascarids parasitic in Snakes. *Ibid.*, vol. 12, p. 411.

30 Baylis, H. A. (1921). A New Genus of Nematodes parasitic in Elephants. *Ibid.*, vol. 13, p. 57.

31 Baylis, H. A. (1922). Notes on some Parasitic Nematodes. (i.) On the genus *Wellcomia*, Sambon, and a New Species of that Genus. (ii.) A New Species of *Ascaris* from an Armadillo. (iii.) Note on Two Species of *Porrocæcum* from Birds. *Ann. and Mag. of Nat. Hist.*, ser. 9, vol. 9, p. 494.

32 Baylis, H. A. (1922). Note on the Habitat and Structure of *Crassicauda*. (Nematoda). *Parasitology*, vol. 14, p. 9.

33 Baylis, H. A. (1923). On the Nematode genus *Streptopharagus*, with some remarks on the genus *Spirocerca*. *Trans. Roy. Soc. Trop. Med. and Hyg.*, vol. 16, p. 486. London.

34 Baylis, H. A. (1923). Report on a Collection of Parasitic Nematodes, mainly from Egypt. Part I. *Ascaridæ* and *Heterakidæ*. Part II. *Oxyuridæ* ; and Part III. *Camallanidæ*, etc. *Parasitology*, vol. 15, pp. 1, 14, and 24.

35 Baylis, H. A. (1923). Note on *Procamallanus spiralis* Baylis, 1923. (Nematoda). *Ibid.*, vol. 15, p. 137.

36 Baylis, H. A. (1923). On the Classification of the *Ascaridæ*. (iii.) A Revision of the genus *Dujardinia* Gedoelst, with a description of a new genus of *Anisakinæ* from a Crocodile. *Ibid.*, vol. 15, p. 223.

37 Baylis, H. A. (1923). (i.) A Filariid from the African Elephant. (ii.) An Ascarid from the Sperm Whale. *Ann. and Mag. Nat. Hist.*, ser. 9, vol. 11, pp. 208, 211.

38 Baylis, H. A. (1923). A New Ascarid from an Otter. *Ibid.*, ser. 9, vol. 11, p. 459.

39 Baylis, H. A. (1923). Some Nematodes of the genus *Cucullanus* from Fishes of the Nile. *Ibid.*, ser. 9, vol. 12, p. 233.

40 Baylis, H. A. (1924). The Male of *Micropleura vivipara* (Nematoda). *Ibid.*, ser. 9, vol. 13, p. 199.

41 Baylis, H. A. (1924). A New Species of *Physaloptera* (Nematoda) from an Australian Lizard. *Ibid.*, ser. 9, vol. 13, p. 309.

41a Baylis, H. A. (1925). Notes on some Australian Parasitic Nematodes. *Ibid.*, ser. 9, vol. 15, p. 112.

41b Baylis, H. A. (1925). On *Gongylonema* collected in Italy during October, 1924, with some observations on the genus. *Jl. Trop. Med. and Hyg.*, p. 71.

41c Baylis, H. A. (1925). On the Identity of *Gongylonema subtile*, Aless. *Ibid.*, p. 361.

41d Baylis, H. A. (1925). On the Species of *Gongylonema* (*Nematoda*) parasitic in Ruminants. *Journ. Comp. Path. and Ther.*, vol. 38, p. 46.

42 Baylis, H. A., and Daubney, R. (1922). Report on the Parasitic Nematodes in the Collection of the Zoological Survey of India. *Memoirs of the Indian Museum*, vol. 7, No. 4, p. 263. Calcutta.

43 Baylis, H. A. and Daubney, R. (1923). Preliminary Descriptions of Three new Parasitic Nematodes. *Ann. and Mag. Nat. Hist.*, ser. 9, vol. 11, p. 333.

44 Baylis, H. A., and Daubney, R. (1923). Note on a New Species of Acuaria (*Nematoda*) from the Adjutant Stork. *Ibid.*, ser. 9, vol. 12, p. 95.

45 Baylis, H. A., and Daubney, R. (1923). A Further Report on Parasitic Nematodes in the Collection of the Zoological Survey of India. *Records of the Indian Museum*, vol. 25, p. 551. Calcutta.

45a Baylis, H. A., and Daubney, R. (1925). A Revision of the Lung-worms of Cetacea. *Parasitology*, vol. 17, p. 201.

46 Baylis, H. A., and Lane, C. (1920). A Revision of the Nematode Family, *Gnathostomidæ*. *Proc. Zool. Soc.* London, Sept., p. 245.

47 Bellingham, O'Bryen (1840–45). Catalogue of Irish Entozoa with Observations. *Ann. and Mag. Nat. Hist.*, London., vol. 4, p. 343 ; vol. 13, pp. 101, 167, 254, 335, 422 ; vol. 14, pp. 162, 251, 317, 396, 471.

48 Beneden, P. J. (1858). Mémoire sur les vers intestinaux. viii. + 376 pp. Paris.

49 Beneden, P. J. (1870). Les cétacés, leurs commensaux et leurs parasites. *Bull. Acad. roy. d. sc. de Belg.*, Brux., vol. 29, p. 347.

50 Beneden, P. J. (1870). Les poissons des côtes de Belgique, leurs parasites et leurs commensaux. *Mém. Acad. roy. d. sc. de Belg.*, Brux., vol. 38, xx. + 100 pp.

51 Beneden, P. J. (1873). Les Parasites des chauves-souris de Belgique. *Ibid.*, vol. 40, 42 pp.

52 Bernard, P. N., and Bauche, J. (1912). Filariose et atherome aortique du buffle et du bœuf. *Bull. Soc. Path. Exot.*, vol. 5, p. 109.

53 Bernard, P. N., and Bauche, J. (1914). Influence du mode de pénétration cutanée ou buccale de " *Stephanurus dentatus*," etc. *Ann. Inst. Past.*, vol. 28, p. 450.

53a Blainville, M. H. D. (1819). Sur un nouveau genre de vers intestinaux, découvert par M. Rhodes et établi par M. Bosc. *Bull. d. sc. Soc. philom. Par.*, Jan., p. 8.

53b Blainville, M. H. D. (1828). Vers. *Dict. d. sc. nat. Par. and Strasb.*, vol. 52, pp. 365–625.

54 Blanc, G. (1912). Un Nématode nouveau (*Streptopharagus armatus* n.g., n. sp.) parasite du Macaque. *C. R. Soc. Biol.*, vol. 72, p. 456.

55 Blanchard, E. (1848–49). Recherches sur l'organisation des vers. *Ann. d. sc. nat., Par., Zool.*, vol. 10., p. 321 ; vol. 11, p. 106 ; vol. 12, p. 5.

55a Blanchard, R. (1889–1890). Traité de Zool. Médicale. Paris.

56 Blanchard, R. (1904). *Tanqua*, n. g., remplaçant *Ctenocephalus* von Linstow. *Arch. Parasitologie*, Paris, vol. 8, p. 478.

57 Bloch, M. E. (1779). Beitrag zur Naturgeschichte der Würmer, welche in anderen Thieren leben. *Beschäft. d. Berl. Gesellsch. naturf. Fr.*, vol. 4, p. 534.

58 Bouilliez, M. (1916). Sur une Filaire du Crapaud de la région du Chari. *Bull. Soc. Path. Exot.*, vol. 9, p. 133.

59 Boulenger, Ch. L. (1914). A List of Nematode Parasites observed in the Alimentary Canal of Sheep in England. *Parasitology*, vol. 7, p. 240.

60 Boulenger, Ch. L. (1915). The Life History of *Nematodirus filicollis* Rud., a Nematode parasite of the Sheep's Intestine. *Ibid.*, vol. 8, p. 133.

61 Boulenger, Ch. L. (1916). Sclerostome Parasites of the Horse in England. I. The genera *Triodontophorus* and *Œsophagodontus*. *Ibid.*, vol. 8, p. 420.

62 Boulenger, Ch. L. (1917). Sclerostome Parasites of the Horse in England. II. New Species of the genus *Cylichnostomum*. *Ibid.*, vol. 9, p. 203.

63 Boulenger, Ch. L. (1920). Sclerostomes of the Donkey in Zanzibar and East Africa. *Ibid.*, vol. 12, p. 27.

64 Boulenger, Ch. L. (1920). On some Nematode Parasites of the Zebra. *Ibid.*, vol. 12, p. 98.

65 Boulenger, Ch. L. (1920). Filariid Worms from Mammals and Birds in the Society's Gardens, 1914–1915. *Proc. Zool. Soc.*, London, Dec., p. 491.

66 Boulenger, Ch. L. (1921). On some Filariid Parasites of Cattle and other Ruminants. *Parasitology*, vol. 12, p. 341.

67 Boulenger, Ch. L. (1921). On some Nematode Parasites of the Camel in India. *Ibid.*, vol. 13, p. 311.

68 Boulenger, Ch. L. (1921). Strongylid Parasites of Horses in the Punjab. *Ibid.*, vol. 13, p. 315.

69 Boulenger, Ch. L. (1922). On *Ascaris vitulorum* Gœze. *Ibid.*, vol. 14, p. 87.

70 Boulenger, Ch. L. (1922). The Structure and Systematic Position of *Strongylus polygyrus*. *Ibid.*, vol. 14, p. 206.

71 Boulenger, Ch. L. (1923). A Nematode (*Falcaustra chapini* n. sp.) Parasitic in a North American Tortoise. *Ibid.*, vol. 15, p. 49.

72 Boulenger, Ch. L. (1923). A Collection of Nematode Parasites from Zanzibar. *Ibid.*, vol. 15, p. 113.

73 Boulenger, Ch. L. (1924). The Filariid of the Camel, *Acanthocheilonema evansi* (Lewis). *Ibid.*, vol. 16, p. 419.

74 Breinl, A. (1913). Nematodes observed in North Queensland. Report for 1911. *Australian Inst. Trop. Med.*, p. 39.

75 Bremser, J. G. (1811). Nachricht von einer beträchtlichen Sammlung thierischer Eingeweidewürmer, und Einladung zu einer literarischen Verbindung, um dieselbe zu vervollkommnen, und sie für die Wissenschaft und die Liebhaber allgemein nützlich zu machen. An Naturforscher überhaupt und an Enthelminthologen insbesondere von der k. k. Naturalienkabinets-Direcktion in Wien. 31 pp.

76 Bremser, J. G. (1819). Ueber lebende Würmer im lebenden Menschen. Ein Buch für ausübende Aerzte. Mit nach der Natur gezeichneten Abbildungen auf vier Tafeln. Nebst einem Anhange über Pseudo-Helminthen. xii. + 284 pp.

77 Bremser, J. G. (1824). Icones Helminthum systema Rudolphi entozoologicum illustrantes. Vienna, pp. 12.

77a Brumpt, E. (1919). Une nouvelle filaire pathogène parasite de l'homme (*Onchocerca cæcutiens*, n. sp. *Bull. Soc. Path. Exot.*, vol. 12, p. 464.

77b Brumpt, E. (1921). Recherches sur le déterminisme des sexes et de l'évolution des Anguillules parasites (*Strongyloides*). *C. R. Soc. Biol.*, vol. 85, p. 149.

78 Brumpt, E. (1922). Précis de Parasitologie. Troisième Edition. xv. + 1216 pp.

79 Cameron, T. W. M. (1923). Studies on two new genera and some little known Species of the Nematode Family *Trichostrongylidæ* Leiper. *Jl. Helminthology*, vol. 1, p. 71.

80 Cameron, T. W. M. (1923). The Anatomy of *Monodontus trigonocephalus* (Rud.) of Sheep. *Ibid.*, vol. 1, p. 99.

81 Cameron, T. W. M. (1923). On the Morphology of *Ollulanus tricuspis* Leuckart, 1865, a Nematode Parasite of the Cat. *Ibid.*, vol. I, p. 157.

82 Cameron, T. W. M. (1924). On *Gaigeria pachyscelis* Railliet and Henry, 1910, a Nematode parasite of Ruminants. *Ibid.*, vol. 2, p. 41.

83 Cameron, T. W. M. (1924). *Dochmoides:* a New genus for the Hookworm, " *Uncinaria* " *stenocephala* Railliet. *Ibid.*, vol. 2, p. 46.

84 Cameron, T. W. M. (1924). On the Nematode genus *Globocephalus* Molin, 1861. *Ibid.*, vol. 2, p. 65.

84a Cameron, T. W. M. (1925). The Trichostrongyle Genus *Graphidioides*. *Ibid.*, vol. 3, p. 163.

85 Cameron, T. W. M., and Ross, I. Clunies (1924). On the Identity of the Kidney Worm of Pigs in New South Wales. *Ibid.*, vol. 2, p. 149.

86 Carus, J. V., and Gerstæcker, C. E. A. (1863). *Handbuch der Zoologie*, vol. 2, p. 1. Leipzig.

86a Castellani, A. (1925). Observations on some Diseases of Central America. *Jl. Trop. Med. and Hyg.*, vol. 28, p. 1.

87 Chandler, A. C. (1918). On a Species of *Hedruris* occurring commonly in the Western Newt, *Notophthalmus torosus*. *Jl. Parasitology*, vol. 5, p. 116.

88 Chandler, A. C. (1924). A new genus of *Trichostrongylid* worms from the Kangaroo. *Parasitology*, vol. 16, p. 160.

89 Chandler, A. C. (1924). New *Filariæ* from Indian Birds. *Ibid.*, vol. 16, p. 398.

90 Chandler, A. C. (1924). Some Parasitic Round Worms of the Rabbit with descriptions of two New Species. *Proc. U. S. Nat. Mus.*, vol. 66, art. 16. Washington.

90a Chandler, A. C. (1925). The species of *Strongyloides* (Nematoda). *Parasitology*, vol. 17, p. 426.

91 Chapin, E. A. (1922). A Species of Round Worm (*Gongylonema*) from Domestic Swine in the United States. *Ibid.*, vol. 62, art. 10.

92 Chapin, E. A. (1924). Nematode Parasites of the Brazilian Land-Tortoise, *Testudo denticulata*. *Ibid.*, vol. 65, art. 13.

93 Chapin, E. A. (1924). Note on *Spironoura affine* Leidy, 1856. Communication to Helminthological Soc. of Washington. *Jl. Parasitology*, vol. 10, p. 212.

93a Chapin, E. A. (1925). Review of the Nematode genera *Syngamus* Sieb. and *Cyathostoma*, E. Blanch. *Jl. Agric. Research*, vol. 30, p. 557.

93b Chapin, E. A. (1925). New Nematodes from North American Mammals. *Ibid.*, vol. 30, p. 677.

94 Ciurea, J. (1911). Ueber *Gnathostoma hispidum* Fedtsch. *Zeit. f. Infekt. parasitäre Krankh. und Hyg. der Haustiere*, vol. 10, p. 288.

95 Ciurea, J. (1912). Ueber *Spiroptera sexalata* Molin aus dem Magen des Hausschweines. *Zool. Jahrb.*, vol. 32, p. 285.

96 Claus, C. R. W. (1885). Lehrbuch der Zoologie. 3. ed. Marburg and Leipzig. xi. + 828 pp.

97 Cobb, N. A. (1898). Extract from MS. report on the Parasites of Stock. *Agric. Gaz. N.S.W.*, vol. 9, pp. 296, 419. Sydney.

98 Cobbold, T. S. (1864). Entozoa : An Introduction to the Study of Helminthology with Reference more particularly to the Internal Parasites of Man. London, 480 pp.

99 Cobbold, T. S. (1869). Entozoa : being a Supplement to the Introduction to the Study of Helminthology. London, 124 pp.

100 Cobbold, T. S. (1870). Description of a new generic type of entozoon from the Aard wolf (*Proteles*) ; with remarks on its affinities, especially in reference to the question of parthenogenesis. *Proc. Zool. Soc.*, London, p. 9.

101 Cobbold, T. S. (1874). Observations on rare parasites from the Horse. *Veterinarian*, Lond., vol. 20, p. 81.

102 Cobbold, T. S. (1877). Discovery of the Adult Representative of Microscopic *Filariæ*. *Lancet*, London, vol. 2, p. 70.

103 Cobbold, T. S. (1879). Parasites : a Treatise on the Entozoa of Man and Animals, including some account of the Ectozoa. xi. + 508 pp. London.

104 Cobbold, T. S. (1882). New Entozoon from the Ostrich. *Jl. Linn. Soc.*, London, vol. 16, p. 184.

105 Cobbold, T. S. (1882). The Parasites of Elephants. *Trans. Linn. Soc., London Zool.*, ser. 2, vol. 2, p. 223.

106 Cobbold, T. S. (1883). On *Simondsia paradoxa* and on its probable Affinity with *Sphærularia bombi*. *Ibid.*, vol. 2, p. 357.

107 Collet-Meygret, G. F. H. (1802). Mémoire sur un ver trouvé dans le rein d'un chien. *J. de phys.*, Par., vol. 55, p. 458.

108   Colucci, V., and Arnone, L. (1897). Di un rarissimo parassita nematoides nello stomaco di cinghiale. *Mem. Acad. d. sc. d. Inst. di Bologna* (1896–97), ser. 5, vol. 6, p. 181.

109   Commes, Ch., and Devanelle, P. (1917). L'Onchocercose aortique bovine dans le Haut-Sénégal-Niger. *Bull. Soc. Path. Exot.*, vol. 10, p. 459.

110   Condamine and Drouilly (1878). Description de la filaire femelle (cause déterminante des boutons hémorrhagiques). *Rec. Méd. Vét.*, vol. 55, p. 1145.

111   Connal, A. (1912). Some Nematode Worms from Lagos. *Jl. Lond. School of Trop. Med.*, vol. 1, p. 229.

111a   Cram, E. B. (1924). A new nematode, *Cylindropharynx ornata*, from the Zebra, with keys to related nematode parasites of the *Equidæ*. *Jl. Agric. Res.*, vol. 28, p. 661.

111b   Cram, E. B. (1924). A new nematode, *Protospirura gracilis*, from the Cat. *Jl. American Vet. Med. Assoc.*, vol. 65, No. 3.

111c   Cram, E. B. (1925). *Cooperia bisonis*, a new nematode from the Buffalo. *Jl. Agric. Res.*, vol. 30, p. 571.

111d   Cram, E. B. (1925). A new genus, *Cylicostomias*, and notes on other genera of the cylicostomes of horses. *Proc. of Helminthological Soc. of Washington.* Reported in *Jl. of Parasit.*, vol. 11, p. 229.

112   Creplin, F. C. H. (1825). Observationes de entozois. Gryphiswaldiæ. x. + 86 pp.

113   Creplin, F. C. H. (1829). *Filariæ* et *Monostomi* speciem novam in *Balæna rostrata* repertam. *Nova acta phys.-med. Acad. nat. curios.*, Bonnæ, vol. 14 (2), p. 871.

114   Creplin, F. C. H. (1839). Eingeweidewürmer, Binnenwürmer, Thierwürmer. *Allg. Encycl. d. Wissensch. u. Künste* (Ersch and Gruber), Leipzig, vol. 32, p. 277.

115   Creplin, F. C. H. (1845–46). Nachträge zu Gurlt's Verzeichniss der Thiere, bei welchen Entozoen gefunden worden sind. *Arch. f. Naturg.*, Berl., 11th year, vol. 1, p. 325 ; and 12th year, vol. 1, p. 129.

116   Daniels, C. W. (1908). Animal Parasites in Man and some of the Lower Animals in Malaya. *Studies from Inst. Med. Rec. Fed. Mal. States*, vol. 3, p. 15.

117   Daubney, R. (1922). The Lesions in Lungworm Disease (" Husk " or " Hoose ") of Cattle. *Journ. Comp. Path. and Therap.*, vol. 35, p. 108.

118   Daubney, R. (1923). A Note on Two Species of the genus *Murshidia* (Nematode, *Strongyloidea*) parasitic in the Wart-hog. *Ann. and Mag. Nat. Hist.*, ser. 9, vol. 11, p. 256.

119   Daubney, R. (1923). Note on the genus *Diaphanocephalus* (Nematoda : *Strongylidæ*), parasitic in Reptiles, with a description of three new Species. *Parasitology*, vol. 15, p. 67.

120   Daubney, R. (1923). The Kidney Worm of Swine : a short redescription of *Stephanurus dentatus* Dies., 1839. *Jl. Comp. Path. and Therap.* vol. 36, p. 97.

121   Daubney, R. (1924). Description of a New Nematode *Œsophagostomum mwanzæ* from the Wart-hog. *Ann. Mag. Nat. Hist.* ser. 9, vol. 13, p. 542.

122   Diesing, K. M. (1839). Neue Gattungen von Binnenwürmern nebst einem Nachträge zur Monographie der Amphistomen. *Ann. Wien. Mus. d. Naturg.*, vol. 2, p. 219.

123   Diesing, K. M. (1851). Systema Helminthum, Berlin, vol. 2, 588 pp.

124   Diesing, K. M. (1855). Sechzehn Gattungen von Binnenwürmern und ihre Arten. *Denkschriften d. K. Akad. d. Wissenschaften*, vol. 9, p. 171. Vienna.

125   Diesing, K. M. (1861). Revision der Nematoden. *Sitzungsb. d. Math.-Naturw. Classe der Akad. der Wissensch.*, vol. 42, p. 595. Vienna.

125a   Dive, G. H., Lafrenais, H. M., and MacArthur, W. P. (1924). A Case of Deposition of the Eggs of *Hepaticola hepatica* in the Human Liver. *Jl. R. A. M. Corps*, vol. 43, p. 1.

126 Drabble, J. (1922). The Kidney Worm of Hogs in New South Wales, *Sclerostomum renium* n. sp. *Jl. Comp. Path. and Therap.*, vol. 35, p. 302, and vol. 36, p. 217.

127 Drasche, R. (1882). Zur Charakteristik der Nematoden-Gattung *Peritrachelius* Diesing. *Verhandl. d. k. k. zool.-bot. Gesellsch.* Wien (1881), vol. 31, p. 187.

128 Drasche, R. (1882–83). Revision der in der Nematoden-Sammlung des k. k. zool. Hofcabinetes befindlichen Original-Exemplare Diesing's und Molin's. *Ibid.*, vol. 32, p. 117 ; vol. 33, pp. 107 ar.d 193.

129 Drasche, R. (1884). Nematoden aus *Testudo græca*. *Ibid.*, vol. 33, p. 325.

130 Dubini, A. (1843). Nuovo verme intestinale umano (*Agchylostoma duodenale*), constituente un sesto genere di nematoidei proprii dell' uomo. *Ann. univ. di med.*, Milano, vol. 106, p. 5.

131 Dujardin, F. (1845). Histoire naturelle des Helminthes ou vers intestinaux, Paris. xvi. + 654 + 15 pp.

132 Eberth, C. J. (1863). Untersuchungen über Nematoden. Leipzig, 77 pp.

133 de Faria, Gomes (1910). Contribution towards the Classification of the Brazilian Entozoa. *Mem. Inst. Oswaldo Cruz*, vol. 2, p. 286.

134 Filho, P., and Pinto, C. F. (1919). Notas sobre a distribuçao geographica dos helminthos no Rio Grande do Sol. I. Indentifiçaçao do *Œsophagostomum radiatum* (Rudolphi, 1803) em Bovinos da Raça Zebú (*Bibos indicus*). *Brazil Med.*, vol. 33, p. 124.

135 Fischer von Waldheim, G. (1798). Sur un nouveau genre der vers intestins, *Cystidicola farionis*, suivi de quelques remarques sur les milieux dans lesquels les vers intestins vivent. *Jl. de phys., chim. et d'hist. nat.*, Paris, vol. 4, p. 304.

136 Fourment, L. (1883). Sur les Filaments ovulaires chez les Nématodes. *C. R. Soc. Biol.*, vol. 35, p. 575.

137 Fourment, L. (1884). Note sur un Nématode nouveau, parasite du Merlan. *Ann. d. Sc. nat. Par. Zool.*, vol. 17, art. 5.

138 Frölich, J. A. (1789). Beschreibungen einiger neuen Eingeweidewürmer. *Naturforscher*, Halle, vol. 24, p. 101.

139 Frölich, J. A. von (1791 and 1802). Beiträge zur Naturgeschichte der Eingeweidewürmer. *Ibid.*, vol. 25, p. 52 ; vol. 29, p. 5.

140 Fülleborn, F. (1908). Ueber *Filaria volvulus* (Leuckart). *Arch. f. Schiffs-u Trop.-hyg.*, vol. 12. Beiheft 7, p. 291.

141 Fülleborn, F. (1908). Ueber Versuche an Hundefilarien und deren Übertragung durch Mücken. *Ibid.*, vol. 12. Beiheft 8, p. 309.

142 Fülleborn, F. (1908). Untersuchungen an menschlichen Filarien und deren Übertragung auf Stechmücken. *Ibid.*, vol. 12. Beiheft 9, p. 357.

143 Fülleborn, F. (1912). Zur Morphologie der *Dirofilaria immitis* Leidy, 1856. *Cent. f. Bakt.* 1 Abt. Orig., vol. 65, p. 341.

144 Fülleborn, F. (1913). Die Filarien des Menschen. *Handbuch der pathogenen mikroorganismen. Kolle und Wassermann*, Jena, p. 185.

145 Fülleborn, F. (1920). Perkutane Infektion bei *Angiostomum nigrovenosum*. *Arch. f. Schiffs-u Trop.-hyg.*, vol. 24, p. 176.

146 Fülleborn, F. (1924). Bermerkungen über die Indentifikation von "Hakenwürmern." *Ibid.*, vol. 28, p. 12.

147 Gaiger, S. H. (1911). Notes on Parasites. *Jl. of Trop. Vet. Science*, Calcutta, vol. 6, p. 292.

148 Galeb, O. (1878). Recherches sur les Entozoaires des Insectes. Organisation et développement des *Oxyuridés*. *Arch. de Zool. expér. et gén.* vol. 7, p. 283. Paris.

149 Galeb, O. (1889). Note sur l'organisation et le développement d'une nouvelle espèce d'entozoaire. *Mém. de l'Inst. égypt.* Le Caire, vol. 2, p. 425.

150 Gedoelst, L. (1911). Synopsis de Parasitologie de l'homme et des animaux domestiques. Bruxelles. xx. + 332 pp.

151 Gedoelst, L. (1916). Notes sur la faune parasitaire du Congo Belge. *Rev. Zool. Africaine* (Bruxelles), vol. 5, p. 1.

152 Gedoelst, L. (1917). Nématodes Parasites du *Sciurus prevosti* de Sumatra. *Ibid.*, vol. 5, p. 153.

153 Gedoelst, L. (1919). Une espèce nouvelle de *Pharyngodon*. *C. R. Soc. Biol.*, vol. 82, p. 869.

154 Gedoelst, L. (1919). Le genre *Histiocephalus* et les espèces qui y ont été rapportées. *Ibid.*, vol. 82, p. 901.

155 Gedoelst, L. (1919). Un Oxyuridé nouveau parasite d'un reptile. *Ibid.*, vol. 82, p. 910.

156 Gedoelst, L. (1919). Un Genre nouveau de *Spiruridæ*. *Ibid.*, vol. 82, p. 1145.

157 Gedoelst, L. (1920). Sur une espèce nouvelle d'Ascaride, parasite du Blaireau. *Ibid.*, vol. 83, p. 1291.

158 Gedoelst, L. (1922). Quelques nématodes parasites de l'Eléphant africain. *Bull. Soc. Path. Exot.*, vol. 15, p. 122.

159 Gedoelst, L. (1923). Le genre *Metastrongylus* Molin, 1861. *Ibid.*, vol. 16, p. 622.

160 Gedoelst, L. (1924). Un Syngame parasite de l'hippopotame. *Annales de Parasitologie humaine et comparée*, vol. 2, p. 307.

160a Gedoelst, L. (1924). Notes de Parasitologie congolaise. *Ann. Soc. Belge. Méd. Trop.*, vol. 4, p. 247.

161 Gedoelst, L. et Liégeois, E. (1922). Note sur le *Streptocara pectinifera* (Neumann). *C. R. Soc. Biol.*, vol. 87, p. 1237.

162 Gendre, E. (1909). Notes d'Helminthologie Africaine (Première Note). *Procès-Verbaux de la Soc. Linn.*, Bordeaux, Jan., 1909, vol. 63.

163 Gendre, E. (1909). Notes d'Helminthologie Africaine (Deuxième Note). Jan., 1909. *Ibid.*, vol. 63.

164 Gendre, E. (1909). Notes d'Helminthologie Africaine (Troisième Note). April, 1909. *Ibid.*, vol. 63.

165 Gendre, E. (1911). Sur quelques espèces d'*Hétérakis* du Dahomey. June, 1911, *Ibid.*, vol. 65.

166 Gendre, E. (1911). Sur une espèce nouvelle d'*Oxysoma*. Oct., 1911. *Ibid.*, vol. 65.

167 Gendre, E. (1912). Sur quelques espèces de Dispharages du Dahomey. Jan., 1912. *Ibid.*, vol. 66.

168 Gendre, E. (1913). Sur une espèce de Dispharage peu connue. Feb., 1913. *Ibid.*, vol. 67.

169 Gendre, E. (1913). Sur une espèce nouvelle de Dispharage. April, 1913. *Ibid.*, vol. 67.

170 Gendre, E. (1913). Notes d'Helmintologie Africaine (Quatrième Note). June, 1913. *Ibid.*, vol. 67.

171 Gendre, E. (1920). Description du mâle d'*Echinuria leptoptili* Gedoelst, Dispharage Parasite du Marabout. May, 1919. *Ibid.*, vol. 72.

172 Gendre, E. (1921). Sur une espèce nouvelle de d'Acuaria, parasite de *Ptilopachys fusus* Vieill. March, 1920. *Ibid.*, vol. 73.

173 Gendre, E. (1921). Un genre nouveau d'*Acuariinæ*. March, 1920. *Ibid.*, vol. 73.

174 Gendre, E. (1921). Sur deux espèces de Nématodes Africains. Jan., 1921. *Ibid.*, vol. 73.

175 Gendre, E. (1921). Notes d'Helminthologie Africaine (Cinquième Note). April, 1921. *Ibid.*, vol. 73.

176 Gendre, E. (1922). Sur un helminthe peu connu *Spiroptera conocephala* Molin. July, 1921. *Ibid.*, vol. 73.

177 Gendre, E. (1922). Sur deux Spiroptères nouveaux voisins de *Spiroptera conocephala* Molin. Nov., 1921. *Ibid.*, vol. 73.

178 Gendre, E. (1922). Notes d'Helminthologie Africaine (Sixième Note). Dec., 1921. *Ibid.*, vol. 73.

179 Gendre, E. (1922). Sur l'Identité des genres *Hadjelia* Seurat et *Gilsonia* Gedoelst et leurs affinités avec le genre *Histiocephalus* Diesing. Dec., 1921. *Ibid.*, vol. 73.

180 Gendre, E. (1923). Sur deux espèces *d'Hadjelia*. Jan., 1922. *Ibid.*, vol. 74.

181 Gendre, E. (1923). Sur quelques espèces *d'Habronema* parasites des oiseaux. Oct., 1922. *Ibid.*, vol. 74.

182 Giles, G. M. J. (1892). On a New Sclerostome from the Large Intestine of Mules. A description of two new Nematode parasites found in sheep. *Scient. mem. by Med. Officers of the Army of India*, part 7, pp. 25 and 45.

183 Gilruth, J. A., and Sweet, G. (1911). *Onchocerca gibsoni* : the Cause of Worm Nodules in Australian Cattle. With Notes on Worm Nests in Australian Cattle and in Camels, by Cleland, J. B., and Johnston, T. H., Government Printer, Sydney. 58 pp.

184 Gilruth, J. A., and Sweet, G. (1912). Further Observations on *Onchocerca gibsoni*, the cause of Worm Nodules in Cattle. *Proc. Roy. Soc. Victoria*, vol. 25 (New ser.), p. 23.

185 Gmelin, J. F. (1790). Systema naturæ, etc., part 6, Vermes, 3021 pp. Lipsiæ.

186 Gœze, J. A. E. (1782). Versuch einer Naturgeschichte der Eingeweidewürmer thierischer Körper. xi. + 471 pp. Blankenburg.

187 Gœze, J. A. E. (1800). Einige Beobachtungen über die Erzeugung der Einge-weidewürmer. In Zeder, 1800, p. 317.

188 Goodey, R. (1923). *Necator americanus* and the Domestic Pig. *Jl. of Helminthology*, vol. 1, p. 161.

189 Goodey, R. (1924). The Anatomy of *Œsophagostomum dentatum* (Rud.) a Nematode parasite of the Pig, with Observations on the Structure and Biology of the Free-living Larvæ. *Jl. Helminthology*, vol. 2, p. 1.

190 Goodey, T. (1924). The Anatomy and Life-History of the Nematode *Rhabdias fuscovenosa* (Railliet) from the Grass Snake *Tropidonotus natrix*. *Ibid.*, vol. 2, p. 51.

191 Goodey, T. (1924). Œsophagostomes of Goats, Sheep, and Cattle. *Ibid.*, vol. 2, p. 97.

192 Goodey, T. (1924). Some New Members of the genus *Œsophagostomum* from the roan Antelope and the Wart-hog. *Ibid.*, vol. 2, p. 135.

193 Goodey, T. (1924). Observations on *Hyostrongylus rubidus* (Hassall and Stiles, 1892) Hall, 1921, from the Stomach of the Pig, with a Note on *Strongylus attenuatus* (Molin, 1860). *Ibid.*, vol. 2, p. 191.

194 Goodey, T. (1924). A Critical Review of Zebrowski's Preliminary Report on Hog Lung-worms. *Ibid.*, vol. 2, p. 198.

195 Goodey, T. (1924). On Two New Species of the Nematode genus *Rhabdias*. *Ibid.*, vol. 2, p. 203.

195a Goodey, T. (1925). *Œsophagostomum longicaudum*, n. sp. from the Pig in New Guinea. *Ibid.*, vol. 3, p. 45.

195b Goodey, T. (1925). *Viannella viscaciæ* n. sp., a Nematode Parasite of the South American rodent *Viscacia viscacia*. *Ibid.*, vol. 3, p. 157.

196 Goodey, T., and Cameron, T. W. M. (1923). Observations on the morphology and Life-history of *Ascaris columnaris* Leidy, a Nematode parasite of the Skunk. *Ibid.*, vol. 1, p. 1.

197 Gordon, R. M. (1922). Ancylostomes recorded from sixty-seven post-mortems performed in Amazonas. *Ann. Trop. Med. and Parasit.*, vol. 16, p. 223.

198 Gordon, R. M. (1922). The Occurrence of Ancylostomes resembling *Necator americanus* amongst domestic Pigs in Amazonas. *Ibid.*, vol. 16, p. 295.

199 Gordon, R. M. (1923). A further Note on the occurrence of Ancylostomes resembling *Necator americanus* amongst domestic Pigs in Amazonas. *Ibid.*, vol. 17, p. 289.

200 Grassi, G. B. (1879). Sovra l'Anguillula intestinale. *R. Ist. lomb. di sc. e lett., Rendic., Milano*, 2 s., vol. 12, p. 228.

201 Graybill, H. W. (1923). A New genus of Nematodes from the domestic Rabbit. *Parasitology*, vol. 15, p. 340.

202 Graybill, H. W. (1924). *Obeliscoides*, a New Name for the Nematode genus *Obeliscus*. *Ibid.*, vol. 16, p. 317.

203 Graybill, H. W. (1924). A New Species of Round Worm of the genus *Trichostrongylus* from the Rabbit. *Proc. U. S. Nat. Mus.*, vol. 66, art. 11.

203a Gurlt, E. F. (1831–32). Lehrbuch der pathologischen Anatomie der Haus-Säugethiere. Nebst einen Anhange, welcher die Beschreibung der bei den Haus-Säugethieren vorkommenden Eingeweidewürmer enthält, vol. 1, xx. + 399 pp. ; vol. 2, xliv. + 462 pp.

204 Hall, M. C. (1913). A New Nematode, *Rictularia splendida*, from the Coyote, with Notes on other Coyote parasites. *Proc. U.S. Nat. Mus., Washington*, vol. 46, p. 73.

205 Hall, M. C. (1916). Nematode Parasites of Mammals of the Orders *Rodentia, Lagomorpha, and Hyracoidea*. *Ibid.*, vol. 50, 258 pp.

206 Hall, M. C. (1918). A Physaloptera from the Dog, with a Note on the Nematode parasites of the Dog in North America. *Jl. Am. Vet. Med. Assoc.*, vol. 6, p. 733.

207 Hall, M. C. (1921). Two new genera of Nematodes, with a note on a neglected Nematode structure. *Proc. U.S. Nat. Mus.*, Washington, vol. 59, p. 541.

208 Hall, M. C. (1922). Lungworms of Domestic Animals. *The Cornell Veterinarian*, vol. 12, p. 131.

209 Hall, M. C. (1923). Internal parasites of Dogs and Cats in the United States, and Treatments for removing these Parasites. *Jl. Amer. Vet. Med. Assoc.*, vol. 63, p. 11.

210 Hallez, P. (1886). Anatomie de l'*Atractis dactilura* (Duj.). *Mem. Soc. d. Sc. de Lille*, ser. 4, vol. 15.

211 Hassall, H., and Stiles, C. W. (1892). *Strongylus rubidus*, a New Species of Nematode, parasitic in Pigs. *Jl. Comp. Med. and Vet. Arch.*, New York, vol. 13, p. 207.

212 Hegt, J. Noordhoek (1910). *Chlamydonema felineum* nov. gen., nov. spec., eine neue parasitisch lebende Nematode. *Tijdsch. der Nederl. Dierk. Vereen.*, ser. 2, part 12. Leiden.

213 Hemprich, F. G., and Ehrenberg, C. G. (1828). Symbolæ physicæ seu icones, etc. *Pars. Zoologica*, Berlin.

214 Henry, A., and Blanc, G. (1912). Le Physaloptère du *Macacus cynomolgus* L. *Bull. Soc. Path. Exot.*, vol. 5, p. 390.

215 Henry, A., et O'Zoux (1909). La Filaire du Foudi (*Filaria ozouxi* Railliet and Henry). *Ibid.*, vol. 2, p. 544.

216 Hesse, A. J. (1923). Description of *Capillaria leucisci* n. sp. found in the Intestine of *Leuciscus phoxinus* Linn. *Jl. Helminthology*, vol. 1, p. 65.

217 Horst, R. (1885). A New Entozoon from *Struthio molybdophanes* Rchw. *Notes Leyden Museum*, vol. 7, p. 263.

218 Hutton, A. (1911). On the Morphology of *Oxyuris ambiguus* Rud., Type of the genus *Passalurus*. *Jl. Lond. School Trop. Med.*, vol. 1, p. 11.

219 Ihle, J. E. W. (1917). Beschrijving van *Strongyloides westeri* n. sp. *Tijdsch. voor Diergeneeskunde*. Afl. 2.

220 Ihle, J. E. W. (1919). *Cylicostomum nanum*, een nieuwe Strongylide van het paard. *Ibid.*, Dl. 46, Afl. 23.

221 Ihle, J. E. W. (1919). Ueber *Ancylostoma perniciosum* Linst. und die Strongyliden des Elefanten. *Bijdr. tot de Dierk.* Afl. 21, p. 97.

222 Ihle, J. E. W. (1920). *Herodontostomum markusi* n. gen., n. sp., eine neue Strongylide des Pferdes *Centralbl. f. Bakt.*, 1 Abt. Orig., vol. 84, p. 43.

223 Ihle, J. E. W. (1920). Eine neue Cylicostomum-Art (*C. mucronatum*) aus dem Darm des Pferdes. *Ibid.*, vol. 84, p. 132.

224 Ihle, J. E. W. (1920). *Cylicostomum brevicapsulatum* n. sp. eine neue strongylide aus dem Darm des Pferdes. *Ibid.*, vol. 84, p. 562.

225 Ihle, J. E. W. (1920). Bemerkungen über die Gattungen *Cylicostomum*, *Poteriostomum* und *Craterostomum*. *Ibid.*, vol. 85, p. 267.

226 Ihle, J. E. W. (1920). Een Anguillulide uit den Darm van het Paard. *Tijdsch. v. Diergeneesk.*, Dl. 47, Afl. 3.

227 Ihle, J. E. W. (1920). Een nieuwe Cylicostomum-soort (*C. brevicapsulatum*), uit den Darm van het Paard. *Ibid.*, Dl. 47, Afl. 5.

228 Ihle, J. E. W. (1920). *Cylicostomum ultrajectinum*, een nieuwe Strongylide uit den Darm van het Paard. *Ibid.*, Dl. 47, Afl. 8.

229 Ihle, J. E. W. (1920). *Uncinaria stenocephala* Railliet. *Ibid.*, Dl. 47, Afl. 14.

230 Ihle, J. E. W. (1921). Das Männchen von *Cylicostomum ultrajectinum*. *Centralbl. f. Bakt.*, 1 Abt. Orig., vol. 85, p. 372.

231 Ihle, J. E. W. (1921). On the genus *Cylicostomum*. *Annals Trop. Med. and Parasit.*, vol. 15, p. 397.

232 Ihle, J. E. W. (1922). Report of the Commission appointed to enquire into the Sclerostomiasis in Holland. I. Zool. Part. Vol. 1. Adult Strongylids (Sclerostomes) inhabiting the large Intestine of the Horse. 118 pp.

233 Ihle, J. E. W. (1922). On *Œsophagostomum apiostomum* (Willach) and some remarks on the Classification of the Strongylidæ. *Bijdr. tot de Dierk.*, Afl. 22, p. 89.

234 Ihle, J. E. W. (1922). Over de verdeeling van het geslacht Cylicostomum. *Tijdschr. v. Diergeneesk.*, Dl. 49, Afl. 4.

235 Ihle, J. E. W. (1924). Over de Nomenclatuur en de Biologie van het geslacht Cylicostomum. *Ibid.*, Dl. 51, Afl. 11.

236 Ihle, J. E. W. (1924). De verdeeling van het geslacht Strongylus. *Ibid.*, Dl. 51, Afl. 17.

236a Ihle, J. E. W. (1925). Verzeichnis der Cylicostomum-Arten der Equiden, mit Bemerkungen über einzelne Spezies. *Centralbl. f. Bakt.*, 1 Abt. Orig. vol. 95, p. 227.

237 Inglis, Vera, and Leiper, R. T. (1912). Bibliography of *Dracontiasis*. *Journ. Lond. School of Trop. Med.*, vol. 2, suppl. no. 1.

238 Irwin-Smith, Vera A. (1920). Nematode parasites of the domestic Pigeon (*Columba livia domestica*) in Australia. *Proc. Linn. Soc. N.S.W.*, Sydney, vol. 45, p. 552.

239 Irwin-Smith, Vera A. (1921). Notes on Nematodes of the genus *Physaloptera*, with Special Reference to those Parasitic in Reptiles. Part 1. *Ibid.*, vol. 46, p. 492.

240 Irwin-Smith, Vera A. (1922). Notes on Nematodes of the genus *Physaloptera*, with Special Reference to those Parasitic in Reptiles. Part 2. A Review of the *Physaloptera* of Lizards. *Ibid.*, vol. 47, p. 53.

241 Irwin-Smith, Vera A. (1922). Notes on Nematodes of the genus *Physaloptera*. Part 3. The *Physaloptera* of Australian Lizards. *Ibid.*, vol. 47, p. 232.

242 Irwin-Smith, Vera A. (1922). A New Nematode parasite of a Lizard. *Ibid.*, vol. 47, p. 311.

243 Jägerskiöld, L. A. (1909). Nematoden aus Ägypten und dem Sudan. *Rictularia* and *Dichelyne*. *Results of Swedish Zool. Exped. to Egypt and White Nile*, 1901, No. 25. Upsala.

244 Jägerskiöld, L. A. (1909). Zur Kenntnis der Nematoden Gattungen *Eustrongylides* u. *Hystrichis*. *Soc. Acta.*, ser. 4, vol. 2, no. 3. Upsala.

245 Jimbo, K. (1914). Ueber die Verbreitung einer Art von *Trichostrongylus*, *T. orientalis* n. sp. als Darmparasiten des Menschen in Japan. *Centralbl. f. Bakt.*, 1 Abt. Orig., vol. 75, p. 53.

246 Johnston, T. H. (1916). A Census of the Endoparasites recorded as occurring in Queensland, arranged under their hosts. *Proc. Roy. Soc. Qld.*, vol. 28, p. 31.

246a Kalantarian, E. V. (1924). On the Parasitic Worms of Armenian Rodents. *Reports of the Tropical Institute of Armenia*, No. 1. [In Russian.]

247 Khalil, M. (1922). A Preliminary Note on some New Nematode parasites from the Elephant. *Ann. Mag. of Nat. Hist.*, ser. 9, vol. 9, p. 212.

248 Khalil, M. (1922). *Galoncus tridentatus* sp. n., a new Ankylostome living in Fibrous Nodules in the Intestine of a Leopard. *Ibid.*, ser. 9, vol. 9, p. 596.

249 Khalil, M. (1922). On the Morphology of the Bursate Nematode, *Brachyclonus indicus* Railliet and Henry, 1910. *Ibid.*, ser. 9, vol. 10, p. 235.

250 Khalil, M. (1922). *Travassosius rufus* gen. et sp. n., a Nematode (*Trichostrongylidæ*) parasitic in the Stomach of the Norwegian Beaver. *Ibid.*, ser. 9, vol. 10, p. 281.

251 Khalil, M. (1922). A Revision of the Nematode Parasites of Elephants, with a description of Four New Species. *Proc. Zool. Soc.*, London, p. 205.

251a Khalil, M. (1924). The Classification of the Family *Ancylostomidæ*. *Reports and Notes of the Public Health Laboratories*, Cairo, No. 6, p. 195.

252 Kotlán, A. (1919). Beiträge zur Helminthologie Ungarns. *Centralbl. f. Bakt.*, 1 Abt. Orig. vol. 83, p. 557.

253 Kotlán, A. (1921). Two New *Cylicostomum* Species from the Horse. *Ann. Trop. Med. and Parasit.*, vol. 14, p. 299.

253a Kuhn, J. (1829). Description d'une nouvelle espèce de Strongle trouvée dans le Marsouin. *Bull. Sci. Nat. et Géol.*, Paris, vol. 17, p. 150.

253b Kuhn, J. (1829). Anatomie comparée de deux espèces de Strongylus, qui vivent dans le Marsouin ; par M. Raspail. [Report by Kuhn.] *Ibid.*, vol. 19, p. 139.

253c Kuhn, J. (1829–1830). Description d'un nouveau genre de l'ordre des Douves, et de deux espèces de Strongles. *Mém. Mus. Hist. Nat.*, Paris, vol. 18, p. 357.

254 Lane, C. (1913). *Agchylostoma ceylanicum*, a New Human Parasite. *Ind. Med. Gazette*, vol. 48, p. 217.

255 Lane, C. (1914). Bursate Nematodes from the Indian Elephant. *Ind. Jl. of Med. Res.*, vol. 2, p. 380.

256 Lane, C. (1914). Suckered Round-Worms from India and Ceylon. *Ibid.*, vol. 2, p. 655.

257 Lane, C. (1915). A Further Note on Bursate Nematodes from the Indian Elephant, *Ibid.*, vol. 3, p. 105.

258 Lane, C. (1915). *Falcaustra falcata*. An Investigation of *Oxysoma falcatum* Linst., 1906. *Ibid.*, vol. 3, p. 109.

259 Lane, C. (1916). The genus *Ancylostoma* in India and Ceylon. *Ibid.*, vol. 4, p. 74.

260 Lane, C. (1916). The genus *Dacnitis* Duj., 1845. *Ibid.*, vol. 4, p. 93.

261 Lane, C. (1917). *Bunostomum kashinathi* and the *Ancylostomidæ*. *Ibid.*, vol. 4, p. 414.

262 Lane, C. (1917). *Gireterakis girardi* (n. g., n. sp.) and other suckered Nematodes. *Ibid.*, vol. 4, p. 754.

263 Lane, C. (1917). *Ancylostoma duodenale* as a Parasite of *Felis tigris*. *Ibid.*, vol. 5, p. 210.

264 Lane, C. (1921). Some Bursate Nematodes from Indian and African Elephants. *Ibid.*, vol. 9, p. 163.

265 Lane, C. (1922). A Preliminary Note on Two Strongylata from Swine in the Pacific. *Ann. Mag. Nat. Hist.*, ser. 9, vol. 9, p. 683.

266 Lane, C. (1922). *Ancylostoma braziliense*. *Annals. Trop. Med. and Parasit.*, vol. 16, p. 347.

267 Lane, C. (1923). The Practice of Medicine in the Tropics, edited by Byam and Archibald, vol. 3.

268 Lane, C. (1923). Some Strongylata. *Parasitology*, vol. 15, p. 348.

269 Lane, C. (1925). The Nematode genus *Raillietostrongylus*. *Parasitology*, vol. 17, p. 192.

270 Leese, A. S. (1911). Indian Camel Filariasis. *Jl. Trop. Vet. Sci.*, Calcutta. vol. 6, p. 400.

271 Leidy, J. (1856). A Synopsis of Entozoa and some of their Ectocongeners observed by the Author. *Proc. Acad. Nat. Sc.*, Phila., vol. 8, p. 42.

272 Leidy, J. (1904). Researches in Helminthology and Parasitology, arranged and edited by J. Leidy, jun. *Smithsonian Misc. Coll.*, vol. 46, 281 pp. Washington.

273 Leiper, R. T. (1907). Two New genera of Nematodes occasionally parasitic in Man. *Brit. Med. Journ.*, June 1st, p. 1296.

274 Leiper, R. T. (1908). Note on the Anatomy of *Cystidicola farionis*. *Parasitology*, vol. 1, p. 193.

275 Leiper, R. T. (1908). An Account of some Helminthes contained in Dr. C. M. Wenyon's Collection from the Sudan. *Third Report Wellcome Research Laboratories, Gordon Memorial College*, Khartoum, p. 187.

276 Leiper, R. T. (1909). *Lagochilascaris minor. Proc. Zool. Soc.*, London, p. 35.

277 Leiper, R. T. (1909). The Structure and Relationships of *Gnathostoma siamense* (Levinsen). *Parasitology*, vol. 2, p. 77.

278 Leiper, R. T. (1909). Description of *Filaria mavis* n. sp., from the Thrush. *The Zoologist*, Sept.

279 Leiper, R. T. (1910). The Entozoa of the *Hippopotamus. Proc. Zool. Soc.*, London, p. 233.

280 Leiper, R. T. (1910). A New Nematode Worm from Trinidad. *Ibid.*, p. 742.

281 Leiper, R. T. (1910). Nematodes. Sjöstedt's Zoologische Kilamendjaro-Meru Exp. (1905–06). Stockholm. Part 22, p. 23.

282 Leiper, R. T. (1910). Guinea-worm in domesticated Animals. *Journ. Trop. Med. and Hyg.*, vol. 13, p. 65.

283 Leiper, R. T. (1911). The Occurrence of *Œsophagostomum apiostomum* as an Intestinal Parasite of Man in Nigeria. *Ibid.*, vol. 14, p. 116.

284 Leiper, R. T. (1911). Notes of Recent and some New Records of Helminthes in Man, of which there are few records. *Jl. Lond. Sch. of Trop. Med.*, vol. 1, p. 16.

285 Leiper, R. T. (1911). Check List of Helminthes Parasitic in Equines. *Ibid.*, vol. 1, p. 22.

286 Leiper, R. T. (1911). Some New Parasitic Nematodes from Tropical Africa. *Proc. Zool. Soc.*, London, June, p. 549.

287 Leiper, R. T. (1911). On the Frequent Occurrence of *Physaloptera mordens* as an Intestinal Parasite of Man in Tropical Africa. *Jl. Trop. Med. and Hyg.*, vol. 14, p. 209.

288 Leiper, R. T. (1911). On the Development and Bionomics of *Trichostrongylus pergracilis. The Grouse in Health and Disease*, London, vol. 1, pp. 218–234.

289 Leiper, R. T. (1911). Report on Onchocerciasis in Cattle with Special Reference to the Structure and Bionomic Characters of the Parasite. *Reports of the Local Govt. Board on Public Health and Medical Subjects*, new ser., no. 45, p. 6; and *Jl. Trop. Med.*, vol. 14, p. 87.

290 Leiper, R. T. (1912). Check List of Helminthes Parasitic in Cattle. *Jl. Lond. School of Trop. Med.*, vol. 1, p. 115.

291 Leiper, R. T. (1913). Observations on certain Helminthes of Man. *Trans. Soc. Trop. Med. and Hyg.*, vol. 6, p. 265.

292 Leiper, R. T. (1913). A New Cylicostome Worm from the Horse in London. *Vet. Journ.*, vol. 69, p. 460.

293 Leiper, R. T. (1913). The Apparent Identity of *Agchylostoma ceylanicum* (Looss, 1911) and *Agchylostoma braziliense* (Faria, 1910). *Jl. Trop. Med. and Hyg.*, vol. 16, p. 334.

294 Leiper, R. T. (1915). Notes of the Occurrence of Parasites presumably rare in Man. *Journ. Roy. Army Med. Corps*, vol. 21, p. 569.

295 Leiper, R. T., and Atkinson, E. L. (1914). Helminthes of the British Antarctic Expedition, 1910–13. *Proc. Zool. Soc.*, London, p. 222.

296 Leiper, R. T., and Atkinson, E. L. (1915). Parasitic Worms : British Antarctic ("Terra Nova") Exp., 1910. *Natural History Report. Zool.* Vol. 2, p. 19.

297 Leuckart, K. G. F. R. (1848). Beschreibung zweier neuen Helminthen. *Arch. f. Naturg.*, Berlin, vol. 1, p. 26.

298 Leuckart, K. G. F. R. (1850). Helminthologische Notizen. *Ibid.*, vol. 1, p. 9.

299 Leuckart, K. G. F. R. (1865). Bericht über die wissenschaftlichen Leistungen in der Naturgeschichte der niederen Thiere während der Jahre 1864 und 1865. (Erste Halfte.) *Ibid.*, vol. 2, p. 165.

300 Leuckart, K. G. F. R. (1865). Zur Entwickelungsgeschichte des *Ascaris nigrovenosa*. Zugleich eine Erwiederung gegen Herrn Candidat Mecznikow. *Arch. f. Anat., Physiol. u. wissensch. Med.*, Leipz., p. 641.

301 Leuckart, K. G. F. R. (1866). Untersuchungen über *Trichina spiralis*. iv. + 120 pp. Leipzig and Heidelberg.

302 Leuckart, K. G. F. R. (1867). Die menschlichen Parasiten und die von ihnen herrührenden Krankheiten. *Ein Hand-und Lehrbuch. f. Naturforscher und Ærzte*, vol. 2. vi. + 256 pp. Leipzig and Heidelberg.

303 Leuckart, K. G. F. R. (1876). Die menschlichen Parasiten und die von ihnen herrührenden Krankheiten, vol. 2, p. 513. Leipzig.

304 Leuckart, K. G. F. R. (1886). The Parasites of man, and the Diseases which Proceed from them. A text-book for Students and Practitioners. Natural History of Parasites in general. Systematic account of the Parasites infesting Man. Protozoa-Cestoda. Transl. from the German, with the co-operation of the author, by William E. Hoyle. xxvi. + 771 pp. Edinburgh.

305 Lingard, A. (1905). Observations on the Filarial Embryos found in the General Circulation of the Equidæ and Bovidæ, and their probable Pathological significance. iv. + 59 pp. London.

306 Linnæus, C. (1758). Systema naturæ per regna tria naturæ, secundum classes, ordines, genera, species, cum characteribus, differentitiis, synonymis, locis. *Editio decima, reformata*, vol. 1, 823 pp. Holmiæ.

307 Linnæus, C. (1767). Idem. Editio duodecima, reformata, vol. 1, pp. 533–1327.

308 Linstow, O. von (1873). Einige neue Nematoden, nebst Bemerkungen über bekannte Arten. *Archiv. f. Naturg.*, Berlin, vol. 1, p. 293.

309 Linstow, O. von (1874). Beobachtungen an *Trichodes crassicauda* Bell. (*Trichosoma crassicauda* Aut.) *Ibid.*, vol. 1, p. 271.

310 Linstow, O. von (1876). Helminthologische Beobachtungen. *Ibid.*, vol. 1, p. 1.

311 Linstow, O. von (1878). Compendium du Helminthologie, Hannover. xxii. + 382 pp.

312 Linstow, O. von (1878). Neue Beobachtungen an Helminthen. *Arch. f. Naturg.*, vol. 1, p. 218.

313 Linstow, O. von (1883). Nematoden, Trematoden und Acanthocephalen, gesammelt von Prof. Fedtschenko in Turkestan. *Ibid.*, vol. I, p. 274.

314 Linstow, O. von (1885). Beobachtungen an bekannten und neuen Nematoden und Trematoden. *Ibid.*, vol. 1, p. 235.

315 Linstow, O. von (1889). Compendium der Helminthologie Nachtrag. Hannover. xvi. + 151 pp.

315a Linstow, O. von (1889). Helminthologisches. *Arch. f. Naturg.*, Berl., vol. 1, p. 235.

316 Linstow, O. von (1898). Nemathelminthen von Herrn Richard Semon in Australien gesammelt. (Zool. Forschungsreisen in Australien und dem Malayischen Archipel. Richard Semon, Jena.) *Denkschr. d. med.-naturw. Gesellsch. zu Jena*, vol. 8, p. 469.

316a Linstow, O. von (1898). Idem. *Zool. Centralbl.*, Leipz., vol. 5, p. 672.

317 Linstow, O. von (1898). Nemathelminthen gesammelt von Herrn Prof. Dr. F. Dahl in Bismarck-Archipel. *Arch. f. Naturg.*, vol. 1, p. 281.

318 Linstow, O. von (1899). Nematoden aus der Berliner zoologischen Sammlung. *Mitt. a. d. Zool. Mus.*, Berlin, vol. 1, p. 3.

319 Linstow, O. von (1899). Zur Kenntnis der Genere *Hystrichis* und *Tropidocerca*. *Arch. f. Naturg.*, Berl., vol. 1, p. 155.

320 Linstow, O. von (1901). Helminthen von den Ufern des Nyassa-Sees, ein Beitrag zur Helminthen-Fauna, von Süd-Afrika. *Jenaische Ztschr. f. Naturw.*, Jena, vol. 35, n. F., vol. 28, p. 409.

321 Linstow, O. von (1901). Beobachtungen an Helminthen des senckenbergischen naturhistorischen Museums, des breslauer zoologischen Instituts und anderen. *Arch. f. mikr. Anat. Bonn.*, vol. 58, p. 182.

322 Linstow, O. von (1902). Beobachtungen an neuen und bekannten Nemathelminthen. *Ibid.*, Bonn., vol. 60, p. 217.

323 Linstow, O. von (1902). *Atractis cruciata* und *Oxyuris monhystera*, zwei neue Nematoden aus *Metopoceros cornutus*. *Centralbl. f. Bakt.*, 1 Abt. Orig., vol. 31, p. 28.

324 Linstow, O. von (1903). Parasiten, meistens Helminthen, aus Siam. *Arch. f. mikr. Anat.*, Bonn., vol. 62, p. 108.

325 Linstow, O. von (1904). Nematoda in the Collection of the Colombo Museum. *Spolia Zeylanica*, vol. 1, p. 91.

326 Linstow, O. von (1904). Beobachtungen an Nematoden und Cestoden. *Archiv. f. Naturg.*, vol. 70, p. 297.

327 Linstow, O. von (1906). Parasites from the Gharial (*Gavialis gangeticus* Geoffr.). *Journ. and Proc. Asiatic Soc.*, Bengal, vol. 2, p. 269.

328 Linstow, O. von (1906). Helminthes from the Collection of the Colombo Museum. *Spolia Zeylanica*, vol. 3, p. 163.

328a Linstow, O. von (1906). Nematodes of the Scottish National Antarctic Expedition, 1902–1904. *Proc. Roy. Soc.*, Edinb., vol. 26, p. 464.

329 Linstow, O. von (1907). Nematoden aus dem Königl. Zoolog. Mus. in Berlin. *Mitteil. a. d. Zool. Mus.*, Berlin, vol. 3, p. 251.

330 Linstow, O. von (1908). Recent Additions to the Collection of Entozoa in the Indian Museum. *Rec. Ind. Mus.*, vol. 2, p. 103.

331 Linstow, O. von (1908). Nematoden und Acanthocephalen aus dem westlichen und zentralen Sudafrika. *Denk. d. med.-naturwiss. Gesellsch.*, vol. 13, p. 23.

332 Linstow, O. von (1909). Parasitische Nematoden. In Brauer's *Die Süsswasserfauna Deutschlands*, Jena, Heft 15, pp. 47–92.

333 Linton, E. (1900). Fish Parasites collected at Woods Hole in 1898. *U.S. Fisheries Commission Bull.*, Washington, vol. 19, p. 267.

334 Linton, E. (1901). Parasites of Fishes in the Woods Hole Region. *Ibid.*, vol. 19, p. 405.

335 Looss, A. (1895). *Strongylus subtilis* n. sp., ein bisher unbekannter Parasit des Menschen in Egypten. *Centralbl. f. Bakt.*, 1 Abt. Orig., vol. 18, p. 161.

336 Looss, A. (1900). Notizen zur Helminthologie Egyptens. III. Die Sclerostomen der Pferde und Esel Egypten. *Ibid.*, vol. 27, p. 150.

337 Looss, A. (1902). Ueber die Giltigkeit des Gattungsnamens *Ankylostomum* Dubini. *Ibid.*, vol. 31, p. 422.

338 Looss, A. (1902). The Sclerostomidæ of Horses and Donkeys in Egypt. *Rec. Egypt. Governm. School of Medicine*, 1901.

339 Looss, A. (1904). Zur Kenntniss des Baues der *Filaria loa* Guyot. *Zool. Jahrbuch.*, Jena, vol. 20, p. 549.

340 Looss, A. (1904). Zum Bau des erwachsenen *Ancylostomum duodenale*. *Centralbl. f. Bakt.*, 1 Abt. Orig., vol. 35, p. 752.

341 Looss, A. (1905). The Anatomy and Life History of *Agchylostoma duodenale*, Dub. A Monograph. Part I. *Rec. Egypt. Govt. School Med.*, Cairo, vol. 3, p. 1.

342 Looss, A. (1905). Die Wanderung der *Ancylostomum und Strongyloides* Larven von der Haut nach dem Darm. *Compt. rend. 6 Cong. internat. de zool.*, Genève, 25 mai, p. 225.

343 Looss, A. (1905). Das Genus *Trichostrongylus* n.g., mit zwei neuen gelegentlichen Parasiten des Menschen. (Notizen zur Helminthologie Ægyptens, 6). *Centralbl. f. Bakteriol.*, 1 Abt. Orig. vol. 39, p. 409.

344 Looss, A. (1911). The Anatomy and Life History of *Agchylostoma duodenale* Dub. A Monograph. Part II. *Rec. Egypt. Govt. School Med.*, Cairo, vol. 4, p. 159.

344a M'Fadyean, J. (1897). Parasitic Gastro-enteritis in Sheep and Lambs. *J. Comp. Path. and Therap.*, Edinburgh and London, vol. 10, pp. 48–63.

345 Macfie, J. W. S. (1924). *Saurositus agamæ* n. g., n. sp. A Filarioid Parasite of the Lizard *Agama colonorum*. *Ann. Trop. Med. and Parasit.*, vol. 18, p. 409.

346 Macfie, J. W. S., and Yorke, W. (1923). *Trichonema tetracanthum*. *Ann. Trop. Med. and Parasit.*, vol. 17, p. 439.

346a Magath, T. B. (1919). *Camallanus americanus*, nov. spec., a Monograph on a nematode species. *Trans. Amer. Microsc. Soc.*, vol. 38, p. 47.

347 Manalang, C. (1924). Note on *Ancylostoma braziliense* as a Human Parasite in the Philippines. *Jl. of Parasitology*, vol. 11, p. 90.

347a Massino, B. J. (1924). On the Nematode Parasites of *Emys orbicularis* from the River Arax. *Reports of the State Experimental Veterinary Institute*, Moscow, vol. 2, No. 1. [In Russian.]

347b Massino, B. (1925). Ein neuer Nematode des Hundes : *Rictularia cahirensis* Jägerskiöld, 1909. *Berl. Tierärztl. Wochenschr.*, vol. 41, p. 67.

348 Maupas, E., and Seurat, L. G. (1912). Sur un Nématode de l'Intestin grêle du Dromadaire. *C. R. Soc. Biol.*, vol. 73, p. 628.

349 Maupas, E., and Seurat, L. G. (1916). Sur le méchanisme de l'accouplement chez les Nématodes. *Ibid.*, vol. 79, p. 614.

350 May, H. G. (1920). Observations on the Nematode genus Nematodirus, with descriptions of New Species. *Proc. U.S. Nat. Mus.*, Washington, vol. 58, p. 577.

351 Mégnin, J. (1885). The Gape Disease of Fowls and the Parasite by which it is Caused. Memoir on a verminous epizootic disease of the pheasantries and on the parasite which causes it, the *Syngamus trachealis* (Sieb.), *Sclerostoma syngamus* (Dies.). *I. Ann. Rep. Bureau Animal Indust.*, *U.S. Dept. Agric.*, Washington (1884), p. 280.

351a Mehlis, E. (1831). Novæ observationes de entozois. Creplin. Isis (Oken) Leipzig, pp. 68–99, 166–199.

352 Miranda, C. (1924). Alguns nematodeos do genero *Aplectana* Railliet and Henry, 1916. *Memorias do Instituto Oswaldo Cruz*, vol. 17, p. 45.

353 Molin, R. (1857). Notizie elmintologiche. *Atti. r. Ist. Veneto di sc., lett. ed arti*, Venezia, vol. 2, pp. 146 and 216.

354 Molin, R. (1858). Versuch einer Monographie der Filarien. *Sitzungsber. d. k. Akad. Wissensch.*, *Wien. math.-naturw. Cl.*, vol. 28, p. 365.

355 Molin, R. (1858). Prospectus helminthum, quæ in prodromo faunæ helmintho-logicæ Venetiæ continentur. *Ibid.*, vol. 30, p. 127.

356 Molin, R. (1859). Nuovi myzelmintha raccolti ed esaminati. *Ibid.*, vol. 37, p. 818.

357 Molin, R. (1859). Cephalocotylea e nematoidea. *Ibid.*, vol. 38, p. 7.

358 Molin, R. (1860). Una Monographia del genere *Spiroptera*. *Ibid.*, vol. 38, p. 911.

359 Molin, R. (1860). Trenta specie di nematoidi. *Ibid.*, vol. 40, p. 331.

360 Molin, R. (1861). Il Sottordine degli acrofalli ordinato scientificamente secondo i risultamenti delle indagini anatomiche ed embriogeniche. *Mem. r. Ist. Veneto di sc. lett. ed arti*, Venezia, vol. 9, p. 427.

361 Molin, R. (1861). Prodromus faunæ helminthologicæ venetæ adjectis disquisi-tionibus anatomicis et criticis. *Denkschr. d. k. Akad. d. Wissensch.*, Wien. *math.-naturw.*, 2 Abt., vol. 19, p. 189.

362 Monnig, H. O. (1924). South African Parasitic Nematodes. *Ninth and Tenth Reports of the Director of Veterinary Education and Research*, April, 1923, Union of South Africa, Dept. of Agriculture, Pretoria, p. 435.

363 Monnig, H. O. (1924). On some New South African Parasitic Nematodes. *Trans. Roy. Soc.*, South Africa, vol. 11, p. 105.

363a Monnig, H. O. (1925). A new Trichostrongylus from South African Sheep. *Ibid.*, vol. 12, p. 243.

364 Mueller, A. (1894). Helminthologische Beobachtungen an bekannten und unbekannten Entozoen. *Arch. f. Naturg.*, Berlin, vol. 1, p. 113.

365 Mueller, A. (1897). Helminthologische Mittheilungen. *Ibid.*, vol. 1, p. 1.

366 Mueller, O. F. (1779–80). Zoologicæ Danicæ seu animalium Daniæ et Norwegiæ rariorium ac minus notorum icones. Havniæ.

367 Mueller, O. F. (1787). Verzeichniss der bisher entdeckten Eingeweidewürmer, der Thiere, in welchen sie gefunden worden, und besten Schriften, die derselben erwähnen. *Naturforschr.*, Halle, vol. 22, p. 33.

368 Neiva, A., Cunha, A. M., and Travassos, L. (1914). Parasitologische Beiträge. *Mem. Inst. Oswaldo Cruz*, vol. 6, p. 180.

369 Neveu-Lemaire, M. (1914). Dédoublement du genre *Nematodirus*. *Bull. Soc. Zool. de France*, vol. 39, p. 293.

370 Neveu-Lemaire, M. (1921). *Crossophorus collaris* Hemprich et Ehrenberg, Ascaride parasite des Damans. *Bull. Soc. Path. Exot.*, vol. 14, p. 390.

371 Neveu-Lemaire, M. (1924). Les Strongylidés du rhinocéros africain. (*Rhinoceros bicornis.*) *Annales de Parasitologie humaine et Comparée*, vol. 2, p. 121. Paris.

372 Neveu-Lemaire, M. (1924). Le femelle de *Khalilia rhinocerotis* Neveu-Lemaire parasite du Rhinocéros Africain (*Rhinoceros bicornis*). *Ibid.*, vol. 2, p. 224.

372a Neveu-Lemaire, M. (1925). Description d'un Strongyle nouveau du Rhinocéros Africain, *Quilonia parva* n. sp. *Ibid.*, vol. 3, p. 290.

373 Nicoll, W. (1907). A Contribution towards a Knowledge of the Entozoa of British Marine Fishes. *Ann. and Mag. of Nat. Hist.*, ser. 7, vol. 19, p. 66.

373a Nishigori, M. (1924). On a New Species of the genus *Hepaticola*. *Jl. Med. Assoc. Formosa*, No. 236, p. 1.

374 Nitzsch, C. L. (1821). Ascaris. *Allg. Encycl. d. Wissensch. u. Künste* (Ersch and Gruber), Leipzig, vol. 6, p. 44.

375 Noc, F., Henry, V., and Esquier, A. (1920). L'Anguillule intestinale de l'homme au Sénégal (*Strongyloides intestinalis* Bavay, 1877). *Bull. Soc. Path. Exot.*, vol. 13, p. 588.

376 Ortlepp, R. J. (1922). A New *Trichostrongyle genus* from an Armadillo, *Euphrectus villosus*. *Ann. and Mag. of Nat. Hist.*, ser. 9, vol. 9, p. 413.

377 Ortlepp, R. J. (1922). A New Species of *Œsophagostomum* (*O. xeri*, sp. n.) from a Rodent (*Xerus setosus*). *Proc. Zool. Soc., Lond.*, June.

378 Ortlepp, R. J. (1922). The Nematode genus *Physaloptera* Rud. *Ibid.*, p. 999.

379 Ortlepp, R. J. (1923). Two New Nematodes collected in the Zoological Gardens of London. *Jl. Helminthology*, vol. 1, p. 61.

380 Ortlepp, R. J. (1923). The Life History of *Syngamus trachealis* (Montagu) v. Siebold, the Gape-worm of Chickens. *Ibid.*, vol. 1, p. 119.

381 Ortlepp, R. J. (1923). Observations on the Nematode genera *Kalicephalus*, *Diaphanocephalus* and *Occipitodontus*, g. n., and on the Larval Development of *Kalicephalus philodryadus* sp. n. *Ibid.*, vol. 1, p. 165.

381a Ortlepp, R. J. (1924). Helminths from Dutch Guiana. *Ibid.*, vol. 2, p. 15.

381b Ortlepp, R. J. (1925). On *Arthrocephalus gambiensis*, n. g., n. sp., a new Anky-lostome from an African mongoose. *Ibid.*, vol. 3, p. 151.

382 Osler, W. (1877). Verminous Bronchitis in Dogs. *Veterinarian*, London, vol. 23, p. 387.

383 Owen, R. (1835). Description of a Microscopic Entozoon infesting the Muscles of the Human Body. *Trans. Zool. Soc.*, London, vol. 1, p. 315.

384 Owen, R. (1836). Anatomical Descriptions of Two Species of Entozoa from the Stomach of a Tiger (*Felis tigris* Linn.), one of which forms a new genus of Nematoidea, *Gnathostoma*. *Proc. Zool. Soc.*, London, p. 123.

385 Pader, J. (1901). Filariose du Ligament Suspenseur du Boulet chez le Cheval. *Archives de Parasitologie*, vol. 4, p. 58.

386 Pagenstecher, H. S. (1865). Die Trichinen, 116 pp. Leipzig.

387 Parona, C. (1894). L'Elmintologia Italiana da suoi primi tempi all' anno 1890. *Atti. r. Università di Genova*, vol. 13, 733 pp.

388 Parona, C., and Stossich, M. (1901). *Œsophagostomum tuberculatum*, n. sp. parassita dei *Dasypus*. *Boll. mus. di zool.*, etc., Genova, 3 pp.

389 Perroncito, E. (1881). Observations sur la développement de *l'Anguillula stercoralis* (Bavay), pseudo-*Rhabditis stercoralis* (mihi) hors de l'organisme humain. *J. de l'anat. et physiol.*, Par., vol. 17, p. 499.

390 Philpot, F. (1922). On *Oswaldocruzia wisei*, a new Nematode from the "Saki" Monkey. *Annals. and Mag. Nat. Hist.*, ser. 9, vol. 10, p. 242.

391 Piana, G. P. (1897). Ricerche sulla morfologia della *Simondsia paradoxa* Cobbold, etc. *Atti Soc. ital. di. Sc. nat.*, Milana, vol. 37, p. 17.

392 Piana, G. P., and Stazzi, P. (1900). Elminti intestinali di una elefantessa. *Arch. d. parasitol.*, Par., vol. 3, p. 509.

393 Quiel, G. (1919). *Poteriostomum* n.g., eine neue, beim Pferde parasitierende Nematodengattung. *Centralbl. f. Bakt.*, Abt. 1, Orig., vol. 83, p. 466.

394 Quiel, G. (1919). Ein neuer Pferdeparasit, *Pseudosclerostomum*, n. g. (Nematode). *Sitz. Ges. naturforsch. Freunde*, Berlin.

395 Railliet, A. (1884). Sur une nouvelle espèce de dochmie de l'intestin du chien. *Bull. et mém. Soc. centr. de méd. vét.*, Par., vol. 38, p. 452.

396 Railliet, A. (1885). Éléments de zoologie médicale et agricole, Paris, 800 pp.

397 Railliet, A. (1889). De l'Occurrence de la Filaire de Médine chez les animaux. *Bull. Soc. Zool. de France*, vol. 14, p. 73.

398 Railliet, A. (1893). Traité de Zool. Méd. et Agricole, 2nd ed. (fasc. 1), Paris, 736 pp.

399 Railliet, A. (1895). Traité de Zoologie Médicale et Agricole, 2nd ed. (fasc. 2), Paris. xv. + 737–1303 pp.

400 Railliet, A. (1899). Évolution sans hétérogonie d'un angiostome de la couleuvre à collier. *C. R. Acad. Sci.*, Paris, vol. 129, p. 1271.

401 Railliet, A. (1900). Observations sur quelques sclérostomiens des ruminants. *Arch. de Parasitol.*, vol. 3, p. 102.

402 Railliet, A. (1902). Sur quelques sclérostomiens parasites des ruminants et des porcins. *C. R. Soc. Biol.*, vol. 54, p. 107.

402a Railliet, A. (1909). *Probstmayria vivipara*, nématode du cheval. *Rec. Méd. Vét.*, Paris, vol. 86, p. 336.

403 Railliet, A. (1915). L'emploi des médicaments dans le traitement des maladies causées par des Nématodes. (Rapport présenté au Congres international vétérinaire de Londres, 1914.) *Rec. Méd. Vét.*, vol. 91, p. 490.

404 Railliet, A. (1916). La Famille des Thelaziidæ. *Journ. of Parasit.*, vol. 2, p. 99.

405 Railliet, A. (1916). Nématodes parasites des Rongeurs. (Review of Hall's paper.) *Rec. Méd. Vét.*, vol. 92, p. 517.

406 Railliet, A. (1916). Sur les Filaires de Batraciens. *Bull. Soc. Path. Exot.*, vol. 9, p. 137.

407 Railliet, A. (1917). L'Oxyurose des Équidés. *Rec. Méd. Vét.*, vol. 93, p. 517.

408 Railliet, A. (1918). Sur un Strongylidé vivant dans des kystes intestinaux chez les grands Félidés. *Bull. Soc. Path. Exot.*, vol. 11, p. 86.

409 Railliet, A. (1918). Un Bunostomien pathogène, parasite de la vésicule bilaire d'un Rongeur africain. *Ibid.*, vol. 11, p. 93.

410 Railliet, A. (1918). Le genre *Dicheilonema* Diesing, 1861. (*Nematoda, Filarioidea.*) *Bull. Soc. Zool. de France*, vol. 43, p. 104.

411 Railliet, A. (1923). Habronèmes et Habronémoses des Équidés. *Rec. Méd. Vét.*, vol. 99, p. 65.

412 Railliet, A. (1923). La véritable *Strongylus tetracanthus* Mehlis et son rôle pathogène. *Ann. d. Parasitol. humaine et comparée*, vol. 1, p. 5.

413 Railliet, A. (1923). Les strongyles (anciens Sclérostomes) et les Strongyloses proprement dites. *Rec. Méd. Vét.*, vol. 99, p. 377.

414 Railliet, A., and Henry, A. (1902). Sur les sclérostomiens des équidés. *C. R. Soc. Biol.*, vol. 54, p. 110.

415 Railliet, A., and Henry, A. (1905). Un nouveau Sclérostomien (*Tridontophorus deminutus*, nov. sp.) parasite de l'homme. *Ibid.*, vol. 58, p. 569.

416 Railliet, A., and Henry, A. (1905). Encore un nouveau Sclérostomien (*Œsophagostomum Brumpti* nov. sp.) parasite de l'homme. *Ibid.*, vol. 58, p. 643.

417 Railliet, A., and Henry, A. (1907). Sur les variations des Strongyles de l'appareil respiratoire des Mammifères. *Ibid.*, vol. 63, p. 751.

418 Railliet, A., and Henry, A. (1907). Némathelminthes parasites. Expéd. Antarctique française (1903–05). Masson & Cie., Paris, vers 14 pp.

419 Railliet, A., and Henry, A. (1909). Sur la classification des *Strongylidæ*. I. *Metastrongylinæ*. *C. R. Soc. Biol.*, vol. 66, p. 85.

420 Railliet, A., and Henry, A. (1909). Sur la classification des *Strongylidæ*. II. *Ankylostominæ*. *Ibid.*, vol. 66, p. 168.

421 Railliet, A., and Henry, A. (1910). Les Thélazies, nématodes parasites de l'œil. *Ibid.*, vol. 68, p. 213.

422 Railliet, A., and Henry, A. (1910). Les Onchocerques, nématodes parasites du tissu conjonctif. *Ibid.*, vol. 68, p. 248.

423 Railliet, A., and Henry, A. (1910). Sur quelques helminthes du *Python sebæ* (Gmelin). *Bull. Soc. Path. Exot.*, vol. 3, p. 94.

424 Railliet, A., and Henry, A. (1910). Deux espèces nouvelles du genre " Aprocta," Linstow. *Ibid.*, vol. 3, p. 152.

425 Railliet, A., and Henry, A. (1910). Nouvelles observations sur les Thélazies, Nématodes parasites de l'œil. *C. R. Soc. Biol.*, vol. 68, p. 783.

426 Railliet, A., and Henry, A. (1910). Quelques Helminthes nouveaux ou peu connus du groupe des Bunostomiens. *Bull. Soc. Path. Exot.*, vol. 3, p. 311.

427 Railliet, A., and Henry, A. (1910). Étude zoologique de l'œsophagostome de Thomas. *Ann. Trop. Med. and Parasit.*, vol. 4, p. 89.

428 Railliet, A., and Henry, A. (1911). Sur une Filaire péritonéale des Porcins. *Bull. Soc. Path. Exot.*, vol. 4, p. 386.

429 Railliet, A., and Henry, A. (1911). Remarques au Sujet des deux Notes de MM. Bauche et Bernard. *Ibid.*, vol. 4, p. 485.

430 Railliet, A., and Henry, A. (1911). Recherches sur les Ascarides des Carnivores. *C. R. Soc. Biol.*, vol. 70, p. 12.

431 Railliet, A., and Henry, A. (1911). Les Helminthes du Nandu. *Paris Bull. Soc. Nat. Acclim.*, vol. 58, p. 573.

432 Railliet, A., and Henry, A. (1911). Helminthes du Porc recueillis par M. Bauche en Annam. *Bull. Soc. Path. Exot.*, vol. 4, p. 693.

433 Railliet, A., and Henry, A. (1912). Observations sur les Strongylidés du genre " *Nematodirus*." *Ibid.*, vol. 5, p. 35.

434 Railliet, A., and Henry, A. (1912). Nématodes vasculicoles des bovins annamites. *Ibid.*, vol. 5, p. 115.

435 Railliet, A., and Henry, A. (1912). Les Œsophagostomiens parasites de l'homme. *Archives de Parasitologie*, vol. 14, p. 562.

436 Railliet, A., and Henry, A. (1912). Quelques Nématodes parasites des Reptiles. *Bull. Soc. Path. Exot.*, vol. 5, p. 251.

437 Railliet, A., and Henry, A. (1913). Observations sur les Nématodes parasites du genre *Aspidodera* Railliet and Henry, 1912. *Bull. Mus. d'Hist. nat.*, p. 93.

438 Railliet, A., and Henry, A. (1913). Contribution à l'étude des Nématodes parasites de l'œil du chien. *Bull. de la Soc. centrale de Méd. Vét.*, p. 200.

439 Railliet, A., and Henry, A. (1913). Un Hæmostrongylus des bronches du Léopard. *Bull. Soc. Path. Exot.*, vol. 6, p. 451.

440   Railliet, A., and Henry, A. (1913). Sur les Œsophagostomiens des Ruminants.
      Ibid., vol. 6, p. 506.

441   Railliet, A., and Henry, A. (1914). Essai de classification des *Heterakidæ*. *Ext.
      IXe. Congrès Internat. Zool.*, Monaco, 1913, p. 674.

442   Railliet, A., and Henry, A. (1915). Sur les Nématodes du genre *Gœzia* Zeder.
      Bull. Soc. Path. Exot., vol. 8, p. 270.

443   Railliet, A., and Henry, A. (1915). Sur les Nématodes du genre *Camallanus*
      Raill. and Henry, 1915. (*Cucullanus* Auct., non Mueller, 1777.) *Ibid.*,
      vol. 8, p. 446.

443a Railliet, A., and Henry, A. (1915). Le parasite de la dermite granuleuse des
      equidés. *Ibid.*, vol. 8, p. 695.

444   Railliet, A., and Henry, A. (1916). Sur les Oxyuridés. *C. R. Soc. Biol.*, vol. 79,
      p. 113.

445   Railliet, A., and Henry, A. (1916). Nouvelles remarques sur les Oxyuridés.
      Ibid., vol. 79, p. 247.

446   Railliet, A., and Henry, A. (1916). Les filaires des Rapaces (Falconiiformes et
      Strigiformes). *Bull. Soc. Path. Exot.*, vol. 9, p. 364.

447   Railliet, A., and Henry, A. (1918). Nématodes parasites du Congo belge. *Ibid.*,
      vol. 11, p. 82.

448   Railliet, A., Henry, A., and Bauche, J. (1914). Sur les Helminthes de l'Eléphant
      d'Asie. *Ibid.*, vol. 7, pp. 129 and 207.

449   Railliet, A., Henry, A., and Bauche, J. (1919). Un nouveau Strongylidé du
      Porc. *Ibid.*, vol. 12, p. 324.

450   Railliet, A., Henry, A., and Joyeux, C. (1913). Un nouveau Strongylidé des
      Singes. *Ibid.*, vol. 6, p. 264.

451   Railliet, A., Henry, A., and Langeron, M. (1912). Le genre *Acanthocheilonema*
      Cobbold, et les Filaires péritonéales des carnivores. *Ibid.*, vol. 5, p. 392.

452   Railliet, A., Henry, A., and Sisoff, P. (1912). Sur les Affinités des Dispharages
      (*Acuaria* Bremser), Nématodes parasites des Oiseaux. *C. R. Soc. Biol.*,
      vol. 73, p. 622.

453   Railliet, A., and Moussu, G. (1892). La filaire des boutons hémorragiques observée
      chez l'âne : découverte du mâle. *Ibid.*, vol. 44, p. 545.

454   Ransom, B. H. (1904). Manson's Eye Worm of Chickens (*Oxyspirura mansoni*),
      with a general review of Nematodes parasitic in the Eyes of Birds. *U.S.
      Dept. of Agriculture*, Bureau of Animal Industry, Bull. No. 60.

455   Ransom, B. H. (1906). The Life History of the Twisted Wire-worm (*Hæmonchus
      contortus*) of Sheep and other Ruminants (Prel. Rep.). *Ibid.*, Circ. 93.

456   Ransom, B. H. (1907). *Probstmayria vivipara* (Probstmayr, 1865), Ransom,
      1907, a Nematode of Horses heretofore unreported from the United
      States. *Trans. Amer. Microscop. Soc.*, vol. 27, p. 33.

457   Ransom, B. H. (1907). Notes on parasitic nematodes, including Descriptions of
      New Genera and Species, and Observations on Life Histories. *U.S. Dept.
      Agric., Bureau Animal Industry*, Circ. 116.

458   Ransom, B. H. (1911). The Nematodes parasitic in the Alimentary Tract of
      Cattle, Sheep, and other Ruminants. *Ibid.*, Bull. 127.

459   Ransom, B. H. (1913). The Life History of *Habronema muscæ* (Carter), a
      parasite of the Horse transmitted by the Housefly. *Ibid.*, Bull. 163.

460   Ransom, B. H. (1916). The Occurrence in the United States of certain Nema-
      todes of Ruminants transmissible to Man. *New Orleans Med. and Surg.
      Journal*, vol. 69, p. 294.

461   Ransom, B. H. (1918). Horse Strongyles in Canada. *Jl. of Amer. Vet. Med.
      Assoc.*, N. S., vol. 6, p. 202.

462   Ransom, B. H. (1924). Hookworms of the genus *Uncinaria* of the Dog, Fox, and
      Badger. *Proc. U.S. Nat. Mus.*, vol. 65, art. 20, p. 1.

463   Ransom, B. H., and Hall, M. C. (1915). The Life History of *Gongylonema
      scutatum*. *Jl. of Parasitology*, vol. 2, p. 80 ; vol. 3, p. 177.

463a Rassowska, R. I. (1924). Nematodes of Cattle in Turkestan. *Reports of the State Experimental Institute*, Moscow, vol. 2, No. 1. [In Russian.]

464 Rauther, M. (1918). Mittheilungen zur Nematodenkunde. *Zool. Jahrb.*, Abth. Anat., vol. 40, p. 441.

465 Riley, W. A. (1920). A Mouse Oxyurid, *Syphacia obvelata*, as a Parasite of Man. *Jl. Parasitology*, vol. 6, p. 89.

466 Riley, W. A., and Chandler, W. L. (1916). The Occurrence of the Giant Nematode on the Liver of a Dog. *Cornell Veterinarian*, Oct., vol. 6.

467 Rivolta, Sebastiano (1884). La natura parassitica delle piaghe estive o gli effetti morbosi di una specie di *Filaria* che si può denominare *Dermofilaria irritans*. *Gior. di anat., ficiol. e patol. d. animali*, Pisa, vol. 16, p. 128.

468 Robert, L. (1922). La Gnathostomose humaine. Œdème ambulant siamois dû à *Gnathostomum spinigerum* (R. Owen, 1836). *Bull. Soc. Path. Exot.*, vol. 15, p. 854.

469 Rodenwaldt, E. (1910). *Filaria kuelzii* n. sp. *Archiv. f. Schiffs. u. Tropenhygiene*, vol. 14, p. 529.

469a Rodhain, J. (1922). Sur une Filaire parasitant le tissu conjunctif sous-cutané de *Agama colonorum* Dum. et Bibr. au Congo Belge. *C. R. Soc. Biol.*, vol. 87, p. 807.

470 Roederer, J. G. (1761). Noch nicht beschriebene Art Würmer im menschlichen Körper. *Götting. Anz. v. gelehrt. Sachen*, vol. 1, p. 243.

471 Romanovitch (1915). Quelques helminthes du Renne (*Tarandus rangifer*). *C. R. Soc. Biol.*, vol. 78, p. 451.

472 Romanovitch (1916). *Deraïophoronema cameli*, n. g., n. sp. *Ibid.*, vol. 79, p. 745.

472a Roubaud, E., et Descazeaux, J. (1921). Contribution à l'histoire de la mouche domestique comme agent vecteur des Habronémoses d'equidés. *Bull. Soc. Path. Exot.*, vol. 14, p. 471.

473 Le Roux, P. L. (1924). Helminths collected from equines in Edinburgh and in London. *Journ. Helminthology*, vol. 2, p. 111.

474 Rudolphi, C. A. (1801–02). Beobachtungen über die Eingeweidewürmer. *Arch. f. Zool. u. Zoot.* Brnschwg., vol. 2, 65 pp., and Fortsetzung der, etc., 66 pp.

475 Rudolphi, C. A. (1808). Entozoorum sive vermium intestinalium historia naturalis, vol. 1. xxvi. + 527 + xxvi. pp. Amstelædami.

476 Rudolphi, C. A. (1809). Entozoorum sive vermium intestinalium historia naturalis, vol. 2, part 1, 457 pp. Amstelædami.

477 Rudolphi, C. A. (1819). Entozoorum synopsis cui accedunt mantissa duplex et indices locupletissimi. x. + 811 pp. Berolini.

478 Sambon, L. W. (1907). Descriptions of some New Species of Animal Parasites. *Proc. Zool. Soc.*, London, p. 282.

478a Sambon, L. W. (1925). Researches on the Epidemiology of Cancer made in Iceland and Italy (July–Oct., 1924). *Jl. Trop. Med. and Hyg.*, p. 39.

479 Schlotthauber (1860). Beiträge zur Helminthologie. *Amtl. Ber. ü. d. 31. Versamml. deutsch. Naturf. u. Ærzte.* Götting. (1854), p. 121.

479a Schmerling, A. A. (1925). Zur Kenntnis der Vogelfilarien (*Squamofilaria* n. gen. und *Diplotriæna artemisiana* n. sp.) von *Coracias garrula* L. *Centralbl. f. Bakt.* Abt. II., vol. 63, p. 267.

480 Schneider, A. (1866). Monographie der Nematoden, Berlin. xiii. + 357 pp.

481 Schrank, F. P. (1788). Verzeichniss der bisher hinlänglich bekannten Eingeweidewürmer, nebst einer Abhandlung über ihre Anverwandtschaften. München, 116 pp.

481a Schulz, R. Ed. S. (1924). *Oxyuridæ* of Armenian Mice. *Reports of the Tropical Institute of Armenia*, vol. 2, No. 1. [In Russian.]

481b Schulz, R. Ed. S. (1924). On the Helminth Parasites of Mice. *Ibid.*, vol. 2, No. 1. [In Russian.]

481c Schwartz, B. (1925). Parasitic Nematodes from Tonkin, Indo-China, including a new species of *Ascaridia*. *Proc. U.S. Nat. Mus.*, vol. 66, art. I.

481d Schwartz, B. (1925). Two new larval Nematodes belonging to the Genus *Porrocæcum* from mammals of the Order Insectivora. *Ibid.*, vol. 67, art. 17.

481e Schwartz, B. (1925). *Ascaridia lineata*, a Parasite of Chickens in the United States. *Jl. Agric. Res.*, vol. 30, p. 763.

482 Setti, E. (1897). Nuovi elminti dell' Eritrea. *Boll. mus. di Zool.*, Genova, 50 pp.

483 Seurat, L. G. (1911). Sur l'habitat et les migrations du *Spirura talpæ* Gmelin (*Spiroptera strumosa* Rud.). *C. R. Soc. Biol.*, vol. 71, p. 606.

484 Seurat, L. G. (1912). Sur la présencé, en Algérie, du *Spiroptera sexalata* Molin, chez le Dromadaire et chez l'Ane. *Ibid.*, vol. 72, p. 174.

485 Seurat, L. G. (1912). Sur la morphologie de l'ovijecteur de quelques Nématodes. *Ibid.*, vol. 72, p. 778.

486 Seurat, L. G. (1912). Sur les Oxyures de *Uromastix acanthinurus* Bell. *Ibid.*, vol. 73, p. 223.

487 Seurat, L. G. (1912). Sur l'appareil génital femelle des Gongylonèmes. *Ibid.*, vol. 73, p. 276.

488 Seurat, L. G. (1913). Sur un Dispharage de la Chevêche et les Affinités du genre *Acuaria* Bremser. *Ibid.*, vol. 74, p. 103.

489 Seurat, L. G. (1913). Sur l'évolution du *Spirura gastrophila* Müll. *Ibid.*, vol. 74, p. 286.

490 Seurat, L. G. (1913). Sur deux Spiroptères du Chat ganté (*Felis ocreata* Gmel.). *Ibid.*, vol. 74, p. 676.

491 Seurat, L. G. (1913). Sur l'existence d'un anneau vulvaire, consécutif a l'accouplement, chez un Nématode. *Ibid.*, vol. 75, p. 326.

492 Seurat, L. G. (1913). Sur l'évolution du *Physocephalus sexalatus* (Molin). *Ibid.*, vol. 75, p. 517.

493 Seurat, L. G. (1913). Le mouton des Hauts-Plateaux de la province d'Alger et ses maladies parasitaires. *Bull. Soc. Hist. Nat. de l'Afrique du Nord*, vol. 4, p. 75.

494 Seurat, L. G. (1913). Sur quelques Nématodes du Sud tunisien. *Ibid.*, vol. 4, p. 126.

495 Seurat, L. G. (1913). Sur le Spiroptère des pies-grièches. *Ibid.*, vol. 4, p. 223.

496 Seurat, L. G. (1914). Sur l'evolution des Nématodes parasites. *IXe. Congrès internat. de Zool.*, Monaco, 1913, p. 623.

497 Seurat, L. G. (1914). Sur un nouveau parasite .de la Cigogne blanche. *Bull. Soc. d'Hist. Nat. de l'Afrique du Nord*, vol. 5, p. 65.

498 Seurat, L. G. (1914). Sur un nouveau parasite de l'Outarde houbara. *Ibid.*, vol. 5, p. 117.

499 Seurat, L. G. (1914). Sur un nouveau parasite du Percnoptère. *Ibid.*, vol. 5, p. 149.

500 Seurat, L. G. (1914). Sur quelques Hétérakis d'Oiseaux. *Ibid.*, vol. 5, p. 195.

501 Seurat, L. G. (1914). Sur deux nouveaux Hétérakis du Sud Algérien. *Ibid.*, vol. 5, p. 222.

502 Seurat, L. G. (1914). Sur les Physaloptères des Rapaces. *Ibid.*, vol. 5, p. 244.

503 Seurat, L. G. (1914). Sur la morphologie de l'ovéjecteur des *Tropidocerca*. *C. R. Soc. Biol.*, vol. 76, p. 173.

504 Seurat, L. G. (1914). Sur un nouveau parasite de la Perdrix rouge. *Ibid.*, vol. 76, p. 390.

505 Seurat, L. G. (1914). Sur un nouveau Nématode parasite des Reptiles. *Ibid.*, vol. 76, p. 724.

506 Seurat, L. G. (1914). Sur un *Tropidocerca* parasite d'un Echassier. *Ibid.*, vol. 76, p. 778.

507 Seurat, L. G. (1914). Sur un Nématode parasite de flammant rose. *Ibid.*, vol. 76, p. 814.

508 Seurat, L. G. (1914). Sur un cas d'Endotokie Matricide chez un Oxyure. *Ibid.*, vol. 76, p. 850.

509 Seurat, L. G. (1914). Sur un nouvel Oxyure des Reptiles. *Ibid.*, vol. 77, p. 96.

510 Seurat, L. G. (1914). Sur un nouvel Habitat et sur la Morphologie du *Subulura allodapa* (Creplin). *Ibid.*, vol. 77, p. 154.

511 Seurat, L. G. (1914). Sur un nouveau Spiroptère du Chat ganté. *Ibid.*, vol. 77, p. 344.

512 Seurat, L. G. (1914). Sur deux Physaloptères tétrahystériens des Reptiles *Ibid.*, vol. 77, p. 433.

513 Seurat, L. G. (1914). Sur une filaire péritonéale du Macroscélide. *Ibid.*, vol. 77, p. 524.

514 Seurat, L. G. (1914). Sur la morphologie de l'appareil génital femelle des Spiruridæ. *C. R. Acad. Sciences*, vol. 159, p. 1016.

515 Seurat, L. G. (1915). Sur deux nouveaux Oxyures du Maroc. *Bull. Soc. Hist. Nat. Afr. Nord*, vol. 6, p. 24.

516 Seurat, L. G. (1915). Un nouveau Physaloptère des Rapaces. *Ibid.*, vol. 6, p. 157.

517 Seurat, L. G. (1915). Sur un nouvel *Ophiostomum* parasite du Gundi. *C. R. Soc. Biol.*, vol. 78, p. 20.

518 Seurat, L. G. (1915). Sur l'existence, en Algérie, du *Dermatoxys veligera* (Rud.) et sur les Affinités du genre *Dermatoxys*. *Ibid.*, vol. 78, p. 75.

519 Seurat, L. G. (1915). Sur deux nouveaux parasites du Renard d'Algérie. *Ibid.*, vol. 78, p. 122.

520 Seurat, L. G. (1915). Sur deux nouveaux Spiroptères des Carnivores. *Ibid.*, vol. 78, p. 157.

521 Seurat, L. G. (1915). Sur les Rictulaires des Carnivores du Nord-Africain et les Affinités du genre *Rictularia*. *Ibid.*, vol. 78, p. 318.

522 Seurat, L. G. (1915). Sur le Cucullan de la Clemmyde lépreuse et les Affinités du genre *Cucullanus*. *Ibid.*, vol. 78, p. 423.

523 Seurat, L. G. (1915). Sur les première Stades évolutifs des Spiroptères. *Ibid.*, vol. 78, p. 561.

524 Seurat, L. G. (1915). Nématodes Parasites. Expédition de MM. Walter Rothschild, E. Hartet et C. Hilgert dans le sud Algérien (Mars and Mai, 1914). *Novitates Zoologicæ*, vol. 22, p. 1.

524a Seurat, L. G. (1915). Sur les conditions de la ponte du Strongle lisse. *Bull. Scient. de la France et de la Belgique*, vol. 48, p. 171.

525 Seurat, L. G. (1916). Sur les Oxyures des Mammifères. *C. R. Soc. Biol.*, vol. 79, p. 64.

526 Seurat, L. G. (1916). Sur l'habitat normal et les affinités du *Protospirura numidica* Seurat. *Ibid.*, vol. 79, p. 143.

527 Seurat, L. G. (1916). Sur l'habitat normal et les affinités du *Rictularia proni* Seurat. *Ibid.*, vol. 79, p. 146.

528 Seurat, L. G. (1916). Sur la quatrième mue d'un Dispharage du Flammant. *Ibid.*, vol. 79, p. 439.

529 Seurat, L. G. (1916). Sur un nouveau type de *Spiruridæ*. *Ibid.*, vol. 79, p. 517.

530 Seurat, L. G. (1916). Sur les Gongylonèmes du Nord-Africain. *Ibid.*, vol. 79, p. 717.

531 Seurat, L. G. (1916). Sur un nouveau Dispharage des Palmipèdes. *Ibid.*, vol. 79, p. 785.

532 Seurat, L. G. (1916). Dispharages d'Algérie. *Ibid.*, vol. 79, p. 934.

533 Seurat, L. G. (1916). Sur les Dispharages des Rapaces. *Ibid.*, vol. 79, p. 1126.

534 Seurat, L. G. (1916). Sur deux filaires des reptiles du Nord-Africain. *Ibid.*, vol. 79, p. 1131.

535 Seurat, L. G. (1916). Contribution à l'étude des formes larvaires des Nématodes parasites hétéroxènes. *Bull. Sci. de la France et de la Belgique*, ser. 7, vol. 49, p. 297.

536   Seurat, L. G. (1917). Physaloptères des Reptiles du Nord-Africain. *C. R. Soc. Biol.*, vol. 80, p. 43.

537   Seurat, L. G. (1917). Sur une Ascaride de la grenouille. *Ibid.*, vol. 80, p. 94.

538   Seurat, L. G. (1917). Physaloptères des Mammifères du Nord-Africain. *Ibid.*, vol. 80, p. 210.

539   Seurat, L. G. (1917). Sur les Affinités du genre *Maupasina* (*Heterakidæ*). *Ibid.*, vol. 80, p. 350.

540   Seurat, L. G. (1917). Une nouvelle filaire péritonéale des rongeurs. *Ibid.*, vol. 80, p. 354.

541   Seurat, L. G. (1917). Sur les Oxyures des Sauriens du Nord-Africain. *Arch. Zool. exp. et gén.*, Paris, LVI., p. 401.

542   Seurat, L. G. (1917). Sur les Spiroptères des Carnivores du Nord-Africain. *Bull. Soc. Hist. Nat. Afr. Nord*, vol. 8, p. 21.

543   Seurat, L. G. (1917). Nématodes de la Perdrix de roche. *Ibid.*, vol. 8, p. 208.

544   Seurat, L. G. (1917). Filaires des reptiles et des Batraciens. *Ibid.*, vol. 8, p. 236.

545   Seurat, L. G. (1918). Nématodes de la Clemmyde lépreuse. *Ibid.*, vol. 9, p. 20.

546   Seurat, L. G. (1918). Nématodes du *Caccabis petrosa* Gmel. (2nd Note). *Ibid.*, vol. 9, p. 50.

547   Seurat, L. G. (1918). Sur le Dispharage de l'Echasse. *Ibid.*, vol. 9, p. 106.

548   Seurat, L. G. (1918). Dimorphisme sexuel chez les Nématodes. *C. R. Soc. Biol.*, vol. 81, p. 1099.

549   Seurat, L. G. (1918). Sur la variation chez les Nématodes. *Ibid.*, vol. 81, p. 1101.

550   Seurat, L. G. (1918). Sur un nouveau Strongle (*Trichostrongylidæ*) de l'Echasse. *Bull. du Mus. d'Hist. Nat.*, p. 113.

551   Seurat, L. G. (1918). Sur les Strongles du Gésier de Palmipèdes. *Ibid.*, p. 345.

552   Seurat, L. G. (1918). Contribution à l'étude de la faune parasitaire de la Tunisie. Nématodes. *Archiv. de l'Inst. Pasteur de Tunis*, vol. 10, p. 243.

553   Seurat, L. G. (1919). Disparages (Nématodes) de l'Afrique mineure. *Novitates Zoologicæ*, vol. 26, p. 179.

554   Seurat, L. G. (1919). Sur la Morphologie du *Proleptus obtusus* Duj. (*Acuariidæ*). *Bull. du Mus. d'Hist. Nat.*, No. 3, p. 166.

555   Seurat, L. G. (1919). Nématodes de la Panthère. *Bull. Soc. d'Hist. Nat. de l'Afrique du Nord*, vol. 10, p. 47.

556   Seurat, L. G. (1919). Extension d'habitat du *Seuratum tacapense* (Seurat). *Ibid.*, vol. 10, p. 206.

557   Seurat, L. G. (1920). Histoire Naturelle des Nématodes de la Berbérie, Algiers, 221 + vi. pp.

558   Seurat, L. G. (1920). *Strongylacantha glycirrhiza*. *C. R. Soc. Biol.*, vol. 83, p. 1472.

559   Seurat, L. G. (1920). Description de la *Filaria martis* Gmel. *Bull. Soc. Hist. Nat. Afr. Nord*, vol. 11, p. 34.

560   Seurat, L. G. (1920). Sur une Filaire du Héron cendré. *Ibid.*, vol. 11, p. 142.

561   Seurat, L. G. (1921). La Filaire du Moineau. *Ibid.*, vol. 12, p. 28.

562   Seurat, L. G. (1921). Orthogénèse des Filaires. *Ibid.*, vol. 12, p. 31.

563   Seurat, L. G. (1921). Variations dans le mode de ramification de la côte dorsale de la bourse caudale du mâle du *Strongylacantha glycirrhiza* Bened. (*Trichostrongylidæ*). *Ibid.*, vol. 12, p. 202.

564   Seurat, L. G. (1921). *Litosoma filaria* Bened. Type d'une nouvelle section de Filaires opisthodelphes. *Bull. Mus. d'Hist. Nat.*, Paris, vol. 27, p. 103.

565   Seurat, L. G., et Neuville, H. (1913). Sur le *Toxascaris leonina* (Linstow). *Ibid.*, vol. 19, p. 16.

566 Shipley, A. E. (1908). Note on *Cystidicola farionis* Fischer. A Thread-worm Parasitic in the Swim-bladder of a Trout. *Parasitology*, vol. 1, p. 190.

566a Shipley, A. E. (1909). The Thread-worms (Nematoda) of the Red Grouse (*Lagopus scoticus*). *Proc. Zool. Soc.*, London, p. 335.

566b Shipley, A. E. (1909). Internal Parasites of Birds allied to the Grouse. *Ibid.*, p. 363.

567 Shipley, A. E., and Hornell, J. (1904–05). The Parasites of the Pearl Oyster. *Rept. to Govt. of Ceylon on Pearl Oyster Fisheries Gulf of Manaar* (Herdman), London, Part 2, p 77 ; Part 3, p. 49.

568 Shipley, A. E., and Hornell, J. (1906). Report on the Cestode and Nematode Parasites from the Marine Fishes of Ceylon. *Ibid.*, Part 5, p. 43.

569 Siebold, C. T. E. von (1835). Helminthologische Beiträge. *Arch. f. Naturg.*, Berlin, vol. 1, p. 45.

570 Siebold, C. T. E. von (1836). Helminthologische Beiträge : zweiter Beitrag. *Syngamus trachealis*. Ein doppelleibiger Eingeweidewurm. *Ibid.*, vol. 1, p. 105.

571 Silva Araujo, A. J. P. (1877). Caso de chyluria, elephancia do escroto, escroto lymphatico, craw-craw e erysipela em um mesmo individuo ; descobrimento da Wuchereria *Filaria* na lympha do escroto. Tratamento pela electricidade com excellentes resultados. *Gaz. med. da Bahia*, vol. 2, p. 492.

572 Skrjabin, K. J. (1916). Nématodes des oiseaux du Turkestan russe. *Annuaire du Mus. Zool. de l'Acad. Impériale de Sciences de Petrograd*, vol. 20, p. 457.

573 Skrjabin, K. J. (1916). Parasitic Trematodes and Nematodes collected by the Expedition of Prof. V. Dogiel and I. Sokolow in British East Africa. *Scientific Results of the Zool. Exped. to British East Africa and Uganda by Prof. V. Dogiel and I. Sokolow in* 1914, vol. 1 (Eng. Trans.), p. 99.

574 Skrjabin, K. J. (1916). Contributions à l'étude de la faune helminthologique du Paraguay. I. Nematodes. *Journ. Russe de Zoologie*, vol. 1, p. 736.

575 Skrjabin, K. J. (1916). Matériaux pour servir à une monographie des Nématodes d'oiseaux. I. Contributions à la connaissance du genre *Aprocta* Linst., 1883. *Annuaire du Musée Zoologique de l'Academie des Sciences de Petrograd*, vol. 21, p. 117.

576 Skrjabin, K. J. (1916). *Seuratia* n. g., nouveau genre de Nématodes d'oiseaux. *C. R. Soc. Biol.*, vol. 79, p. 971.

577 Skrjabin, K. J. (1917). *Aprocta microanalis* n. sp., nouvelle Filaire des yeux d'oiseaux. *Ibid.*, vol. 80, p. 303.

578 Skrjabin, K. J. (1917). Sur quelques Nématodes des Oiseaux de la Russie. *Parasitology*, vol. 9, p. 460.

579 Skrjabin, K. J. (1921). La stéphanurose des porcs et son agent. *Bull. Soc. Path. Exot.*, vol. 14, p. 47.

579a Skrjabin, K. J. (1923). Beitrag zur kenntnis der Vogelfilarien Russlands. *Revue de Microbiologie et Épidémiologie*, vol. 2, p. 27 and p. 90. [In Russian.]

580 Skrjabin, K. J. (1923). *Hastospiculum varani*, n. gen., n. sp. Eine neue Filaria der Reptilien. *Russian Journ. of Trop. Med.*, vol. 1, p. 40 and p. 57. [In Russian.]

581 Skrjabin, K. J. (1923). Parasitic Nematodes of the Fresh Water Fauna of European and part of Asiatic Russia. Moscow, pp. 1–98 + i. to xxxiii., with 20 plates.

582 Skrjabin, K. J. (1924). Sur le genre *Metastrongylus* Molin, 1861. *C. R. Soc. Biol.*, vol. 90, p. 1215.

582a Skrjabin, K. J. (1924). On the Parasitic Helminths of the Turkestan Desert and Steppes. *Reports of the State Experimental Institute*, Moscow, vol. 2, No. 1. [In Russian.]

582b Sleggs, G. F. (1925). A Strongyloid Nematode, *Warrenius bifurcatus* n. sp., from the Richardson ground squirrel. *Parasitology*, vol. 17, p. 410.

582c Smit, H. J., and Notosoediro, R. (1923). Nog eenige Strongyliden van het Paard op Java III. and IV. *Nederl.-Ind. Bl. v. Diergeneesk. en Dierent*, vol. 34, p. 446 ; and vol. 35, p. 28.

583 Smith, A. J., Fox, H., and White, C. Y. (1908). Contributions to Systematic Helminthology. *Univ. of Penn. Med. Bull.*, vol. 20, p. 283.

584 Solowiow, P. Th. (1912). Vers parasitaires des Oiseaux du Turkestan. *Ann. Mus. Zool.*, Pétrograd, vol. 17, p. 86.

585 Sonsino, P. (1889). Studi e notizie elmintologiche. *Atti Soc. tosc. di sc. nat., Pisa, proc. verb.*, vol. 6, p. 224.

586 Sonsino, P. (1890). Un nuovo *Heterakis* del *Gallus domesticus, Heterakis differens* mihi. *Ibid.*, vol. 7, p. 136.

587 Spaul, E. A. (1923). Notes on some Nematodes from East African Hosts. *Annals and Mag. Nat. Hist.*, ser. 9, vol. 11, p. 218.

587a Steiner, G. (1921). *Phlyctainophora lamnæ* n. g., n. sp., eine neue parasitische Nematodenform aus *Lamna cornubica* (Heringshai). *Centralbl. f. Bakt. Orig.*, vol. 86, p. 591.

588 Steiner, G. (1924). Some Nemas from the Alimentary Tract of the Carolina Tree Frog (*Hyla carolinensis* Pennant). *Jl. of Parasitology*, vol. 11, p. 1.

589 Stephens, J. W. W. (1903). A New Human Nematode, *Strongylus gibsoni* n. sp. *Ann. Trop. Med. and Parasit.*, vol. 2, p. 315.

590 Stephens, J. W. W. (1916). Nemathelminthes. In Fantham, Stephens, and Theobald's *Animal Parasites of Man*, London, pp. 360–474.

591 Stewart, F. H. (1914). Studies in Indian Helminthology, No. 1. *Rec. Ind. Mus.*, vol. 10, p. 165.

592 Stiles, C. W. (1892). On the Anatomy of *Myzomimus scutatus* (Mueller, 1869) Stiles, 1892. (Notes on Parasites, 12). *Festschr. z. 70, Geburtst. R. Leuckart's*, Leipz., Oct. 7th, p. 126.

592a Stiles, C. W. (1892). A Word in regard to the Filaridæ found in the Body Cavity of Horses and Cattle ; on the presence of *Strongylus ostertagi* (Ostertag, 1890) Stiles, 1892, in America ; a Word in regard to Dr. Francis's *Distomum texanicum. Jl. Comp. M. and Vet. Arch.*, New York, vol. 13, p. 143.

593 Stiles, C. W. (1901). *Uncinariosis (Anchylostomiasis)* in Man and Animals in the United States. *Texas Med. News*, Austin, vol. 10, p. 523.

594 Stiles, C. W. (1903). Clinical Diagnosis of Intestinal Parasites. *Jl. Amer. Med. Assoc.*, vol. 41, pp. 172 and 310.

595 Stiles, C. W. (1907). The Zoological Characters of the Roundworm genus *Filaria* Mueller, 1787, with a list of the Thread Worms reported for Man. *Bull. 34, Hyg. Lab., U.S. Pub. Health and Mar. Hosp. Serv.*, Washington, p. 31.

596 Stiles, C. W., and Brown, G. (1924). Nomenclature of the Nematode genera *Belascaris* 1907, *Toxascaris* 1907, and *Toxocara* 1905. *Proc. of Helminthological Soc. of Washington.* Reported in *Jl. of Parasitology*, vol. 11, p. 92.

597 Stiles, C. W., and Brown, G. (1924). The Type Species of *Monodontus* Molin, 1861. *Proc. of Helminthological Soc. of Washington.* Reported in *Jl. of Parasit.*, vol. 11, p. 96.

597a Stiles, C. W., and Brown, Gertrude (1924). The present status of the Parasitic Nematode family *Ascaridæ. Public Health Reports Treasury Depart., U.S.*, vol. 39, No. 32, p. 1957.

598 Stiles, C. W., and Hassall, A. (1899). Internal Parasites of the Fur Seal. (In Jordan, David Starr, et al. The Fur Seals and Fur Seal Islands of the North Pacific Ocean, part 3, pp. 99–177. Washington.)

599 Stiles, C. W., and Hassall, A. (1905). The Determination of Generic Types, and a List of Round-worm genera, with their original and type species. *U.S. Dept. of Agric., Bureau of Animal Industry, Bull.* No. 79.

600 Stiles, C. W., and Hassall, A. (1920). Index-catalogue of Medical and Veterinary Zoology : Roundworms. *Treasury Dept. U.S. Public Health Service, Hygienic Laboratory, Bull.* No. 114.

601 Stossich, M. (1888). Il genere *Heterakis* Dujardin. *Glasnik hrv. nar. drutžva, Zagreb*, vol. 2, p. 277.

602 Stossich, M. (1896). Il genere *Ascaris* Linné. Lavoro monografico. *Boll. Soc. adriat. di sc. nat. in Trieste*, vol. 17, p. 9.

603 Stossich, M. (1896). Ricerche elmintologiche. *Ibid.*, vol. 17, p. 121.

604 Stossich, M. (1897). Filarie e spiroptere. Lavoro monografico. *Ibid.*, vol. 18, p. 13.

604a Stossich, M. (1900). Contributo allo studio degli elminti. *Ibid.*, vol. 20, p. 1.

605 Stossich, M. (1904). Sopra alcuni nematodi. *Ann. Mus. Zool. d. r. Univ. di Napoli*, vol. 1, p. 1.

606 Strassen, O. K. L. Zur. (1907). *Filaria medinensis* und *Ichthyonema*. *Verhandl. d. deutsch. zool. Gesellsch.*, Leipzig, p. 110.

607 Sweet, G. (1909). The Endoparasites of Australian Stock and Native Fauna, Part 2. New and Unrecorded Species. *Proc. Roy. Soc. Vict.*, vol. 21, new ser., p. 503.

608 Sweet, G. (1914). Investigations into the Occurrence of Onchocerciasis in Cattle and Associated Animals in Countries other than Australia. *Government Printer*, Melbourne, 53 pp.

609 Taylor, E. L. (1924). On the Ascarids of the Dog and Cat. *Ann. Trop. Med. and Parasit.*, vol. 18, p. 243.

610 Taylor, E. L. (1924). Notes on some Nematodes in the Museum of the Liverpool School of Tropical Medicine. *Ibid.*, vol. 18, p. 601.

611 Taylor, E. L. (1925). Notes on some Nematodes in the Museum of the Liverpool School of Trop. Med. II. *Ibid.*, vol. 19, p. 57.

611a Taylor, E. L. (1925). On the genus *Kiluluma*. *Ibid.*, vol. 19, p. 53.

612 Taylor, Louise (1899). Our present knowledge of the Kidney Worm of Swine, *Sclerostoma pinguicola*. *Sixteenth Ann. Rep. Bur. Animal Industry*, Washington, p. 612.

613 Thapar, G. S. (1924). On *Kiluluma* Skrjabin, a genus of Strongylid nematodes parasitic in the African Rhinoceros. *Jl. Helminthology*, vol. 2, p. 209.

613a Thapar, G. S. (1925). On the Morphology and Systematic Position of *Echinopharynx*, a new genus of Bursate Nematode from *Testudo tabulata*. *Ibid.*, vol. 3, p. 19.

613b Thapar, G. S. (1925). On some new members of the Genus *Kiluluma* from the African Rhinoceros. *Ibid.*, vol. 3, p. 63.

613c Thapar, G. S. (1925). Studies on the Oxyurid Parasites of Reptiles. *Ibid.*, vol. 3, p. 83.

614 Theiler, A., and Robertson, W. (1916). Investigations into the Life-History of the Wire-worm in Ostriches. *Third and Fourth Reports of the Director of Vet. Research*, Nov., 1915. Pretoria, p. 293.

615 Theiler, G. (1923). The Strongylids and other Nematodes parasitic in the Intestinal Tract of South African Equines. *Thèse présentée à la Faculté des sciences de l'Université de Neuchâtel*. Pretoria.

616 Theiler, G. (1924). Two New Species of Nematodes from the Zebra. *Trans. Roy. Soc. South Africa*, vol. 11, p. 197.

616a Thiel, P. H. van (1925). Deux Nématodes nouveaux d'un singe hurleur de suriname. *Ann. de Parasit.*, vol. 3, p. 171.

617 Thomas, J. L. (1924). Studies of the Life-History of *Trichosomoides crassicauda* (Bellingham). *Jl. Parasitology*, vol. 10, p. 105.

618 Thornton, H. (1924). The Relationship between the *Ascarids* of Man, Pig, and Chimpanzee. *Ann. Trop. Med. and Parasit.*, vol. 18, p. 99.

619 Thornton, H. (1924). A Review of the Œsophagostomes in the Collection of the Liverpool School of Tropical Medicine. *Ibid.*, vol. 18, p. 393.

620 Travassos, L. (1913). Ueber die brazilianischen Arten der Subfamilie *Heterakinæ* Railliet u. Henry. *Mem. do Instituto Oswaldo Cruz*, vol. 5, p. 271.

621 Travassos, L. (1914). Contribution to the Study of Brazilian Helminthology. III. A New genus of the family *Heterakidæ* Railliet and Henry. *Ibid.*, vol. 6, p. 137.

622 Travassos, L. (1914). Beiträge zur Kenntnis der brasilianischen Helminthenfauna. IV. Ueber die brasilianischen Arten des genus *Tetrameres* Creplin, 1846. *Ibid.*, vol. 6, p. 150.

623 Travassos, L. (1914). Trichostrongylinæ brazileiras. *Braz. Med.*, An. 28, pp. 163 and 183.

624 Travassos, L. (1914). Trichostrongylideos brazileiros. *Ibid.*, p. 325.

625 Travassos, L. (1915). Sobre as especies brazileiras do genero *Tetrameres* Creplin, 1846. *Ibid.*, Anno 29, p. 297.

626 Travassos, L. (1915). Trichostrongylideos brazileiros. *Ibid.*, An. 29, p. 388.

627 Travassos, L. (1915). Contribuições para o conhecimento da fauna helmintolojica brazileira. V. Sobre as especies brasileiras do genero *Capillaria* Zeder, 1800. *Memorias do Inst. Oswaldo Cruz*, vol. 7, p. 146.

628 Travassos, L. (1917). Nematodes parasitos de roedores. *Brazil Medico*, An. 31, p. 35.

629 Travassos, L. (1917). Tetrameridæ brazileiras. *Ibid.*, An. 31, p. 65.

630 Travassos, L. (1917). Trichostrongylidæ brazileiras. *Oswaldocruzia* n. gen. *Ibid.*, An. 31, p. 73.

631 Travassos, L. (1917). Alguns helminthos da colleção do Instituto Bacteriologico de S. Paulo. *Ibid.*, An. 31, p. 99.

632 Travassos, L. (1917). Informações sobre a familia *Kathlanidæ*, n. nom. *Revista da Sociedade Brasileira de Sciencias*, p. 83.

633 Travassos, L. (1918). Trichostrongylidæ brazileiras. *Ibid.*, p. 193.

633a Travassos, L. (1918). Contribuição para o conhecimento da fauna helmintolojica brazileira. *Revista do Museu Paulista*, vol. 10, p. 217.

634 Travassos, L. (1919). Contributions à l'étude de la Faune helminthologique du Brésil. No. VIII. Les espèces brésiliennes du genre *Tetrameres* Creplin, 1846. *Mem. Inst. Oswaldo Cruz*, vol. 11, p. 63.

635 Travassos, L. (1919). Material Helmintolojico da Ilha Trinidade. *Archiv. Mus. Nacional*, vol. 22, p. 161.

636 Travassos, L. (1919–20). Esboço de uma chave geral dos Nematodes parasitos. (*Soc. Braz. Sc.*, 1919.) *Rev. de Vet. Zoot.*, vol. 10, p. 59. 1920.

637 Travassos, L. (1920). Contributions à l'étude de la faune helminthologique du Brésil. IX. Les espèces du genre *Spinicauda* n. g. *Mem. Inst. Oswaldo Cruz*, vol. 12, p. 41.

638 Travassos, L. (1920). Contributions à l'étude de la faune helminthologique du Brésil. X. Les espèces du genre *Turgida*. *Ibid.*, vol. 12, p. 66.

639 Travassos, L. (1919–20). Contribuição para a Sistematica dos *Ascaroidea*. (Soc. Brasileira de Sciencias, 1919.) *Arch. da Esc. Sup. de Agric. e. Med. Veter.*, Nictheroy, vol. 4, p. 15.

639a Travassos, L. (1920). Contribuições para o conhecimento da fauna helmintolojica brasileira. *Oxyascaridæ* n. fam. *Ibid.*, vol. 4, p. 17.

640 Travassos, L. (1919–20). Genero *Florencioia* Trav., 1919. *Ibid.*, vol. 4, p. 21.

641 Travassos, L. (1921). Nematodeos nóvos. I. *Brazil Med.*, Anno 35, vol. 2, p. 367.

642 Travassos, L. (1921). Contributions à l'étude de la Fauna helminthologique du Brésil. XIII. Essai Monographique sur la famille des *Trichostrongylidæ* Leiper, 1909. *Mem. Inst. Oswaldo Cruz*, vol. 13 (Trans.), p. 1.

643 Travassos, L. (1922). Contributions to the Knowledge of the Brazilian Helminthological Fauna. XVI. *Cruzia tentaculata* (Rud., 1819). *Ibid.*, vol. 14, p. 66.

644 Travassos, L. (1922). Notas helmintolojicas. *Braz. Med.*, Anno 36, vol. 1, p. 256.

645 Travassos, L. (1923). Informações sobre a fauna helmintolojica de Matto Grosso. Oxyuroidea-Kathlanidæ. *A Folha Med.*, 4, p. 29.

646 Travassos, L. (1923). Informações sobre a fauna helmintolojica de Matto Grosso. Oxyuroidea-Oxyuridæ. *Ibid.*, 4, p. 35.

647 Travassos, L. (1923). Informaçoes sobre a fauna helmintolojica de Matto Grosso. Oxyuroidea-Heterakidæ. *Ibid.*, 4, p. 58.

647a Travassos, L. (1924). Pesquizas scientificas realizadas em Angra dos Reis. *Ibid.*, vol. 5, p. 152.

648 Travassos, L., and Horta (1915). *Acheilostoma paranecator* n. sp. Novo Nematode Parasita do *Equus asinus. Braz. Med.*, An. 29, p. 389.

649 Treutler, F. A. (1793). Observationes pathologico-anatomicæ auctarium ad helminthologiam humani corporis continentes. Lipsiæ. iv. + 44 pp.

650 Turkhud, D. A. (1920). Dracontiasis in Animals. *Ind. Jl. Med. Res.*, vol. 7, pp. 727.

651 Turner, M. (1920). On the Nematode Parasites of a Chapman's Zebra. *Proc. Zool. Soc.*, London, p. 441.

652 Turner, M. (1921). On some Helminth Parasites from an East African Rock Rabbit (*Procavia* sp.). *Trans. Roy. Soc. Trop. Med. and Hyg.*, vol. 15, p. 182.

652a Turner, W. Y. (1915). The Morphology of *Filaria sagitta* v. Linstow, 1907, from the Heart of *Tragelaphus sylvaticus* in Nyasaland. *Jl. Helminthology*, vol. 3, p. 15.

653 Veglia, F. (1916). The Anatomy and Life-History of the *Hæmonchus contortus* (Rud.). *Third and Fourth Reports of the Director of Vet. Res.*, Nov., 1915, p. 349. Pretoria.

654 Veglia, F. (1923). Preliminary Notes on the Life-History of *Œsophagostomum columbianum. Ibid.*, Ninth and Tenth Reports, p. 803.

655 Vevers, G. M. (1920). Report on Entozoa collected from Animals which died in the Zoological Gardens of London during Eight Months of 1919–20. *Proc. Zool. Soc.*, London, p. 405.

656 Vevers, G. M. (1922). On the Parasitic Nematoda collected from Mammalian Hosts which died in the Gardens of the Zoological Society of London during the Years 1919–21; with a Description of Three New Genera and Three New Species. *Ibid.*, Dec.

657 Vevers, G. M. (1923). Some New and Little Known Helminths from British Guiana. *Jl. of Helminthology*, vol. 1, p. 35.

658 Viborg, E. N. (1795). Sammlung von Abhandlungen für Thierärzte und Œkonomen. Copenhagen.

659 Walton, A. C. (1923). Some New and Little Known Nematodes. *Jl. Parasitology*, vol. 10, p. 59.

659a Ward, H. B. (1895). The Parasitic Worms of Man and Domestic Animals. *Studies Zool. Lab., Univ. Nebraska*, p. 225.

660 Ward, H. B. (1907). Iconographia Parasitorum hominis, No. 70. *Studies from the Zool. Lab.*, Nebraska.

661 Ward, H. B. (1916). Gongylonema in the Rôle of a Human Parasite. *Jl. Parasitology*, vol. 2, p. 119.

661a Ward, H. B. (1916). Nematoda. *Reference Handbook of Medical Sciences*, New York, pp. 676–704.

662 Ward, H. B., and Magath, T. B. (1916). Notes on some Nematodes from Freshwater Fishes. *Jl. Parasitology*, vol. 3, p. 57.

663 Ware, F. (1924). Two Bursate Nematodes from the Indian Elephant. *Jl. Comp. Path. and Therap.*, vol. 37, p. 278.

663a Ware, F. (1925). On a Nematode of the Genus *Ostertagia. Jl. Comp. Path. and Therap.*, vol. 38, p. 38.

663b Wedl, K. (1855). Helminthologische Notizen. *Sitzungsb. d. Math.-Naturw. Classe der Akad. der Wissensch.*, Wien., vol. 16, p. 371.

664 Wedl, K. (1861–62). Zur Helminthenfauna Ægyptens. *Ibid.*, vol. 44, pp. 225, 463.

665 Wiegmann, A. F. A. (1835). Bericht über die Fortschritte der Zoologie im Jahre 1834 (Entozoon). *Arch. f. Natur.*, vol. 1, p. 301.

666 Wigdor, M. (1918). Two New Nematodes common in some Fishes of Cayuga Lake. *Jl. Parasitology*, vol. 5, p. 29.

666a Witenberg, G. (1925). Notes on Strongylidæ of Elephants. *Parasitology*, vol. 17, p. 284.

667 Wostokow, W. J. (1905). Strongylidæ des poumons des mammifères domestiques de la Ville de Charkow. *Rec. des Travaux de l'Institut Vét. de Charkow*, vol. 7, No. 2.

668 Yokogawa, S. (1920). A New Nematode from the Rat. *Jl. Parasitology*, vol. 7, p. 29.

668a Yokogawa, S. (1922). On a new species of *Physaloptera* (*Physaloptera formosana*) and the tumour caused by this parasite. *Trans. Jap. Path. Soc.*, 12.

668b Yokogawa, S. (1925). On a new species of Nematode, *Gongylonema orientale*, found in Formosa. *Jl. Parasitology*, vol. 11, p. 195.

669 Yorke, W., and Blacklock, B. (1915). Ankylostomiasis in Dogs in Sierra Leone. *Ann. Trop. Med. and Parasit.*, vol. 9, p. 425.

670 Yorke, W., and Blacklock, B. (1917). The Occurrence of *Ancylostoma ceylanicum* in West African Dogs. *Ibid.*, vol. 11, p. 69.

671 Yorke, W., and Macfie, J. W. S. (1918). Strongylidæ in Horses. I. *Cylicostomum longibursatum* sp. n. II. *Cylicostomum minutum* sp. n. III. *Cylicostomum nassatum* Looss, var. *parvum. Ibid.*, vol. 11, pp. 399, 405, 411.

672 Yorke, W., and Macfie, J. W. S. (1918). Strongylidæ in Horses. IV. *Gyalocephalus capitatus* Looss. V. *Gyalocephalus equi* sp. n. *Ibid.*, vol. 12, pp. 79, 91.

673 Yorke, W., and Macfie, J. W. S. (1919). Strongylidæ in Horses. VI. *Cylicostomum pseudo-catinatum* sp. n. VII. *Cylicostomum pateratum* sp. n. VIII. Species found in American Horses. *Ibid.*, vol. 12, p. 273 ; vol. 13, pp. 57, 137.

674 Yorke, W., and Macfie, J. W. S. (1920). Strongylidæ in Horses. IX. *Cylicostomum tridentatum* sp. n. *Ibid.*, vol. 14, p. 153.

675 Yorke, W., and Macfie, J. W. S. (1920). Strongylidæ in Horses. X. On the genus *Poteriostomum* Quiel. *Ibid.*, vol. 14, p. 159.

676 Yorke, W., and Macfie, J. W. S. (1920). Strongylidæ in Horses. XI. Species found in West Africa and Jamaica. *Ibid.*, vol. 14, p. 165.

677 Yorke, W., and Macfie, J. W. S. (1920). Strongylidæ in Horses. XII. *Cylindropharynx rhodesiensis* sp. n. *Ibid.*, vol. 14, p. 169.

678 Yorke, W., and Macfie, J. W. S. (1920). Strongylidæ in Horses. XIII. *Cylicostomum triramosum* sp. n. *Ibid.*, vol. 14, p. 175.

679 Yorke, W., and Macfie, J. W. S. (1921). The Anatomy of *Oxyuris equi* (Schrank, 1788), Rud. 1803, and *Enterobius vermicularis* (Linn., 1758), Leach, 1853. *Trans. Roy. Soc. Trop. Med. and Hyg.*, vol. 15, p. 148.

680 Yorke, W., and Southwell, T. (1920). *Crossocephalus zebræ* n. sp. *Ann. Trop. Med. and Parasit.*, vol. 14, p. 127.

681 Zeder, J. G. H. (1800). Erster Nachtrag zur Naturgeschichte der Eingeweidewürmer mit Zufässen und Anmerkungen herausgegeben. xx. + 320 pp. Leipzig.

682 Zeder, J. G. H. (1803). Anleitung zur Naturgeschichte der Eingeweidewürmer. xvi. + 432 pp. Bamberg.

682a Zschokke, F. (1884). Recherches sur l'organisation et la distribution zoologique des vers parasites des poissons d'eau douce. *Arch. de Biol., Gand, Leip. and Par.*, vol. 5, p. 153.

682b Zschokke, F. (1896). Zur Faunistik der parasitischen Würmer von Süsswasser fischen. *Centralbl. f. Bakteriol.*, 1 Abt., vol. 19, p. 772.

683 Zürn, F. A. (1882). Die Schmarotzer auf und in dem Körper unserer Hau säugethiere, sowie die durch erstere veranlassten Krankheiten, deren Behandlung und Verhütung. I. Theil : Tierische Parasiten, Weimar, xvi. + 316 pp.

684 Zykov, V. P. (1902). Wo sollen wir den Zwischenwirt des *Cystoopsis acipenseri*, N. Wagn. suchen ? *Biol. Centralb.*, vol. 22, p. 229. Leipzig.